S0-BXN-367

PROGRESS IN CLINICAL AND BIOLOGICAL RESEARCH

RECENT TITLES

Vol 50: **Rights and Responsibilities in Modern Medicine: The Second Volume in a Series on Ethics, Humanism, and Medicine,** Marc D. Basson, *Editor*

Vol 51: **The Function of Red Blood Cells: Erythrocyte Pathobiology,** Donald F. H. Wallach, *Editor*

Vol 52: **Conduction Velocity Distributions: A Population Approach to Electrophysiology of Nerve,** Leslie J. Dorfman, Kenneth L. Cummins, and Larry J. Leifer, *Editors*

Vol 53: **Cancer Among Black Populations,** Curtis Mettlin and Gerald P. Murphy, *Editors*

Vol 54: **Connective Tissue Research: Chemistry, Biology, and Physiology,** Zdenek Deyl and Milan Adam, *Editors*

Vol 55: **The Red Cell: Fifth Ann Arbor Conference,** George J. Brewer, *Editor*

Vol 56: **Erythrocyte Membranes 2: Recent Clinical and Experimental Advances,** Walter C. Kruckeberg, John W. Eaton, and George J. Brewer, *Editors*

Vol 57: **Progress in Cancer Control,** Curtis Mettlin and Gerald P. Murphy, *Editors*

Vol 58: **The Lymphocyte,** Kenneth W. Sell and William V. Miller, *Editors*

Vol 59: **Eleventh International Congress of Anatomy,** Enrique Acosta Vidrio, *Editor-in-Chief.* Published in 3 volumes:
Part A: **Glial and Neuronal Cell Biology,** Sergey Fedoroff, *Editor*
Part B: **Advances in the Morphology of Cells and Tissues,** Miguel A. Galina, *Editor*
Part C: **Biological Rhythms in Structure and Function,** Heinz von Mayersbach, Lawrence E. Scheving, and John E. Pauly, *Editors*

Vol 60: **Advances in Hemoglobin Analysis,** Samir M. Hanash and George J. Brewer, *Editors*

Vol 61: **Nutrition and Child Health: Perspectives for the 1980s,** Reginald C. Tsang and Buford Lee Nichols, Jr., *Editors*

Vol 62: **Pathophysiological Effects of Endotoxins at the Cellular Level,** Jeannine A. Majde and Robert J. Person, *Editors*

Vol 63: **Membrane Transport and Neuroreceptors,** Dale Oxender, Arthur Blume, Ivan Diamond, and C. Fred Fox, *Editors*

Vol 64: **Bacteriophage Assembly,** Michael S. DuBow, *Editor*

Vol 65: **Apheresis: Development, Applications, and Collection Procedures,** C. Harold Mielke, Jr., *Editor*

Vol 66: **Control of Cellular Division and Development,** Dennis Cunningham, Eugene Goldwasser, James Watson, and C. Fred Fox, *Editors.* Published in 2 Volumes.

Vol 67: **Nutrition in the 1980s: Constraints on Our Knowledge,** Nancy Selvey and Philip L. White, *Editors*

See pages 507–508 for previous titles in this series.

Vol 68: **The Role of Peptides and Amino Acids as Neurotransmitters,** J. Barry Lombardini and Alexander D. Kenny, *Editors*

Vol 69: **Twin Research 3, Proceedings of the Third International Congress on Twin Studies,** Luigi Gedda, Paolo Parisi and Walter E. Nance, *Editors.* Published in 3 Volumes:
Part A: **Twin Biology and Multiple Pregnancy**
Part B: **Intelligence, Personality, and Development**
Part C: **Epidemiological and Clinical Studies**

Vol 70: **Reproductive Immunology,** Norbert Gleicher, *Editor*

Vol 71: **Psychopharmacology of Clonidine,** Harbans Lal and Stuart Fielding, *Editors*

Vol 72: **Hemophilia and Hemostasis,** Doris Ménaché, D.M. Surgenor, and Harlan D. Anderson, *Editors*

Vol 73: **Membrane Biophysics: Structure and Function in Epithelia,** Mumtaz A. Dinno and Arthur B. Callahan, *Editors*

Vol 74: **Physiopathology of Endocrine Diseases and Mechanisms of Hormone Action,** Roberto J. Soto, Alejandro De Nicola, and Jorge Blaquier, *Editors*

Vol 75: **The Prostatic Cell: Structure and Function,** Gerald P. Murphy, Avery A. Sandberg, and James P. Karr, *Editors.* Published in 2 volumes:
Part A: **Morphologic, Secretory, and Biochemical Aspects**
Part B: **Prolactin, Carcinogenesis, and Clinical Aspects**

THE PROSTATIC CELL: STRUCTURE AND FUNCTION

PART A

MORPHOLOGIC, SECRETORY, AND BIOCHEMICAL ASPECTS

THE PROSTATIC CELL: STRUCTURE AND FUNCTION

PART A

MORPHOLOGIC, SECRETORY, AND BIOCHEMICAL ASPECTS

Editors

GERALD P. MURPHY, MD, DSc
Director, Roswell Park Memorial Institute
Director, National Prostatic Cancer Project
Buffalo, New York

AVERY A. SANDBERG, MD
Department of Genetics and Endocrinology
Roswell Park Memorial Institute
Buffalo, New York

JAMES P. KARR, PhD
Deputy Director for Scientific Affairs
National Prostatic Cancer Project
Buffalo, New York

ALAN R. LISS, INC. • NEW YORK

Address all Inquiries to the Publisher
Alan R. Liss, Inc., 150 Fifth Avenue, New York, NY 10011

Printed in the United States of America.

Library of Congress Cataloging in Publication Data

Main entry under title:

The Prostatic cell.

(Progress in clinical and biological research; 75A-75B)
Proceedings of a workshop conducted by the National Prostatic Cancer Project and held at Roswell Park Memorial Institute, Buffalo, N.Y., Mar. 5–7, 1981.
Includes bibliographical references and index.
Contents: pt. A. Morphologic, secretory, and biochemical aspects – pt. B. Prolactin, carcinogenesis, and clinical aspects.
1. Prostate gland – Cancer – Congresses. 2. Cancer cells – Congresses. 3. Prostate gland – Congresses. I. Murphy, Gerald Patrick. II. Sandberg, Avery A. III. Karr, James P. IV. National Prostatic Cancer Project. V. Series. [DNLM: 1. Prostate – Cytology – Congresses. WI PR668E v. 75 / WJ 750 P965 1981]
RC280.P7P78 616.99'463 81-17146
ISBN 0-8451-0075-0 (set) AACR2
ISBN 0-8451-0161-7 (pt. A)
ISBN 0-8451-0162-5 (pt. B)

THE PROSTATIC CELL: STRUCTURE AND FUNCTION

A Workshop Organized by the National Prostatic Cancer Project Buffalo, New York, March 5–7, 1981

Chairmen, Organizing Committee

James P. Karr, PhD
Avery A. Sandberg, MD
Gerald P. Murphy, MD, DSc

Host

Roswell Park Memorial Institute

Contents of Part A

PROSTATIC SECRETIONS

UNIQUE PROSTATIC PROTEINS

TRACE METALS

Contributors to Part A

Khalil Ahmed, Department of Laboratory Medicine and Pathology, University of Minnesota; Veterans Administration Medical Center, Toxicology Research Laboratory, 4801 East 54th Street, Minneapolis, Minnesota 55417 **[55]**

Neil G. Anderson, Department of Pharmacology, University of Colorado School of Pharmacy, Campus Box 297, Boulder, Colorado 80309 **[177]**

Gerhard Aumüller, Department of Anatomy and Cell Biology, Philipps-Universität at Marburg, Robert-Koch-Strasse 6, 3550 Marburg, West Germany **[409]**

Evelyn R. Barrack, Department of Urology and Oncology Center, The James Buchanan Brady Urological Institute, The Johns Hopkins University School of Medicine, Baltimore, Maryland 21205 **[1]**

Richard J. Bartlett, Department of Pediatrics and Cancer Research Center, University of North Carolina, Chapel Hill, North Carolina 27514 **[351]**

S. Battersby, Tenovus Institute for Cancer Research, Welsh National School of Medicine, Heath, Cardiff, United Kingdom, CF4 4XX **[479]**

Per Björk, AB Leo Research Laboratories, Box 941, S-251 Helsingborg, Sweden **[391]**

D. Bossyns, Laboratorium voor Experimentele Geneeskunde en Laboratorium voor Biochemie, Faculteit Geneeskunde, Katholieke Universiteit Leuven, Rega Instituut, Minderbroedersstraat 10, B-3000, Leuven, Belgium **[339]**

N. Bruchovsky, Department of Cancer Endocrinology, Cancer Control Agency of British Columbia, 2656 Heather Street, Vancouver, British Columbia, Canada, V5Z 3J3 **[161]**

M.E. Burns, Department of Biochemistry, Boston University School of Medicine, Boston, Massachusetts 02118 **[417]**

Kjell Carlström, Hormone Laboratory, Sabbatsberg Hospital, Box 6401, S-113 82 Stockholm, Sweden **[391]**

J.A. Chandler, Tenovus Institute for Cancer Research, Welsh National School of Medicine, Heath, Cardiff, United Kingdom, CF4 4XX **[475]**

Chawnshang Chang, Department of Biochemistry, The Ben May Laboratory for Cancer Research, The University of Chicago, 950 East 59th Street, Chicago, Illinois 60637 **[381]**

Andrew Chiarodo, National Organ Site Programs Branch, Division of Resources, Centers and Community Activities, National Cancer Institute, Bethesda, Maryland 20205 **[xxv]**

The number in brackets following a contributor's affiliation is the opening page of that contributor's article.

T. Ming Chu, Department of Diagnostic Immunology Research and Biochemistry, Roswell Park Memorial Institute, 666 Elm Street, Buffalo, New York 14263 **[435]**

Leland W.K. Chung, Department of Pharmacology, University of Colorado School of Pharmacy, Boulder, Colorado 80309 **[177]**

Donald S. Coffey, Department of Urology and Oncology Center, The James Buchanan Brady Urological Institute, The Johns Hopkins University School of Medicine, Baltimore, Maryland 21205 **[1]**

Gary A. Croghan, Department of Diagnostic Immunology Research and Biochemistry, Roswell Park Memorial Institute, 666 Elm Street, Buffalo, New York 14263 **[435]**

Gerald R. Cunha, Department of Anatomy, University of Colorado Health Sciences Center School of Medicine, Denver, Colorado 80262 **[177]**

Karen A. Curto, Department of Pharmacology and Toxicology, West Virginia University Medical Center, Morgantown, West Virginia 26506 **[459]**

P. De Moor, Laboratorium voor Experimentele Geneeskunde en Laboratorium voor Biochemie, Faculteit Geneeskunde, Katholieke Universiteit Leuven, Rega Instituut, Minderbroedersstraat 10, B-3000, Leuven, Belgium **[339]**

Michael P. Donovan, Department of Pharmacology and Toxicology, West Virginia University Medical Center, Morgantown, West Virginia 26506 **[459]**

William R. Fair, Division of Urology, Washington University School of Medicine, 4960 Audubon Avenue, St. Louis, Missouri 63110 **[247]**

Wells E. Farnsworth, Department of Biochemistry, Chicago College of Osteopathic Medicine, 1122 East 53rd Street, Chicago, Illinois 60615 **[225]**

Björn Forsgren, AB Leo Research Laboratories, Box 941, S-251 09 Helsingborg, Sweden **[391]**

Frank S. French, Department of Pediatrics, University of North Carolina, Chapel Hill, North Carolina 27514 **[351]**

D.K. Fujii, Departments of Medicine and Ophthalmology, Cancer Research Institute and University of California Medical Center, San Francisco, California 94143 **[95]**

L. Giguere, Department of Medicine and Ophthalmology, Cancer Research Institute and University of California Medical Center, San Francisco, California 94143 **[95]**

D. Gospodarowicz, Departments of Medicine and Ophthalmology, Cancer Research Institute and University of California Medical Center, San Francisco, California 94143 **[95]**

Said A. Goueli, Department of Laboratory Medicine and Pathology, Toxicology Research Laboratory, University of Minnesota, Veterans Administration Medical Center, Minneapolis, Minnesota 55417 **[55]**

John T. Grayhack, Department of Urology, Northwestern University Medical School, 303 East Chicago Avenue, Chicago, Illinois 60611 **[231]**

Jan-Åke Gustafsson, Department of Medical Nutrition, Karolinska Institutet, Box 60400, S-104 01 Stockholm, Sweden **[391]**

Ferenc Gyorkey, Departments of Pathology, Pharmacology, and Virology, Baylor College of Medicine and Veterans Administration Medical Center, 2002 Holcombe Boulevard, Houston, Texas 77211 **[491]**

Barry M. Heatfield, Department of Pathology, University of Maryland School of Medicine, 10 South Pine Street, Baltimore, Maryland 21201 **[25]**

Walter Heyns, Laboratorium voor Experimentele Geneeskunde, Rega Instituut, Leuven, Belgium **[339, 409]**

Richard A. Hiipakka, Department of Biochemistry, The Ben May Laboratory for Cancer Research, The University of Chicago, 950 East 59th Street, Chicago, Illinois 60637 **[381]**

Bertil Högberg, Department of Pharmacology, Karolinska Institutet, Box 60400, S-104 01 Stockholm, Sweden **[391]**

Julius S. Horoszewicz, Department of Viral Oncology, Roswell Park Memorial Institute, 666 Elm Street, Buffalo, New York 14263 **[435]**

John T. Isaacs, Department of Urology and Oncology Center, The James Buchanan Brady Urological Institute, The Johns Hopkins University School of Medicine, Baltimore, Maryland 21205 **[1]**

William B. Isaacs, Department of Urology and Oncology Center, The James Buchanan Brady Urological Institute, The Johns Hopkins University School of Medicine, Baltimore, Maryland 21205 **[1]**

Stephen C. Jacobs, Department of Urology, The Medical College of Wisconsin, 9200 West Wisconsin Avenue, Milwaukee, Wisconsin 53226 **[325]**

Sheila M. Judge, Department of Biochemistry, The Ben May Laboratory for Cancer Research, The University of Chicago, 950 East 59th Street, Chicago, Illinois 60637 **[381]**

James P. Karr, National Prostatic Cancer Project, 666 Elm Street, Buffalo, New York 14263 **[xxvii]**

Manabu Kuriyama, Department of Diagnostic Immunology Research and Biochemistry, Roswell Park Memorial Institute, 666 Elm Street, Buffalo, New York 14263 **[435]**

Russell K. Lawson, Department of Urology, The Medical College of Wisconsin, 9200 West Wisconsin Avenue, Milwaukee, Wisconsin 53226 **[325]**

Oscar A. Lea, Department of Pharmacology, University of Bergen, Bergen, Norway **[351]**

Chung Lee, Department of Urology, Northwestern University Medical School, 303 East Chicago Avenue, Chicago, Illinois 60611 **[145, 231]**

Susan S. Leong, Department of Viral Oncology, Roswell Park Memorial Institute, 666 Elm Street, Buffalo, New York 14263 **[435]**

Shutsung Liao, Department of Biochemistry, The Ben May Laboratory for Cancer Research, The University of Chicago, 950 East 59th Street, Chicago, Illinois 60637 **[381]**

A. Mariotti, Departments of Urology and Pharmacology, West Virginia University Medical Center, Morgantown, West Virginia 26506 **[133]**

M. Mawhinney, Department of Pharmacology, West Virginia University Medical Center, Morgantown, West Virginia 26506 **[133]**

M.G. McLoughlin, Division of Urology, Department of Surgery, University of British Columbia, Vancouver, British Columbia, Canada, V5Z 1L7 **[161]**

J. Mous, Laboratorium voor Experimentele Geneeskunde en Laboratorium voor Biochemie, Faculteit Geneeskunde, Katholieke Universiteit Leuven, Rega Instituut, Minderbroedersstraat 10, B-3000, Leuven, Belgium **[339]**

R.E. Muller, Department of Biochemistry, Boston University School of Medicine, Boston, Massachusetts 02118 **[417]**

J. Müntzing, AB Leo, Research Laboratories, Box 941, S-251 09 Helsingborg, Sweden **[137]**

Gerald P. Murphy, National Prostatic Cancer Project and Roswell Park Memorial Institute, 666 Elm Street, Buffalo, New York 14263 **[xxvii, 435]**

Blake Lee Neubauer, Lilly Research Laboratories, Eli Lilly and Company, Indianapolis, Indiana 46285 **[177]**

Claudia M. Noyes, Department of Medicine, University of North Carolina, Chapel Hill, North Carolina 27514 **[351]**

Amy K. Oberhauser, Department of Biochemistry, The Ben May Laboratory for Cancer Research and the University of Chicago, 950 East 59th Street, Chicago, Illinois 60637 **[381]**

Lawrence D. Papsidero, Department of Diagnostic Immunology Research and Biochemistry, Roswell Park Memorial Institute, 666 Elm Street, Buffalo, New York 14263 **[435]**

Richard F. Parrish, Washington University School of Medicine, 4960 Audubon Avenue, St. Louis, Missouri 63110 **[247]**

B. Peeters, Laboratorium voor Experimentele Geneeskunde en Laboratorium voor Biochemie, Faculteit Geneeskunde, Katholieke Universiteit Leuven, Rega Instituut, Minderbroedersstraat 10, B-3000, Leuven, Belgium **[339]**

Peter Petrusz, Department of Anatomy, University of North Carolina, Chapel Hill, North Carolina 27514 **[351]**

Patricia C. Phelps, Department of Pathology, University of Maryland School of Medicine, 10 South Pine Street, Baltimore, Maryland 21201 **[25]**

Å. Pousette, Department of Medical Nutrition, Karolinska Institutet, Box 60400, S-104 01 Stockholm, Sweden **[25, 391]**

P.S. Rennie, Department of Cancer Endocrinology, Cancer Control Agency of British Columbia, 2656 Heather Street, Vancouver, British Columbia, Canada, V5Z 3J3 **[161]**

Audrey K. Rocco, Department of Pharmacology, University of Colorado School of Pharmacy, Boulder, Colorado 80309 **[177]**

W. Rombauts, Laboratorium voor Experimentele Geneeskunde en

Laboratorium voor Biochemie, Faculteit Geneeskunde, Katholieke Universiteit Leuven, Rega Instituut, Minderbroedersstraat 10, B-3000, Leuven, Belgium **[339]**

Betty Rosoff, Department of Biology, Stern College, Yeshiva University, 245 Lexington Avenue, New York, New York 10016 **[447]**

Diane Haddock Russell, Department of Pharmacology, University of Arizona Health Sciences Center, Tucson, Arizona 85724 **[207]**

Avery A. Sandberg, Department of Genetics and Endocrinology, Roswell Park Memorial Institute, 666 Elm Street, Buffalo, New York 14263 **[xxvii, 75]**

N. Savion, Departments of Medicine and Ophthalmology, Cancer Research Institute and University of California Medical Center, San Francisco, California 94143 **[95]**

Carl P. Schaffner, Waksman Institute of Microbiology, Rutgers - The State University of New Jersey, P.O. Box 759, Piscataway, New Jersey 08854 **[279]**

Karen Schilling, Department of Biochemistry, The Ben May Laboratory for Cancer Research, The University of Chicago, 950 East 59th Street, Chicago, Illinois 60637 **[381]**

Darrel W. Stafford, Department of Zoology, University of North Carolina, Chapel Hill, North Carolina 27514 **[351]**

Michael T. Story, Department of Urology, The Medical College of Wisconsin, 9200 West Wisconsin Avenue, Milwaukee, Wisconin 53226 **[325]**

J.-P. Tauber, Departments of Medicine and Ophthalmology, Cancer Research Institute and University of California Medical Center, San Francisco, California 94143 **[95]**

Peter F. Tauber, Department of Obstetrics and Gynecology, University of Essen, Essen, West Germany **[265]**

John A. Thomas, Department of Pharmacology and Toxicology, West Virginia Medical Center, Morgantown, West Virginia 26506 **[459]**

Timothy C. Thompson, Department of Pharmacology, University of Colorado School of Pharmacy, Boulder, Colorado 80309 **[177]**

B.G. Timms, Tenovus Institute for Cancer Research, Welsh National School of Medicine, Heath, Cardiff, United Kingdom CF4 4XX **[475]**

M.P. To, Department of Cancer Endocrinology, Cancer Control Agency of British Columbia, 2656 Heather Street, Vancouver, British Columbia, Canada, V5Z 3J3 **[161]**

A.M. Traish, Department of Biochemistry, Boston University School of Medicine, Boston, Massachusetts 02118 **[417]**

Benjamin F. Trump, Department of Pathology, University of Maryland School of Medicine, 10 South Pine Street, Baltimore, Maryland 21201 **[25]**

Luis A. Valenzuela, Department of Pathology, St. Joseph's Intercommunity Hospital, 2605 Harlem Road, Buffalo, New York 14225 **[435]**

David H. Viskochil, Departments of Pediatrics and Biochemistry,

University of North Carolina, Chapel Hill, North Carolina 27514 **[351]**
I. Vlodavsky, Departments of Medicine and Ophthalmology, Cancer Research Institute and University of California Medical Center, San Francisco, California 94143 **[95]**
Michael P. Waalkes, Department of Pharmacology and Toxicology, West Virginia University Medical Center, Morgantown, West Virginia 26506 **[459]**
Ming C. Wang, Department of Diagnostic Immunology Research and Biochemistry, Roswell Park Memorial Institute, 666 Elm Street, Buffalo, New York 14263 **[435]**
Elizabeth M. Wilson, Departments of Pediatrics and Biochemistry, University of North Carolina, Chapel Hill, North Carolina 27514 **[351]**
Michael J. Wilson, Department of Laboratory Medicine and Pathology, Toxicology Research Laboratory, University of Minnesota, Veterans Administration Medical Center, Minneapolis, Minnesota 55417 **[55]**
H.H. Wotiz, Departments of Biochemistry and Urology, Boston University School of Medicine, Boston, Massachusetts 02118 **[417]**
Lourens J.D. Zaneveld, Departments of Physiology and Biophysics, and Obstetrics and Gynecology, University of Illinois at the Medical Center, P.O. Box 6998, Chicago, Illinois 60680 **[265]**

Contents of Part B: Prolactin, Carcinogenesis, and Clinical Aspects

PROLACTIN

CARCINOGENS AND ENZYME INDUCTION

CLINICAL STUDIES

Contributors to Part B

John A. Arcadi, Department of Biology, Whittier College Cancer Research Laboratory, Whittier College, Whittier, California 90608

Frederick H. Batzold, Department of Biochemistry, Albany Medical College, Albany, New York 12208

E. **Borgström,** Department of Urology, Karolinska Institutet, Stockholm, Sweden

David Brandes, Department of Pathology, The Johns Hopkins School of Medicine and Baltimore City Hospitals, Baltimore, Maryland 21224

Leif Busk, Department of Toxicology, Swedish Food Administration, S-751 26 Uppsala, Sweden

Sham-Yuen Chan, Department of Microbiology, Lobund Laboratory, University of Notre Dame, Notre Dame, Indiana 46556

Andrew Chiarodo, National Organ Site Programs Branch, Division of Resources, Centers and Community Activities, National Cancer Institute, Bethesda, Maryland 20205

Hans Deutsch, Department of Toxicology and Experimental Pathology, c/o Dr. Karl Thomae GmbH, Biberach/Riss, West Germany

D.R. Fahmy, Tenovus Institute for Cancer Research, Welsh National School of Medicine, Heath, Cardiff, United Kingdom, CF4 4XX

Isaiah J. Fidler, Cancer Metastasis and Treatment Laboratory, National Cancer Institute Frederick Cancer Research Center, P.O. Box B, Frederick, Maryland 21701

Hans Glaumann, Department of Pathology, Huddinge Hospital, S-141 86, Huddinge, Sweden

K. **Griffiths,** Tenovus Institute for Cancer Research, Welsh National School of Medicine, Heath, Cardiff, United Kingdom, CF4 4XX

Jan-Åke Gustafsson, Department of Medical Nutrition, Karolinska Institutet, Box 60400, S-104 01 Stockholm, Sweden

Tapio Haaparanta, Department of Pathology, Huddinge Hospital, S-141 86, Huddinge, Sweden

Miasnig Hagopian, Section on Chemical Carcinogenesis, Mason Research Institute, Worcester, Massachusetts 01605

M.E. Harper, Tenovus Institute for Cancer Research, Welsh National School of Medicine, Heath, Cardiff, United Kingdom, CF4 4XX

Bertil Högberg, Department of Pharmacology, Karolinska Institutet, Box 60400, S-104 01 Stockholm, Sweden

Christoph Hohbach, Department of Toxicology and Experimental Pathology, c/o Dr. Karl Thomae GmbH, Biberach/Riss, West Germany

Myong Won Kahng, Department of Pathology, University of Maryland School of Medicine, 10 South Pine Street, Baltimore, Maryland 21201

James P. Karr, National Prostatic Cancer Project, 666 Elm Street, Buffalo, New York 14263

John A. Katzenellenbogen, Department of Chemistry, University of Illinois School of Chemical Sciences, 461 Roger Adams Laboratory, Box 37, 1209 West California, Urbana, Illinois 61801

Edward J. Keenan, Departments of Surgery and Pharmacology, Hormone Receptor Laboratory, University of Oregon Health Sciences Center School of Medicine, 3181 Southwest Sam Jackson Park Road, Portland, Oregon 97201

Elaine D. Kemp, Departments of Surgery and Pharmacology, University of Oregon Health Sciences Center School of Medicine, 3181 Southwest Sam Jackson Park Road, Portland, Oregon 97201

Leon Lack, Department of Pharmacology, Duke Medical Center, Box 3185, Durham, North Carolina 27710

Joseph Meites, Department of Physiology, Neuroendocrine Research Laboratory, Michigan State University, East Lansing, Michigan 48824

Gerald P. Murphy, National Prostatic Cancer Project and Roswell Park Memorial Institute, 666 Elm Street, Buffalo, New York 14263

W.B. Peeling, Department of Urology, St. Woolos' Hospital, Newport, Gwent, United Kingdom

Vladimir Petrow, Department of Pharmacology, Duke Medical Center, Box 3185, Durham, North Carolina 27710

C.G. Pierrepoint, Tenovus Institute for Cancer Research, Welsh National School of Medicine, Heath, Cardiff, United Kingdom, CF4 4XX

Morris Pollard, Department of Microbiology, Lobund Laboratory, University of Notre Dame, Notre Dame, Indiana 46556

S. Poolsawat, Department of Biology, Whittier College Cancer Research Laboratory, Whittier College, Whittier, California 90608

George Poste, Smith Kline and French Laboratories, Philadelphia, Pennsylvania 19101

Åke Pousette, Department of Medical Nutrition, Karolinska Institutet, Box 60400, S-104 01 Stockholm, Sweden

Elizabeth E. Ramsey, Departments of Surgery and Pharmacology, University of Oregon Health Sciences Center School of Medicine, 3181 Southwest Sam Jackson Park Road, Portland, Oregon 97201

Avery A. Sandberg, Department of Genetics and Endocrinology, Roswell Park Memorial Institute, 666 Elm Street, Buffalo, New York 14263

P.E.C. Sibley, Tenovus Institute for Cancer Research, Welsh National School of Medicine, Heath, Cardiff, United Kingdom, CF4 4XX

Nelson H. Slack, National Prostatic Cancer Project, Roswell Park Memorial Institute, 666 Elm Street, Buffalo, New York 14263

W. Roy Slaunwhite, Jr., Department of Biochemistry, State University of New York at Buffalo Schools of Medicine and Dentistry, Buffalo, New York 14214

Emil R. Smith, Department of Pharmacology, University of Massachusetts Medical School, 55 Lake Avenue North, Worchester, Massachusetts 01605

Mary W. Smith, Department of Pathology, University of Maryland School of Medicine, 10 South Pine Street, Baltimore, Maryland 21201

Peter Söderkvist, Departments of Medical Nutrition and Pharmacology, Karolinska Institutet, Box 60400, S-104 01 Stockholm, Sweden

Rune Toftgård, Departments of Medical Nutrition and Pharmacology, Karolinska Institutet, Box 60400, S-104 01 Stockholm, Sweden

Frank M. Torti, Division of Oncology, Stanford University School of Medicine, Stanford, California 94305

Benjamin F. Trump, Department of Pathology, University of Maryland School of Medicine, 10 South Pine Street, Baltimore, Maryland 21201

Heinz Ueberberg, Department of Toxicology and Experimental Pathology, c/o Dr. Karl Thomae GmbH, Biberach/Riss, West Germany

Willard J. Visek, University of Illinois, 190 Medical Sciences Building, 506 South Matthews Avenue, Urbana, Illinois 61801

Mukta M. Webber, Division of Urology, Department of Surgery, University of Colorado Health Sciences Center, Box C-319, 4200 East 9th Avenue, Denver, Colorado 80262

Raphael J. Witorsch, Department of Physiology, Medical College of Virginia School of Basic Sciences, Virginia Commonwealth University, Box 551, Richmond, Virginia 23298

Foreword: Organ Site Programs Overview

The National Organ Site Programs of the National Cancer Institute consist of grant-suppported National Projects of targeted cancer research. The program was established to stimulate research on important but neglected cancer problems that had not attracted a level of effort commensurate with the research leads available or with the mortality and morbidity associated with them. Currently there are four National Organ Site Projects concerned with cancer of the urinary bladder, large bowel, pancreas, and prostate. The overall strategy of each Project has been to share major responsibility between the National Cancer Institute and scientists throughout the nation for planning and coordinating a multidisciplinary research program aimed at prevention as well as decreased morbidity and mortality from the disease. Under the leadership of a national project director, this working cadre of laboratory and clinical scientists has developed a national plan of research within which priorities are identified in the areas of Etiology and Epidemiology, Detection and Diagnosis, and Treatment. This forms the basis for soliciting grant applications to help fulfill the aims and objectives of the national plan. Thus, the National Organ Site Programs permit the pursuit of targeted research through investigator-initiated efforts and the application of a spectrum of research disciplines to cancer at specific organ sites. It has involved the biomedical community in a unique scientific and managerial partnership with the National Cancer Institute. The effect has been to create research interest and activities where little existed before.

The National Prostatic Cancer Project, with Gerald P. Murphy as National Project Director, periodically conducts workshops on a timely basis to assess the state of the art in areas deemed ready for immediate implementation. In other instances, workshops are held with the objective of creating an atmosphere in which divergent topics are reviewed and brought into current focus, such that a cross fertilization of disciplines and ideas may stimulate thought for new investigational emphasis and direction. This book is one of two volumes that record the proceedings of such a workshop, entitled *The Prostatic Cell: Structure and Function,* held at Roswell Park Memorial Institute, Buffalo, New York, March 5-7, 1981.

The cordial hospitality and organizational effort mounted by the staff of Roswell Park Memorial Institute contributed to the success of the workshop. Special thanks are also extended to the participants.

June 1981

Andrew Chiarodo, PhD
Chief, National Organ Site Programs Branch
Divison of Resources, Centers and Community Activities
National Cancer Institute
Bethesda, Maryland

Preface

In planning the Workshop on the structure and function of the prostatic cell, the aim of the organizers was to assemble a program that would cover aspects of prostatic morphology, physiology, biochemistry, and pathology that had not been explored in depth at previous meetings of a similar nature. The more than fifty papers that were ultimately presented bear witness to the rapid development now taking place in these areas of investigation. Current research is expanding our knowledge not only of the normal prostate but also of the factors leading to the primary diseases of the gland: benign prostatic hypertrophy and cancer.

Because of the large amount of material presented at the Workshop, it was decided to publish the proceedings in two volumes. This first volume is concerned with the morphology, secretion, and unique proteins of the prostate.

In view of the complexity of the prostate, the reader's attention is directed first to nuclear and cytoplasmic mechanisms. Next, papers concerned with the gland on a grosser scale examine stromal-parenchymal interactions. Discussions of prostatic secretion, presented in the third section, make an important contribution to a subject that has been relatively little studied.

Since previous conferences had dealt extensively with steroid receptor proteins in the prostate, the Workshop focused on other proteins that are unique to the prostate. The papers from that session are presented next. The final section is devoted to work on trace metals in normal and abnormal prostatic tissue. Even though the presence of high concentrations of these metals – particularly zinc – has been known for many years, little has been done until recently to shed light on their role and function.

The reader should not assume that the two volumes of Workshop proceedings represent the last word on prostatic function, biochemistry, and pathology, for we have only scratched the surface of an understanding of that complicated gland, the prostate. The organizers hope that these presentations will give encouragement and direction to further research in the field.

We wish to thank the colleagues with whom we consulted about the program and whose help and interest made the Workshop a success.

Avery A. Sandberg, MD
James P. Karr, PhD
Gerald P. Murphy, MD, DSc

NUCLEAR AND CYTOPLASMIC MECHANISMS

The Prostatic Cell: Structure and Function
Part A, pages 1–24

The Relationship of Cellular Structure and Function: The Matrix System

John T. Isaacs, Evelyn R. Barrack, William B. Isaacs, and Donald S. Coffey

INTRODUCTION

The shape of a cell may be directly involved in determining cellular functions such as proliferation and differentiation processes [1]. For example, Folkman and Moscona [2] could precisely control the shape of normal cells in vitro by varying the substratum adhesiveness of the culture plates to which the cells were attached. With appropriate control experiments, the authors concluded that cell shape was coupled to DNA synthesis and cell growth. They discussed their findings in relation to such phenomena as density-dependent inhibition of cell growth and anchorage dependence; these authors also discussed the possible relationship of cell shape to response to serum growth factors [2]. Gospodarowicz, Greenburg, and Birdwell [3] observed that the mitogenic response of a given cell was also determined by the cell shape. They observed that corneal epithelial cells adopted a flattened shape when maintained in vitro on plastic and were sensitive to fibroblast growth factor, but not to epidermal growth factor. In contrast, when these cells were maintained on a layer of collagen they assumed a tall columnar form and responded to epidermal growth factor. With additional experiments, they concluded that the extracellular matrix upon which the cells rested determined the cell shape that in turn regulated the cell's proliferation properties. Cause and effect have not been resolved in final detail; nevertheless, these types of experiments are generating what may become compelling evidence to support such structure-function relationships.

If cell shape does directly control cell replication and differentiation it is important to resolve what determines and modulates cell shape and how these events might be transmitted within the cell to control nuclear functions. First we will focus on evidence that an extracellular matrix interacts with a cell to regulate cellular differentiation; we propose that this interaction may be transmitted to the nuclear matrix by way of the cytoplasmic skeleton.

There is much evidence to support the hypothesis that intercellular interactions and the extracellular matrix may have a role in the control of proliferation and cytodifferentiation. The extracellular matrix as it exists *in vivo* may be broadly defined as the external supporting structure upon which cells reside and consists of the basement membrane, collagens, proteoglycans, glycosaminoglycans, acidic polysaccharides, and other complex components of the ground substance that are not fully characterized. The extracellular matrix has often been implicated as an important factor in the control of genetic expression, particularly with respect to epithelial and mesenchymal interactions [4,5]. In addition, the potential of certain types of extracellular collagen to redirect cell differentiation has been demonstrated by the remarkable interaction of demineralized bone collagen matrix with mature fibroblasts to induce the redifferentiation of these cells to form new chondroblasts and chondrocytes. With time, these newly differentiated cells form new bone and even undergo hemopoiesis through the formation of new bone marrow [6,7]. In these experiments, it was concluded that direct contact of fibroblasts with the isolated extracellular bone matrix collagen dictated the redifferentiation process. Significantly, these effects were specific for collagen isolated from bone.

Gospodarowicz and his associates [3] suggest that transformed cells may have escaped the restrictions normally imposed on cell proliferation by cellular morphology. This suggestion was based on previous reports that the transformation of cells is usually accompanied by a relative loss of anchorage dependence, a lower requirement for growth factors, and the acquired ability to grow in suspension cultures. The control of cellular morphology of fibroblasts may involve, in part, the cell surface glycoprotein fibronectin. Yamada et al[8] have demonstrated that the addition of isolated fibronectin to transformed fibroblasts in culture could cause the reversal of cellular morphology back towards the normal state, and this was accompanied by a partial restoration of both cell adhesiveness and contact growth inhibition.

It now appears that epithelial cells attach to the basement membrane by a protein similar but not identical to fibronectin; this protein has been termed laminin. In addition, collagen is a generic term, and it is now apparent that there are several distinct forms of collagen, and Type IV is the one predominating in the basement membrane. A recent review has been published describing these cell adhesion proteins and their specificity for the different types of collagen [9].

It is unknown at present how the extracellular matrix recognizes, interacts with, and directs the cell membrane components to bring about changes in cell morphology and, consequently, cellular function. Nevertheless, there have been recent advances in our knowledge of the dynamic aspects and modifications of cell membrane organization [10]. How these extracellular matrix-plasma membrane interactions may be transmitted internally to the cell to alter cell shape is unclear [1]. At present, it seems reasonable to assume that some of the components of the cytoskeleton, such as the microfilaments and microtubules, may be involved directly in determining cellular morphology [11]. There is much interest in defining the properties of these structural protein components, particularly with regard to their role in cell motility and cytokinesis.

Much less information is available to evaluate a mechanism by which cell shape might regulate nuclear shape or function. Indeed, the relationship of nuclear function to nuclear shape requires clarification. In this regard, nuclear swelling has been recognized to be associated with active nucleic acid synthesis. Classical experiments by Harris [12,13] and Graham et al [14] have demonstrated that nuclear enlargement is a prerequisite for, rather than a consequence of, increased synthesis and accumulation of nucleic acids. Agents that swell isolated nuclei in vitro have also been shown to release nuclear DNA template restrictions [15,16]. In addition, many hormone-stimulated cells, as well as cancer cells, are characterized by alterations in nuclear morphology [17–20]. Ritter [18] and Chung and Coffey [19] have demonstrated that in the prostate gland nuclear volume and composition can be correlated with androgen stimulation (Fig. 1). This raises the important question of what regulates nuclear structure and volume.

The nuclear matrix, the structural framework component of the nucleus, has been postulated to be involved in nuclear swelling phenomena [21–25]. In addition, it has also been reported that newly synthesized DNA is associated with the nuclear matrix [26–30, 92–94].

It still remains to be determined whether structural alterations which have been induced can be transmitted directly by chemomechanical linkage from the extracellular matrix through the cytomatrix to the nucleus, and whether these changes represent primary events in the control of cell differentiation and replication. A central concept of this presentation is that the tissue contains a series of connecting reticular matrix networks that provide a solid phase support, capable of dynamic changes in organization. Thus, changes in the extracellular matrix may produce conformational alterations in a series of matrix systems that are directly coupled internally to the nucleus and thereby alter nuclear morphology and function. The term "matrix" is chosen because it is defined generally as "the groundwork on which anything is cast or the basic material on which a thing develops" [31]. It is visualized that these matrices form the supportive structural framework of the cell and its component parts (see Fig. 2 for summary). This entire matrix system is referred to as the tissue matrix. The matrix of a cellular component may be associated with other elements such as protein and nucleic acids, many of which are removed during the fractionation or isolation steps. A matrix system is usually revealed by extracting membrane lipids with detergent and removing many soluble proteins in low and high ionic strength solutions. Remnants of RNA and DNA may be removed enzymatically by RNase and DNase treatment. The residual insoluble components which comprise the matrix will vary according to the individual method used for the isolation [95]. The total tissue matrix is visualized to be composed of the following (see Fig. 3).

EXTRACELLULAR MATRIX

Basement membrane
Collagens
Proteoglycans, glycosaminoglycans, acidic polysaccharides
Ground substance (chemical nature undefined)

CYTOMATRIX (CYTOSKELETON)

Cytoplasmic matrix
- plasma membrane matrix
- reticulum matrix of the ground substance
- microfilament, microtubule, and intermediate filament networks

Nuclear matrix
- residual nuclear envelope, pore complex, lamina
- interchromatinic network
- residual nucleolus

CYTOMATRIX (CYTOSKELETON)

Gentle lysis of cells with mild detergent to remove membrane lipids has been used in numerous studies to reveal the existence of an elaborate internal structure or cytoskeleton within the cytoplasm [32,33]. Many studies have indicated that this cytoskeleton is composed primarily of microtubules, actin, myosin, keratin, and intermediate filaments of approximately 100 Å and other minor high molecular weight proteins of 200K–250K daltons; these residual cytoskeletons have been revealed in many types of cells following treatment with the non-ionic detergent NP-40 or Triton X-100 [32–41]. Many soluble proteins are lost from the cell following detergent treatment and only about a half dozen major polypeptide bands remain with the residual cytoskeleton, as revealed by SDS-polyacrylamide electrophoresis.

Electron microscopy of these isolated cytoskeletons reveals residual elements of the plasma membrane, reticular network, polyribosomes, 100 Å filaments, and the nucleus [32,33].

Penman has reported an apparent association of polyribosomes with the isolated cytoskeleton and their dissociation by treatment with either RNase or cytochalasin B [33]. Sabatini and his colleagues [41,42] have isolated rough and smooth microsomal membrane fractions from rat liver and extracted them with the non-ionic detergent Kyro EOB. They observed two residual integral proteins in the rough microsome fraction that were not present in smooth microsomes.

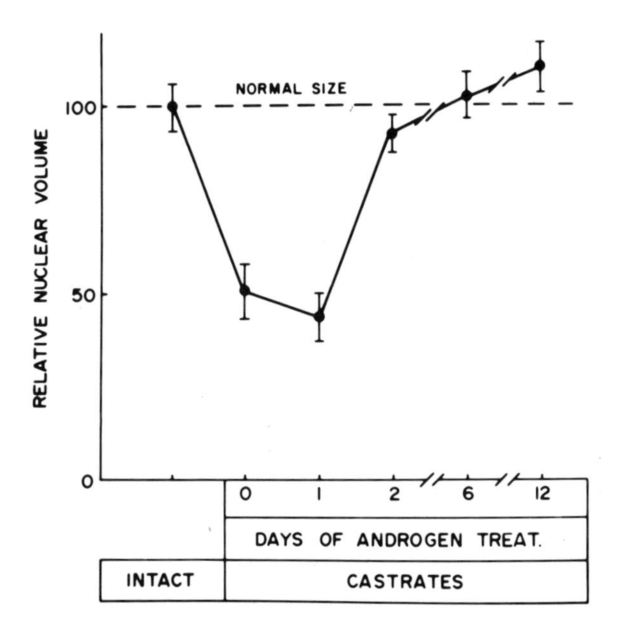

Fig. 1. Change in rat ventral prostate nuclear volume with androgen treatment. Figure is plotted from data presented by Ritter [18].

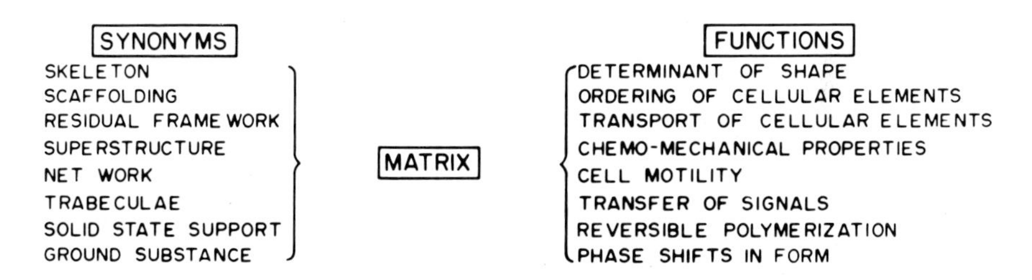

Fig. 2. Synonyms that have appeared that have been used for cellular matrix structures and some proposed functions.

These proteins had apparent molecular weights of 63K and 65K daltons and were resistant to extraction from the microsomal membranes by neutral detergents, alkali, or acid treatment; however, they could be solubilized by deoxycholate or trypsin treatment. Evidence was presented that these residual structural proteins were in close proximity to bound ribosomes and the suggestion was made that they may be involved in the ribosome binding sites on the endoplasmic reticulum [42].

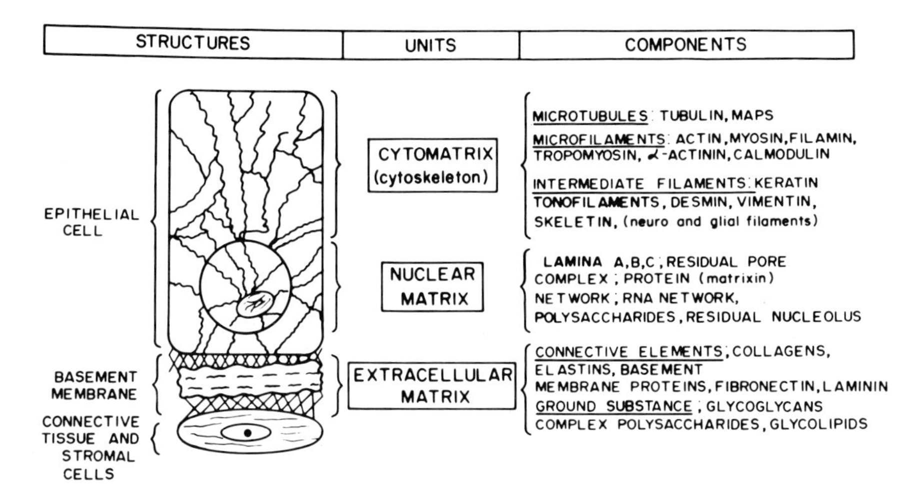

Fig. 3. A schematic of the overall tissue matrix system with some of the proteins identified as to their tissue location.

Many of these microfilamentous structures in the cytoskeleton appear to be associated directly with the nuclear membrane, and it is suggested that they may directly affect nuclear function. Since these filaments extend from the plasma membrane to the nucleus, they may provide a direct chemomechanical link for the communication of plasma membrane events through the cytoplasm to the nucleus; however, this hypothesis remains to be established.

NUCLEAR MATRIX

For many years, it was believed that the nuclear membrane maintained the integrity of the eukaryotic nucleus. High molarity salt solutions (1 M NaCl) were used first by Zbarsky and Georgiev [43–46] and later by Busch and his colleagues [47,48] to extract the majority of the DNA from the nucleus. This treatment left a relatively intact lipid-containing nuclear membrane that encompassed the nucleus, which still contained residual internal structures. The later development of mild non-ionic detergents (Triton X-100) made it possible to extract the nuclear membrane lipid components. Thus, a series of extractions of nuclei with detergent, hypotonic, and hypertonic solutions could remove over 98% of the total nuclear phospholipid, DNA and RNA, and 90% of the nuclear proteins [49,50]; yet the nuclei maintained their spherical integrity (Fig. 4). Electron microscopy of this insoluble structure revealed a matrix system that was composed of residual elements of the nuclear membrane and nuclear pore complexes, surrounding an internal fibrillar network that extended from the periphery to residual elements

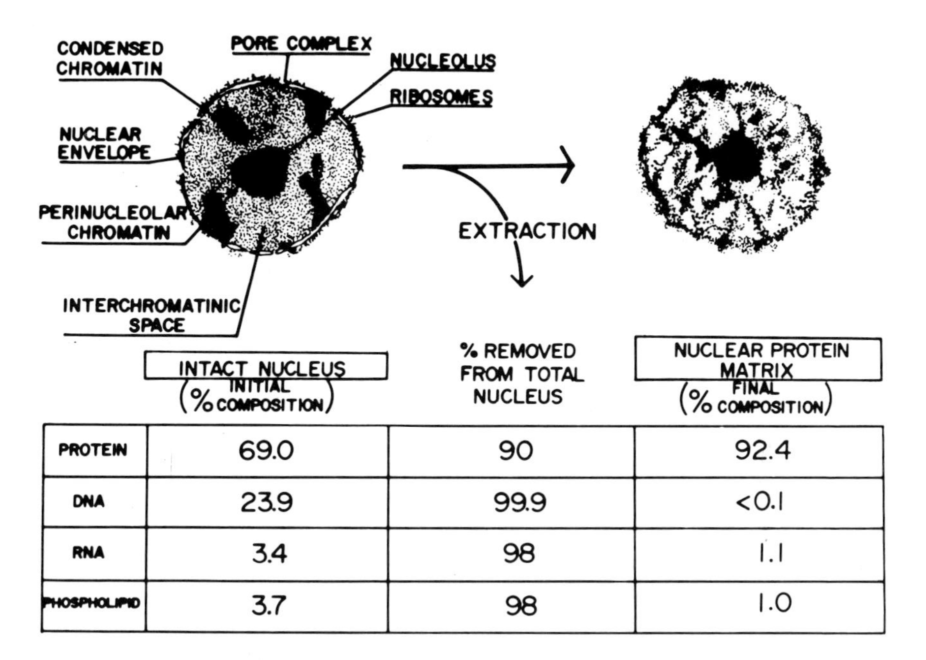

	INTACT NUCLEUS INITIAL (% COMPOSITION)	% REMOVED FROM TOTAL NUCLEUS	NUCLEAR PROTEIN MATRIX FINAL (% COMPOSITION)
PROTEIN	69.0	90	92.4
DNA	23.9	99.9	<0.1
RNA	3.4	98	1.1
PHOSPHOLIPID	3.7	98	1.0

Fig. 4. Schematic of the isolation of the nuclear matrix from rat liver. Isolated nuclei were treated with triton X-100, low ionic strength buffer, 2 M NaCl, and then treated with RNase and DNase. For specific details consult [1]. The amount of DNA and RNA remaining varies with the extent of nuclease treatment.

of the nucleolus (Fig. 5). This residual nuclear structure was first isolated from rat liver nuclei, characterized and termed the nuclear matrix [49,50]. The nuclear matrix represented only 5–10% of the total nuclear protein, and yielded only a few major polypeptide bands on sodium dodecyl sulfate polyacrylamide gel electrophoresis [50]. The prominent protein fractions have apparent molecular weights of 60K–70K daltons, and by partial tryptic digest fingerprinting techniques, appear to be structurally related [1,50]. In addition, there are several clusters of minor polypeptides of approximately 50K and 100K–200K daltons [50].

Utilizing the regenerating rat liver as a model of DNA synthesis, it was possible to demonstrate that newly synthesized DNA, labeled with tritiated thymidine, was first associated with a small fraction of DNA that is tightly bound to the nuclear matrix. With time the label progressed to the non-matrix bulk fraction of the nuclear DNA, which could be extracted during the preparation of the nuclear matrix [26]. Recently, it has been proposed that DNA is replicated at fixed sites, termed replisomes, and that these sites are associated with the nuclear matrix [27,29]. DNA is visualized to move as loops through the replisome

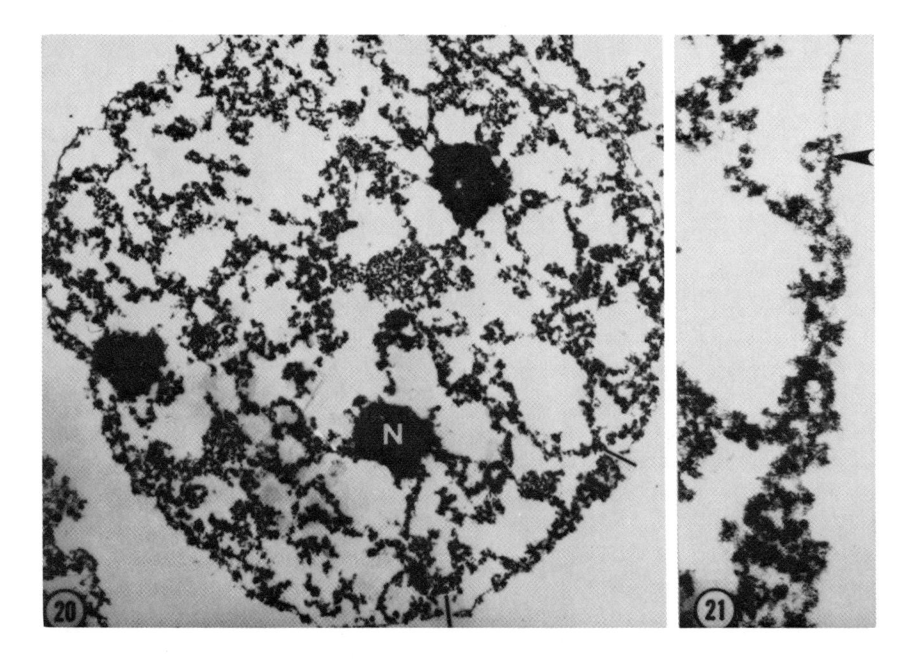

Fig. 5. An electron micrograph of one nuclear matrix sphere isolated from rat liver nuclei. Photo 20 (× 15,000) is the entire matrix sphere. The area in the lower right quadrant of photo 20, marked by the bars, is magnified to yield photo 21 (× 42,000). N = residual nucleolus. The arrow in photo 21 indicates a residual pore complex in the peripheral lamina area.

and in the process becomes replicated into daughter strands [27] (Fig. 6). The DNA loops are attached at their base to the matrix and the loops are in a state of supercoiling [28] (Fig. 7).

In addition to DNA replication, it appears that the nuclear matrix may be associated with many other dynamic aspects of nuclear function, as reviewed in Fig. 8 [1]. These include: protein phosphorylation [51,52]; heterogeneous nuclear RNA synthesis [53–55] and RNA transport [53]; association with viral DNA synthesis [56] and newly formed viral proteins [57], including [56] the T (transformation) antigen; nuclear swelling processes [22]; binding of carcinogens [58]; and specific steroid binding sites [59,60].

Structures similar to the rat liver nuclear matrix have been isolated from the nuclei of many other types of cells such as Tetrahymena [61], HeLa [62], Chinese hamster ovary [63], chicken erythrocytes [64], slime mold [30], mouse liver [65], chicken liver, and rat prostate [59]. The properties of the nuclear matrix and additional details regarding its isolation and characterization have been reviewed [1,21,66,91].

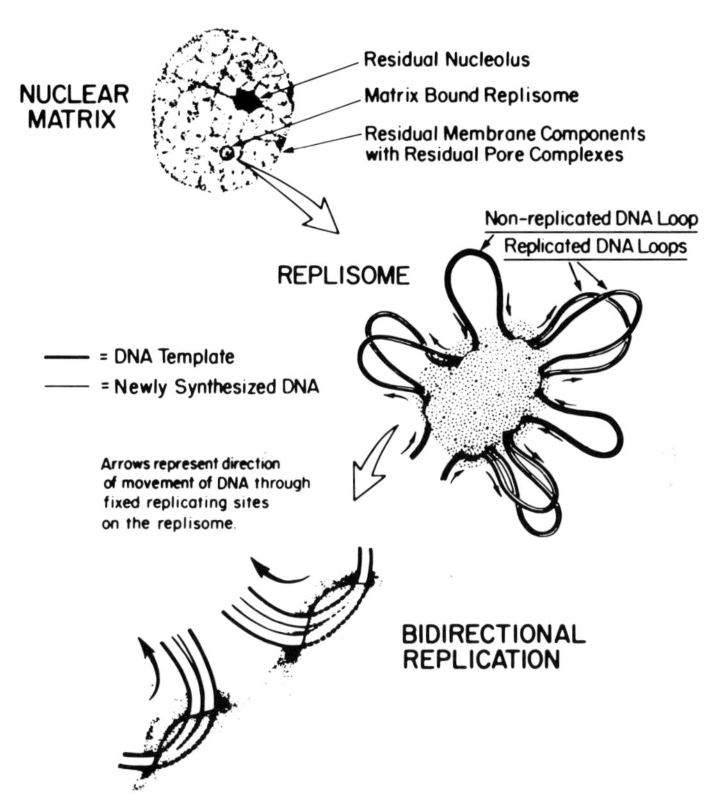

Fig. 6. Proposed model for fixed site of DNA replication on the nuclear matrix. The top drawing in the figure represents a nuclear matrix. The middle drawing shows a cluster of fixed replication complexes forming a replisome. DNA is bound via the replication complexes in alternating replicated and nonreplicated loops. The bottom drawing shows one fixed replication complex with the DNA being reeled through as it is replicated. The process shown would result in a bidirectionally replicated section of DNA with the origin of replication at the center of the replicated loop. (For details of evidence for this model consult [27,28].)

STEROIDS BIND TO THE NUCLEAR MATRIX

The interaction of steroid hormones with the nucleus of target tissues is widely believed to be an essential part of the mechanism by which these hormones modulate nuclear events. However, the precise nature of this nuclear interaction has not been fully resolved [67–69]. Although nuclear binding sites for steroid hormones have been reported to be located on the nuclear membrane [70], nuclear ribonucleoprotein particles [71], DNA [68], chromatin, and fractions thereof

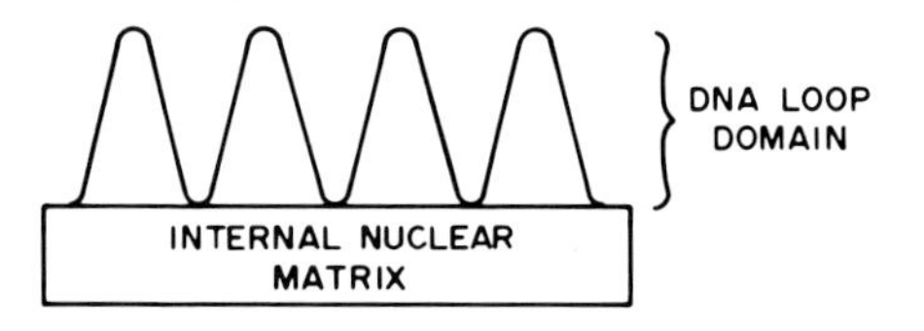

EACH LOOP:

1.) 10-30 MICRONS

2.) 50,000-200,000 NUCLEOTIDE BASE PAIRS

Fig. 7. A schematic of the loops attached at their base and the indicated sizes of each loop. See [27,28] for details.

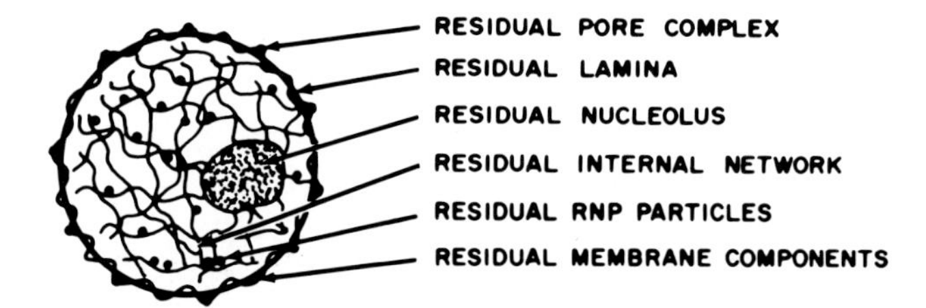

- LIPID FREE
- REPRESENTS ONLY 10% OF TOTAL NUCLEAR PROTEINS. CONTAINS RELATED PROTEINS
- SITE OF ATTACHMENTS OF DNA LOOPS
- CONTAINS FIXED SITES FOR DNA SYNTHESIS
- ASSOCIATED WITH HnRNA
- SPECIFIC BINDING OF HORMONES
- PROTEINS PHOSPHORYLATED
- MAY HAVE DYNAMIC PROPERTIES

Fig. 8. A schematic of the morphological components of the nuclear matrix and some of the biological properties identified with these structures.

[69,72], the role of each of these putative receptors or acceptors in the mechanism of steroid hormone action has not been elucidated. Nuclear receptors also have been characterized following fractionation of nuclei with hypertonic salt solutions (eg, 0.3–0.6 M KCl or NaCl). Thus, a great deal of effort has been directed at correlating hormone responses with the levels of steroid binding activity in these salt-soluble nuclear extracts [73–75]. Yet this salt-extractable steroid-binding

component does not always represent 100% of the total nuclear binding; in many cases, a significant amount of steroid binding activity remains resistant to solubilization by high concentrations of salt (reviewed in [59]). For example, the identification of specific estrogen binding sites in salt-insoluble nuclear subfractions of the rat uterus is of particular interest because of the proposed correlation of this binding with estrogen-induced growth of the immature rat uterus [76]. In their study, Clark and Peck [76] concluded that the number of salt-resistant nuclear binding sites for estradiol was identical with the number of sites required for maximal uterine growth, and they proposed that these salt-resistant binding sites may represent specific nuclear acceptor sites. A similar observation has been reported by Ruh and Baudendistel [77], who have suggested that these salt-resistant estradiol binding sites may be involved in events that result in the replenishment of cytoplasmic receptors [78].

Some have questioned the concept of a distinct salt-resistant class of nuclear receptors [79], suggesting instead that they represent salt-soluble nuclear receptors entrapped in the gelatinous DNA pellet that results from the exposure of nuclei to high concentrations of salt. Barrack et al have demonstrated, however, that this salt-resistant estradiol binding component cannot be solubilized even under hypertonic conditions that allow the extraction of greater than 99% of the total nuclear DNA [59,60]. This nuclear steroid binding appears to be associated with the nuclear matrix component [59,60]. The work of Barrack et al [59] may be summarized as follows:

The nuclear matrix of an estrogen-responsive tissue (chicken liver) and of an androgen target tissue (rat ventral prostate) contains binding sites for estradiol and dihydrotestosterone, respectively. The binding of steroids to these sites is saturable, high affinity ($K_d \sim 10^{-9}M$), steroid-specific (liver binds estrogens, prostate binds androgens), and heat- and pronase-sensitive. The levels of these matrix-associated steroid binding sites change in response to manipulation of the hormonal status of the animal. Thus, the liver nuclear matrix of laying hens contains a significant number of estradiol binding sites, whereas that of untreated chicks or roosters contains very few sites. Treatment of chicks or roosters with a dose of estrogen that stimulates the liver to synthesize vitellogenin leads to a marked increase in the number of estradiol binding sites associated with the liver nuclear matrix. In the rat ventral prostate, the nuclear matrix-associated binding sites for dihydrotestosterone that are present in intact adults essentially disappear within 24 hours after castration. Androgen replacement therapy restores, within 1 hour, the number of matrix binding sites for dihydrotestosterone to normal levels. Inhibitors of proteolysis (phenylmethylsulfonyl fluoride) are essential for the protection of these androgen binding sites. Conditions that lead to the solubilization of the internal network material of the nuclear matrix also result in the extraction of 70–85% of the specific dihydrotestosterone binding sites from the matrix; a limited number of binding sites still remain associated with the peripheral lamina. For specific details of the aforementioned study consult the original publication [59].

EXTRACELLULAR MATRIX

Many classical studies in developmental biology have clearly implicated the extracellular matrix as having an important function in directing or controlling cellular differentiation [4]. For example, Cunha has provided an excellent review of the role of epithelial-stromal interactions in the development of the urogenital tract [80]. Reid and her associates [81] have isolated an insoluble cell-free tissue component that interacts with isolated cells in culture to maintain in vitro hormonal response and a state of cellular differentiation and growth. This residual tissue component that has been termed the biomatrix [81] is composed in part of connective tissue fibers such as collagen, basement membrane, elastin, and other insoluble proteins and polymers that resist solubilization after DNase and RNase treatment, extraction in low and high ionic strength solutions (2 M NaCl) and treatment with detergent (1% deoxycholate).

Similar biomatrix systems have been isolated from the prostate gland and appear to have a differential effect on prostate epithelial cells in culture.

How external signals are transmitted to the cell nucleus by the touching of the cell to the biomatrix is a fundamental question and is remindful of the many previous observations that cell contact with extracellular matrix components such as collagen or the mesenchyme elements can profoundly alter epithelial cell shape and function [1–9].

CANCER CELL NUCLEI

One of the hallmarks of the cancer cell is the enlargement of the nucleus, nucleolus, and the abnormal form and staining of the chromatin. The nuclear membrane is often invaginated and tortuous in appearance [20]. This might suggest that components that control nuclear shape may be altered within the cancer cell [21]. Since the nuclear matrix represents a skeletal component of the nucleus it has been suggested to serve a role as the determinant of nuclear shape and structure [1]. Indeed, there is a report that the nuclear matrix might be altered in cancer cells when compared to normal cells [82]. Since DNA synthesis remains in an "on" state in the cancer and it fails to cease growth, it is of interest that the structure that determines the shape of the nucleus also plays a paramount function in DNA synthesis. It is unknown whether abnormalities in the shape of the nucleus via changes in the nuclear matrix might also account for the abnormalities in DNA synthesis and growth control in the cancer cell; however, it is an intriguing possibility.

PROTEIN PROFILES AND CANCER

Over the last few years there has been increasing evidence that there may be a direct relationship between changes in the protein components of the cytoskeletal structure of cancer cells and their altered growth characteristics. Several studies have established that there is a marked alteration in the organization of the major contractile proteins actin and myosin in cancer cells [83,84]. There are also reports that the content of other cytoskeleton-associated proteins such as microtubule complexes [85], fibronectin [86], and calmodulin [87] are also significantly changed in transformed cells. Therefore, comparisons of the protein profiles of normal and cancer tissue might well reveal major differences.

One simple method for comparing protein profiles between normal and cancer tissue is by the use of one-dimensional sodium dodecyl sulfate-polyacrylamide gel electrophoresis (1-D SDS gels). This 1-D SDS gel system allows one to separate SDS-soluble proteins according to their respective molecular weights. While most tissues contain a large number of common proteins, the relative quantitative amounts of each of the individual proteins usually vary widely in different tissues. In this regard, a protein profile can be obtained based not simply on the presence or absence of particular protein bands, but upon the relative abundance of the respective protein bands for each tissue. For example, Figure 9 presents the densitometric tracings of the 1-D SDS gels of six normal rat tissues. Clearly many of the same protein bands, stained with Coomassie blue, are present in all six normal tissues; however, the relative abundance of the individual protein bands is completely unique for each tissue. The relative abundance of the individual protein bands, as determined by densitometric scan of the 1-D SDS gels, can be used to quantitatively rank each of these proteins. Indeed, Irwin and Dauphinais have recently proposed that each normal tissue can be uniquely classified by a tissue-specific code based upon the relative abundance of their SDS-solubilized proteins [88]. For comparative purposes 1-D SDS gel analysis was performed on several of the Dunning R-3327 rat prostate adenocarcinoma tumor lines to see if they resemble the normal rat prostate in their protein profiles (Fig. 10). The Dunning lines examined were: 1) the R3327-H tumor, a slow growing (20 day doubling time), androgen sensitive, well differentiated adenocarcinoma; 2) the R-3327-HI tumor, a slow growing (20 day doubling time), androgen insensitive, well differentiated adenocarcinoma; and 3) the R-3327-AT tumor, a fast growing (2–3 day doubling time), androgen insensitive, anaplastic carcinoma. The histologies of these tumors are presented in Figure 11.

Since the original Dunning tumor, from which all other R-3327 tumor lines are derived, arose spontaneously from the dorsal lobe of an aged Copenhagen male rat, the tumor protein profiles should be compared directly versus the normal dorsal prostatic lobe. In Figure 9, however, the prostatic ventral lobes and the dorsolateral complex as a group are individually presented. Nevertheless,

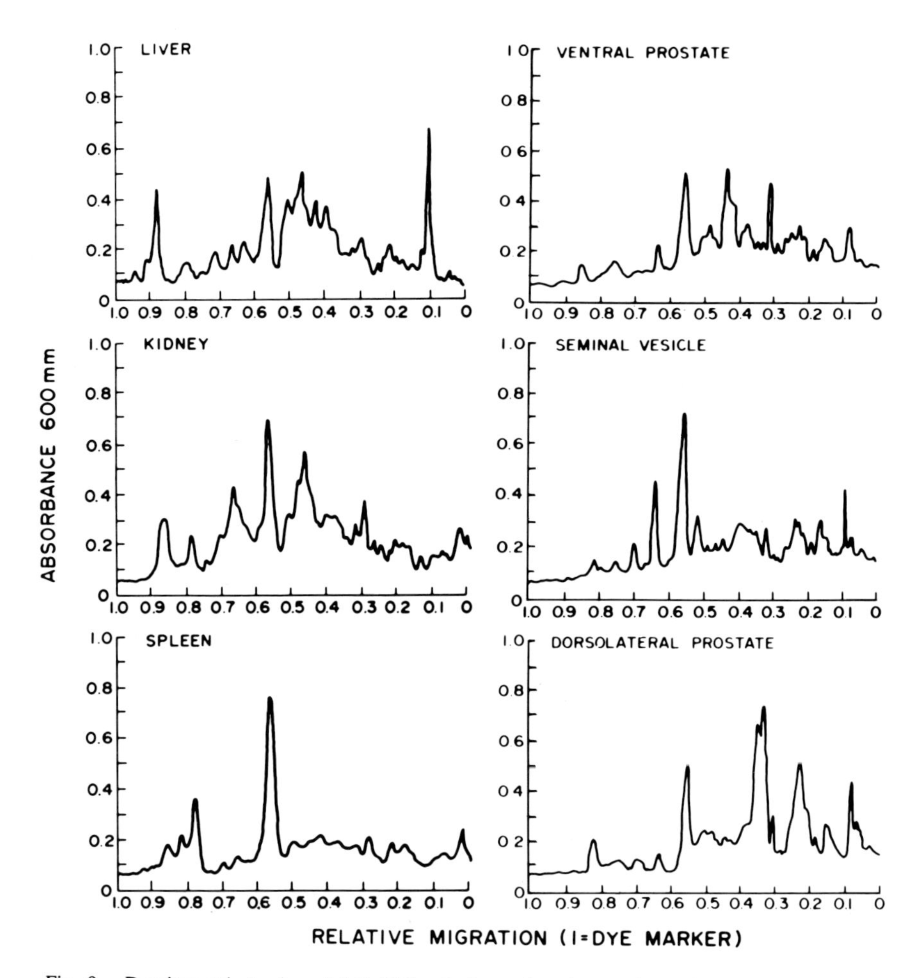

Fig. 9. Densitometric tracing of 1-D SDS gel electrophoretic protein profiles of various normal tissues. SDS-10% gel electrophoresis was performed on whole homogenates of various tissues (50 μg of total protein/gel) as reported by Isaacs et al [89].

comparison of Figures 9 and 10 reveals two major points. First, all the Dunning tumor lines, regardless of their histological appearance or growth characteristics, resemble each other very closely by 1-D SDS gels. Note that in Figure 10 a spontaneous mammary tumor is also presented for comparison and it does not resemble the prostatic tumors. Chemically induced rat hepatomas also have been examined (not shown), and they too do not resemble the R-3327 tumor group profile. Therefore the relatedness between the three R-3327 tumors is not simply related to the tumor state but is probably due to the common origin of these

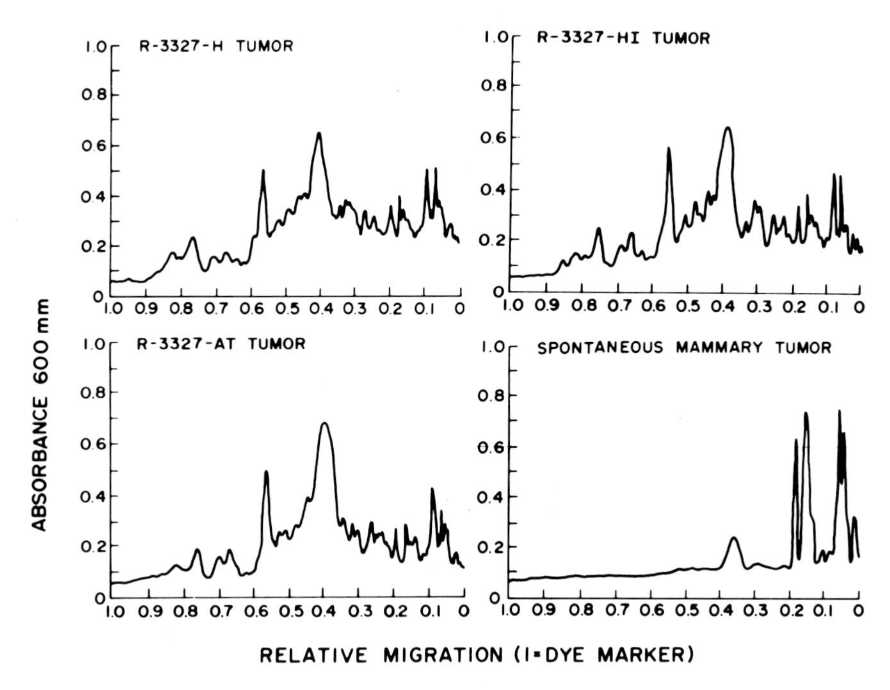

Fig. 10. Densitometric tracing of protein profiles of R-3327 prostatic tumors and mammary tumors as described in Figure 9.

three tumors. The second point of comparing Figures 9 and 10 is that the Dunning tumors only generally resemble the dorsolateral prostate. Major differences have occurred in the protein profiles of these Dunning tumors as compared to normal prostatic tissue.

These 1-D SDS gel findings were initially reported in 1979 [89]. We have since extended these studies to two-dimensional analyses of the tissue protein profiles. By using the standard method of O'Farrell, whole homogenates of normal and tumor tissue were solubilized with 9.5 M urea, 5% β-mercaptoethanol, 2% NP-40, and 2% ampholine (LKB) (solubilization buffer) and run first on isoelectric focusing gels (1st dimension) following in the second dimension by 10% SDS-gel resolution [90]. Using this 2-D gel technique, it is easily possible to uniquely identify each of the four prostatic lobes of the rat, Figure 12. The boxed-in areas in this figure refer to zones of the gel where major protein spot differences occur in comparing the dorsal, lateral, ventral, and anterior rat prostate. Several of these zones contain more than one protein spot. For example, areas A and B each have at least four distinct spots. By comparing the presence to absence of these individual protein spots in the A–E zones, it is possible to

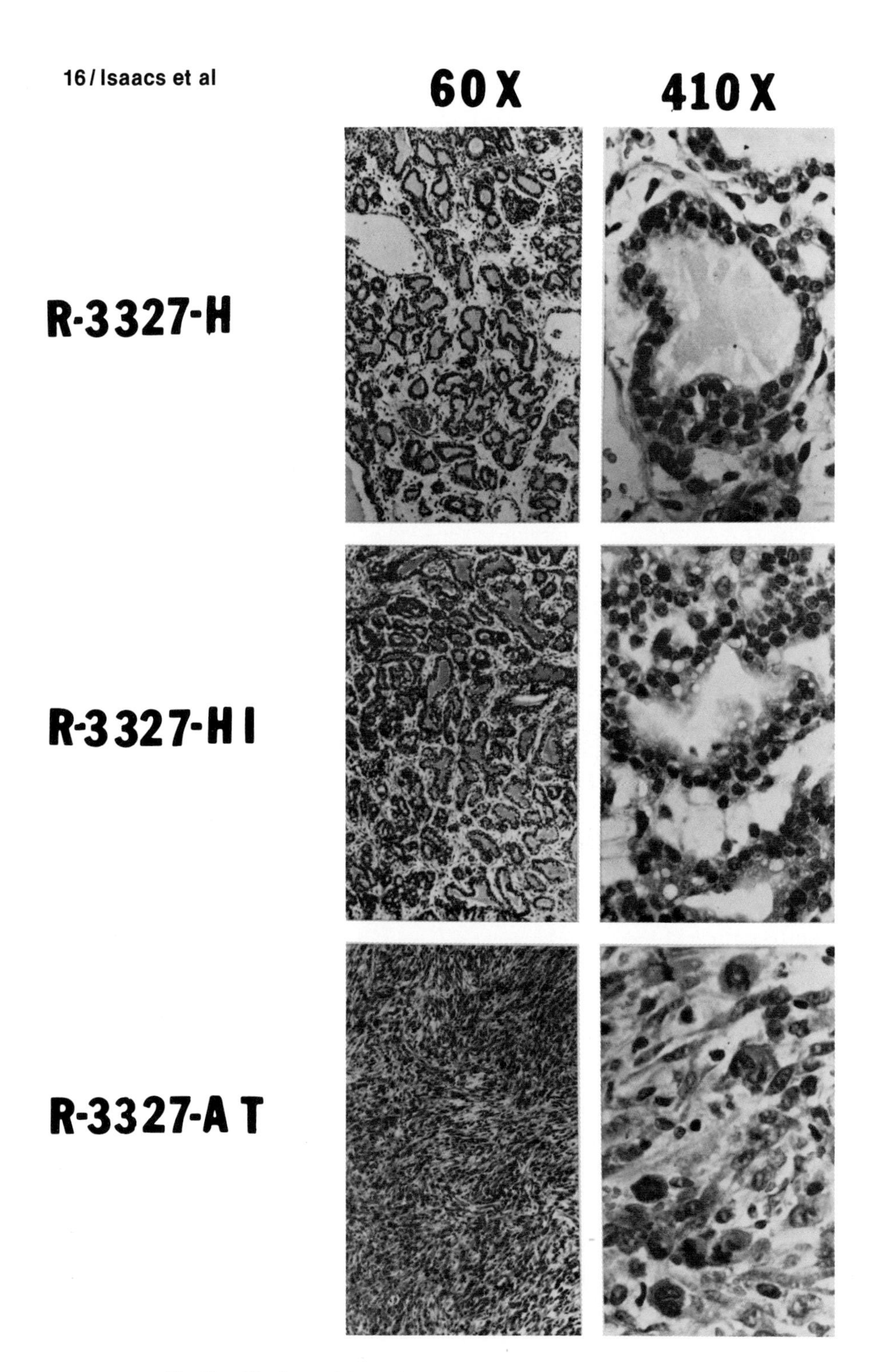

Fig. 11. Histology of the various Dunning R-3327 rat prostatic tumors.

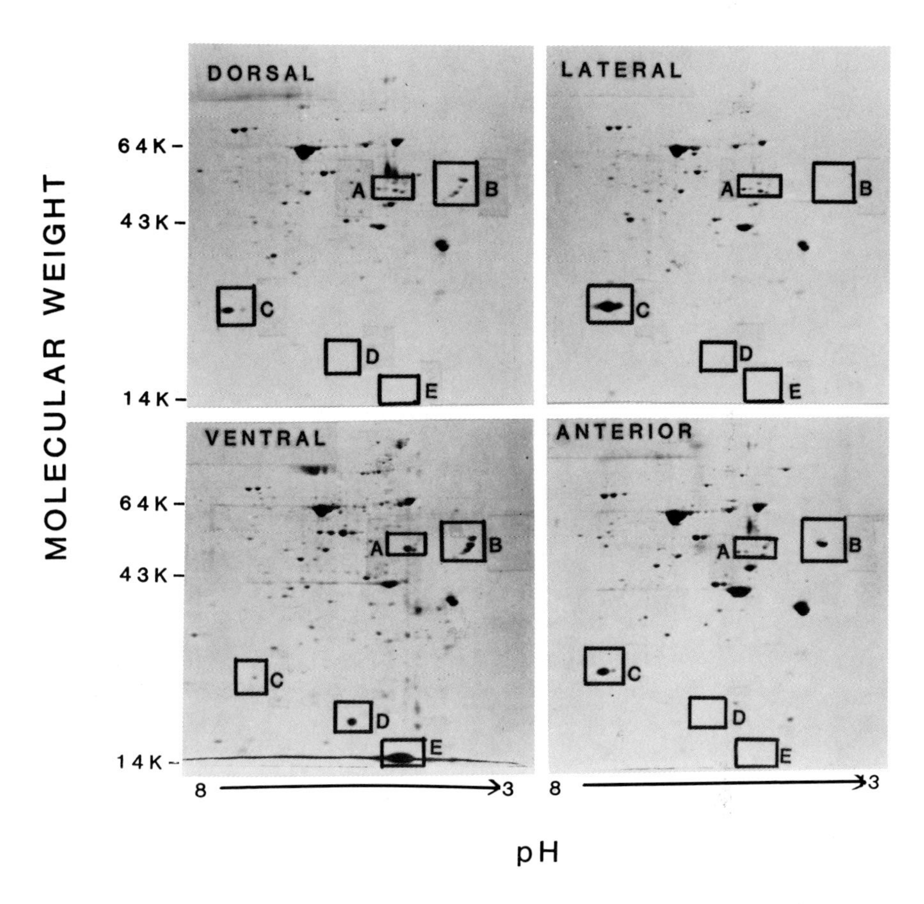

Fig. 12. 2-D gels of the various normal rat prostatic lobes. First dimension was with a pH gradient from 8–3.5. Second dimension was run in a SDS-10% gel.

uniquely identify each normal rat prostatic lobe. These differences are summarized in Table I, and they demonstrate the power of this type of analysis to characterize tissue. Figure 13 compares the 2-D gel of the three Dunning R-3327 tumors. Comparison of Figures 12 and 13 reveals that there are many more protein spots for the tumors than for the normal prostate, regardless of which lobe is compared. One explanation for this difference is that there are changes in the solubility characteristics of the tumor proteins as compared to proteins from normal prostate allowing more of them to dissolve in the original solubil-

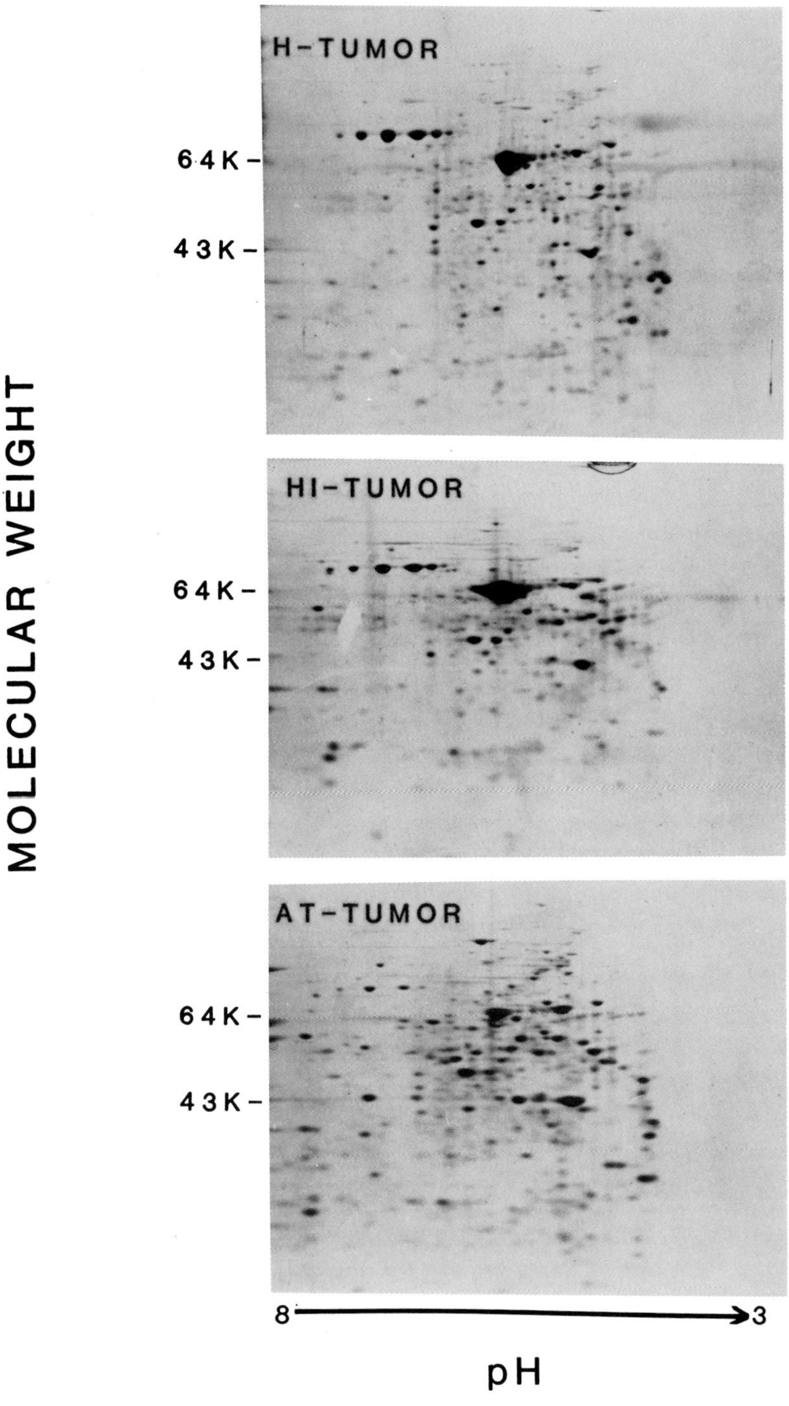

Fig. 13. 2-D Gels of Dunning R-3327 tumors performed as described in Figure 12.

TABLE I. Comparison of proteins in various lobes of the rat prostate by two-dimensional electrophoretic gel analysis

Rat prostate lobes	Localization of proteins (zones on 2-D gels)											
	A				B				C		D	E
	1	2	3	4	1	2	3	4	1	2	1	1
Dorsal	+	+	+	+	+	+	+	+	+	+	−	−
Lateral	+	+	+	+	−	−	−	−	+	+	−	−
Ventral	−	−	+	+	+	+	+	+	−	+	+	+
Anterior (coagulating gland)	+	+	−	+	+	−	−	−	+	+	−	−

ization buffer. Another possibility is that normal prostatic lobes are programmed to express only a limited number of proteins in relatively high levels, these proteins being related to the unique phenotypic differentiation of the particular prostatic lobe. The prostatic tumors may have lost this differentiation so that now the numerous "housekeeping" proteins, always present, become a larger fraction of the total protein pool.

Since a constant amount of total protein is applied to each gel, this could result in the detection of spots in tumors which are also present in normal tissue but which in some tissues are at too low a relative protein content to be detected. Regardless of why there are many more protein spots seen for the prostatic tumors than for any of the normal prostatic lobes, an additional observation is apparent from comparing the 2-D gels of the tumors and normal prostatic tissue. The observation is that the tumors only generally resemble the normal dorsal prostate. Major changes in the protein profiles, as revealed by 2-D gels, have occurred in going from the normal dorsal prostate to the Dunning R-3327-H tumor.

Further protein changes are evident when the R-3327-HI and AT tumors are compared to H tumors from which each was originally derived. There is, however, a very distinct relatedness between the H, HI, and AT tumors.

The present findings demonstrate that profound changes in the relative abundance of total proteins occurs with the development of prostatic cancer. These changes may be of only a quantitative nature (ie, amount of individual proteins) but it is also possible that qualitative changes in the proteins (ie, altered proteins) may also occur. Much more work will need to be done to resolve this important question.

In summary, we visualize an overall tissue matrix system that is capable in part of controlling cellular function through phase shifts in cellular structure. The direction of these phase shifts and the mechanism of control remain to be elucidated, but the concept is indicated in the schematic of Figure 14.

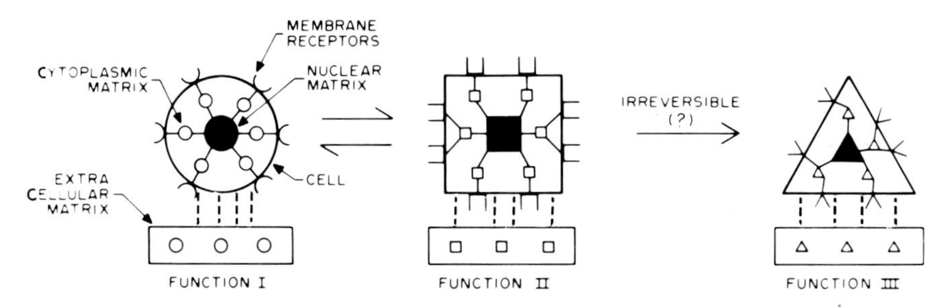

Fig. 14. A schematic of the concept of interlocking phase shifts in tissue structural elements associated with changes in cellular function (hypothesis).

REFERENCES

1. Shaper J H, Pardoll D M, Kaufmann S H, Barrack E R, Vogelstein B, Coffey D S: The relationship of the nuclear matrix to cellular structure and function. Adv Enz Reg 17: 213–248, 1979.
2. Folkman J, Moscona A: Role of cell shape in growth control. Nature 273: 345–349, 1978.
3. Gospodarowicz D, Greenburg G, Birdwell C R: Determination of cellular shape by the extracellular matrix and its correlation with the control of cellular growth. Cancer Res 38: 4155–4171, 1978.
4. Grobstein C: Developmental role of intercellular matrix: Retrospective and prospective. In Slarkin H C, Grenlich R C, Brinkley B R, Porter K R (eds): "Extracellular Matrix Influence on Gene Expression." New York: Academic Press, 1975, pp 9–16.
5. Hay E D: Cell matrix interaction in embryonic induction. In Brinkley BR, Porter KR (eds): "International Cell Biology' Biology." New York: Rockefeller University Press, 1977, pp 50–57.
6. Reddi A H: Collagen and cell differentiation. In Ramachadran G N, Reddi A H (eds): "Biochemistry of Collagen." New York: Plenum, 1976, pp 449–478.
7. Reddi A H, Anderson W A: Collagenous bone matrix induced endochondral ossification and hemopoiesis. J Cell Biol 69: 557–572, 1976.
8. Yamada K M, Yamada S S, Pastan I: Cell surface protein partially restores morphology, adhesiveness and contact inhibition of movement to transformed fibroblasts. Proc Natl Acad Sci USA 73: 1217–1221, 1976.
9. Kleinman H K, Klebe R J, Martin G R: Role of collagenous matrices in the adhesion and growth of cells. J Cell Biol 88: 473–485, 1981.
10. Nicolson G L, Poste G, Ji T H: The dynamics of cell membrane organization. In Poste G, Nicolson G L (eds): "Dynamic Aspects of Cell Surface Organization. Vol. 3, Cell Surface Reviews." Amsterdam: North Holland Publishing Co., 1977.
11. Goldman R, Pollard T, Rosenbaum J (eds): "Cell Motility," Books A, B and C. Cold Spring Harbor Conference on Cell Proliferation, Cold Spring Harbor Laboratory, 1976.
12. Harris, H: "Nucleus and Cytoplasm." 2nd Edition, Oxford: Clarendon Press, 1978.
13. Harris H: "Cell Fusion." Oxford: Clarendon Press, 1970.
14. Graham C F, Arms K, Gurdon J B: The induction of DNA synthesis by egg cytoplasm. Dev Biol 14: 349–381, 1966.

15. Coffey D S, Barrack E R, Heston W D W: The regulation of nuclear DNA template restrictions by acidic polymers. Adv Enz Reg 12: 219–266, 1974.
16. Arnold E A, Yawn D H, Brown D G, Wyllie R C, Coffey D S: Structural alteration in isolated rat liver nuclei after removal of template restrictions by polyanions. J Cell Biol 53: 737–757, 1972.
17. Cavazos L F, Melampy R M: Cytological effects of testosterone propionate on epithelium of rat seminal vesicle. Endocrinology 54: 644–648, 1954.
18. Ritter C: Androgen-stimulated restoration in rat seminal vesicle and prostate epithelial cells. Endocrinology 84: 844–854, 1969.
19. Chung L W K, Coffey D S: Biochemical characterization of prostate nuclei. I. Androgen-induced changes in nuclear proteins. Biochem Biophys Acta 247: 570–583, 1971.
20. Bernhard W, Granboulan N: The fine structure of the cancer cell nucleus. Exp Cell Res (suppl) 9: 19–53, 1963.
21. Berezney R, Coffey D S: The nuclear protein matrix: Isolation, structure and function. Adv Enz Reg 14: 63–100, 1976.
22. Wunderlich F, Herlan G: A reversibly contractile nuclear matrix: Its isolation, structure and composition. J Cell Biol 73: 271–278, 1977.
23. Riley D E, Keller J M: Cell cycle dependent changes in nonmembranous nuclear ghosts from HeLa cells. J Cell Sci 29: 129–146, 1978.
24. Herlan G, Quevedo R, Wunderlich F: Structural transformation of the nuclear matrix in situ. Exp Cell Res 115: 103–110, 1978.
25. Wunderlich F, Giese G, Bucherer C: Expansion and apparent fluidity decrease of nuclear membranes induced by low Ca/Mg. Modulation of nuclear membrane lipid fluidity by the membrane associated nuclear matrix proteins. J Cell Biol 79: 479–490, 1978.
26. Berezney R, Coffey D S: Nuclear protein matrix: Association with newly synthesized DNA. Science 189: 291–293, 1975.
27. Pardoll D M, Vogelstein B, Coffey D S: A fixed site of DNA replication in eucaryotic cells. Cell 19: 527–536, 1980.
28. Vogelstein B, Pardoll D, Coffey D S: Supercoiled loops and eucaryotic DNA replication. Cell 22: 79–85, 1980.
29. Dijkwel P, Mullenders L, Wanka F: Analysis of the attachment of replicating DNA to a nuclear matrix in mammalian interphase nuclei. Nucleic Acid Res 6: 219–230, 1979.
30. Hunt B F, Vogelstein B: Association of newly replicated DNA with the nuclear matrix of *Physarum polycephalum*. Nucleic Acid Res 9: 349–363, 1981.
31. Friel J P (ed): "Dorland's Medical Dictionary." 25th Edition, Philadelphia: W. B. Saunders, 1974.
32. Osborn M, Weber K: The detergent resistant cytoskeleton of tissue culture cells includes the nucleus and microfilament bundles. Exp Cell Res 106: 339–349, 1977.
33. Lenk R, Ransom L, Kaufman Y, Penman S: A cytoskeleton structure with associated polyribosomes obtained from HeLa cells. Cell 10: 67–78, 1977.
34. Brinkley B R, Fuller G M, Highfield D P: Cytoplasmic microtubules in normal and transformed cells in culture: Analysis by tubulin antibody immunofluorescence. Proc Natl Acad Sci USA 72: 4981–4985, 1975.
35. Felix H, Strauli P: Different distribution pattern of 100 Å filaments in resting and locomotive leukemia cells. Nature 261: 604–606, 1976.
36. Goldman R D, Lazarides E, Pollack R, Weber K: Distribution of actin in non-muscle cells: Use of actin antibody in localization of actin within microfilament bundles of mouse 3T3 cells. Exp Cell Res 90: 333–344, 1975.
37. Hartwig J H, Stoessel T P: Isolation and properties of actin, myosin and a new actin-binding protein in rabbit alveolar macrophages. J Biol Chem 250: 5696–5705, 1975.

38. Lazarides E: Immunofluorescence studies on the structure of actin filaments in tissue culture cells. J Histochem Cytochem 23: 507–528, 1975.
39. Lazarides E: Actin, α-actinin and tropomyosin interaction in the structural organization of actin filaments in non-muscle cells. J Cell Biol 68: 202–219, 1976.
40. Lazarides E, Weber K: Actin antibody: Specific visualization of actin filaments in non-muscle cells. Proc Natl Acad Sci USA 71: 2268–2272, 1974.
41. Kreibich G, Ulrich B A, Sabatini D D: Proteins of rough microsomal membranes related to ribosome binding. I. Identification of ribophorins I and II, membrane proteins characteristic of rough microsomes. J Cell Biol 77: 464–487, 1978.
42. Kreibich G, Freienstein C M, Pereyra B N, Ulrich B L, Sabatini D D: Proteins of rough microsomal membranes related to ribosome binding. II. Cross-linking of bound ribosomes to specific membrane proteins exposed at the binding sites. J Cell Biol 77: 488–506, 1978.
43. Zbarsky I B, Debov S S: Proteins of cell nuclei. Dokl Akad Nauk SSSR 63: 795–798, 1948.
44. Zbarsky I B, Georgiev G P: Cytological characteristics of protein and nucleoprotein fractions of cell nuclei. Biochim Biophys Acta 32: 301–302, 1959.
45. Georgiev G P, Chentsov J S: The structural organization of nucleochromosomal ribonucleoproteins. Exp Cell Res 27: 570–572, 1962.
46. Zbarsky I B, Dmitrieva N P, Yermolayeva L P: On the structure of tumor cell nuclei. Exp Cell Res 27: 573–576, 1962.
47. Narayan K S, Steele W J, Smetana K, Busch H: Ultrastructural aspects of the ribonucleoprotein network in nuclei of Walker tumor and rat liver. Exp Cell Res 46: 65–77, 1967.
48. Steele W J, Busch H: Studies on the ribonucleic acid component of the nuclear ribonucleoprotein network. Biochim Biophys Acta 129: 54–67, 1963.
49. Berezney R, Coffey D S: Identification of a nuclear protein matrix. Biochem Biophys Res Commun 60: 1410–1417, 1974.
50. Berezney R, Coffey D S: Nuclear matrix: Isolation and characterization of a framework structure from rat liver nuclei. J Cell Biol 73: 616–637, 1977.
51. Allen S L, Berezney R, Coffey D S: Phosphorylation of nuclear proteins in regenerating rat liver nuclei. Biochem Biophys Res Commun 75: 111–116, 1977.
52. Gerace L, Blobel G: The nuclear envelope lamina is reversibly depolymerized during mitosis. Cell 19: 277–287, 1980.
53. Herman R, Weymouth L, Penman S: Heterogeneous nuclear RNA-protein fibers in chromatin-depleted nuclei. J Cell Biol 78: 663–674, 1978.
54. Long B H, Huang C Y, Pogo A O: Isolation and characterization of the nuclear matrix in Friend erythroleukemia cells: Chromatin and heterogeneous RNA interactions with the nuclear matrix. Cell 18: 1079–1090, 1979.
55. van Eekelen C A G, van Venrooij W J: mRNA and its attachment to nuclear protein matrix. J Cell Biol 88: 554–563, 1981.
56. Buckler-White A J, Humphrey G W, Pigiet V: Association of Polyoma T antigen and DNA with the nuclear matrix from lytically infected 3T6 cells. Cell 22: 37–46, 1980.
57. Deppert W: Simian virus 40 (SV40)-specific proteins associated with the nuclear matrix isolated from adenovirus type 2-SV40 hybrid virus-infected HeLa cells carry SV40-U antigen. J Virol 26: 165–178, 1978.
58. Hemminki K, Vainio H: Preferential binding of benzo(a)pyrene into nuclear matrix fraction. Cancer Lett 6: 167–173, 1979.
59. Barrack E R, Coffey D S: The specific binding of estrogens and androgens to the nuclear matrix of sex hormone responsive tissues. J Biol Chem 255: 7265–7275, 1980.
60. Barrack E R, Hawkins E F, Allen S L, Hicks L L, Coffey D S: Concepts related to salt resistant estradiol receptors in rat uterine nuclei: Nuclear matrix. Biochem Biophys Res Commun 79: 829–836, 1977.

61. Herlan G, Wunderlich F: Isolation of a nuclear protein matrix from Tetrahymena macronuclei. Cytobiologie 13: 291–296, 1976.
62. Hodge L D, Mancini P, Davis F M, Heywood P: Nuclear matrix of HeLa S_3 cells. J Cell Biol 72: 194–208, 1977.
63. Hildebrand C E, Okinaka R T, Gurley L R: Existence of a residual nuclear protein matrix in cultured hamster cells. J Cell Biol 67: 169a, 1975.
64. Shelton K R, Cochran D L: In vitro oxidation of intrinsic sulfhydryl groups yield polymers of the predominant polypeptides in the nuclear envelope fraction. Biochemistry 17: 1212–1216, 1978.
65. Comings D E, Okada T A: Nuclear proteins. III. The fibrillar nature of the nuclear matrix. Exp Cell Res 103: 341–360, 1976.
66. Berezney R: Dynamic properties of the nuclear matrix. In Busch H (ed): "The Cell Nucleus." New York: Academic Press, 1979, vol 7, pp 413–456.
67. Gorski J, Gannon F: Current models of steroid hormone action: A critique. Ann Rev Physiol 38: 425–450, 1976.
68. Yamamoto K R, Alberts B M: Steroid receptors: Elements for modulation of eukaryotic transcription. Ann Rev Biochem 45: 721–746, 1976.
69. Thrall C L, Webster R A, Spelsberg T C: Steroid receptor interaction with chromatin. In Busch H (ed): "The Cell Nucleus." New York: Academic Press, 1978, pp 461–529.
70. Jackson V, Chalkley R: The binding of estradiol-17 β to the bovine endometrial nuclear membrane. J Biol Chem 249: 1615–1626, 1974.
71. Liao S, Liang T, Tymoczko J K: Ribonucleoprotein binding of steroid- "receptor" complexes. Nature New Biol 241: 211–213, 1973.
72. Senior M B, Frankel F R: Evidence for two kinds of chromatin binding sites for the estradiol-receptor complex. Cell 14: 857–863, 1978.
73. Lazier C: ^{3}H-Estradiol binding by chick liver nuclear extracts: Mechanism of increase in binding following estradiol injection. Steroids 26: 281–298, 1975.
74. Fang S, Anderson K M, Liao S: Receptor proteins for androgens. On the role of specific proteins in selective retention of 17β-hydroxy-5α-androstan-3-one by rat ventral prostate in vivo and in vitro. J Biol Chem 244: 6584–6595, 1969.
75. VanDoorn E, Craven S, Bruchovsky N: The relationship between androgen receptors and the hormonally controlled responses of rat ventral prostate. Biochem J 160: 11–21, 1976.
76. Clark J H, Peck E J Jr: Nuclear retention of receptor-oestrogen complex and nuclear acceptor sites. Nature 260: 635–637, 1976.
77. Ruh T S, Baudendistel L J: Different nuclear binding sites for antiestrogen and estrogen receptor complexes. Endocrinology 100: 420–426, 1977.
78. Ruh T S, Baudendistel L J: Antiestrogen modulation of the salt-resistant nuclear estrogen receptor. Endocrinology 102: 1838–1846, 1978.
79. Traish A, Müller R E, Wotiz H H: Binding of estrogen receptor to uterine nuclei. Salt extractable versus salt-resistant receptor-estrogen complexes. J Biol Chem 252: 6823–6830, 1977.
80. Cunha G R: Epithelial-stromal interactions in the development of the urogenital tract. Int Rev Cytol 47: 137–192, 1976.
81. Rojkind M, Gatmaitan Z, Mackensen S, Giambrone M D, Ponce P, Reid L M: Connective tissue biomatrix: Its isolation and utilization for long-term cultures of normal rat hepatocytes. J Cell Biol 87: 255–263, 1980.
82. Berezney R, Basler J, Hughes BB, Kaplan SC: Isolation and characterization of the nuclear matrix from Zajdela ascites hepatoma cells. Cancer Res 39: 3031–3039, 1979.
83. Pollack R, Osborn M, Weber K: Patterns of organization of actin and myosin in normal and transformed cultured cells. Proc Natl Acad Sci USA 72: 994–998, 1975.
84. Tucker R W, Sanford K F, Frankel F R: Tubulin and actin in paired nonneoplastic cells in

vitro. Fluorescent antibody studies. Cell 13: 629–642, 1978.
85. Brinkley B R, Miller C L, Fuseler J W, Pepper D A, Wible L J: Cytoskeletal changes in cell transformation to malignancy. In Saunders G F (ed): "Cell Differentiation and Neoplasia." 1978, pp 419–450.
86. Hynes R O: Cell surface proteins and malignant transformation. Biochim Biophys Acta 458: 73–107, 1976.
87. Watterson D M, Van Eldik L J, Smith R E, Vanaman T C: Calcium-dependent regulatory protein of cyclic nucleotide metabolism in normal and transformed chicken embryo fibroblasts. Proc Natl Acad Sci USA 73: 2711–2715, 1976.
88. Irwin D, Dauphinais I D: A tissue-specific code based upon the abundance of SDS-solubilized proteins. Anal Biochem 92: 193–198, 1979.
89. Isaacs J T, Isaacs W B, Coffey D S: Models for development of non-receptor methods for distinguishing androgen-sensitive and -insensitive prostatic tumors. Cancer Res 39: 2652–2659, 1979.
90. O'Farrell, P H: High resolution two-dimensional electrophoresis of proteins. J Biol Chem 250: 4007–4021, 1975.
91. Agutter PS, Richardson JCW: Nuclear non-chromatin proteinaceous structures: Their role in the organization and function of the interphase nucleus. J Cell Sci 44: 395–435, 1980.
92. McCready SJ, Godwin J, Mason DW, Brazell IA, Cook PR: DNA is replicated at the nuclear cage. J Cell Sci 46: 365–386, 1980.
93. Smith HC, Berezney R: DNA polymerase α is tightly bound to the nuclear matrix of actively replicating liver. Biochem Biophys Res Commun 97: 1541–1547, 1980.
94. Berezney R, Buchholtz LA: Dynamic association of replicating DNA fragments with the nuclear matrix of regenerating liver. Exp Cell Res 132: 1–13, 1981.
95. Kaufmann SH, Coffey DS, Shaper JH: Considerations in the isolation of rat liver nuclear matrix, nuclear envelope, and pore complex lamina. Exp Cell Res 132: 105–123, 1981.

The Prostatic Cell: Structure and Function
Part A, pages 25-53

The Role of the Cytoskeleton and Related Components in Normal and Neoplastic Prostatic Epithelium

Benjamin F. Trump, Barry M. Heatfield, and Patricia C. Phelps

INTRODUCTION

Within the last 7–8 years the cytoskeleton has received much attention, which has revealed its important role in many cell activities. It is known to be present in all eukaryotic cells and to be involved in cell shape, mobility, mitosis, attachment, pinocytosis, and malignant transformation. In addition it helps direct intracellular particle motility during phagocytosis and secretion, and is able to respond to many cell-surface signals by regulating the motility of cell surface receptors for immunoglobulins, lectins, and hormones. Transformed cells and preneoplastic and neoplastic tissues, which are known to express altered cell functions, have been studied as potential models for observing modifications in the cytoskeletal system. The finding of a relevant modification(s) could be useful as a marker for early neoplasia and for the understanding of the neoplastic process.

As described in more detail below, the cytoskeleton is made up of four major components: microtubules, microfilaments, intermediate filaments, and microtrabeculae. The microtubules have been intensely studied and are believed to interact with the microfilaments in a significant manner and to play a supportive or framework-like role, though other functions have also been proposed. Microtubule-associated proteins (MAPs) may function in the assembly of microtubules from the protein tubulin. The microfilaments consist of actin and associated proteins. The intermediate filaments are called tonofilaments in epithelial cells and are known to contain keratin and prekeratin proteins. They are seen in abundance in epidermal cells and are also commonly found at desmosomal attachment sites. The microtrabeculae are represented by an interconnecting network of thin strands, which attach to many types of organelles as well as to the plasma membrane.

A number of studies in the literature report data on the cytoskeletal elements in transformed cells and in preneoplastic and neoplastic tissues as compared to their normal counterparts. These will be presented in detail following a brief consideration of available methods for studying the cytoskeleton.

Techniques available for studying the cytoskeleton include morphologic and immunocytochemical methods at both the light microscope (LM) and transmission electron microscope (TEM) level on cell and tissue preparations. Indirect immunofluorescence and the peroxidase-antiperoxidase (PAP) procedure of Sternberger [1] can be routinely used on fixed material with equivalent results by LM and TEM, providing the antibody is monospecific for the filament protein to be studied and that proper tissue preparation and/or embedding is followed. Some of the more elegant work has been performed on cells using cytoskeletal preparations and indirect immunofluorescence. Prior to fixation, cells on coverslips are treated with a nonionic detergent such as Triton X-100 in stabilizing buffer (e.g., suitable for microtubules) in order to remove cell membranes. The isolated cytoskeletons are then fixed in glutaraldehyde, washed, and incubated with the primary antibody, then washed and incubated with the secondary antibody tagged with fluorescein-isothio-cyanate (FITC), or other analogous compounds. The results are readily visible in the fluorescence microscope. The Sternberger PAP technique is very sensitive for small amounts of antigen and can also be used for cytoskeletal preparations. This technique involves several steps. Again the cells are first incubated with the primary antisera (usually made in rabbits), washed, and then incubated with an excess of a second antisera raised in goats by immunization with rabbit immunoglobulins (GAR), and again washed. This step is followed by incubation with the PAP complex (a purified immuno-complex of horseradish peroxidase made in rabbits), which will attach to the remaining binding site of the GAR antisera. After a final wash a substrate such as diaminobenzidine (DAB) is applied, which undergoes oxidation and polymerization to a dense reaction product visible by both LM and TEM. A shorter method of cell fixation is also possible using 3% PSB-buffered formaldehyde and then opening cell membranes by exposure to 100% acetone at –20°C before performing the immunochemical techniques.

For LM study of tissue cytoskeletal elements preliminary work has been done by the immunofluorescence procedure on unfixed or briefly fixed frozen sections and by the PAP method on formaldehyde-fixed paraffin-embedded sections. Using these techniques keratin has been successfully located by Schlegel et al [2] and Franke et al [3], while actin was identified by Gabbiani et al [4].

Poor antibody penetration and adequate morphological preservation at the ultrastructural level have been major problems in the identification of cytoskeletal elements. However, a recent study has localized myosin, actin, and tropomyosin in the rat intestine by TEM immunoperoxidase techniques [5].

Study of cell junctions has been performed by TEM of routine, heavy metal-stained ultrathin sections of plastic-embedded fixed tissues, isolated membrane preparations negatively stained with heavy metals, and by examination of thin metal film replicas of freeze-fractured, freeze-etched tissues. A general consideration of these techniques in the morphologic characterization of cell junctions can be found in the excellent review by Weinstein et al [6].

Microtrabeculae have been characterized by stereo images of whole, cultured cells taken with the high voltage TEM. Such cells have been prepared in a variety of ways to eliminate the possibility of artifact as detailed by Wolosewick and Porter [7].

THE CYTOSKELETON—STRUCTURE, FUNCTION, PATHOLOGY

Microtubules/MAPs

Microtubules, first isolated and purified from homogenates of mammalian brain by Weisenberg and co-workers [8,9], are similar in all cells, and are sometimes the most abundant and largest of the filamentous structures found in the cytoplasm, being 25 nm in diameter, with a hollow core 15 nm in diameter. Microtubules may be of indefinite length. They are composed of unbranched polymers of the protein tubulin. Tubulin exists as a dimer of two nonidentical subunits, α- and β-tubulin. Thirteen longitudinal rows (protofilaments) of dimers in a circular array comprise the wall of the tubule. Polymerized tubulin exists in dynamic equilibrium with unpolymerized tubulin. Polymerization of tubulin is Mg^{++}-dependent and is inhibited by calcium. Other conditions which can interfere with tubulin polymerization and microtubule assembly include temperature, pressure, pH, anesthetics, and antimitotic compounds such as vinblastin, cholchicine, Ca^{++} ionophores, and others.

Recently, microtubule-associated proteins (MAPs) have been characterized from microtubules assembled in vitro [10]. They appear as fine filamentous projections decorating the surface of microtubules as seen by TEM [11,12]. There are at least two MAPs which have been isolated: MAP 1 and MAP 2, whose subunit molecular weight is greater than 300,000 daltons. The presence of MAPs appear to facilitate the initial rate and total amount of assembly of microtubules from tubulin subunits in vitro by lowering the critical concentration of tubulin needed for polymerization. The MAPs, which coat the surface of the microtubule, may confer stability and prevent or retard dissasembly [13]. They may also be involved in cross-bridging of microtubules where they occur in bundles as in the marginal bands which form structural units in nucleated erythrocytes [13,14].

Microtubules participate, most notably, in formation of the spindle apparatus during chromosome separation at anaphase, although they are not contractile. Movement of chromosomes is thought to involve a polymerization-depolymerization mechanism or, alternatively, interaction between adjacent microtubules or with other cytoplasmic proteins [13]. In a recent paper, Brinkley et al [15] have clearly identified microtubular organizing centers (MTOC) in the cytoplasm of 3T3 cells by studying tubulin polymerization after colcemid treatment using indirect immunofluorescent methods. They concluded that most interphase cells in G1 phase contain a single MTOC. As the cells progress through S-phase, two MTOCs are apparent. Most cytoplasmic microtubules appeared to be assembled in close proximity to the centrioles. The number and arrangement of microtubules in cultured cells is dependent on a number of variables, including the stage of the cell cycle and type of substrate used. Microtubules may be distributed in linear arrays parallel to the axis of elongated cell processes in some cells. In epithelial cells, a three-dimensional, lattice-like network is more common. It has been suggested that microtubules are limited to cell membrane proteins via intermediate macromolecules [16], and may also interact with actin, intermediate filaments, and related proteins, as well as intracellular organelles. Thus, in addition to spindle formation, alteration in microtubules could affect cell shape, motility, secretory activity, etc. MAPs probably play a significant role in the formation and stabilization of microtubules.

Alterations in the pattern of distribution of microtubules, or the rate of polymerization, possibly involving MAPs, may account for changes in cell structure and function associated with disease states, particularly neoplasia. However, consistent differences in the number of microtubules, amount of tubulin, or association with plasma membrane components in neoplastic vs normal cells have not yet been clearly demonstrated, although significant alterations in the pattern of distribution of microtubules in neoplastic cells may exist. Brinkley et al [17] and Fonte and Porter [18] found that virus-transformed cells had fewer and more randomly arranged microtubules than normal cells. Miller et al [19] also found fewer microtubules in transformed cells. Others [20–23] have not found significant differences in the population and organization of microtubules between normal and transformed cells.

Recently, Rubin and Warren [24] reported that transformed rat kidney cells had only half the number of microtubules as normal cells, but that both had the same total amount of tubulin. Asch et al [25] found no consistent differences in microtubules in primary cell lines from normal, preneoplastic, and neoplastic mammary epithelium, but in one secondary cell line from a mammary tumor they saw an abnormal, intricate microtubule network.

Microfilaments

Actin/myosin. The contractile filament component, actin, is 6–8 nm in diameter and consists of double-stranded polymers. Actin is known to exist in both a monomeric (globular) form and a polymerized (filamentous) state, which are in dynamic equilibrium. In nonmuscle cells, actin is associated with the proteins α-actinin, filamin, tropomyosin, and myosin. The filaments exist individually as a meshwork or as bundles or cables, and can be visualized by TEM and, more specifically, by immunocytochemical techniques. Actin filaments and associated myosin proteins are involved in contraction in muscle and nonmuscle cells, and are probably responsible for orientation of a number of structures such as microvilli of epithelial cells in the intestine and kidney.

Differences in the quantity and distribution of microfilaments between normal and transformed cells have been reported. Gabbiani et al [4] found increased numbers of contractile filaments (actin/myosin) by immunofluorescence studies of cancer cells of human skin, oral cavity, and mammary gland, particularly at tumor margins. Actin/myosin staining correlated with the presence of microfilaments. Similarly, McNutt [26] noted an increase in microfilaments at the advancing margins of invasive tumors of the skin. In contrast, Pollack et al [27] observed few, if any, actin cables in cells transformed by oncogenic viruses. Modification of contractile proteins, such as an increase in their number indicated above, may account for increased motility and, thus, invasiveness [4]. Asch et al [25] did not detect differences in microfilaments in primary cell lines from normal, preneoplastic, and neoplastic mammary epithelium, but saw a reduction in actin cables in one secondary cell line from a mammary tumor. Myosin has been localized in the cytoplasm next to the plasma membrane in tumors of human breast, stomach, bronchi, skin, esophagus, and kidney [28]. Tumor cells were more strongly positive than normal cells, although the pattern of immunofluorescence varied depending on tumor type. The apparent increase in myosin in these tumor cells may be related to cell shape and polarity, in addition to cell movement. The interrelationship between actin filaments and the plasma membrane, which may determine cell locomotion, etc, is unclear, but may involve other proteins such as calmodulin (see below), which is a structural protein tightly associated with the filament core of microvilli, and may play an important role in calcium-dependent activity of contractile proteins as well as other calcium-dependent phenomena [29].

Intermediate filaments. This class of filaments consists of protein polymers, and although they are similar in diameter (7–11 nm) in many cell types, they can differ in the type of constitutent protein. To date, several categories have been described based on differences in protein chemistry.

Prekeratin/keratin. Tonofilaments in epithelial cells consist of the protein prekeratin and/or keratin. Typically, tonofilaments exist in small bundles scattered in the cytoplasm, and often terminate in desmosomal junctions (see below). Keratin is virtually specific for epithelium, and can be demonstrated morphologically by TEM and by immunologic techniques. Tonofilaments are particularly abundant in the epidermis, and have been described in basal cells of normal prostatic epithelium, but not in secretory cells or prostatic adenocarcinomas [2]. In a variety of other human tumors, Schlegel et al [2] obtained positive staining for keratin in squamous cell carcinoma and transitional cell tumors; negative or minimal staining was observed in mammary adenocarcinoma, undifferentiated lung carcinoma, and in adenocarcinoma of the colon and kidney. In squamous cell carcinoma of the lung, the quantity of tonofilaments may be increased [30]. In addition, the tonofilament bundles in these tumors formed an extensive branching and anastomosing network. In pseudopodia, these bundles were very dense and it is possible that they may be involved in invasive activity of tumor cells. Yuspa and colleagues [31] have reported interesting data on changes in spontaneously transformed mouse epidermal cells. They find that the cells in all transformed lines had lower than normal quantities of keratin, as determined by radioimmunoassay. In addition, transformed cells were able to grow in media containing high calcium concentrations (7.0 mM), whereas their normal counterparts could not. This suggests that keratin filaments could be associated with a calcium-regulated blockage of normal cell proliferation.

Desmin. Intermediate filaments in smooth muscle cells contain desmin as a major subunit protein. It has been suggested that desmin can form complexes with actin, and may function as a network to interlink myofibrils as a mechanical unit, as well as attachment of myofibrils to the plasma membrane [32].

Vimentin. Various mesenchymal cells and certain epithelia, such as endothelial cells from human umbilical cord, have intermediate filaments consisting principally of the protein vimentin [33], which is immunologically distinct from prekeratin or desmin.

At present, intermediate sized filaments may be involved in cell locomotion, transport, and organelle movement, as well as maintenance of cell shape and intracellular support. Alterations in intermediate filaments accompanying malignant transformation could account for some aspects of the malignant phenotype.

Microtrabecular Lattice

Stereomicroscopy by high voltage TEM reveals an irregular, but nonrandom, three-dimensional lattice throughout the cytoplasm of a variety of cultured cells (rat kidney, human fibroblasts, and others) prepared in different ways to exclude the possibility of preparation artifact [7,34]. Comprising the lattice are slender strands, 3–6 nm in diameter. The microtrabeculae form an open meshwork interconnecting various organelles, even microtubules and microfilaments, and are confluent with the inner surface of the plasma membrane. The slender strands of the lattice may coat the surface of actin filaments [35]. It has been estimated that the protein-rich lattice accounts for up to 20% of the cell volume.

Recently, it was proposed that the microtrabecular lattice may "organize the diverse components of the cell into a functional unity—the cytoplast—and mediate regulated and directed transport in the cell" [35].

As yet, however, little information is available on alterations under pathologic conditions, including neoplasia. Nevertheless, it is likely that changes in the conformation of this lattice could result in significant effects on cell shape and movement, as postulated for other cytoskeletal elements discussed in this paper. For example, under conditions of energy depletion, the lattice collapses, often resulting in aggregation of organelles near the center of the cell.

Associated Components

Calmodulin. Calmodulin is an intracellular receptor protein for calcium, and appears to mediate calcium-dependent cell activities including metabolism of cyclic nucleotides and glycogen, calcium transport, secretion, motility, cell shape, and division. Calmodulin has been characterized by Dedman et al [36], and a monospecific antibody has been prepared [37], which has great potential as an immunocytochemical marker [38]. By immunofluorescence, the distribution of calmodulin is sometimes coincident with actin-containing stress fibers [37], and has been demonstrated to be present in various cells and tissues [39,40].

In certain transformed mammalian cells, the concentration of calmodulin was double that observed in normal cells [41]. This increase was found to result from increased synthesis of calmodulin. Since calcium-dependent assembly-disassembly of microtubules in vitro may be mediated by calmodulin [42], alterations in this protein may explain differences in the amount and distribution of several cytoskeletal components in neoplastic cells as compared to normal cells. In the absence of calmodulin, high concentrations of [Ca^{++}] would be required to exert the same effects (eg, microtubule assembly-dissasembly).

Cell junctions. Briefly, there are three major classes of junctional complexes based on ultrastructural characteristics. These classes are: 1) tight (occludens) junctions, 2) gap (nexus) junctions, and 3) desmosomes (adherens). These can be further divided according to the configuration at the cell surface, ie, a belt-like zone around the cell periphery (eg, zonula occludens), disc shape (eg, macula adherens or desmosome; gap junctions), etc. Both tight junctions and gap junctions involve intermembrane contact of adjacent cells, whereas adjacent membranes are separated by a narrow space in the case of desmosomes.

1) Tight junctions appear to involve fusion of the plasma membranes of adjacent cells in areas of contact. These junctional complexes usually occur in a continuous band around the apical perimeter of many types of epithelial cells and provide a highly selective barrier to the passage of molecules from the adjacent milieu into the intercellular space or in the reverse direction, and are

important in the regulation of osmotic and electrochemical gradients across epithelia.

Alterations in tight junctions often accompany cell injury of various etiologies [6]. These include morphologic changes as well as reduction or loss of function as a permeability barrier. In certain neoplasms, ie, transitional cell carcinoma of the bladder, or squamous cell carcinoma of the uterine cervix, focal discontinuity or even loss of tight junctions (zonulae occludentes) may occur, the severity of which, in some instances, appears to be correlated with the degree of cellular anaplasia. The factors responsible for such alterations may be multiple, including genetic or extracellular, microenvironmental factors [6].

2) In gap junctions, the surfaces of adjacent cells are separated by a narrow 2–4 nm space or gap which provides a pathway for communication by permiting passive movement of ions and small molecules between adjacent cells across the gap [43] via hydrophilic channels [44–46]. Gap junctions (or connexons [47]) are composed of six subunits and are reported to rotate forming "open" or "closed" configurations [48]. It is suggested that in the "open" configuration, particles with a molecular weight of up to 800 daltons can be accomodated. Passage of informational molecules between cells via gap junctions may be important in the coordination of tissue activities, such as metabolism, growth, and differentiation [49].

Gap junctions may be absent in the majority of liver cells during early periods of regeneration in response to partial hepatectomy [50]. In some malignant tumors, there may be reduction in number or loss of gap junctions. For example, in human cervical carcinomas, a deficiency of gap junctions has been noted [6,51,52]. Loss of these complexes may occur at an early stage of tumor progression, complicating assessment of their role in malignant transformation. One important known uncoupling condition is elevated [Ca^{++}]—known to occur in regenerating and neoplastic cells [29].

3) Desmosomes are characterized by focal approach of surfaces of adjacent cells to within 25–35 nm. Moderately electron-dense material is present in this intervening space. At the midplane is a thin zone of very dense material. Tonofilaments are attached to the thickened inner surfaces of the subjacent plasma membranes and from there pass into the adjacent cytoplasm, sometimes forming dense bundles. Hemidesmosomes (half desmosomes) resemble desmosomes and appear to serve as attachment sites between some epithelia and the underlying stroma. Desmosomes and hemidesmosomes appear to provide points of strong attachment among epithelial cells and between epithelia and connective tissue.

Alteration in the number or integrity of desmosomes accompanies neoplasia in several human tissues. In neoplastic bladder epithelium, desmosomes may be incomplete; one half of a desmosome may be present along the plasma membrane of only one of two adjacent cells [53]. Epidermoid (squamous) carcinomas of the lung may show increased numbers of desmosomes compared to the cell of origin. In metastases to the liver in humans [54] and in experimental animals [55], well-defined desmosomes are formed between tumor and hepatic parenchymal cells, indicating that specialized junctional complexes can be assembled even between dissimilar neoplasic and non-neoplastic tissues. Alterations in demosomal junctions have also been described in normal tissues, and in non-neoplastic states [6]. In addition, McNutt [26] noted a decrease in the number of hemidesmosomes at the marginal edge of invasive carcinoma of the skin.

CYTOSKELETON AND PROSTATIC EPITHELIUM

Although interest in the cytoskeleton and its role in normal and altered cells is increasing, little attention has been given to this important system in prostatic epithelium. It is the purpose of the present paper to describe results of our recent preliminary studies and review the possibilities of how the cytoskeleton might function in the normal and abnormal prostate.

Methods of Study

In our laboratory specimens of normal prostatic epithelium were obtained from patients studied at immediate autopsy. Using this technique, we are able to collect the entire prostate within a few minutes of death [56]. In addition to non-neoplastic prostate, specimens of adenocarcinoma were collected at the time of surgery for comparative studies.

Following sampling, tissues were fixed in mixed aldehydes [57] for correlative LM, TEM, and scanning electron microscopy (SEM), or were prepared for culture.

For TEM, fixed tissues were washed three times in 0.2 M cacodylate buffer containing 7% sucrose, then postfixed in 1% osmium tetroxide. The washed tissues were stained with 1% uranyl acetate en bloc and dehydrated through graded alcohols, propaline oxide, and embedded in Epon 812. Light microscopy was performed on 1-μm sections stained with toluidine blue [58]. Ultrathin sections were then prepared and stained with uranyl magnesium acetate and lead citrate prior to examination in a JEOL 100B TEM.

For SEM, osmium-fixed tissues were rinsed in 0.2 M cacodylate buffer and transferred to saturated thiocarbohydrazide [59] in distilled water for 20 minutes at room temperature. Such treated specimens were then washed several times in distilled water, placed in osmium tetroxide for 30–60 minutes, dehydrated through graded ethanols, and critical point dried with liquid CO_2. These specimens were mounted on aluminum stubs with silver conductive paint, sputter-coated with gold-palladium for 5 minutes, and examined with an AMR 1000 SEM.

For culture, tissues were cut into 1–2 mm slices with razor blades in a laminar flow hood, and placed in L-15 medium [60] in Petri dishes. They were then trimmed into small (approximately 1 × 1 × 10 mm) pieces with a scalpel, gently rinsed in L-15, and transferred to 60-mm Petri dishes. About 3–4 pieces were added per dish. The medium consisted of 3 ml of CMRL-1066, supplemented with 0.1 mg per ml hydrocortisone hemisuccinate, 1 mg/ml bovine recrystalyzed insulin, 2 mm L-glutamine, 5% heat-inactivated fetal bovine serum, and antibiotics [61]. The culture dishes were then incubated in controlled atmosphere chambers gassed with a mixture of 45% O_2, 50% N_2, and 5% CO_2. The chambers were positioned on a rocker platform, rocked at 10 cycles per minute which permited alternate exposure and submersion of the explant surface, and incubated at 37°C. The medium and atmosphere were replaced three times each week. Under these conditions, viable prostatic epithelium was cultured for periods up to 6 months.

Preliminary experiments were performed to determine the presence of microtubules in outgrowth cells from a single case of adenocarcinoma of the prostate. Cytoskeletal preparations were made by exposing the cells to Triton X-100 (in stabilizing buffer) for several minutes, followed by fixation in 3% glutaraldehyde and treatment with a low concentration of fresh buffered sodium borohydride. The cells were then stained for indirect immunofluorescence by incubation for 45 minutes at 37°C with a primary monospecific, affinity-purified rabbit antitubulin antibody (kindly provided by B.R. Brinkley, Baylor College, Houston, Texas). They were then washed and incubated with fluorescein-tagged, goat anti-rabbit IgG and viewed and photographed using a Zeiss Photomicroscope III adapted for epifluorescence and equipped with a 490 excitor filter and a 510 reflector filter.

Structure of the Normal Prostatic Epithelium

Closely packed arrays of epithelial cells cover folds and papillary extensions of the wall of glandular acini in normal human prostate as seen by SEM (Fig. 1). Separating the acini is dense fibromuscular stroma. The rounded apical surface of these epithelial cells in the active gland is covered with a variable number of microvilli and occasional elevated secretory blebs (Fig. 2). Openings in the apical plasma membrane also characterize some of these cells, although their significance is unclear [62].

By TEM, the prostatic glands are lined by a pseudo-stratified epithelium. Secretory cells extend from the basal lamina to the lumen, while the basal cells lie along the basal lamina but do not reach the lumen (Fig. 3).

Secretory cells. The secretory cells are columnar to tall cuboidal with a nucleus located in the basal portion (Fig. 3). The apical portion of the cells is characterized by numerous vacuolar structures which may contain smaller vesicles. Other organelles are present, including a well-developed supranuclear Golgi complex, mitochondria, sparse profiles of rough endoplasmic reticulum (RER), an occasional lipid droplet, free polysomes, and lysosomes. The apical

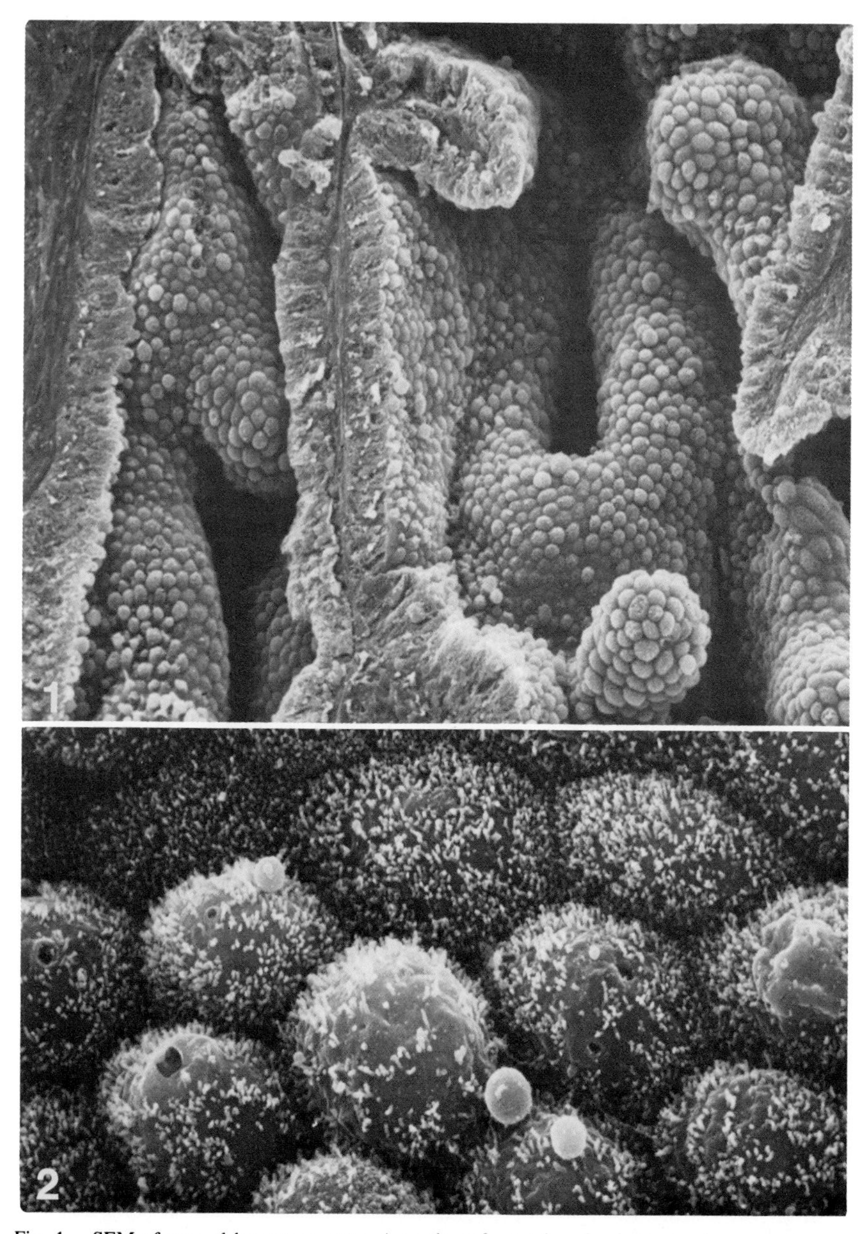

Fig. 1. SEM of normal human prostate. A portion of a sectioned acinus reveals compact arrays of epithelial cells with convex apical surfaces covering narrow folds or papillary-like projections of the acinar wall. The stroma appears thin and delicate between ajacent layers of epithelial cells covering folds of the acinar wall. (Courtesy, SEM, Inc.) 300×.

Fig. 2. Numerous short microvilli, together with occasional secretory blebs, characterize apical surfaces of epithelial cells seen in Figure 1. (Courtesy, Dr. Hayato Sanefuji.) 4,000 ×.

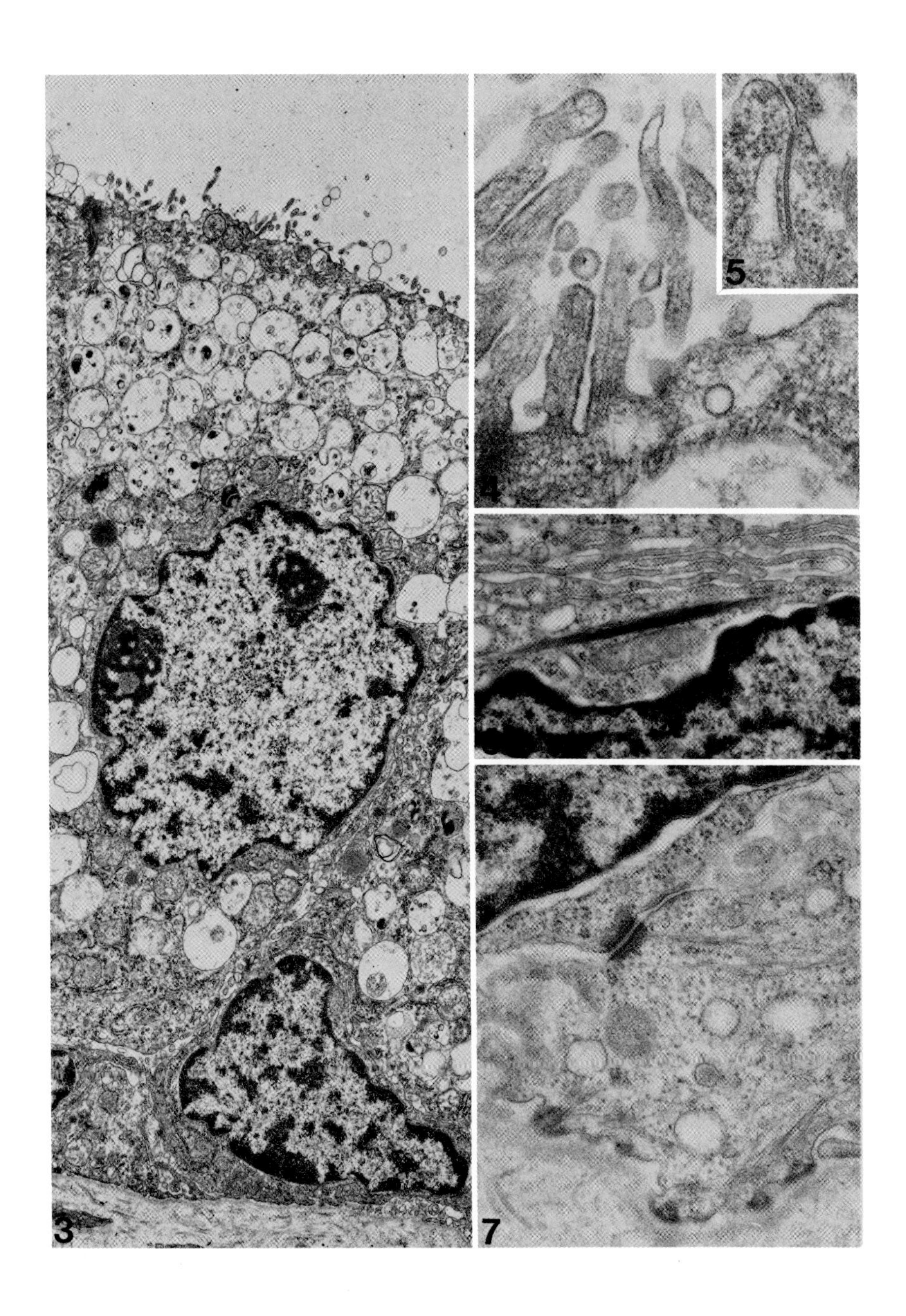
3
4
5
7

surface is typically covered with microvilli (Fig. 4), but in some instances, bulging cytoplasmic blebs project toward the lumen, in which membrane-bound structures resembling pinched-off blebs are seen. Typical junctional complexes including well-formed tight junctions, gap junctions (Figs. 4,5), and desmosomes are observed along the lateral surfaces, which are irregular with small membrane folds (Fig. 6).

Cytoskeletal elements are observed in thin sections, and include thin filaments (presumed to be actin), intermediate filaments (presumed to be keratin), and microtubules. The thin filaments are especially prominent in the cell apex where they occur in the area of the terminal web and longitudinally within the microvilli (Fig. 4). These filaments presumably also attach to the adjacent cell membrane, thereby assisting in the maintenance of microvilli shape. Intermediate filaments are seen throughout the cell, and are noted in clusters along the lateral margins where they may be responsible for folding of the plasma membrane. They are especially prominent in close proximity to desmosomes. Microtubules, though not abundant in secretory cells, are occassionally seen scattered throughout the cytoplasm.

Basal cells. The basal cells are triangular or flattened cells which lie along the basal lamina and appear nestled among the basal profiles of secretory cells (Fig. 3). They possess somewhat hyperchromatic nuclei (Fig. 3,6) with inconspicuous nucleoli and have a high nucleus to cytoplasm ratio. In contrast to secretory cells, basal cells lack secretory vacuoles and have a poorly developed Golgi complex. They display junctional complexes including well-formed desmosomes (Fig. 7), and have extensive plasma membrane folds along their mar-

---

Fig. 3. TEM of pseudostratified prostatic epithelium showing principal morphologic features of secretory cells and basal cells. Secretory cells are columnar and extend from the basal lamina to the lumen. The cytoplasm is packed with vacuoles enclosing vesicular profiles. The apical surface is covered with microvilli and occasional plasma membrane blebs. Basal cells are positioned along the basal lamina at the junction between the epithelium and stroma. These cells are triangular or flattened in shape, possess a small nucleus with condensed chromatin, and lack secretory vacuoles. (Courtesy, Academic Press, Inc.) 8,000 ×.

Fig. 4. Apical surface of secretory cell showing a tight junctional complex (lower left) and numerous microvilli supported by microfilaments (actin). 40,000 ×.

Fig. 5. Example of a gap junction along the lateral margins of two adjacent secretory cells. 20,000 ×.

Fig. 6. Tonofilament bundles within the cytoplasm of a basal cell. Also shown are interdigitating surface folds. 12,000 ×.

Fig. 7. Desmosome between adjacent basal cells, and possible hemidesmosome-like condensations along the lower margin of a basal cell, adjacent to the basal lamina. 12,000 ×.

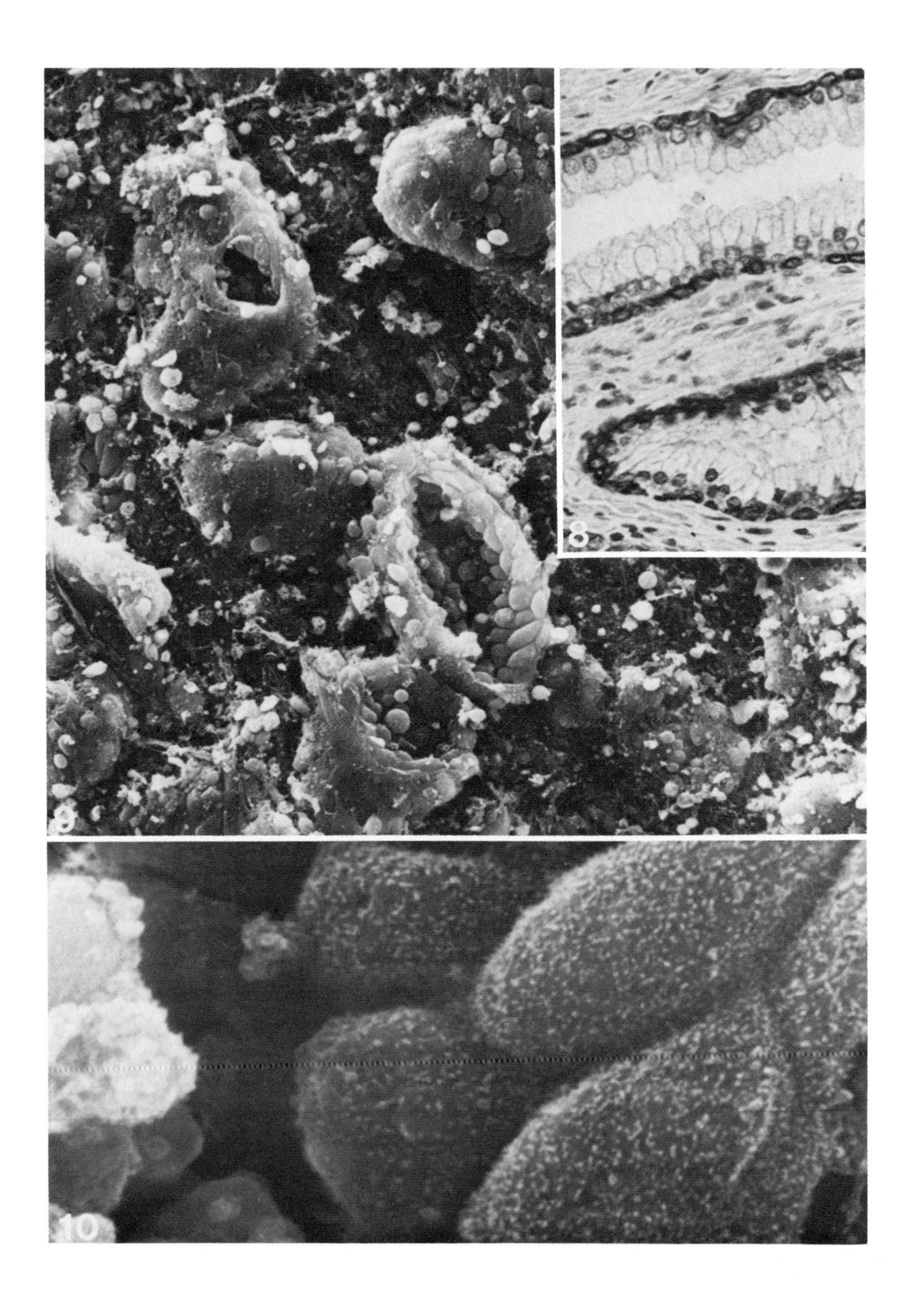
8
9
10

gins (Fig. 6). Lysosomes and numerous polysomes are present, together with striking bundles of keratin filaments (Fig. 6), identified immunologically (Fig. 8) by Schlegel et al [2]. Along the basal lamina are condensations of cytoplasmic material which may represent hemidesmosomes (Fig. 7). Well-formed bundles of actin filaments are not obvious within these cells. Basal cells have been regarded as "reserve cells" [63–66]. In explant cultures, basal cells possess the capacity to incorporate tritiated thymidine, migrate, and assume secretory characteristics [67].

Structure of Adenocarcinoma

SEM of cut surfaces of surgical specimens of well-differentiated prostatic adenocarcinoma (Fig. 9) reveals numerous small acinar structures consisting of compact arrangements of tumor cells. Individual tumor cells which line the small acini possess rounded apical surfaces covered with variable numbers of shortened microvilli (Fig. 10).

By TEM, the cells of well-differentiated adenocarcinomas of the prostate are cuboidal or columnar and, typically, only a single layer of cells is present; basal cells are absent (Fig. 11). Normal secretory vacuoles are seen; however, cell surfaces and cytoskeletal components are markedly different. The well-formed apical microvilli of normal secretory cells are either absent or scanty (Fig. 12). The microfilaments of the cell apex and those along the base of the cells are markedly disorganized. Junctional complexes can still be seen (Figs. 12,13), although gap junctions may be decreased in number. Other elements of the cytoskeleton, eg, microtubules and filaments (actin?) are occassionally encountered (Fig. 14).

Prostatic Epithelium in Culture

Normal prostate. Our results of long-term explant culture of normal human prostate have revealed a number of interesting changes that relate to the activities of the secretory and basal cells, and of the cytoskeleton. During early

---

Fig. 8. LM of paraffin-embedded, normal prostatic acinar epithelium stained for keratin by immunocytochemistry using the peroxidase-antiperoxidase (PAP) technique. Reaction product is localized in basal cells. (Courtesy, Dr. Susan Banks-Schlegel.) 400 ×.

Fig. 9. SEM of the cut surface of well-differentiated, prostatic adenocarcinoma showing various profiles of small acinar structures exposed at the cut surface of the specimen. 600 ×.

Fig. 10. Several tumor cells of one acinus shown in Figure 9. Rounded apical surfaces are decorated with stubby microvilli; occasional secretory blebs are seen. 4,000 ×.

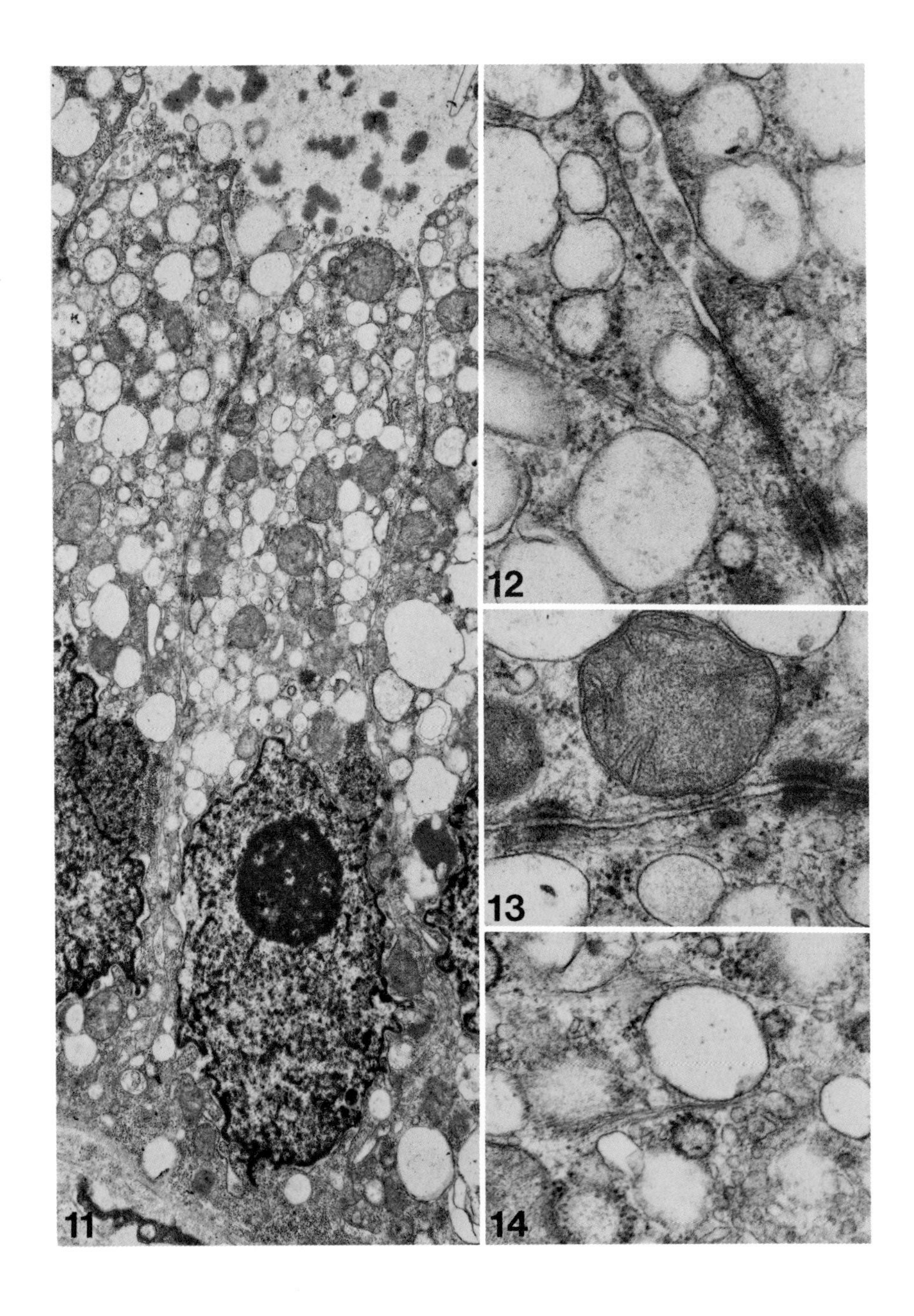
11
12
13
14

periods of culture, we noted degeneration and necrosis of the secretory columnar cells in acini. However, basal cells remained viable, and following sloughing of secretory cells the ducts and acinar structures became recolonized by cells with epithelial features, including microvilli, junctional complexes, large Golgi complexes (Figs. 15–17), and basal lamina. Scattered keratin filaments, also found in bundles, and microtubules were sometimes seen. During colonization basal cells incorporated tritiated thymidine and subsequently migrated onto and covered the cut surface of the explant. Vacuoles containing mucosubstances were present within their apices. It is our hypothesis at the present time that the secretory cells fail to survive under culture conditions; instead the explants are repopulated by proliferating basal cells which undergo mucus metaplasia.

In cultured or fresh explants of normal human prostate xenografted into the nude (athymic) mouse, tonofilament bundles were sometimes very conspicuous in basal cells, but inconspicuous in secretory cells (Fig. 18).

Prostatic adenocarcinoma. When adenocarcinomas are cultured in vitro, the cells readily cover cut surfaces of the explant as in normal prostate. The appearance of the cells, however, is remarkably different. Multiple layers of squamous-like cells are seen. The cells are very irregular in shape, both by SEM (Fig. 19) and TEM (Fig. 20). Cell junctions are scarce or absent (Fig. 20). Filopodia contact adjacent cells (Fig. 19). Large bundles of thin filaments are arranged parallel to the cell membrane, but are not inserted into the membrane forming villi (Fig. 21). Microtubules are sometimes seen (Fig. 22).

In preliminary experiments, outgrowth cells from a single case of adenocarcinoma of the prostate showed a conspicuous complement of microtubules stained with the indirect immunofluorescent technique. Prostate outgrowth cells possessed many microtubules with somewhat variable patterns of distribution (Fig. 23). Some large cells (Fig. 23a) had long straight microtubules, which extended from the perinuclear region in parallel arrays. Near the periphery most micro-

---

Fig. 11. TEM of a small acinus of well-differentiated prostatic adenocarcinoma. Tumor cells possess numerous secretory vacuoles as in normal prostate. A single, large nucleolus is present in the nucleus of one cell. Basal cells are absent. 8,000×.

Fig. 12. Tight junctional complex and desmosome (lower right) of prostatic tumor cells are illustrated. 30,000×.

Fig. 13. Several desmosomes attach two adjacent tumor cells. 40,000×.

Fig. 14. Aggregates of filaments (actin?) in the cytoplasm of a tumor cell. 30,000×.

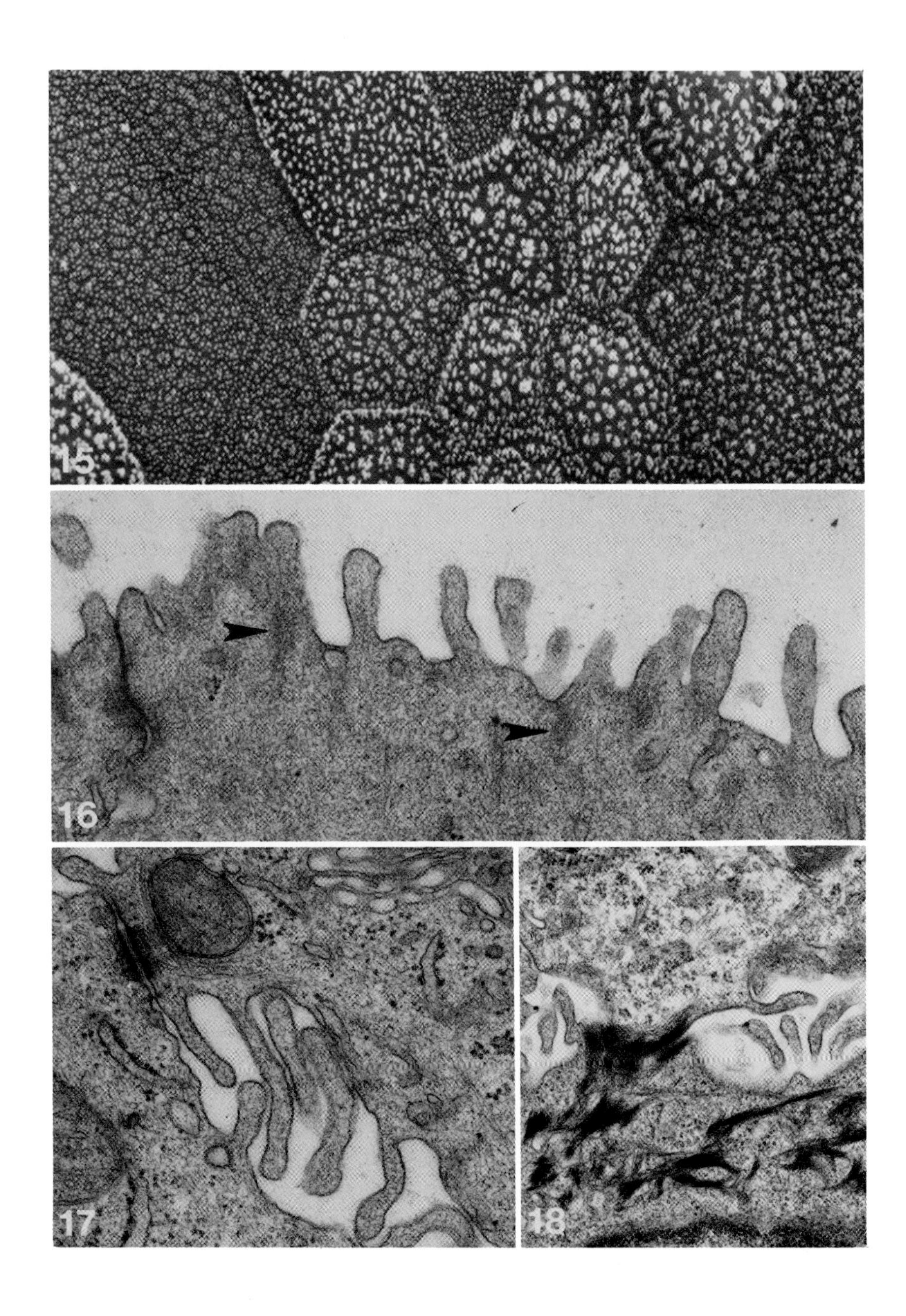
15
16
17
18

tubules appeared to bend or overlap. The smaller cells (Fig. 23b,c) had numerous microtubules which extended in various directions and were arranged in complex meshwork patterns. Additional data are needed to determine whether malignant cells in the prostate can be distinguished from their normal counterparts by means of altered cytoskeletal filament patterns.

Carcinogen-treated normal prostate. Cells of normal prostate explants treated with the direct-acting carcinogen, MNNG, appear similar to cultured explants of adenocarcinoma [62,68]. By SEM, cells on explant surfaces are piled up, lack orientation, and contact neighboring cells with cytoplasmic extensions (Fig. 24). By TEM, the cells also show few tight junctions or desmosomes (Fig. 25).

DISCUSSION

It is apparent that the prostatic epithelium possesses components of the cytoskeleton comparable to those of other cell types, and which are seemingly altered in neoplasia as well. In this section, some of these aspects will be discussed, followed by a consideration of control mechanisms in normal cells and possible alterations in neoplasia.

Our in vitro observations indicate altered cell junctions and junctional-cytoskeletal relationships in adenocarcinomas of the prostate or in normal prostate treated with carcinogens. Several types of junctions appear to be decreased, however. Most important conceptionally is reduction in the number of gap junctions which are the sites of cell-cell communication and macromolecular transfer. It has been reported by Lowenstein [69] in a series of articles that transformed

---

Fig. 15. SEM showing tightly packed epithelial cells of basal cell origin covering surfaces of prostatic explants after culture for 5 weeks. Cells are polygonal with stubby microvilli that vary in number and length. Borders between adjacent cells are delineated by narrow ridges (condensations) of microvilli. 2,000 ×.

Fig. 16. TEM of the apical portion of a basal cell derivative on the surface of an explant after culture for 9 weeks. A tight junction connects the perimeter of two adjacent cells (left). Microvilli contain filamentous cores (arrow heads), which extend for a short distance into the adjacent cytoplasm. 40,000 ×.

Fig. 17. As in Figure 16. A desmosome (upper left), lateral membrane folds (bottom) without supporting microfilaments, and well-developed Golgi cisternae (upper right) are shown. 40,000 ×.

Fig. 18. Illustrated are bundles of tonofilaments present in a basal cell of fresh human prostate xenografted into a nude mouse for 1 week. Some tonofilaments are associated with a desmosome (left) attaching the basal cell (below) to a secretory cell (above). 20,000 ×.

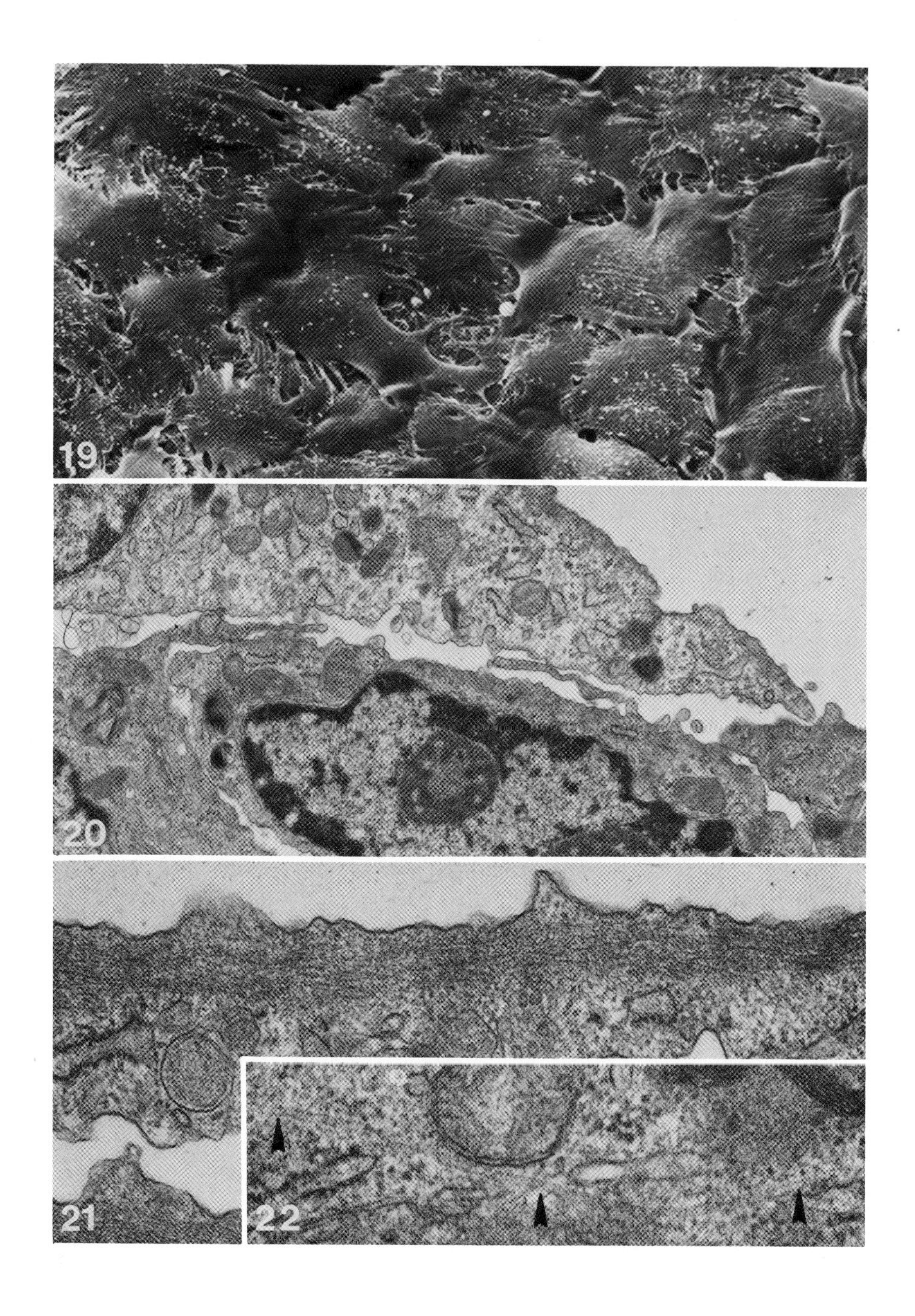
19
20
21
22

cells in vitro have decreased gap junctions and decreased cell-cell communication. This has also been observed in carcinomas of the cervix and bladder. Interestingly, Lowenstein also has documented in some experiments that increased levels of intracellular calcium can precipitate gap junction association. The decreased numbers of desmosomes and, subsequently, lack of attachment sites for intermediate filaments could also obviously result in cell-shape changes. Bulger and Trump [70] reported on treatment of isolated flounder kidney tubules with calcium-free media with or without calcium chelating agents. They noted that as desmosomes separated rapid shape changes occurred presumably due to the release of cell attachments and the tension of contractile filaments against an otherwise unsupported system.

The pattern of distribution of microtubules demonstrated by immunofluorescence in cultured adenocarcinoma cells may be distinctive though variable from cell to cell. In general the pattern is similar to that which we have previously observed in cultures of bronchial carcinomas, in contrast to normal bronchial epithelium. In the future, it would be useful to develop methods to demonstrate and compare such patterns in sections of normal and neoplastic prostatic epithelia in order to explore the utility of alterations in these patterns as possible markers for preneoplasia and neoplasia.

Normally, most of the keratin stainable by the immunoperoxidase technique is found in basal cells in normal human prostate in contrast to secretory cells. In our experience, modification in the amount of keratin often occurs in cultured cells. Keratin filaments are present in the outgrowth and these are also maintained in xenotransplants. As we noted previously [67], the cells colonizing explants and present in the outgrowth of such explants are believed to be derived from proliferation of basal cells. It is also of interest that squamous metaplasia that

---

Fig. 19. SEM of an explant of well-differentiated adenocarcinoma of prostate after culture for 8 weeks. The explant surface is covered with neoplastic cells which tend to pile up and contact adjacent cells with pseudopodial or filopodial extensions. The apical surfaces show the presence of irregular folds or tiny blebs of the plasma membrane. 2,000×.

Fig. 20. TEM of neoplastic cells covering surfaces of explants as in Figure 19. Junctional complexes (tight junctions, desmosomes, gap junctions) are absent). (Courtesy, SEM, Inc.) 16,000×.

Fig. 21. Apical portion of two adjacent explant-cultured tumors cells, as in Figure 19. Arrays of microfilaments (actin?) parallel the cell surface. Note absence of plasma membrane specializations (eg, microvilli). 30,000×.

Fig. 22. Profile of a microtubule (arrow heads) in a tumor cell on explant surfaces as in Figure 19. 30,000×.

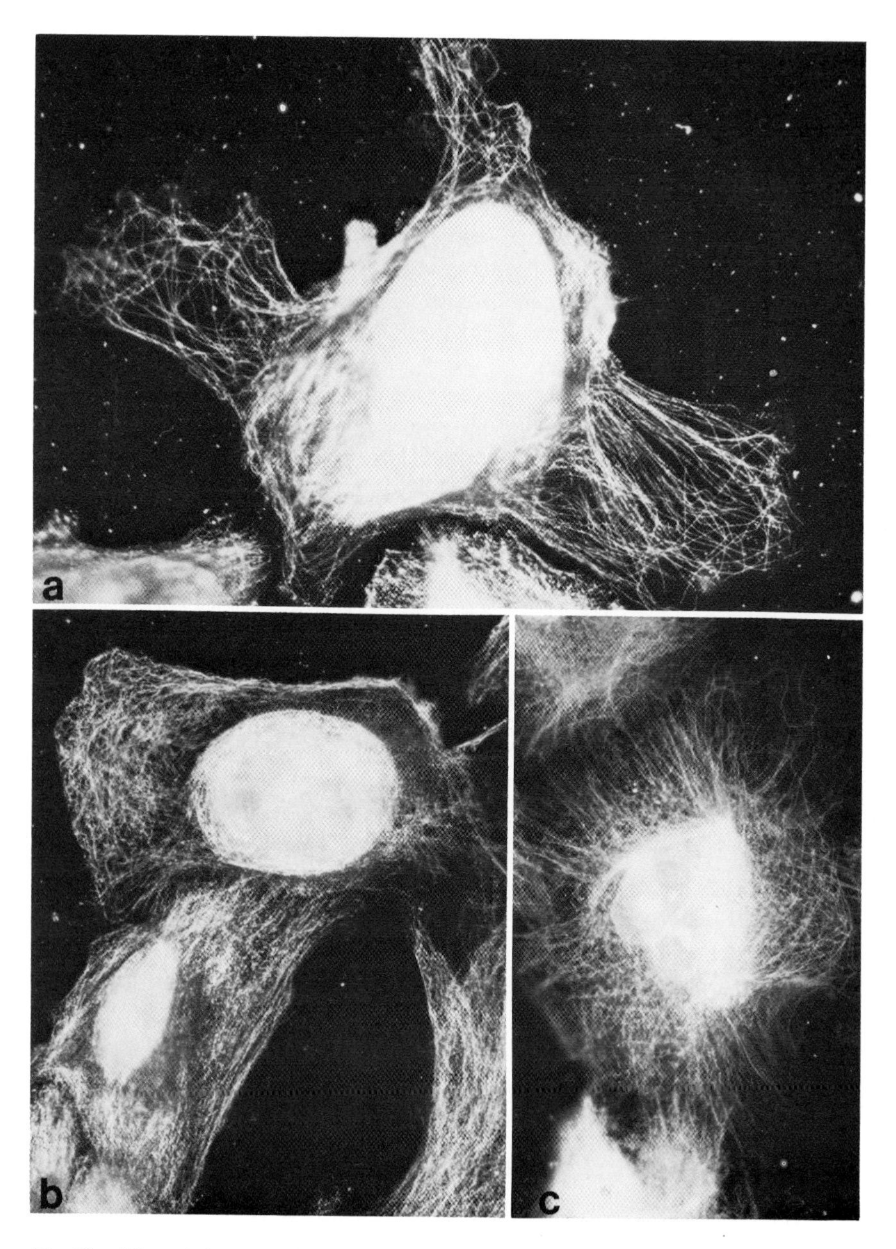

Fig. 23. Microtubule display in outgrowth cells from explant of prostatic adenocarcinoma. Pattern variations are seen: a) Large cell with many straight microtubules except at the periphery; b,c) small cells with numerous microtubules arranged in a meshwork. (Indirect immunofluoresence techniques using affinity-purified tubulin antisera, courtesy B. R. Brinkley, Houston, Texas.) 600×.

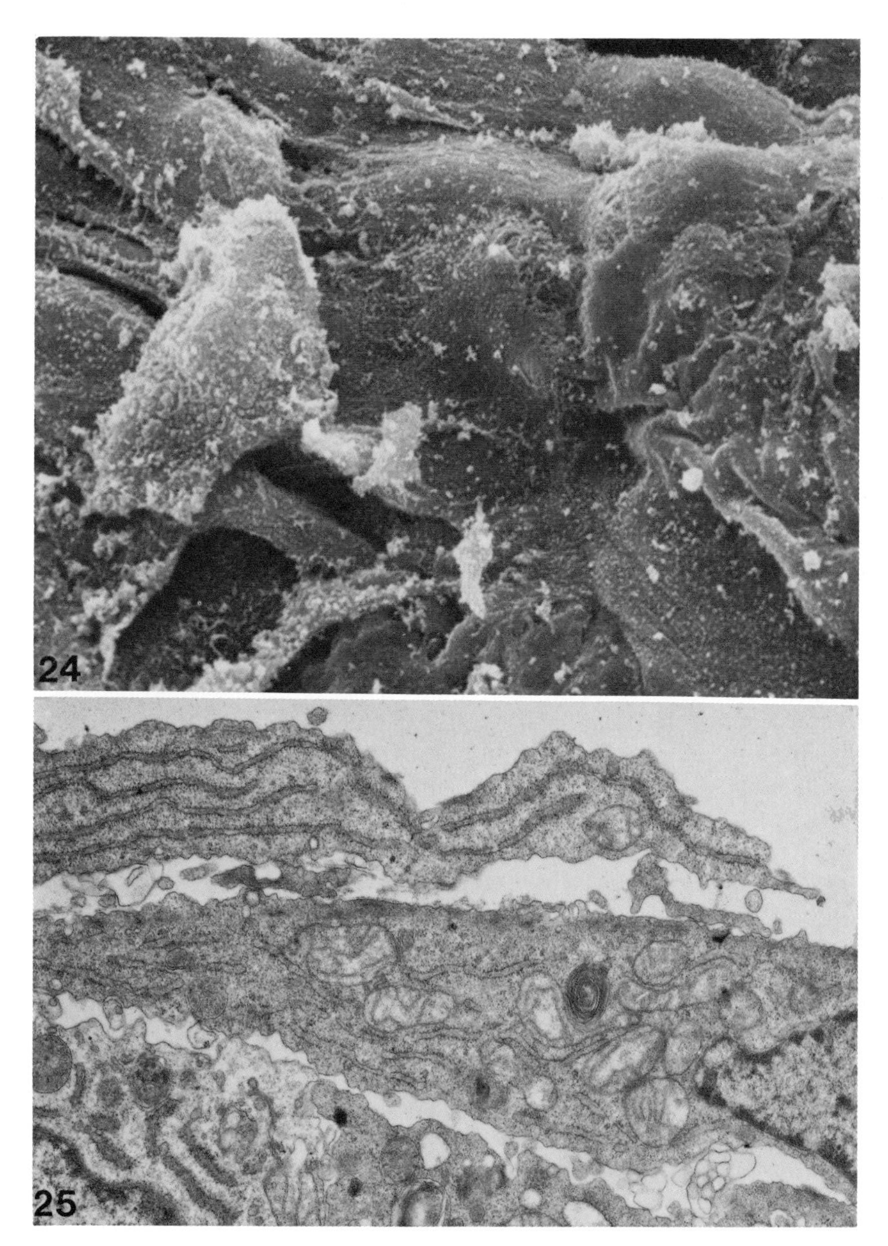

Fig. 24. SEM of an explant of normal prostate after four weekly doses of MNNG (10 μg/ml) in vitro. Cells are piled up and possess morphologic features similar to those of cultured cells of prostatic adenocarcinoma explants (Fig. 19). (Courtesy, Dr. Hayato Sanefuji.) 1,500×.

Fig. 25. TEM of cells of an explant of normal prostate treated with MNNG as in Figure 24. Morphologic features resemble those of cultured explants of adenocarcinomas as seen in Figure 20. Junctional complexes and plasma membrane specializations are absent. (Courtesy, SEM, Inc.) 16,000×.

occurs in aging, and especially after estrogen therapy for prostatic adenocarcinoma, may represent a cytoskeletal change modulated by hormone-receptor interaction. We hypothesize, based on the work of Yuspa et al [31] on the skin, that this effect of estrogen is possibly mediated through regulation of intracellular calcium, which is known in other cells to be at least one environmental factor resulting in increased keratin fibrils within cells.

Many other roles for the cytoskeleton in normal and abnormal prostatic epithelium are unexplored. It is likely, for example, that these elements play a deterministic role in the secretory process in the prostate. It has been suggested in other cells that the vectorial movement of secretory or absorptive vacuoles is constrained by channels created by microtubules [35]. The force exerted on these vacuoles is probably a function of the microtrabecular network and actin filaments working in concert. Other possible roles for the cytoskeletal complex which are more speculative, but essentially important, include a direct nongenetic role in cytoplasmic inheritance which could even be involved in determining and maintaining the phenotype of cancer cells.

Thus, it seems probable that changes of the cytoskeleton will be found to play an important role in the alterations in structure and function that occur during the development of neoplasia in the prostate. Among the more obvious alterations seen so far is the marked change in cell shape which is exhibited by neoplastic cells of the prostate, particularly in vitro. Also of interest is the fact that we have produced very similar if not identical morphologic changes by treating normal prostatic epithelium in vitro with carcinogens. Among the more striking alterations are the conspicuous shape changes which are characterized by loss of regular, well-developed villi, separation at intercellular spaces, and reduction or loss of cell junctions. It is reasonable to assert that all of these changes are choreographed by modulations of elements of the cytoskeleton. It is evident from our preliminary observations that alterations of presumed actin filament-membrane relationships are involved in the altered appearance of the microvilli. It is also probable that in migrating neoplastic cells in culture large bundles of thin filaments or stress fibers are conspicuous along the margins of the cell and at the advancing edges, as described for other cell types.

As has already been indicated, the normal shape characteristics of a given cell phenotype are maintained by interactions of microtubules, thin filaments, and intermediate filaments with the cell membrane and at cell junctions. Thus, the normal shape of both basal and secretory cells must be maintained by these interactions. Modification of the cytoskeleton can cause rapid changes in cell shape. Such modification can be a result of a number of influences including hormones, toxins, cyclic nucleotides, energy depletion, and modification of cell membrane integrity with a variety of compounds, including carcinogens. Although the details have not been elucidated, current evidence favors a messenger role for ionized calcium in this modification [29]. The level of calcium in the cells is controlled by active extrusion mechanisms at the cell surface. These mechanisms involve calcium ATPases and sodium/calcium exchange driven by sodium-potassium ATPase and internal sequestration in mitochondrial and endoplasmic reticulum membranes, which actively accumulate calcium and control its level in the cytosol. Normally, calcium is maintained at low levels in the cytosol, approximately 10^{-6}–10^{-7} M, and when elevations above these levels occur, phenomena such as disorganization or contraction of actin, and depolymerization of microtubules may occur. Most of the actions of calcium are mediated indirectly via the calmodulin-Ca^{++} complex. Through the use of antibodies to calmodulin, it has been found that calmodulin is associated with actin filaments in interphase nuclei and with the spindle-fibers during mitosis. As mitosis proceeds, calmodulin probably mediates the dissolution of microtubules in the region of the centrioles during anaphase and telophase. It is of interest that neoplastic cells have a 2–3-fold increase in the intracellular concentration of calmodulin but no change in the total amount of tubulin, thus raising the calmodulin to tubulin ratio [41]. This may well modify the relationships of both microtubules and microfilaments, and the cytoskeleton as a whole. Recent data from our laboratory and of that of Cameron [71] indicate changes in ion ratios in transformed cells, including increased levels of sodium and decreased levels of potassium. This implies active sodium-potassium exchange and an increased level of calcium. All of these factors, therefore, may play a role in modifying the cell shape seen in altered cells.

In a recent review by Lechner et al [72], it was pointed out that a transfer of cultures was facilitated by culture medium in which sodium was replaced by potassium. This resulted in better passage, but also decreased viability. According to the principles mentioned above and reviewed recently by Trump et al [29], such replacement would totally inhibit sodium-calcium exchange and result in an increased calcium content in the cells. This may explain why the cells round up and detach, and why cell division is initiated. Such an explanation could account for behavioral modification in malignant transformation.

CONCLUSIONS

Knowledge of the pathobiology of the cytoskeleton in many cells is rapidly advancing, but little is presently known about the mammalian prostate in this regard. Cytoskeletal elements are evident in human prostate, but differ in basal and secretory cell types. Marked alterations in the cytoskeleton are revealed in neoplastic prostatic epithelium in vitro, and may play an important role in the process of malignant transformation. Of particular interest for the future will be refined studies on the cytoskeleton and its interaction with cell constituents, as well as its role in the expression of the malignant phenotype.

ACKNOWLEDGMENTS

We thank Mrs. Pat Miller for skillfully typing the manuscript and Mr. Carl Larsson and staff for photographic prints. Work reported in this paper was supported by NIH grant CA 15798, through the National Prostatic Cancer Project, Buffalo, New York.

REFERENCES

1. Sternberger LA: Immunocytochemistry. New York: John Wiley and Sons, 1979.
2. Schlegel R, Banks-Schlegel S, McLeoud J, and Pinkus G: Immunoperoxidase localization of keratin in human neoplasms. Am J Pathol 101: 41–50, 1980.
3. Franke WW, Schmid FE, Freudenstein C, Appelhans B, Osborn M, Weber K, Keenan TW: Intermediate-sized filaments of the prekeratin type in myoepithelial cells. J Cell Biol 84: 633–654, 1980.
4. Gabbianni G, Csank-Brassert J, Schneeberger JC, et al: Contractile proteins in human cancer cells. Immunofluorescent and electron microscopic study. Am J Pathol 83: 457–474, 1976.
5. Drenckhahn D, Groschel-Stewart V: Localization of myosin, actin, and tropomyosin in rat intestinal epithelium: Immunohistochemical studies at the light and electron microscope level. J Cell Biol 86:475–482, 1980.
6. Weinstein RS, Alroy J, Pauli BU: Pathobiology of cell junctions. In Trump BF, Jones RT, Laufer A (eds): "Pathobiology of Human Disease." New York: Gustav Fisher 1981 (in press).
7. Wolosewick JJ, Porter KR: Microtrabecular lattice of the cytoplasmic ground substance. J Cell Biol 82: 114–139, 1979.
8. Weisenberg RC, Borisy GG, Taylor EW: The colchicine-binding protein of mammalian brain and its relation to microtubules. Biochemistry 7: 4466–4478, 1968.
9. Weisenberg RC: Microtubule formation in vitro in solutions containing low calcium concentration. Science 177: 1104–1105, 1972.
10. Sloboda RD, Rudolph SA, Rosenbaum JL, Greengard P: Cyclic AMP-dependent endogenous phosphorylation of a microtubule-associated protein. Proc Natl Acad Sci USA 72: 177–181, 1975.
11. Sloboda RD, Rosenbaum JL: Decoration and stabilization of intact, smooth-walled microtubules with microtubule-associated proteins. Biochemistry 18: 48–55, 1979.
12. Kim H, Binder LL, Rosenbaum JL: The periodic association of MAP 2 with brain microtubules in vitro. J Cell Biol 80: 266–276, 1979.
13. Sloboda RD: The role of microtubules in cell structure and cell division. Am Sci 68: 290–298, 1980.
14. Barrett LA, Dawson RB: Avian erythrocyte development: Microtubules and the formation of the disk shape. Dev Biol 36: 72–81, 1974.
15. Brinkley BR, Cox SM, Pepper DA, et al: Microtubule assembly sites in cultured mammalian cells: Analysis by tubulin immunofluorescence and electron microscopy. Proc. 37th Ann. E.M.S.A. Meeting. Baton Rouge: Publishing Division Claitor's, 1979, pp. 14–17.
16. Nicolson GL, Poste G, Ji TH: The dynamics of cell membrane organization. In Poste G, Nicolson GL (eds): "Dynamic Aspects of Cell Surface Organization. Cell Surface Reviews." Amsterdam: North Holland Pub Co, Vol 3, 1976, pp 1–27.
17. Brinkley BR, Fuller GM, Highfield DP: Cytoplasmic microtubules in normal and transformed cells in culture: Analysis by tubulin antibody immunofluorescence. Proc Natl Acad Sci USA 72: 4981–4985, 1975.
18. Fonte V, Porter K: Topographic changes associated with the viral transformation of normal cells

to tumorigenicity. In: Eighth Int. Cong. on Electron Microscopy, Australian Acad Sci. Canberra: Sanders and Goodchild, pp 334–335, 1974.
19. Miller CL, Fuseler JW, Brinkley BR: Cytoplasmic microtubules in transformed mouse x non-transformed human cell hybrids: Correlation with in vitro growth. Cell 12: 319–331, 1977.
20. Osborn M, Weber K: The display of microtubules in transformed cells. Cell 12: 561–571, 1977.
21. Tucker RW, Sanford KK, Frankel FR: Tubulin and actin in paired non-neoplastic and spontaneously transformed neoplastic cell lines in vitro: Fluorescent antibody studies. Cell 13: 629–642, 1978.
22. DeMey J, Joniau M, DeBrabander M, et al: Evidence for unaltered structure and in vivo assembly of microtubules in transformed cells. Proc Natl Acad Sci USA 75: 1339–1343, 1978.
23. Watt FM, Harris H, Weber K, et al: The distribution of actin cables and microtubules in hybrids between malignant and non-malignant cells, and in tumours derived from them. J Cell Sci 32: 419–432, 1978.
24. Rubin RW, Warren RH: Organization of tubulin in normal and transformed rat kidney cells. J Cell Biol 82: 103–113, 1979.
25. Asch BB, Medna D, Brinkley BR: Microtubules and actin-containing filaments of normal, preneoplastic, and neoplastic mouse mammary epithelial cells. Cancer Res 39: 893–907, 1979.
26. McNutt NS: Ultrastructural comparison of the interface between epithelium and stroma in basal cell carcinoma and control human skin. Lab Invest 35: 132–142, 1976.
27. Pollack RE, Osborn M, Weber K: Patterns of organization of actin and myosin in normal and transformed cultured cells. Proc Natl Acad Sci USA 72: 994–998, 1975.
28. Macartney JC, Trevithick MA, Kricka L, et al: Identification of myosin in human epithelial cancers with immunofluorescence. Lab Invest 41: 437–445, 1979.
29. Trump BF, Berezesky IK, Phelps PC: Sodium and calcium regulation and the role of the cytoskeleton in the pathogenesis of disease: A review and hypothesis. SEM, Inc., AMF O'Hare, Illinois, 1981 (submitted).
30. Inoue S, Dionne GP: Tonofilaments in normal human bronchial epithelium and in squamous cell carcinoma. Am J Pathol 88: 345–354, 1977.
31. Yuspa SH, Hawley-Nelson P, Koehler B, Stanley JR: A survey of transformation markers in differentiating epidermal cell lines in culture. Cancer Res 40: 4694–4703, 1980.
32. Lazarides E, Hubbard BD: Immunological characterization of the subunit of the 100 Å filaments from muscle cells. Proc Natl Acad Sci USA 73: 4344–4348, 1976.
33. Franke WW, Schmid E, Osborn M, et al: Intermediate-sized filaments of human endothelial cells. J Cell Biol 81: 570–580, 1979.
34. Buckley IK: Three dimensional fine structure of cultured cells: Possible implications for subcellular motility. Tiss Cell 7: 51–72, 1975.
35. Porter KR, Tucker JB: The ground substance in the living cell. Sci Am 244: 57–67, 1981.
36. Dedman JR, Potter JD, Jackson RL, Johnson JD, Means AR: Physicochemical properties of rat testis Ca-dependent regulator protein of cyclic nucleotide phosphodiesterase. J Biol Chem 252: 8415–8422, 1977.
37. Dedman JR, Welsh MJ, Means AR: Ca-dependent regulator. J Biol Chem 253: 7515–7521, 1978.
38. Means RM, Dedman JR: Calmodulin—an intracellular calcium receptor. Nature 285: 73–77, 1980.
39. Welsh MJ, Dedman JR, Brinkley BR, Means AR: Tubulin and calmodulin: Effects of microtubule and microfilament inhibitors on localization in the mitotic apparatus. J Cell Biol 81: 624–634, 1979.
40. Lin CT, Dedman JR, Brinkley BR, Means AR: Localization of calmodulin in rat cerebellum by immunoelectron microscopy. J Cell Biol 85: 473–480, 1980.

41. Chafouleas JG, Pardue RL, Brinkley BR, Dedman JR, Means AR: Regulation of intracellular levels of calmodulin and tubulin in normal and transformed cells. Proc Natl Acad Sci USA 78: 996–1000, 1981.
42. Marcum JM, Dedman JR, Brinkley BR, Means AR: Control of microtubule assembly-disassembly by calcium-dependent regulator protein. Proc Natl Acad Sci USA 75: 3771–3775, 1978.
43. Gilula NB, Reeves OR, Steinbach A: Metabolic coupling, ionic coupling and cell contacts. Nature 235: 262–265, 1972.
44. Goodenough DA, Revel JP: A fine structural analysis of intercellular junctions in the mouse liver. J Cell Biol 45: 272–290, 1970.
45. Makowski L, Caspar DLD, Phillips WC, Goodenough DA: Gap junction structures. II. Analysis of the x-ray diffraction data. J Cell Biol 74: 629–645, 1977.
46. McNutt NS, Weinstein RS: The ultrastructure of the nexus. A correlated thin-section and freeze-cleave study. J Cell Biol 47: 666–688, 1970.
47. Goodenough DA: In vitro formation of gap junction vesicles. J Cell Biol 68: 220–231, 1976.
48. Unwin PNT, Zampighi G: Structure of the junction between communicating cells. Nature 283: 545–549, 1980.
49. Pitts JD: In Brinkley BR, Porter KR (eds): "International Cell Biology." New York: Rockefeller University Press, 1977, p 43.
50. Yancey SB, Easter D, Revel JP: Cytological changes in gap junctions during liver regeneration. J Ultrastruct Res 67: 229–242, 1979.
51. McNutt NS, Weinstein RS: Carcinoma of the cervix; deficiency of nexus intercellular junctions. Science 165: 597–599, 1969.
52. McNutt NS, Hershberg RA, Weinstein RS: Further observations on the occurrence of nexuses in benign and malignant human cervical epithelium. J Cell Biol 51: 805–825, 1971.
53. Weinstein RS, Zel G, Merk FB: Quantitation of occludens, adherens, and nexus cell junctions in human tumors. In Schultz J, Block RE (eds): "Membrane Transformation in Neoplasia." New York: Academic Press, 1974, pp 127–146.
54. Jesudason ML, Iseri OA: Host-tumor cellular junctions: An ultrastructural study of hepatic metastasis of bronchogenic oat cell carcinoma. Hum Pathol 11: 66–69, 1980.
55. Iseri OA, Shamsuddin AKM: Host-tumor cellular junctions in spontaneous metastases to the liver. Lab Invest 42: 125, 1980.
56. Trump BF, Valigorsky JM, Jones RT, Mergner WJ, Garcia JH, Cowley RA: The application of electron microscopy and cellular biochemistry to the autopsy. Observations on cellular changes in human shock. Hum Pathol 6: 499–516, 1975.
57. McDowell EM, Trump BF: Histologic fixatives suitable for diagnostic light and electron microscopy. Arch Pathol Lab Med 100: 405–414, 1976.
58. Trump, BF, Smuckler EA, Benditt EP: A method for staining epoxy sections for light microscopy. J Ultrastruct Res 5: 343–348, 1961.
59. Kelley RO, Dekker RAF, Bluemink JG: Ligand-mediated osmium binding: Its application in coating biological specimens for scanning electron microscopy. J Ultrastruct Res 45: 254–258, 1973.
60. Leibovitz A: The growth and maintenance of tissue-cell cultures in free gas exchange with the atmosphere. Am J Hyg 78: 173–183, 1963.
61. Sanefuji H, Heatfield BM, Trump BF: Studies on carcinogenesis of human prostate. I. Technique for long-term explant culture. Tiss Cult Assoc Manual 4: 855–856, 1978.
62. Heatfield BM, Sanefuji H, Trump BF: Studies on carcinogenesis of human prostate. IV. Comparison of normal and neoplastic prostate during long-term explant culture. SEM/III, SEM, Inc., AMF O'Hare, Illinois pp 645–655, 1979.
63. Brandes D, Kirchheim D, Scott WW: Ultrastructure of the human prostate: Normal and neoplastic. Lab Invest 13: 1541–1560, 1964.

64. Mao P, Angrist A: The fine structure of the basal cell of human prostate. Lab Invest 15: 1768–1782, 1966.
65. Fisher ER, Sieracki JC: Ultrastructure of human normal and neoplastic prostate. Pathol Annual 5: 1–26, 1970.
66. Dermer GB: Basal cell proliferation in benign prostatic hyperplasia. Cancer 41: 1857–1862, 1978.
67. Heatfield BM, Sanefuji H, Trump BF: Long-term explant culture of normal human prostate. In Harris CC, Trump BF, Stoner GD (eds): "Methods in Cell Biology, Vol. 21, Normal Human Tissue and Cell Culture, Part B, Endocrine, Urogenital and Gastrointestinal Systems." New York: Academic Press, Chap 8, 1980, pp 171–194.
68. Sanefuji H, Heatfield BM, Trump BF: Studies on carcinogenesis of human prostate. V. Effects of the carcinogen N-methyl-N′-nitro-N-nitrosoguanidine (MNNG) on normal prostate during long-term explant culture. SEM/III, SEM, Inc., AMF O'Hare, Illinois, pp 657–663, 1979.
69. Loewenstein WR, Kanno Y, Socolar SJ: The cell-to-cell channel. Fed Proc 37: 2645–2650, 1978.
70. Bulger RE, Trump BF: Ca^{++} and K^{+} ion effects on ultrastructure of isolated flounder kidney tubules. J Ultrastruct Res 28: 301–319, 1969.
71. Cameron IL, Smith NKR: Energy dispersive x-ray microanalysis of the concentration of elements in relation to cell reproduction in normal and in cancer cells in vivo. SEM/II, SEM, Inc., AMF O'Hare, Illinois, pp 463–474, 1980.
72. Lechner JF, Babcock MS, Marnell M, Narayan KS, Kaighn ME: Normal human prostate epithelial cell cultures. In Harris CC, Trump BF, Stoner GD (eds): "Methods in Cell Biology, Vol. 21, Normal Human Tissue and Cell Culture, Part B, Endocrine, Urogenital and Gastrointestinal Systems." New York: Academic Press, Chap 9, 1980, pp 195–225.

The Prostatic Cell: Structure and Function
Part A, pages 55–74

Biochemistry of Protein Kinase Reactions in the Prostate in Relation to Androgen Action

Khalil Ahmed, Michael J. Wilson, and Said A. Goueli

INTRODUCTION

This contribution provides a brief overview of our work, including some unpublished data, relating to various aspects of nuclear protein kinases of rat ventral prostate with special reference to their possible role in the events related to the mechanism of androgen action in this target organ. A more detailed account of chromatin controls in the prostate and phosphoprotein biochemistry has previously been given [1–3]. Likewise, for general aspects of biochemistry and biology of androgen action, it is recommended that the reader consult some of the other comprehensive review articles [4–10].

Much work on androgen action and nuclear protein phosphorylation [1–3,11,12] has led to the concept that translocation of the cytosol 5α-dihydrotestosterone-receptor complex to the nucleus and its binding to chromatin constituents (or acceptor sites) results in the activation of chromatin, leading to enhanced transcription. Evidence has been provided that early physical changes in chromatin occur which may be commensurate with its altered activities [13,14]. Observations along these lines emphasize the importance of investigations dealing with prostatic chromatin controls to delineate those activities which may be influenced most rapidly and profoundly by the presence or absence of an androgenic stimulus.

It is generally believed that chromatin proteins play a regulatory role in the control of transcription. Among these proteins, histones appear to be intimately involved in nucleosome structure and generally exert a gene repressive activity. On the other hand, a large body of data gained from work with a variety of experimental models suggests that nonhistone proteins and their phosphorylated derivatives may serve as positive regulatory agents (for reviews see, eg, [2,15–19]). This latter concept is based upon the observation that nonhistone proteins stimulate RNA synthesis in vitro in a tissue-specific manner [20,21] and that many of these nonhistone proteins are "acidic" nonhistone phosphoproteins [22]. Studies of Kleinsmith et al [23], showing a marked reduction in initiation sites available for transcription in chromatin reconstituted with dephosphorylated nonhistone proteins, have provided further support to the above concepts. It may be added that the nonhistone phosphoprotein complex in chromatin has now been shown to be comprised not only of highly acidic proteins but also proteins which have pI values near neutral or somewhat basic range (for references see [24]). Indeed, it appears that almost 40% of the ^{32}P radioactivity incorporated into chromatin-associated phosphoproteins is attributable to some of these basic nonhistone phosphoproteins [24].

Following the original observation of Kleinsmith et al [25] that intact lymphocytes showed an early enhancement of ^{32}P-incorporation into nuclear phosphoproteins during stimulation by phytohemagglutinin, we provided the first evidence of an increased rate of phosphorylation of nonhistone proteins in vitro in nuclei obtained from a tissue in which gene action was elicited in vivo; ie, testosterone action in rat ventral prostate [26–28], and isoproterenol-stimulated submandibular gland [29].

The above studies from this laboratory, taken together with earlier work of Langan [30], Kleinsmith and Allfrey [31], and other concurrent reports [32,33] strongly suggested the presence of protein kinase activities intrinsic to the cell nucleus. Direct evidence of changes in chromatin-associated protein kinase activity in association with altered genome activity was provided by us [34–37], and has been substantiated in a variety of experimental models of gene activation or cell growth (for references see, eg, [2,3,17,18,38]). It should also be mentioned that whereas the enzymes engaged in the phosphorylation of nonhistone proteins appear to be predominantly c-AMP-independent protein kinases, the translocation of c-AMP-dependent kinase or its subunits into the nucleus has also been demonstrated in response to specific stimuli, especially where c-AMP may be involved as a secondary messenger. In the prostatic nucleus the c-AMP-dependent protein kinase component represents only a small part of the total enzyme activity (for discussion see eg [2,38,39]).

In summary, then, given that nuclear protein phosphorylation appears to represent an integral aspect of regulation of gene expression, it would seem reasonable that modulations in the activities of associated protein kinases are critical. In the context of androgen action in the prostate, one would expect profound effects of androgen withdrawal and administration on these reactions, and this will be the focus of further discussion in this paper.

PROSTATIC NUCLEAR PROTEIN KINASE REACTIONS

As mentioned above, we originally described that the rate of phosphorylation of nuclear proteins (studied in purified nuclei in vitro) was greatly reduced when nuclei were isolated from prostates of rats orchiectomized for 4–5 days. This decline was prevented when animals were maintained on androgen therapy following castration. In order to determine if the phosphorylation of prostatic nuclear proteins correlated with androgen-stimulated gene activity in this organ, we examined the effect of a single injection of testosterone given to orchiectomized rats [26–28]. Prostatic nuclei from these animals were prepared and in vitro incorporation of ^{32}P from γ-^{32}P-ATP into the nuclear protein was determined. As shown in Table I, under these conditions a preponderant portion of the ^{32}P radioactivity was present in the nonhistone proteins. Testosterone treatment for a period of 30 minutes produced a marked increase in the rate of phosphorylation of these proteins. This effect was target-tissue specific since it was not observed in nuclei from liver under the same conditions. Experiments based on in vivo incorporation of ^{32}P into nuclear phosphoproteins in response to androgen treatment of castrated rats provided further support of these observations [40–42].

TABLE I. Effect of castration and testosterone treatment on the initial rates of ^{32}P incorporation into nuclear phosphoproteins[a,b]

	^{32}P Incorporation (nmoles/mg protein/hr)[c]		
Source	Total phosphoproteins	Nonhistone phosphoproteins	Histone phosphoproteins
Ventral prostate			
Normal	25.6 ± 0.5	55	6
Castrated controls[d]	6.2 ± 0.7	9.9 ± 2.2	2.8 ± 1.0
Castrated, single injection of testosterone at 30 minutes[e]	9.5 ± 0.4	17.8 ± 3.5	3.5 ± 0.8
Castrated, maintained with daily testosterone injections[f]	24.9 ± 0.4	55	6

[a]Adapted from [3,27,28].

[b]Rats used in these experiments were orchiectomized for 112–137 hours.

[c]The phosphorylation reactions were carried out for 1 minute in medium consisting of 5 mM $MgCl_2$, 115 mM NaCl, 30 mM Tris-HCl, pH 7.5 at 37°C, and 3.5 mM [γ-^{32}P]ATP. Time-course experiments demonstrated that the incorporation of radioactivity into nuclear phosphoproteins was measured within the linear range for nuclei from rats of differing androgenic status.

[d]Castrated control rats received 0.2 ml of sesame oil 30 minutes prior to sacrifice. The values for orchiectomized rats receiving a daily treatment with 0.2 ml sesame oil were not significantly different from those shown here for rats receiving a single injection of oil.

[e]These rats received a single injection of testosterone propionate (2 mg in 0.20 ml sesame oil) 30 minutes prior to sacrifice.

[f]Testosterone maintained, castrated animals received a daily subcutaneous dose of 1 mg testosterone propionate in 0.2 ml sesame oil.

Using exogenous substrates, initial studies of protein kinase activity associated with prostatic nuclei from normal and orchiectomized animals suggested that the androgenic status of the animal influenced this activity [1,36]. These data also hinted at possible multiplicity and differential androgen sensitivity of prostatic nuclear-associated protein kinase activity, and work was undertaken to explore this in detail.

Chromatin-Associated Protein Kinase Activity

Purified chromatin from rat ventral prostate nuclei, and also a nonhistone protein (NHP) fraction derived therefrom, were found to contain protein kinase activity towards exogenous as well as endogenous protein substrates [2,3,37,43]. The optimal characteristics of various reactions were established; these included requirements for Mg^{2+}, NaCl, a $-SH$ protective agent such as dithiothreitol, and polyamines in the case of nonhistone proteins or partially dephosphorylated

TABLE II. Comparison of the enzymic properties of histone kinase and acidic phosphoprotein kinase associated with nucleolar, extranucleolar, and chromatin subfractions from rat ventral prostate nuclei[a,b]

	Nucleolus		Extranucleolus	Chromatin	
Property	LRH	DPV	DPV	LRH	DPV
pH optima	8.0–8.2	7.1	7.4, 8.4	8.0–8.2	7.0–7.4, 7.89
Mg^{2+}, optima (mM)	8	5–8	3–6	6	5
Mn^{2+}, substitution (% compared to optimal Mg^{2+})	30	60	40[c]	30	40
NaCl, optimal (mM)	120	160	160	80	200
Dithiothreitol (% stimulation)	67	58	—	37	64
Km values for ATP (mM)	0.02	0.02 0.05 1.05	0.05 0.24	0.01	0.04 0.41
Km values for protein substrate (mg/ml)	2	0.03 0.06 1.9	0.06 0.44 1.9	0.9	0.3
Effect of orchiectomy (% decrease in activity at 24 hr)	2	42	26	8	53

[a]These data are taken from [3, 37, 46–48].

[b]Histone kinase and acidic phosphoprotein kinase activities associated with nucleolar, extranucleolar, and chromatin fractions were determined using lysine-rich histones (LRH) and dephosphophosvitin (DPV) as substrates. For experimental details, please see above references.

[c]The activity in the presence of 0.5 mM Mn^{2+} (compared with Mg^{2+}) was 40% but was only 15% at 5 mM Mn^{2+}.

phosvitin (DPV) as substrates. (For details on the use of the latter as a model acidic-protein substrate, see [44]). Further, the euchromatin fraction as compared with heterochromatin was found to contain a larger portion of enzyme activity [3,45]. Several of the kinetic characteristics of the chromatin-associated activity (summarized in Table II) were highly suggestive of the presence of multiple enzyme activities. These included different Km values for protein substrates, for ATP, and multiple pH optima, etc.

As shown in Fig. 1A, chromatin-associated protein kinase activity towards DPV (as compared with histone as substrate) was highly sensitive to the androgenic status of the animal and decreased by 50% within 18 hours postorchiectomy (expressed per unit of DNA or protein). Androgen replacement therapy in the castrated animal prevented these changes [2,3,37]. The time course of this activity upon androgen deprivation follows closely the loss of nuclear receptors for androgen and is as extensive as the decline in RNA polymerase under these conditions [3]. In contrast to the rapid decline of the acidic-protein kinase, the chromatin associated activity toward histone decreased much more slowly; eg, it was reduced by only 10% at 18 hours postorchiectomy. It may be noted that at early times postcastration, eg, at 24 hours, there is only a minimal change in the protein/DNA ratio of chromatin, when a marked decline in the associated protein kinase activity is apparent. In a preliminary study, the effect of a single injection of testosterone propionate (1 mg/100 gm body weight) in animals,

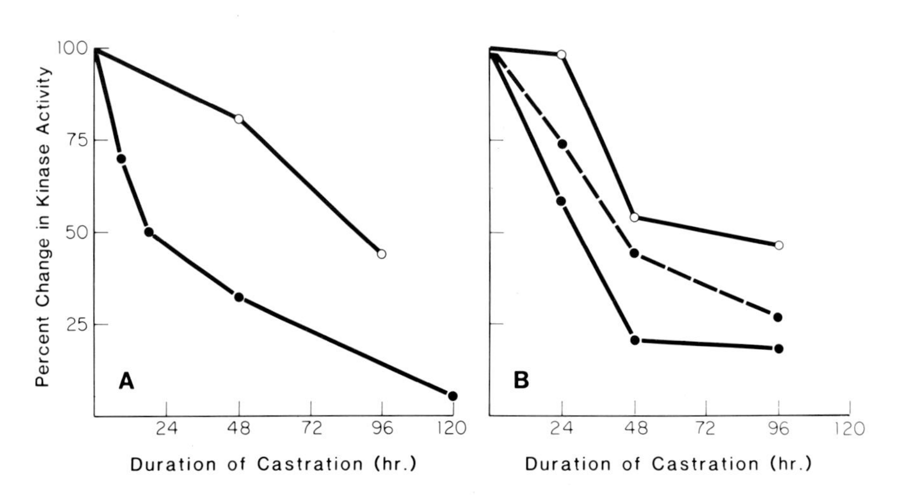

Fig. 1. The effects due to castration on the protein phosphokinase activities of chromatin (A) and nucleolus and extranucleolar material (B) of rat ventral prostate. The protein kinase activities were assayed with dephosphophosvitin (●) and lysine-rich histones (○) as model protein substrates. In B, kinase activities of the nucleolus are shown with solid lines, whereas that associated with the extranucleolar material is depicted with a dashed line. These data are adapted from [37, 47, 48].

previously castrated for 48 to 96 hours, was also determined with respect to the chromatin-associated protein kinase activities. At 1–2 hours after the injection, there was a variable (10–60%) but significant increase in the enzyme activity towards DPV but not towards lysine-rich histone as substrate. At 4 hours this increase was abolished and was followed by a large increase near 12 hours. The latter may relate to other cellular growth activities or the eventual onset of DNA synthesis [49], since it continued to increase for 48 hours after daily injections of testosterone. A thorough analysis of these responses, however, must await further separation and purification of the various enzyme activities, since, as shown later, the system is highly heterogeneous and differential responses of an individual kinase activity could be masked [2].

Nucleolar-Associated Protein Kinase

Nucleolar and extra-nucleolar fractions were isolated from purified nuclei of rat ventral prostate. As summarized in Table II, the general characteristics of protein kinase activities associated with these fractions also revealed the presence of multiple enzymes [2,3,46–48]. Further, nucleolus-associated protein kinase activities toward lysine-rich histone and acidic-phosphoprotein substrates showed differential responses to altered androgenic status of the animal; eg, at 24 hours postorchiectomy little change was observed in the former kinase activity, whereas the latter declined significantly more rapidly. On the other hand, the acidic-protein kinase activity in the extra-nucleolar fraction as compared with that in the nucleolus declined less rapidly as a result of orchiectomy (Table II and Fig. 1B).

Effects of Antiandrogens

To further confirm that the androgen effects on prostatic nuclear protein kinase reactions are mediated via the androgen-receptor complex, we examined the effects of antiandrogens (cyproterone acetate and flutamide) on prostatic chromatin-associated protein kinases [3,50]. Intact adult male rats when treated with either flutamide or cyproterone acetate produced both time- and dose-dependent declines in acidic-phosphoprotein kinase activity. At a daily dose of 10 mg of either antiandrogen for 48 hours, the decline in activity was about 36%. The ability of antiandrogens to compete with testosterone with regard to its effect on prostatic chromatin-associated acidic-phosphoprotein kinase activity and phosphorylation of endogenous chromosomal proteins was examined by simultaneous treatment of castrated rats with testosterone and antiandrogens for 48 hours (Table III). Both antiandrogens were effective in doing so, and at a dose 100-fold greater than that of testosterone propionate (on a molar basis) flutamide gave 55% and cyproterone acetate 27% reduction in acidic-protein kinase activity compared with appropriate controls. The phosphorylation of endogenous proteins in chromatin was even more sensitive to antiandrogen treatment under the same

TABLE III. Effect of competition of antiandrogens and testosterone in 48-hour castrated rats on the phosphorylation of endogenous prostatic chromatin proteins and chromatin-associated protein phosphokinase activities[a,b]

		Percent of testosterone-treated controls[c]		
Testosterone propionate	Antiandrogen	Endogenous protein	DPV	LRH
0.01 mg/100 gm	Oil only	100	100	100
Oil only	Oil only	46	36	81
0.01 mg/100 gm	Flutamide, 10-fold	65	86	97
0.01 mg/100 gm	Flutamide, 100-fold	41	55	76
0.01 mg/100 gm	Cyproterone acetate, 10-fold	70	79	95
0.01 mg/100 gm	Cyproterone acetate, 100-fold	45	73	86

[a]For details see [50].
[b]Animals were castrated and injected at two independent subcutaneous sites with testosterone propionate and antiandrogen, both of which were suspended in sesame oil. The testosterone-treated castrated control animals received hormone and oil; the castrate controls were injected with sesame oil at both sites. The antiandrogens cyproterone acetate and flutamide were administered in two doses; one at a 10-fold and the other at a 100-fold higher concentration than the testosterone propionate dose on a molar basis. Injections of oil, hormone, or antiandrogen were given immediately upon castration, at 24 hours, and finally at 48 hours just prior to sacrifice.
[c]Phosphorylation of endogenous chromatin proteins was measured using a reaction mixture containing 30 mM Tris-HCl, pH 7.5 at 37°C, 5 mM $MgCl_2$, 1 mM dithiothreitol, 0.1 mM [γ-^{32}P]ATP (specific radioactivity 30,000 dpm/nmole), 30 mM NaCl, and approximately 50 μg of prostatic chromatin protein. The time of reaction was 1 minute. Protein kinase activity toward DPV and LRH were assayed as described in [37, 48].

conditions, and declined by 65–69% in each case. As observed in the response to orchiectomy, chromatin-associated histone kinase activity was less sensitive to antiandrogen treatment.

Fractionation of Nuclear-Associated Protein Kinases

Since the above-described results suggested the presence of multiple protein kinases in the prostatic nucleus, a detailed fractionation and purification of these enzymes was undertaken to determine their substrate specificities and the nature of their androgenic control. We have made some progress in this direction [51], as described in the following.

A nuclear protein kinase extract was prepared by sonication of purified nuclei in a buffered medium and fractionated with the aid of DEAE-Sephadex A-25 column chromatography. The protein kinase activity in the extract was assayed in the presence of dephosphophosvitin (DPV), lysine-rich histone (LRH), and prostatic nonhistone proteins (NHP) as substrates. The kinase activities towards DPV or LRH were quantitatively recovered by this method. However, the recovery of activity towards NHP could not be estimated accurately because of technical difficulties, but appears to be about 20% of that present in the nucleus.

In Figure 2 are presented the chromatographic profiles of protein kinase activities towards various substrates showing their distribution in the flow-through and bound fractions. The ratios of flow-through and bound fractions were 60:40, 50:50, and 80:20 for DPV, LRH, and NHP substrates, respectively. The bound fraction was eluted primarily at 0.25–0.30 M $(NH_4)_2SO_4$ concentration. However, with NHP as substrate a small but highly reproducible activity was also evident at 0.15–0.20 M $(NH_4)_2SO_4$; DPV or LRH were not phosphorylated by this enzyme. It may be noted that each of the above protein kinase assays was carried out under conditions optimized for the given substrate, and under these conditions the activity towards the other substrates was minimal. This strongly

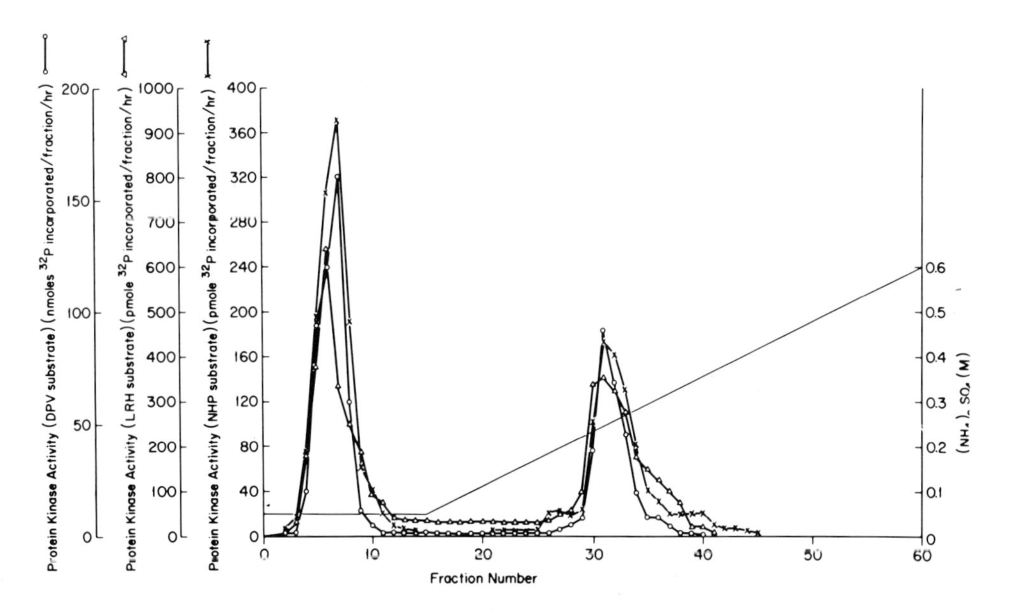

Fig. 2. DEAE-Sephadex column chromatographic profile of prostatic nuclear protein phosphokinases. The protein kinase activities were determined using DPV (o———o), LRH (△———△), and NHP (X———X) as substrates. The recovery of each protein phosphokinase activity from the DEAE-Sephadex column was routinely 85% of the activity originally applied to it. This percent recovery of protein kinase activities from DEAE-Sephadex columns was not affected when the nuclear kinase extracts from orchiectomized rats were investigated, as in Figures 3–5. Reproduced from [51] with permission.

TABLE IV. Effect of c-AMP and of c-AMP-dependent protein kinase inhibitor on the activity of kinases fractionated by DEAE-sephadex column chromatography

		Percent change in protein kinase activity in the presence of	
Column fractions	Substrates	c-AMP	c-AMP-dependent protein kinase inhibitor
Flow through	LRH	0	−70
Peak fraction	DPV	0	+15
	NHP	0	+50
Bound fractions			
Eluted at 0.15–0.2 M $(NH_4)_2SO_4$	NHP	0	+25
Eluted at 0.25–0.3 M $(NH_4)_2SO_4$	LRH	0	+20
	DPV	0	+20
	NHP	0	+20

The enzymic activities of pooled fractions of the individual protein phosphokinases in the presence or absence of c-AMP (2 and 10 μM) or the c-AMP-dependent protein kinase inhibitor protein (40 μg/100 μl assay) were determined as described by Goueli et al [51]. Data taken from [51].

suggests that even though none of the above peak fractions represents a pure enzyme, the activities toward different substrates are not entirely due to an overlap of a kinase activity towards different substrates. Initial studies on further fractionation of the DPV kinase activity in the bound fraction have suggested the presence of at least two enzymes [52]. A number of other observations included in the ensuing description further substantiate the multiplicity of kinase activities in each fraction.

None of the above enzymes was stimulated by c-AMP; however, the inhibitor of c-AMP-dependent protein kinase markedly reduced the activity of LRH kinase present in the flow-through peak, but stimulated all the other enzyme activities. This suggests that only the former represents the catalytic subunit of the cytosol c-AMP-dependent histone kinase (Table IV).

The effects due to orchiectomy for 24- or 48-hour periods on the activity towards various substrates in the above-described protein kinase fractions are demonstrated in Figures 3–5. These manipulations did not alter the percent recovery of kinase activities from the nucleus and hence the observed alterations in activity after castration should represent actual changes in enzyme activity or concentration.

The kinase activity towards DPV (Fig. 3) was reduced in the flow-through peak by about 20% at 24 hours, and 48% at 48 hours postorchiectomy. The

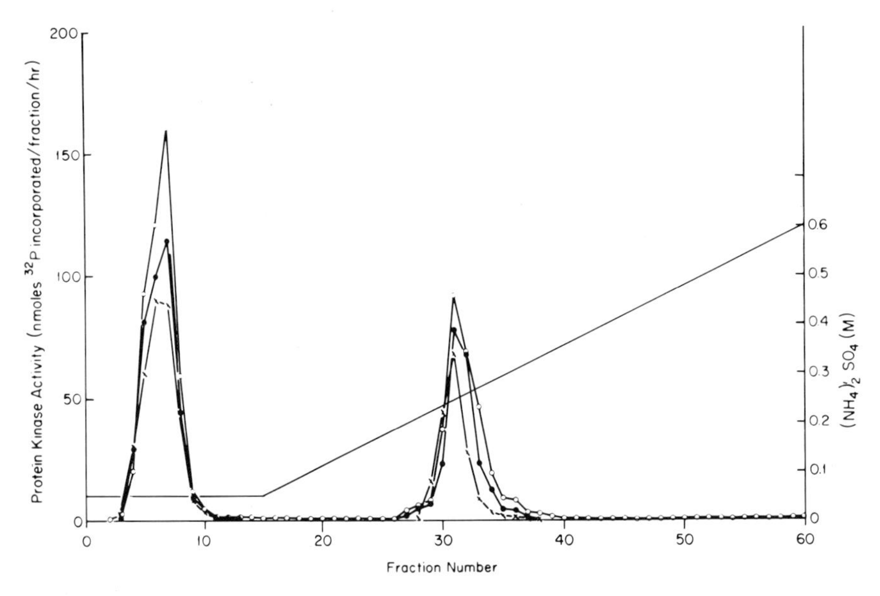

Fig. 3. The effects due to orchiectomy on the protein phosphokinase activities toward DPV isolated from DEAE-Sephadex column. Protein kinases were extracted from prostatic nuclei prepared from intact (○———○), 24-hour castrated (●———●), and 48-hour castrated (X———X) rats. All other details were the same as for Figure 2. Reproduced from [51] with permission.

activity in the bound peak was reduced by 33% and 50% under the same conditions. The kinase activity towards LRH (Fig. 4) was virtually unchanged in either the flow-through or bound fractions at 24 hours postorchiectomy, but at 48 hours it had increased nearly 250% in each fraction. On the other hand, the various protein kinase activities towards NHP as substrate (Fig. 5) demonstrated differential responses to orchiectomy. The activity in the flow-through peak was relatively insensitive to androgen deprivation in that it was unchanged at 24 hours, although by 48 hours it had declined by 50%. The bound activity (eluting at 0.25–0.30 M $(NH_4)_2SO_4$) was the most sensitive to androgenic status of the animal and retained less than 20% of the activity at 24 hours postorchiectomy. Interestingly, the activity specific towards NHP (eluting at 0.15–0.20 M

Fig. 5. Changes due to orchiectomy on protein phosphokinase activities toward NHP separated by DEAE-Sephadex column chromatography. Protein kinases were extracted from prostatic nuclei prepared from intact (○———○), 24-hour castrated (●———●), and 48-hour castrated (X———X) rats. All other details were the same as given in the legend to Figure 3. Reproduced from [51] with permission.

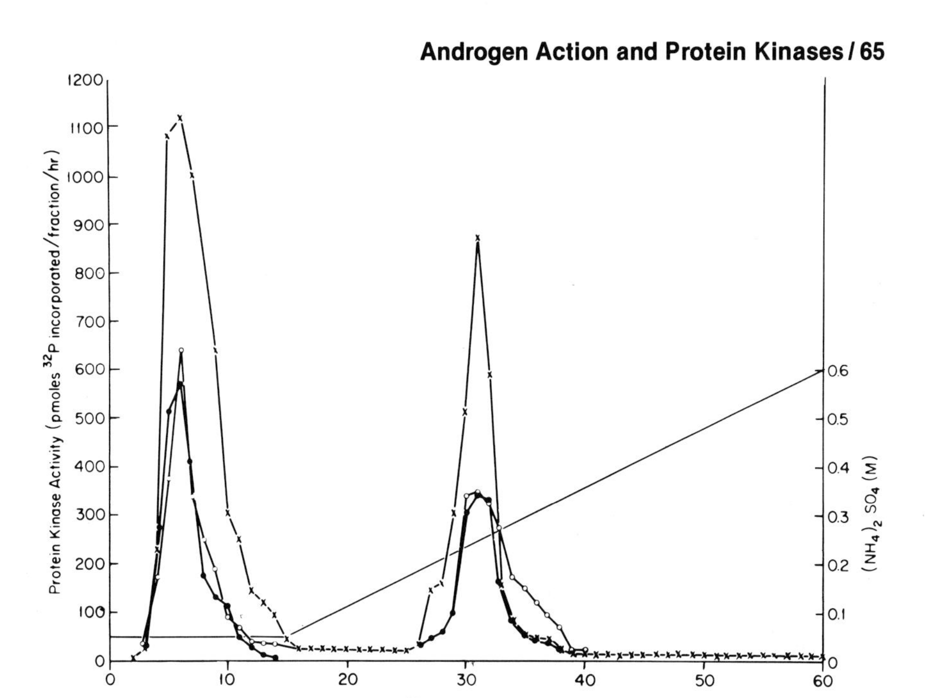

Fig. 4. The effects owing to orchiectomy on LRH protein phosphokinase activities obtained in the DEAE-Sephadex column elution profile. Protein kinases were extracted from prostatic nuclei prepared from intact (○——○), 24-hour castrated (●——●), and 48-hour castrated (X——X) rats. All other details were the same as for Figure 3. Reproduced from [51] with permission.

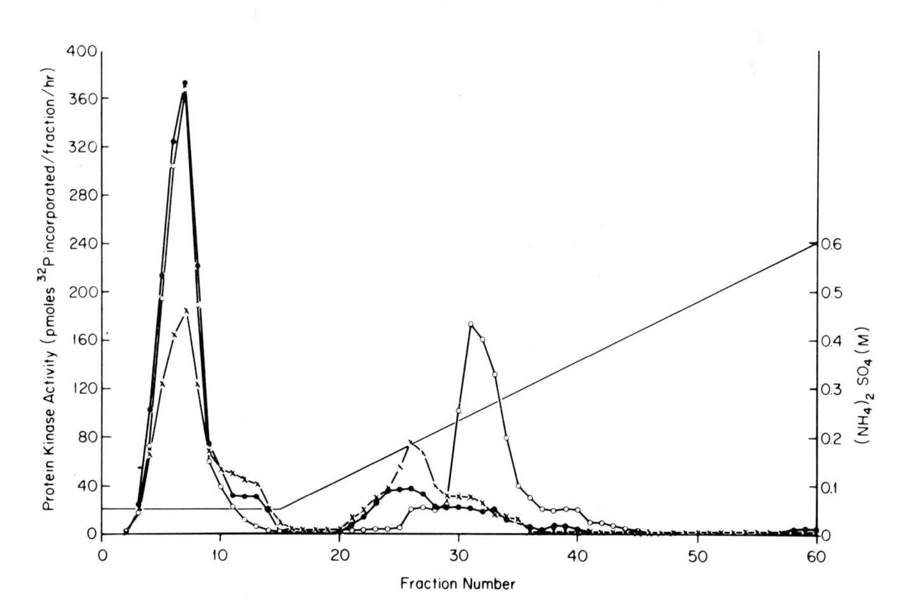

$(NH_4)_2SO_4$), which was very low in preparations from normal animals, demonstrated an *increase* of nearly 100% at 24 hours, and 200% at 48 hours following androgen deprivation.

Responses of Cytosol c-AMP-Dependent and -Independent Protein Kinases

We have also investigated the changes in cytosol protein kinases in response to altered androgenic status of the animal. Prostatic cytosol c-AMP-dependent protein kinase was resolved into type I and type II activities. The relative proportion of these was 10–15% and 85–90%, respectively. c-AMP-Independent protein kinase (active towards DPV) was also obtained from the cytosol fraction. All of these activities showed little change at 24 hours postorchiectomy (Table V). Furthermore, no change in the proportions of the type I and type II enzymes was observed as a result of castration [54,55]. These results are in agreement with those of Reddi et al. [56] and Tsang and Singhal [57], but not with those of Fuller et al. [58]. As also observed by others [57,59], marked changes were found only after longer periods of castration (eg, 96 hours), when a decline in activity per gland was observed. This reduced enzyme activity, however, had a higher specific activity, which may be a reflection of the loss of other cytosol proteins following prolonged castration.

PROSTATIC NUCLEAR PHOSPHOPROTEIN PHOSPHATASES

Although the primary focus of this presentation is on the prostatic nuclear protein kinases, a few remarks on the phosphoprotein phosphatases are warranted since these enzymes may also be involved in controlling the level of phosphorylation of various nuclear proteins.

TABLE V. Effect of castration on c-AMP-dependent and c-AMP-independent protein kinases of rat ventral prostate cytosol[a]

	Histone kinase (+c-AMP)[b]		DPV kinase (c-AMP-independent)[b]	
	Total activity/prostate (nmoles ^{32}P/min)	Specific activity (nmoles ^{32}P/mg protein/min)	Total activity/prostate (nmoles ^{32}P/min)	Specific activity (nmoles ^{32}P/mg protein/min)
Intact	10.0	0.7	8.3	0.5
24-hr castration	11.7	0.9	6.9	0.5
96-hr castration	1.8	1.6	1.5	1.3

[a]Data taken from [54,55].

[b]c-AMP-Dependent and -independent protein kinases were assayed using total histone and DPV as substrates, respectively. Where present, c-AMP was at 2×10^{-6} M. The assays were based on the procedure of Goueli et al [53].

TABLE VI. Comparison of the properties of phosphatases associated with the nucleus of rat ventral prostate[a]

Property	Acidic phosphoprotein phosphatase[b]	Histone phosphatase[c]	Alkaline phosphatase[d]
		Substrate	
	[^{32}P]phosvitin	^{32}P-labeled lysine-rich histone	p-nitrophenyl phosphate
pH optimum	6.7	7.1	9.5–10.3
EDTA, 1 mM (% activity)	23	90	2
2-Mercaptoethanol, 3 mM (% activity)	99	140	10
NaCl, 0.2 M (% activity)	52	57	96
Inhibitors (% activity)			
NaF, 10 mM	37	36	96
Ammonium molybdate, 1 mM	81	64	—
ATP, 1 mM	34	18	—
48-hr Orchiectomy (% of intact controls)	69	81	232

[a]Adapted from [47,60–62]. Sonicates of Triton X-100 washed nuclei were used as the source of enzyme.
[b]Acidic phosphoprotein phosphatase activity was assayed by measuring the release of $^{32}P_i$ from [^{32}P]phosvitin. The reaction medium included 1 mM $MgCl_2$, 32 mM imidazole-HCl (final reaction pH 6.7 at 37°C), and 0.8 mg of [^{32}P]phosvitin in a final volume of 0.25 ml.
[c]The histone phosphatase activity was determined by the release of $^{32}P_i$ from ^{32}P-labeled lysine-rich histone and was assayed in a final volume of 0.25 ml containing 3 mM 2-mercaptoethanol, 48 mM Tris-HCl (final reaction pH 7.1 at 37°C), and 125-200 μg ^{32}P-labeled lysine-rich histone.
[d]The alkaline phosphatase activity was determined by the p-nitrophenol split from p-nitrophenyl phosphate. The reaction medium included 3 mM p-nitrophenyl phosphate and 50 mM sodium carbonate-bicarbonate buffer (final reaction pH 9.68 at 37°C).

The prostatic nucleus was found to contain protein phosphatase activities towards ^{32}P-labeled histone and phosvitin as substrates (Table VI). In addition, an alkaline phosphatase active towards p-nitrophenyl phosphate as substrate was observed. All of these enzymes had distinct characteristics suggesting a multiplicity among them as well. However, the protein phosphatases were relatively insensitive to early changes in the androgenic status of the animal. One would have expected their activity to be enhanced following orchiectomy; rather, there was a small decline at 48 hours postcastration. The alkaline phosphatase activity, whose function is not clear, however, increased rapidly following androgen deprivation. The above work on prostatic nuclear phosphoprotein phosphatase needs to be expanded to determine activities towards endogenous nonhistone phosphoproteins. Nevertheless, it would appear that nuclear protein kinases, rather than phosphatases, are involved in rapid modulation of nuclear protein phosphorylation in response to androgenic status of the animal [2,3,49,60–66]. Naturally, the relative impact of a phosphatase activity (though unchanging) would be enhanced or diminished with alterations in the protein kinase activities.

CONCLUSIONS

The results described above provide evidence that the prostatic nucleus contains multiple protein kinase activities as determined by distinct differences in their properties and discrete subnuclear localization. This conclusion is further reinforced by the remarkable apparent differential androgen sensitivity of various enzymes. As previously described [2,3], since phosphatases associated with the nucleus do not demonstrate as rapid a change in activities as do the protein kinases, it would appear, at least in early responses to androgen, that levels of nuclear protein phosphorylation may be primarily regulated via the protein kinase reactions. Complementing these studies are also our observations (not described in this paper) that modulations in the activities of protein kinases occur (distinct from the appearance of endogenous substrates) at different periods of time during postnatal development of the prostate [2,3,67,68].

In the work described above on prostatic nuclear protein kinase reactions in relation to androgen action, our approach thus far has been to carry out a systematic analysis of these enzymes (with the goals being their eventual purification and determination of substrate specificity) in order to establish the temporal changes in their activities in response to androgen withdrawal. Thus, enzymes which demonstrate rapid changes in activity following androgen deprivation (ie, those which turn over rapidly) would be excellent candidates for a possible role in the early events involved in the mediation of androgen action. However, a complete picture of the turnover of various enzymes will be developed only after the effects of a single injection of androgen administered to castrated animals are also documented. This is problematic because of the heterogeneity of the nuclear protein kinases (and differential responses to androgenic status demonstrated by decrease or increase of enzyme activities) and, therefore, further definition of specific controls in this system must await the purification of various enzymes and determination of their substrate specificities.

In Table VII are documented some parameters of early androgen action in the prostatic nucleus as they compare with changes in protein kinase activities. There appears to be a remarkable temporal relation between the activity of certain protein kinases (eg, which show marked decreases within 24 hours postorchiectomy) and the quantity of nuclear androgen receptors as well as the activity of

TABLE VII. Effects of orchiectomy on androgen-sensitive parameters of rat ventral prostate nuclei

Activity	% Change	
	24-hr	48-hr
Nuclear protein kinase fractions		
DPV substrate		
flow through	–20	–40
bound	–33	–53
histone substrate		
flow through	0	+250
bound	0	+250
NHP substrate		
flow through	0	–50
bound		
eluted at 0.15–0.20 M $(NH_4)_2SO_4$	+100	+200
eluted at 0.25–0.30 M $(NH_4)_2SO_4$	–84	–84
RNA polymerase	–52	–73
Nuclear receptor	–93	–94

Data adapted from [6,51,69].

RNA polymerase. We therefore postulate that these enzymes may be especially important with respect to the early androgen action in this target organ. On the other hand, the enzymes which show an enhancement in activity upon castration also deserve attention since they may play a role in the decline of androgen-dependent activities of the prostate or its regression. This concept is in concert with the demonstration of a regression-associated increase of a protein kinase in a breast tumor cell line [39]. Perhaps the NHP kinase (eluting at 0.15–0.2 M $(NH_4)_2SO_4$ which is very low in normal animals but increases rapidly on castration) and histone kinases (which increase around 48 hours postorchiectomy) serve similar functions. Again, a definitive answer to these possibilities will be forthcoming only when these enzymes are further purified and their natural substrates are identified. Nonetheless, the above-described results strongly suggest that the presence or absence of specific protein kinase reactions may be critical for discrete steps in the mediation of androgen action.

As discussed by Mathis et al [70], it is recognized that altered chromatin structure preceding transcription may depend on three consecutive or simultaneous events: a) relaxation of higher order of chromatin; b) conversion of nucleosome to an "active" form; and c) interaction of "factors" to bind and initiate RNA synthesis at specific sites. Given these considerations, the mechanism(s) by which prostatic nuclear protein kinase activities are modulated in response to altered androgenic status of the animal, and the site(s) of their action in the sequence of events related to androgen action in the prostate, especially the control of transcription, remain to be elucidated. Therefore, much of the ensuing discussion is somewhat speculative and is presented to determine possible future directions for experimental approaches.

The observation that changes in activity of different protein kinases occur at different times following androgen deprivation suggests that phosphorylation (and conceivably dephosphorylation) of different substrates may be critical at discrete moments. A number of possibilities may thus be visualized for the role(s) of protein kinases in the early action of androgen. As suggested in Figure 6, it is plausible that upon androgen-receptor complex interaction with chromatin, modulations in protein kinases may occur in different temporal sequences, thus exerting their influence in one or more steps in the proposed scheme. In the first instance it may be that the interaction of androgen-receptor complex with chromatin directly influences the activity of some of the protein kinase reactions (step 1).

In step 2 where protein kinase reactions may be modulated or participate in activity of the chromatin, it is implied that alterations in the activity of these enzymes may be owing to a physical conformational change in chromatin in response to androgen-receptor complex binding as described by others [13,14]. Such conformational changes could affect the relationship of kinases and their endogenous protein substrates. Other examples by which conformational changes in nuclear protein substrates have been attributed to enhance the nuclear protein kinase reactions are known [3,43,71]. On the other hand, at this stage (step 2)

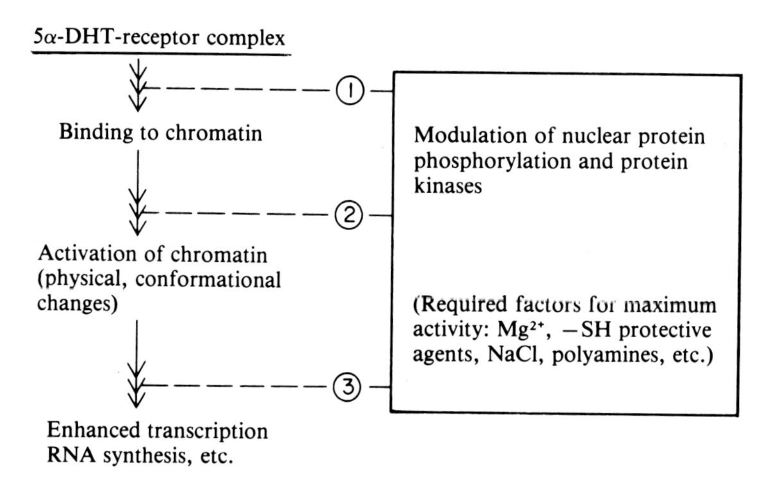

Fig. 6. Androgen-mediated chromatin controls in the prostate.

it is equally conceivable that the activation of chromatin follows the action of one or more protein kinases.

The third locus of protein kinase involvement (step 3) may relate to the possible actions of these enzymes on the RNA polymerase (ie, by phosphorylation of the polymerase itself), or by formation of specific phosphoprotein-polymerase complexes, or by specific phosphoprotein-DNA complexes, with the eventual result that efficient operation of the polymerase reaction proceeds. It should be remarked that at any of the above-mentioned steps where alterations in kinase activities could occur, they may also be due to increased amounts of kinases or their substrates (by synthesis and/or transport to nucleus), or conformational changes in the enzymes and/or substrates.

It has been reported [72] that phosphorylation of chromatin enhances its acceptor activity for androgen-receptor complex. Early modulation of protein kinases (step 1) in response to androgen may, therefore, play a crucial role at this level. The acceptor proteins appear to be present in both the loosely bound and tightly bound nonhistone protein fractions of chromatin [9,12]. Much protein kinase activity is associated with the loosely bound proteins of chromatin and several nonhistone proteins in this fraction are highly phosphorylated in a tissue-specific manner [3,24]. Further observations on prostatic nuclear protein kinases should aid in integrating some of the above concepts.

ACKNOWLEDGMENTS

The original investigations described in this paper were supported in part by research grant CA 15062 awarded by the National Cancer Institute, D.H.H.S., and by the General Medical Fund of the Veterans Administration.

REFERENCES

1. Ahmed K: Phosphoprotein metabolism in primary and accessory sex tissues. In Thomas JA, Singhal RL (eds): "Molecular Mechanisms of Gonadal Hormone Action. Advances in Sex Hormone Research." Baltimore: University Park Press, 1975, Vol 1, pp 129–165.
2. Ahmed K, Wilson MJ: Chromatin controls in the prostate. In Busch H (ed): "The Cell Nucleus." New York: Academic Press, 1978, Vol 6, pp 409–459.
3. Ahmed K, Wilson MJ, Goueli SA, Norvitch ME: Testosterone effects on the prostatic nucleus. In Busch H (ed): "Effects of Drugs on the Cell Nucleus." New York Academic Press, 1979, pp 419–454.
4. Price D, Williams-Ashman HG: The accessory reproductive glands of mammals. In Young WC (ed): "Sex and Internal Secretions." Baltimore: Williams and Wilkins, 1961, pp 366–488,.
5. Mann TJ: "The Biochemistry of Semen and of the Male Reproduction Tract." London: Methuen, 1964.
6. Liao S, Fang S: Receptor-proteins for androgens and the mode of action of androgens on gene transcription in ventral prostate. Vitam Horm 27:17–90, 1969.
7. Williams-Ashman HG, Reddi AH: Actions of vertebrate sex hormones. Ann Rev Physiol 33:31–82, 1971.

8. Mainwaring WIP: "The Mechanisms of Action of Androgens." New York: Springer-Verlag, 1977.
9. Liao S, Mezzetti G, Chen C: Androgen receptor and early biochemical responses. In Busch H. (ed): "The Cell Nucleus." New York: Academic Press, 1979, Vol 7, pp 201–227.
10. Ahmed K, Wilson MJ, Goueli SA, Steer RC: Functional biochemistry. In Hafez ESE, Spring-Mills E (eds): "Perspectives of Human Reproduction." Ann Arbor: Ann Arbor Science Publishers, 1979, Vol 6, pp 69–108.
11. Nyberg LM, Wang TY: The role of the androgen-binding nonhistone proteins in the transcription of prostatic chromatin. J Steroid Biochem 7:267–273, 1976.
12. Hiremath ST, Loor RM, Wang TY: Isolation of an androgen receptor from salt extract of rat prostatic chromatin. Biochem Biophys Res Commun 97:981–986, 1980.
13. Mainwaring WIP, Jones DM: Influence of receptor complexes on the properties of prostate chromatin, including its transcription by RNA polymerase. J Steroid Biochem 6:475–481, 1975.
14. Loor RM, Hu AL, Wang TY: Structurally altered and transcriptionally activated rat prostate chromatin induced by androgens. Biochim Biophys Acta 477:312–321, 1977.
15. Allfrey VG: DNA-binding proteins and transcriptional control in prokaryotic and eukaryotic systems. In Cameron IL, Jeter JR Jr (eds): "Acidic Proteins of the Nucleus." New York: Academic Press, 1974, pp 1–27.
16. Olson MOJ, Busch H: Nuclear proteins. In Busch H (ed): "The Cell Nucleus." New York: Academic Press, 1974, vol 3, pp 211–268.
17. Kleinsmith, LJ: Phosphorylation of nonhistone porteins. In Busch H (ed): "The Cell Nucleus." New York: Academic Press, 1978, vol 6, pp 221–261.
18. Stein GS, Stein JL, Thomson JA: Chromosomal proteins in transformed and neoplastic cells: A review. Cancer Res. 38:1181–1201, 1978.
19. Busch H: The cell and its function. In "Cancer and Chemotherapy." New York: Academic Press, 1980, vol 1, pp 21–76.
20. Gilmour RS, Paul J: Role of nonhistone components in determining organ specificity of rabbit chromatins. FEBS Lett 9:242–244, 1970.
21. Kamiyama M, Wang TY: Activated transcription from rat liver chromatin by nonhistone proteins. Biochim Biophys Acta 228:563–576, 1971.
22. Teng CS, Teng CT, Allfrey VG: Studies of nuclear acidic proteins: Evidence for their phosphorylation, tissue specificity, selective binding to deoxyribonucleic acid, and stimulatory effects on transcription. J Biol Chem 246:3597–3609, 1971.
23. Kleinsmith, LJ, Stein J, Stein G: Dephosphorylation of nonhistone proteins specifically alters the pattern of gene transcription in reconstituted chromatin. Proc Natl Acad Sci USA 73:1174–1178, 1976.
24. Ahmed K, Davis AT, Goueli SA, Wilson MJ: Phosphorylation of a nonhistone protein fraction which coextracts with the high-mobility-group proteins of chromatin. Biochem Biophys Res Commun 96:326–332, 1980.
25. Kleinsmith LJ, Allfrey VG, Mirsky AE: Phosphorylation of nuclear protein early in the course of gene activation in lymphocytes. Science 154: 780–781, 1966.
26. Ahmed K: Effect of testosterone on nuclear phosphoproteins of rat ventral prostate. Pharmacologist 12:229, 1970.
27. Ahmed K: Studies on nuclear phosphoproteins of rat ventral prostate: Incorporation of ^{32}P from [γ-^{32}P]-ATP. Biochim Biophys Acta 243:38–48, 1971.
28. Ahmed K, Ishida H: Effects of testosterone on nuclear phosphoproteins in rat ventral prostate. Molec Pharmacol 7:323–327, 1971.
29. Ishida H, Ahmed K: Studies on phosphoproteins of submandibular gland nuclei isolated from isoproterenol-treated rats. Exp Cell Res 78:31–40, 1973.

30. Langan TA: A phosphoprotein preparation from liver nuclei and its effect on the inhibition of RNA synthesis by histones. In Konigsberger VV, Bosch L (eds): "Regulation of Nucleic Acid and Protein Biosynthesis." Amsterdam: Elsevier, 1967, pp 233–242.
31. Kleinsmith LJ, Allfrey VG: Nuclear phosphoproteins. II. Metabolism of exogenous phosphoprotein by intact nuclei. Biochim Biophys Acta 175:136–141, 1969.
32. Kamiyama M, Dastugue B, Defer N, Kruh J: Liver chromatin nonhistone proteins. Partial fractionation and mechanism of action on RNA synthesis. Biochim Biophys Acta 277:576–583, 1972.
33. Takeda M, Yamamura H, Ohga Y: Phosphoprotein kinases associated with rat liver chromatin. Biochem Biophys Res Commun 42:103–110, 1971.
34. Ahmed K: Increased phosphorylation of nuclear phosphoproteins in precancerous liver. Res Commun Chem Pathol Pharmacol 9:771–774, 1974.
35. Ishida H, Ahmed K: Studies on chromatin-associated protein phosphokinase of submandibular gland from isoproterenol-treated rats. Exp Cell Res 84:127–136, 1974.
36. Ahmed K, Davis AT: Protein phosphokinase activity associated with rat ventral prostate chromatin. In: "Proceedings of the Symposium on Normal and Abnormal Growth of the Prostate." Springfield: CC Thomas, 1975, pp 317–327.
37. Ahmed K, Wilson MJ: Chromatin-associated protein phosphokinases of rat ventral prostate: Characteristics and effects of androgenic status. J Biol Chem 250:2370–2375, 1975.
38. Jungmann RJ, Kranias EG: Nuclear phosphoprotein kinases and the regulation of gene transcription. Int J Biochem 8:819–830, 1977.
39. Cho-Chung YS: On the interaction of cyclic AMP-binding protein and estrogen receptor in growth control. Life Sci 24:1231–1240, 1979.
40. Schauder P, Starman BJ, Williams RH: Effect of testosterone on phenol-soluble nuclear acidic proteins of rat ventral prostate. Proc Soc Exp Biol Med 145:331–333, 1974.
41. Kadohama N, Anderson KM: Nuclear nonhistone proteins from rat ventral prostate cell under going hypertrophy or hyperplasia. Exp Cell Res 99:135–145, 1976.
42. Kadohama N, Anderson KM: Acetylation and phosphorylation of nuclear proteins from growing or dividing rat ventral prostate cells. Can J Biochem 55:513–520.
43. Ahmed K, Wilson MJ, Goueli SA, Williams-Ashman HG: Effects of polyamines on prostatic chromatin- and nonhistone-protein associated protein kinase reactions. Biochem J 176:739–750, 1978.
44. Ahmed K, Wilson MJ, Davis AT: Phosvitin phosphate content: Implications for protein kinase assay. Biochim Biophys Acta 377:80–83, 1975.
45. Norvitch ME, Wilson MJ, Ahmed K: Distribution of protein phosphokinases and chromosomal phosphoproteins in heterochromatin and euchromatin of rat ventral prostate. Eur J Cell Biol 22: 78, 1980.
46. Wilson MJ, Ahmed K: Localization of protein phosphokinase activities in the nucleolus distinct from extranucleolar regions in rat ventral prostate nuclei. Exp Cell Res 93:261–266, 1975.
47. Wilson MJ, Ahmed K: The differential response of prostatic nucleolar and extranculeolar protein phosphokinase activities following androgen deprivation. Endocr Res Commun 3:63–69, 1976.
48. Wilson MJ, Ahmed K: Enzymic characteristics and effects of testosterone treatment on nucleolar- and chromatin-associated histone phosphokinase activity of rat ventral prostate. Exp Cell Res 106:151–157, 1977.
49. Coffey DS, Shimazaki J, Williams-Ashman HG: Polymerization of deoxyribonucleotides in relation to androgen-induced prostatic growth. Arch Biochem Biophys 124:184–198, 1968.
50. Wilson MJ, Davis AT, Ahmed K: Effects of antiandrogens (cyproterone acetate and flutamide) on the activity of nuclear protein phosphokinases and phosphatases of rat ventral prostate. Molec Pharmacol 17:212–217, 1980.

51. Goueli SA, Steer RC, Wilson MJ, Ahmed K: Partial purification and differential androgen sensitivity of protein kinases from nuclei of rat ventral prostate. Eur J Biochem 113:45–51, 1980.
52. Goueli SA, Ahmed K: Multiplicity of the rat ventral prostate nuclear protein kinases in a fraction bound to DEAE-sephadex Fed Proc 40:1720, 1981.
53. Goueli SA, Slungaard R, Wilson MJ, Ahmed K: A modified paper-binding procedure for the assay of nucleus associated protein phosphokinases. J Pharmacol Meth 3:235–242, 1980.
54. Ahmed K, Goueli SA, Wilson MJ, Novitch ME, Steer RC, Tse EY: Protein kinase reactions of the rat ventral prostate nucleus. Proc Pan Am Congr Andrology II, Mexico City, 1981, (in press).
55. Tse EY, Wilson MJ, Ahmed K: Responses of cytosolic protein kinases to changing androgenic status in rat ventral prostate Fed Proc 40:1607, 1981.
56. Reddi AH, Ewing LL, Williams-Ashman HG: Protein phosphokinase reactions in mammalian testis: Stimulatory effects of adenosine 3′,5′-cyclic monophosphate on the phosphorylation of basic proteins. Biochem J 122:333–345, 1971.
57. Tsang BK, Singhal RL: Androgenic effects on protein kinases and cyclic AMP-binding protein in the ventral prostate. Res Commun Chem Pathol Pharmacol 13:697–712, 1976.
58. Fuller DJM, Byus CV, Russell DH: Specific regulation by steroid hormones of the amount of type I cyclic AMP-dependent protein kinase holoenzyme. Proc Natl Acad Sci USA 75:223–227, 1978.
59. Ichii S, Iwanaga Y, Ikeda A: Effects of sex hormones on the activity of protein kinases in rat ventral prostate and uterus. Endocrinol Jpn 20:33–37, 1973.
60. Wilson MJ, Ahmed K: Presence and androgen control of an alkaline phosphatase in the nucleus of rat ventral prostate. Biochim Biophys Acta 429:439–447, 1976.
61. Wilson MJ, Ahmed K: Enzymic properties and effects of androgen on nuclear histone phosphatase activity of rat ventral prostate. Exp Cell Res 117:71–78, 1978.
62. Wilson MJ, Ahmed K, Fischbach TJ: Acidic-phosphoprotein phosphatase activity of rat ventral prostate nuclei: Apparent lack of effect of androgens. Biochim Biophys Acta 542:12–20, 1978.
63. Wilson MJ, Ahmed K: Comparison of the effects of androgens on nuclear histone kinase and phosphatase activities of rat ventral prostate. Endocrinology 98:75.
64. Wilson MJ, Ahmed K, Fischbach TJ: Acidic phosphoprotein phosphatase of the prostatic nucleus: Enzymic properties and the effects of androgens. Fed Proc 36:389, 1977.
65. Wilson MJ, Goueli SA, Ahmed K: Separation of nuclear protein phosphatases active toward acidic and basic phosphoprotein substrates. 11th Int Congr Biochem Abstr, Toronto, p 48, 1979.
66. Wilson MJ, Goueli SA, Ahmed K: Partial purification of nuclear protein phosphatases of rat ventral prostate. Proc 6th Int Congr Endocrinol, Melbourne, p 545, 1980.
67. Norvitch ME, Wilson MJ, Ahmed K: Chromatin-associated protein phosphokinase activities in rat ventral prostate during sexual maturation. 3rd Int Conf Differentiation, Minneapolis, p 31, 1978.
68. Norvitch ME, Wilson MJ, Ahmed K: Phosphoproteins and phosphokinase activities of ventral prostate chromatin during sexual maturation in the rat (submitted for publication).
69. van Doorn E, Craven S, Bruchovsky N: The relationship between androgen receptors and the hormonally controlled responses of rat ventral prostate. Biochem J 160:11–21, 1976.
70. Mathis D, Oudet P, Chambon P: Structure of transcribing chromatin. Prog Nucleic Acids Res 24:1–55, 1980.
71. Kaplowitz PB, Platz RD, Kleinsmith LJ: Nuclear phosphoproteins. 3. Increase in phosphorylation during histone-phosphoprotein interaction. Biochim Biophys Acta 229:739–748, 1971.
72. Klyzsejko-Stefanowicz L, Chiu JF, Tsai YH, Hnilica LS: Acceptor proteins in rat androgenic tissue chromatin. Proc Natl Acad Sci USA 73:1954–1958, 1976.

The Prostatic Cell: Structure and Function
Part A, pages 75–92

The Prostatic Cell: Chromosomal and DNA Analyses

Avery A. Sandberg

Like all somatic cells, those of the prostate contain a full complement (2n) of DNA organized during the interphase stage of the cell cycle essentially as diffuse chromatin. The latter is probably organized within the nuclei of the cells of the prostate no differently than in nuclei of other organs and tissues [1,2] (Fig. 1), though the functional expression of the chromatin in prostatic cells which endows them with their functions and morphology must be uniquely prostatic. The exact status of the chromatin during, and the duration of, the various stages of the cell cycle in the disparate varieties of prostatic cells have not been rigorously established (Fig. 2). An exception is the later stage of the cell cycle (prophase, metaphase) in which the chromatin of the prostatic cell is transformed into distinct chromosomes, whose number and morphology are identical to those of all other somatic cells in the body [3] (Fig. 3). Under conditions of neoplasia the amount of chromatin (DNA) and/or the number and morphology of chromosomes undergo changes [3] (Fig. 4).

Of all the organs in the body, we do know some parameters which control the *total* amount of DNA in the prostate, ie, the influence of hormonal factors, primarily testosterone, on the size, cellular composition, and DNA content of the gland. Thus, it has been shown that following castration the total amount of DNA (ie, the total number of cells) greatly decreases and can be induced to return to almost normality upon the administration of testosterone [4] (Fig. 5). Furthermore, testosterone does have the potential of stimulating the replication of chromatin within nuclei. Whether other hormonal substances (eg, prolactin, estrogens, etc) have a similar influence has not been established with certainty, though it would appear that if such influence does exist it does not have the intensity of testosterone. The role these hormones or any other substances or factors play in inducing and/or maintaining abnormal DNA amounts and function, such as those seen in neoplasia, has not been clarified.

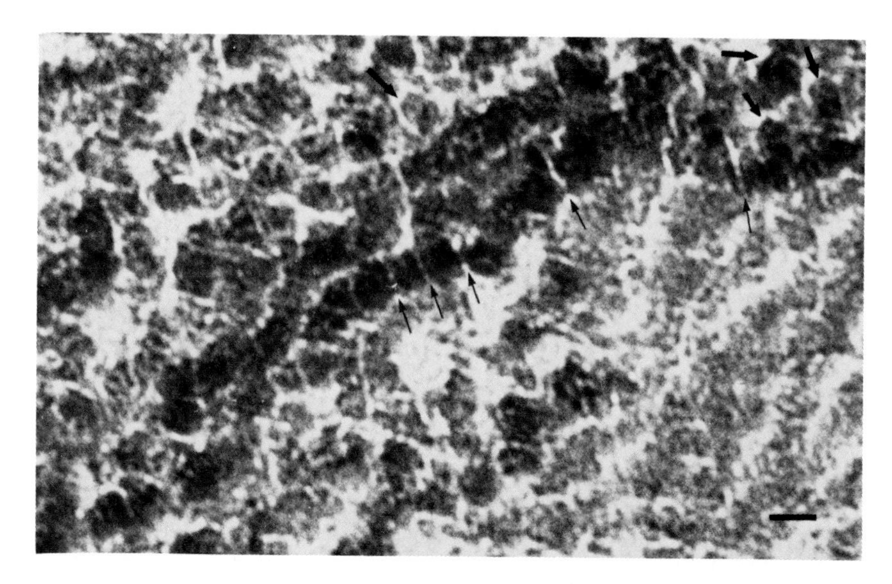

Fig. 1. An electron microscopic picture of the structure of chromatin in a nucleus showing the arrangement of the hexagonal nucleosomes in situ. In all probability this arrangement is characteristic of all somatic cells of the body, including those of the prostate, though the functions of these nucleosomes vary from one cell to another to allow for specific differentiation and functions in different organs and tissues [2].

MEASUREMENTS OF DNA IN PROSTATIC CELLS

Some features of DNA (eg, staining with certain reagents such as Feulgen's, fluorescence characteristics) afford under optimal conditions an opportunity for measuring with great accuracy the amount of DNA per nucleus [6–10]. However, close attention must be given to the control values for the tissue being examined and the stage of the cell cycle of the cells in which such measurements are being performed. The latter is particularly crucial since replication of DNA during interphase (S-phase) occurs asynchronously, a situation which cannot be ascertained with DNA measurements [3]. Thus, a normal nucleus may have a substantial part, if not all, of its DNA replicated and yet not be recognized by photometric measurements and, thus, yield a spuriously high value for the amount of DNA present in a normal cell. Only in anaphase does the nucleus contain an exact amount of 2n DNA. Thus, the DNA value obtained during that stage can serve most reliably as a control value. The value obtained in mature lymphocytes, which replicate their DNA very slowly over a prolonged period of time, is usually taken as the control DNA value. However, small variations in DNA, such as

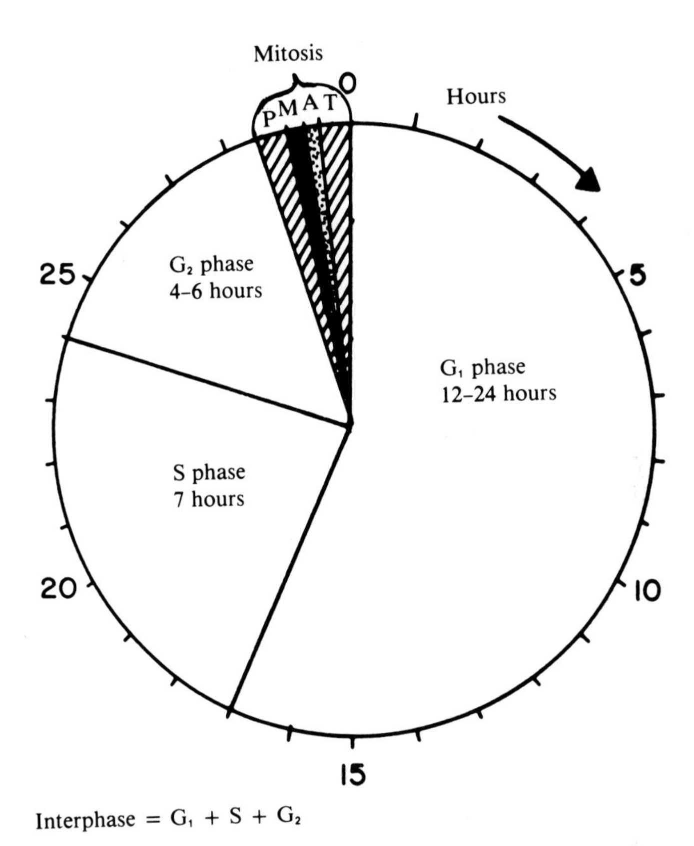

Fig. 2. A schematic presentation of the cell cycle of human cells showing the duration of the various periods. Though the lengths of these periods may vary from one tissue to another, the important facets to be remembered are that duplication of the DNA occurs only during the S-phase and that the amount of DNA will, thus, vary considerably whether it is measured early or late in the S-phase. In very late S-phase the amount of DNA may approach twice the normal (4n), whereas prior to that, increased amounts of DNA may be encountered and spuriously interpreted as abnormal when in fact the cell is undergoing normal duplication of its DNA.

those associated with an extra or missing small chromosome, constituting less than 5% of the total amount of cellular DNA, cannot be ascertained accurately and reliably with the various photometric measurements, nor can changes in morphology of chromosomes leading to profound alterations in cell function (particularly neoplasia) be established with such methodology. Thus, DNA measurements carry with them these limitations, though the data obtained appear to have yielded some worthwhile information regarding, in particular, neoplastic

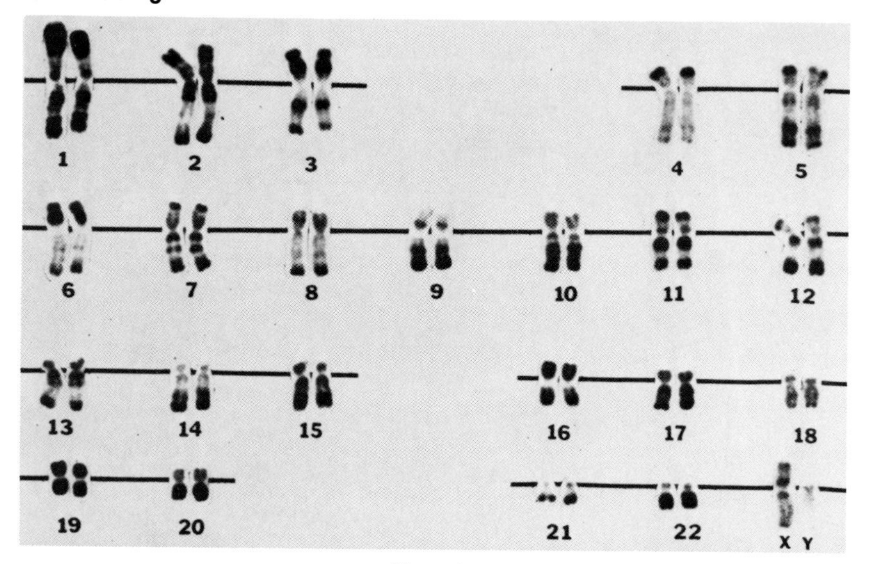

Figure 3

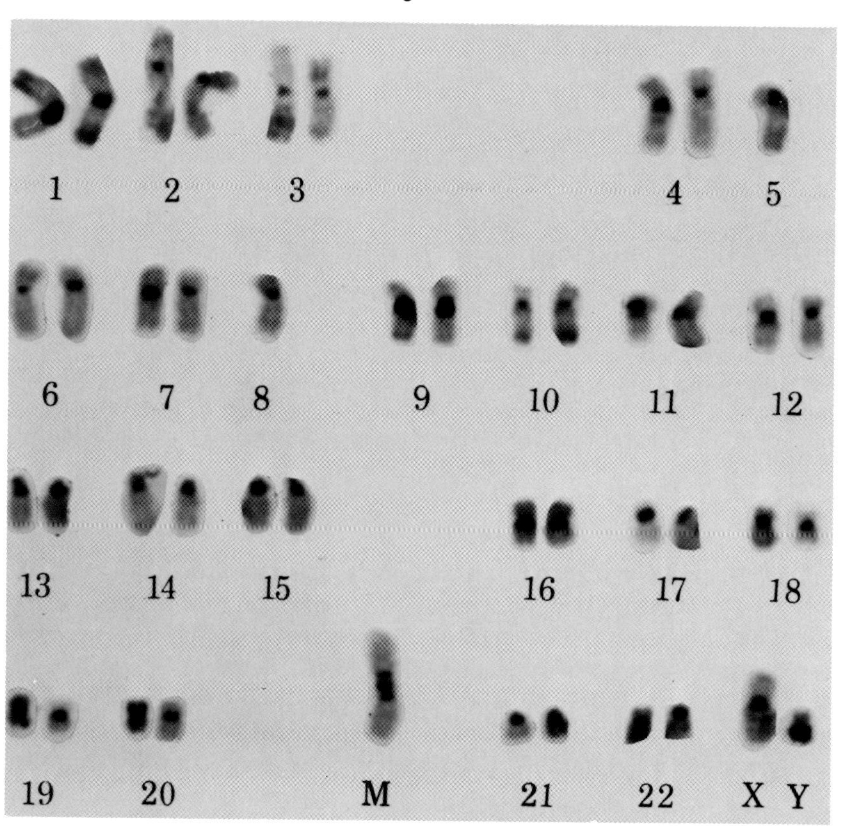

Figure 4

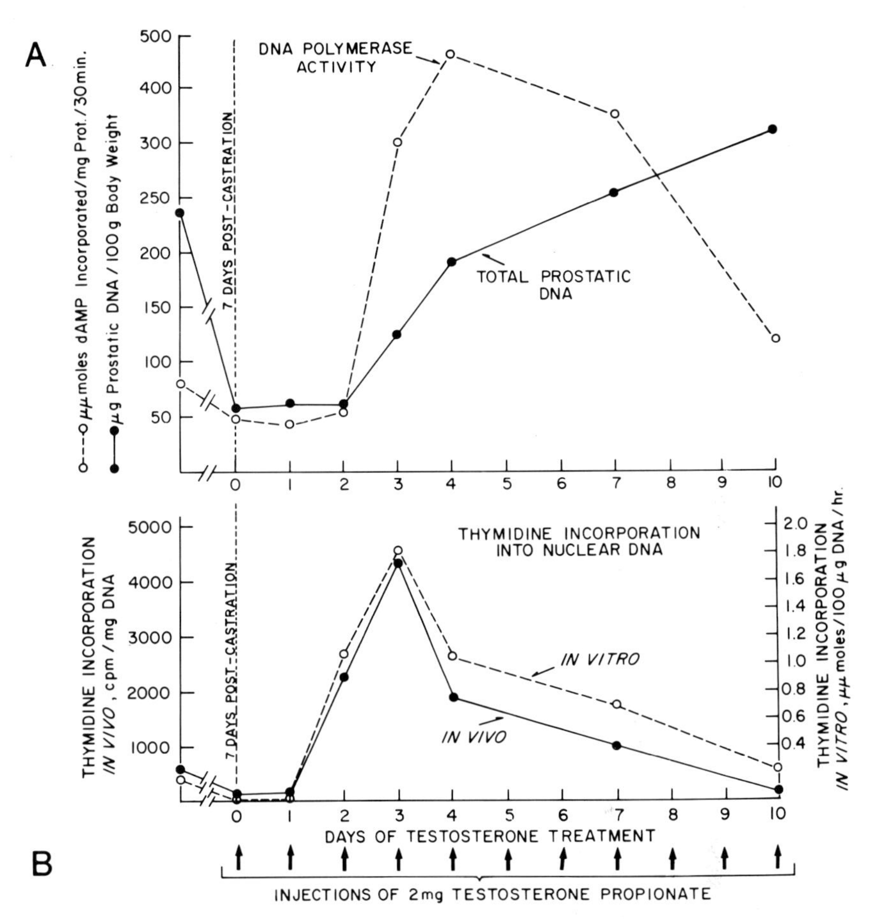

Fig. 5. Effects of castration and exogenous androgen administration on: A) total DNA in the rat ventral prostate, and B) rate of DNA synthesis determined by ^{3}H-thymidine incorporation when administered in vivo and by incubation of ^{3}H-thymidine for 1 hour with minced ventral prostatic tissue in vitro. DNA was isolated from the tissue and the specific activity of the incorporated labeled thymidine determined. The results indicate definite stimulation of DNA synthesis by the testosterone administration [4].

Fig. 3. Karyotype of the 46 chromosomes of a normal cell showing the R-banding pattern of the chromosomes. The normal human karyotype consists of 22 pairs of autosomes and 2 sex chromosomes (XY in the male; XX in the female). The banding patterns (in this case R-banding) do not differentiate one cell in the body from another, since the bands appear to be the same in all somatic cells of an individual. Any deviation from the normal number of 46 chromosomes (diploid number = 2n) and/or morphology of the chromosomes is compatible with neoplastic abnormalities [3].

Fig. 4. A hypodiploid (less than 46 chromosomes) karyotype of a cancer cell containing a marker (M) chromosome of dicentric nature. Such a marker almost invariably indicates a neoplastic state. Note the missing chromosomes in groups 5 and 8, though it is not clear whether these have contributed to the genesis of the marker, which remained unidentified. The presence of marker chromosomes carries with it definite prognostic implications in certain conditions [25].

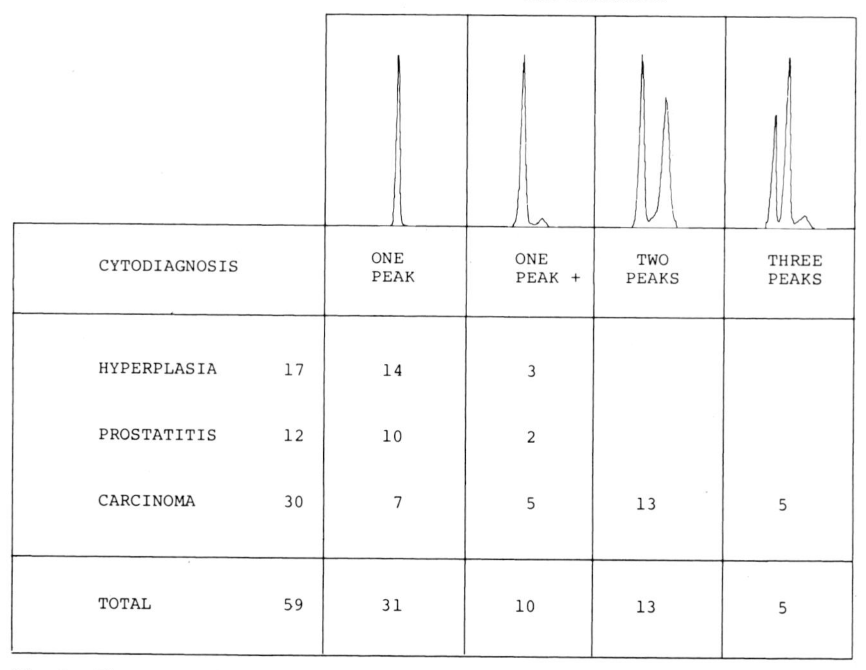

CYTODIAGNOSIS		ONE PEAK	ONE PEAK +	TWO PEAKS	THREE PEAKS
HYPERPLASIA	17	14	3		
PROSTATITIS	12	10	2		
CARCINOMA	30	7	5	13	5
TOTAL	59	31	10	13	5

Fig. 6. Flow cytometric DNA analysis in 59 cases with prostatic disease taken from Frederiksen et al [11]. Typical histograms are shown on top and recorded as peaks below. Each histogram was based on the analysis of about 50,000 nuclei. The ordinate indicates cells per channel in relative units and the abscissa the relative fluorescence intensity (channel number). One peak indicates all counted nuclei in the diploid DNA area, one peak plus an additional small fraction of less than 10% tetraploid nuclei and 2 or 3 peaks represent significant hyperdiploid cell populations. It must be realized that even though the peaks are shown in diploid and tetraploid areas, there is no guarantee that the distribution of chromosomes and/or their morphology are normal, since pseudodiploid and pseudotetraploid cells, as well as those near completion of the DNA replication cycle, may give similar pictures.

Figs. 7–11. Figures have been taken from Bichel et al [12]. In this study flow microfluorometry and transrectal fine needle biopsies of human prostatic carcinomas were utilized. Figure 7 shows the values obtained in 5 benign prostatic hyperplasias, with all the values falling rather sharply within the 2n (diploid) range. In Figure 8 five well differentiated prostatic carcinomas are shown with 4 of them having a minor population of cells with 4n amount of DNA. Figure 9 shows 5 moderately differentiated prostatic carcinomas with only 3 showing distribution abnormalities of the DNA in the 4n range. Figure 10 depicts 5 moderately differentiated prostatic carcinomas with definite abnormalities in the distribution of the DNA. Nuclei with 4n or more DNA predominated in 3 of the tumors and in the other 2 constituted a significant proportion of the cells. Figure 11 shows 2 poorly differentiated prostatic carcinomas with a high proportion of the cells being in the 4n range.

As already indicated, the exact constitution of these cells cannot be determined on the basis of any DNA determination, since the amount of DNA may be normal or a multiple of the normal; yet the nuclei may have a very abnormal karyotypic distribution. However, in cases where mitotic cells suitable for chromosome analysis cannot be obtained, measurement of DNA may be of help in the evaluation of prostatic tumors.

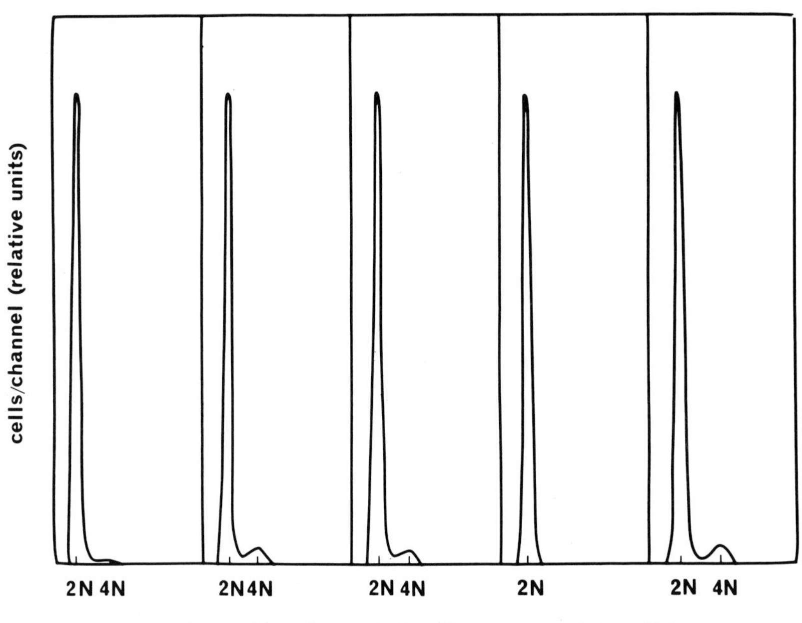

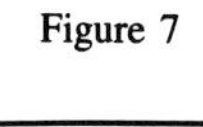
Figure 7

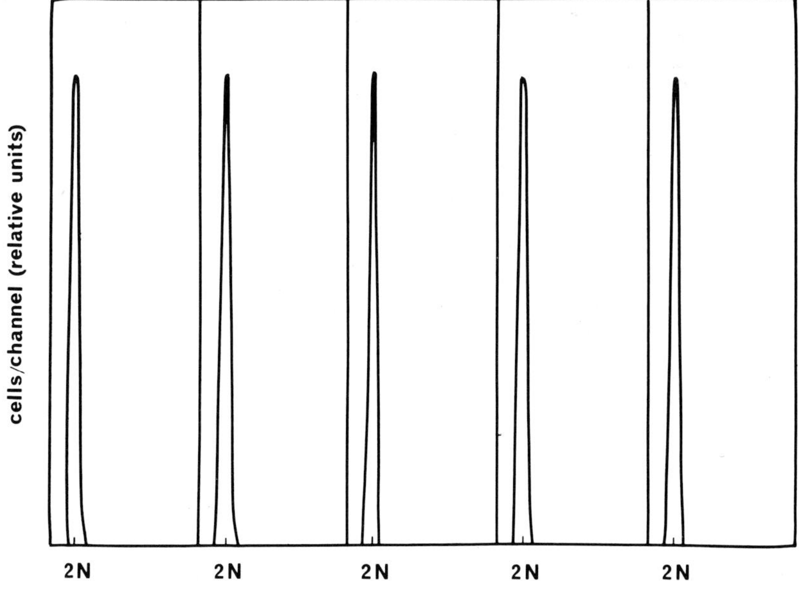

Figure 8

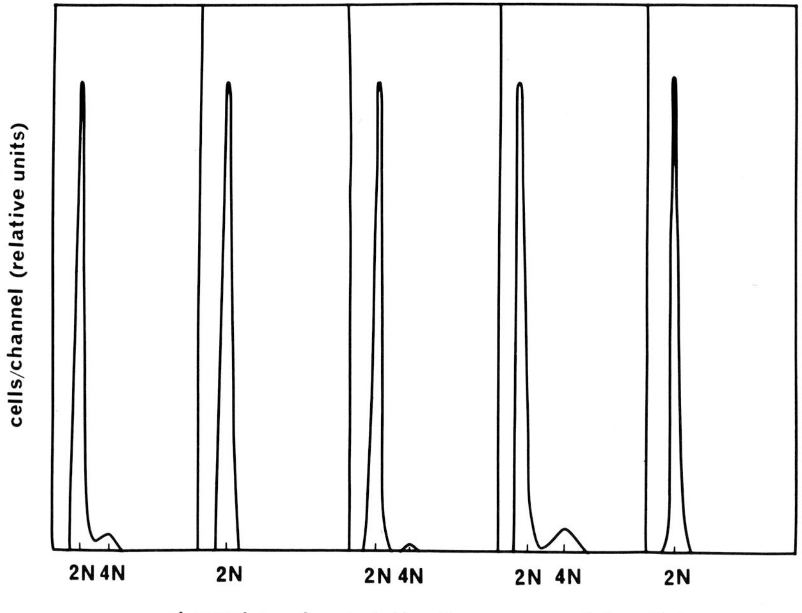

Figure 9

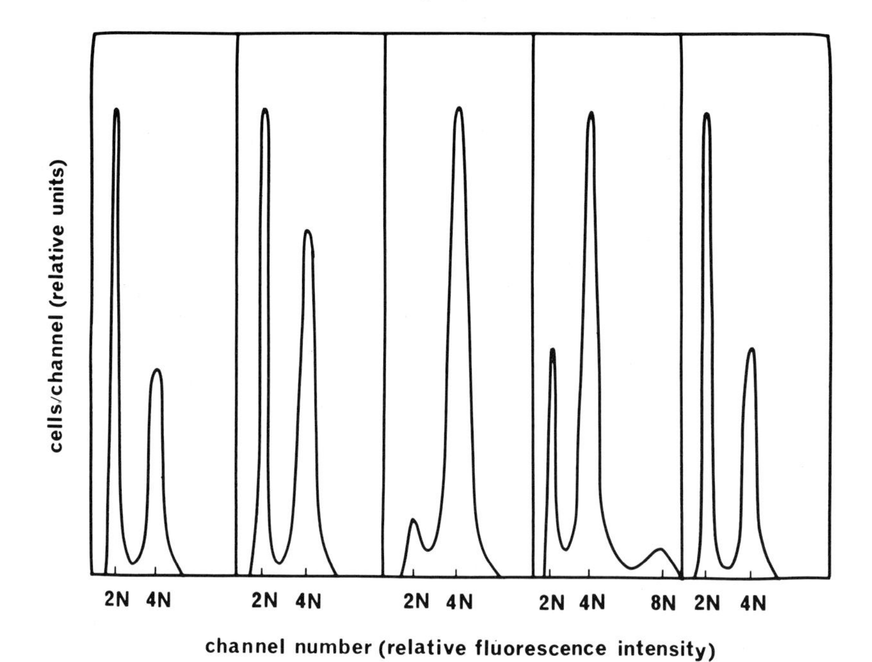

Figure 10

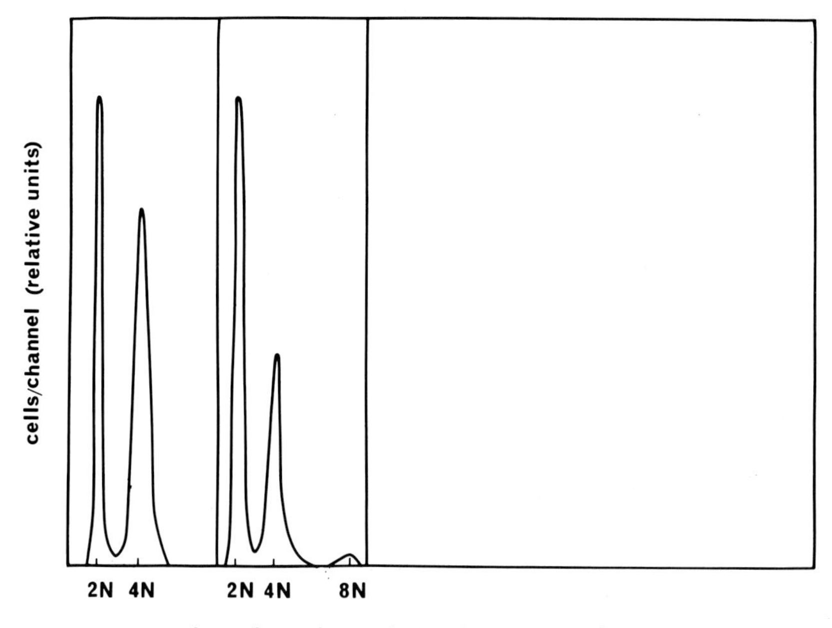

Figure 11

conditions associated with the prostate. Thus, studies on cellular DNA content of cancer of the prostate have been published and correlated with prognosis [11–15]. However, these methodologies lack the specificity and morphologic detail of chromosome analysis, particularly regarding the possibility of a specific change characterizing all or some cancers of the prostate.

Studies based on DNA content in prostatic cancers indicate that ploidy may have some relationship to response to estrogens, ie, all but one of the 9 triploid and hexaploid tumors did not respond to estrogen therapy, sharply contrasting with 22 of 24 diploid and tetraploid tumors that did not respond [15]. It will be important to ascertain with chromosomal studies whether this particular relationship is maintained under the more rigorous karyotypic analysis.

In another study [11], transrectal fine-needle aspiration biopsies were obtained in 59 patients with cancer of the prostate, and in 9 with benign prostatic hypertrophy (BPH) and prostatitis and analyzed with cytometric DNA measurements. One major peak in the DNA histogram was observed in the biopsies from BPH, prostatitis, and in some of the carcinomas. A DNA histogram with a second or third peak was always compatible with carcinoma and was found in the tumors of patients with cancers of various stages. The authors suggested that patients with hyperploid cancers in Stages I or II could benefit from early treatment [6].

In a subsequent study by the above group [16], prostatic transrectal fine-needle aspiration biopsies and flow cytometric analysis of single cell DNA content were carried out in 8 patients with untreated cancer of the prostate before and at frequent intervals during treatment with estrogens. Before treatment, the undifferentiated tumors were characterized by hyperploid cell populations, whereas diploid cells were found in well differentiated tumors. During treatment a change towards diploidy in DNA was observed about 3–6 months after initiation of therapy in the hyperploid cancers. Cytometric DNA analysis, according to these authors [16], may be of value in following patients with prostatic cancer, particularly those of poorly differentiated types.

In the above studies the presence of diploid cells, as revealed through cellular DNA content, must be interpreted with caution, since pseudodiploid cells (cells containing 46 chromosomes but either of abnormal distribution and/or morphology) would not only escape detection but also could readily register as diploid in cytometric analysis and yet be abnormal karyotypically. The latter is invariably the case in carcinoma of the prostate, as well as in that of other organs.

In another study [17] the effects of estracyt in 81 patients with advanced prostatic carcinoma, mainly estrogen resistant, were investigated by single cell cytophotometric analysis of the DNA content of the various cancers. In 9 of the cases the authors showed that the DNA content in poorly differentiated tumors decreased significantly more after estracyt than after conventional estrogen therapy and that during progression of the disease, despite estracyt therapy, no decrease in DNA content was seen, even after chemotherapy with cytoxan or 5-FU. The authors indicate that single cell microscanning cytophotometric analysis appears to be an interesting clinical, as well as an experimental, approach to obtain quantitative information about therapy-induced changes in cancer of the prostate.

Single cell cytophotometric analysis of nuclear DNA was first introduced by Sprenger et al, [18,19]. This showed that tumor cell populations and benign cells of the prostate can be distinguished with this method. Sprenger et al, [13,14] also analyzed the DNA content of prostatic carcinomas treated with estrogens. However, serial DNA analysis had not been published until the findings of Leistenschneider and Nagel appeared [13,17]. The latter authors also indicated that in contrast to their method, DNA flow-through cytophotometry seems to be of limited value for nuclear DNA determination, since it yields high rates of false negative and false positive results in prostatic cancer [19]. In a previous study the same authors [13] showed that under appropriate conditions of therapy, the nuclear DNA content of prostatic carcinomas can decrease to levels usually found in adenomas. The authors assumed that the latter contain exclusively diploid cells, though the possibility always exists that slight deviations from diploidy may, in fact, characterize some adenomas or variable proportions of cells in all adenomas and, yet, remain undetected with the methods used. This remains an area to be investigated further.

CHROMOSOME ANALYSIS IN PROSTATIC DISEASE

Detailed chromosome analyses in relatively large series of human prostatic cancers, either primary or metastatic, are egregiously lacking [3]. We reported [20] the presence of an isochromosome 17,i(17q), established with Q and G-banding, in the metastatic cells in the bone marrow of a patient with prostatic cancer. Direct marrow chromosome preparations showed a mode of 70 chromosomes with considerable scattering in counts and the presence of about 15% diploid metaphases with 46 chromosomes. The latter cells were undoubtedly of normal cell origin. A prostatic cancer with hypodiploidy and no marker chromsomes was described by Sekine [21].

The preponderant number of human cancers is characterized by chromosomal abnormalities [3]. These may be of subtle nature—a slight change in morphology as revealed by various banding techniques and/or the presence or absence of one of the small chromosomes and translocation without an apparent loss of chromosomal material—or may consist of profound modifications of the human genome with a large number of chromosomes, occasionally exceeding 100, accompanied by varying numbers of morphologically abnormal (marker) chromosomes. Banding analyses have afforded an opportunity to ascertain the origin of such marker chromosomes in most of the tumors, though frequently only some of the markers can be identified, whereas others remain too complex for such identification. Important is the fact that certain human cancers (lymphomas, cancer of the ovary, mixed tumor of the parotid, meningiomas) have been shown to be characterized by specific karyotypic changes [3,22–24] (Fig. 12).

In addition, certain nonrandom chromosome changes are associated with rather specific subgroups of leukemia and lymphoma and with therapeutic and prognostic facets of these diseases [3]. In bladder cancer, the presense or absence of markers has definite implications in the recurrence and prognosis of noninvasive cancers of the bladder; ploidy of the tumors also appears to be related to survival [25,26].

Obviously, a search must be made to ascertain whether similar karyotypic specificity characterizes various tumors and cancers of the prostate. Unfortunately, to date the number of prostatic cancers which has been analyzed karytotypically remains very small, and this area awaits future exploration.

DNA measurements have indicated that severe variations from diploidy occur in prostatic cancer, yet little information based on chromosome analysis in prostatic cancer is available. This is probably due to a number of factors. One of these is the small number of mitotic figures usually observed upon direct analysis

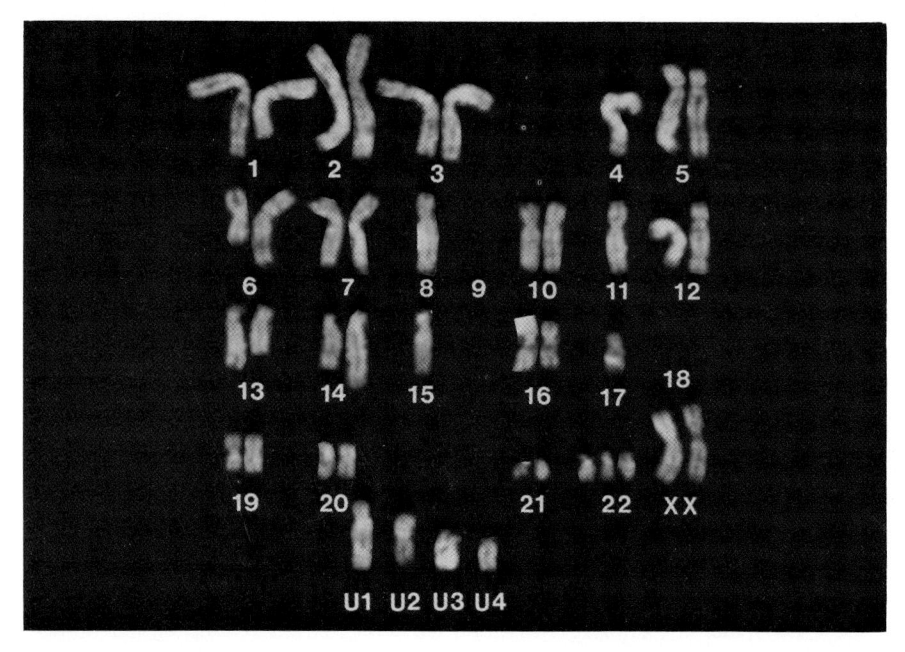

Fig. 12. Karyotype of a cell from an ovarian serous pseudocystadenocarcinoma showing a specific chromosome change, ie, t(6;14). The exchange of material between chromosomes 6 and 14 results in considerable elongation of the long arm of a chromosome 14 and shortening of the long arm of 6. Note missing chromosomes in some groups, an extra one in one group, and the presence of 4 unidentified markers whose origin could not be established with certainty but may be related to some of the missing chromosomes. Specific changes, similar to the 6;14 translocation of cystadenocarcinoma, must be established in prostatic cancer on the basis of detailed cytogenetic analysis of a large number of tumors.

of the tumors. Since it is possible that when such tumors are subjected to in vitro culture, particularly for relatively prolonged periods of time, selection of one karyotype over another may occur, the one selected in vitro may not necessarily reflect the in vivo condition. Thus, we must seek means by which to increase the number of mitotic cells in prostatic tumors at the time of analysis. Another reason for frequent failure of karyotypic analysis in prostatic cancer is the fact that often there is considerable supportive stromal tissue in the tumor, and this mitigates against optimal preparations for chromosome analysis. However, recent developments in cytogenetic methods for examining cancerous tissues [22,26,27], including that of the prostate, should go a long way towards yielding results elucidating and bearing importantly upon the karyotypic picture observed in prostatic cancer.

CHROMOSOME ANALYSIS IN ESTABLISHED CELL LINES FROM PROSTATIC CANCER

The limitations of chromosome analysis in established cell lines, as indicated above, are related to the uncertainty as to whether the findings obtained following long term culture of prostatic cancer cells are identical or at least very similar to those present in the original tumor [3]. Until this aspect is rigorously established, the cytogenetic findings obtained on such established cell lines must be interpreted with this reservation in mind. Nevertheless, the chromosome findings on established cell lines are of some interest and undoubtedly reflect in vivo events and, hence, are of considerable interest.

Cytogenetic information is available on 5 established cell lines of prostatic cancer origin (Table I). Each one of these is characterized by hyperdiploidy with high modal chromosome numbers and the frequent presence of markers [29–38] (Figs. 13–16).

One cell line studied with Q-banding revealed the cells to be completely aneuploid with a modal chromosome number in the hypertriploid range [29]. At least 10 distinctive marker chromosomes were identified. However, the modal chromosome number shifted from 62 to 55 with time in culture (between the 5th and 50th passage), and certain karyotypic variability occurred. In another cell line [29], originating from a primary prostatic adenocarcinoma, 28% of the cells were found to te pseudodiploid and 72% pseudotetraploid. All metaphases examined were partially trisomic for chromosome 9 and lacked a demonstrable Y chromosome. The overall karyotypic patterns of the cell lines studied, as well as their marker chromosomes, clearly distinguished these lines from other cancer

TABLE I. Epithelial cell lines originating from cancers of the prostate

Line identification	Source	Tumorgenicity	Chromosome number and karyotype	References
DU-145	Brain metastasis	Nude mice agar	64,Y 3 markers	[29]
PC-3	Vertebral metastasis	Nude mice	58 10 markers	[32]
HPC-36	Primary tumor	Not done	Hyperdiploid	[35]
1013 L	Primary tumor		77–84,Y	[37]
LNCaP	Lymph node metastasis	Nude mice	80–94 more than 5 markers	[36]

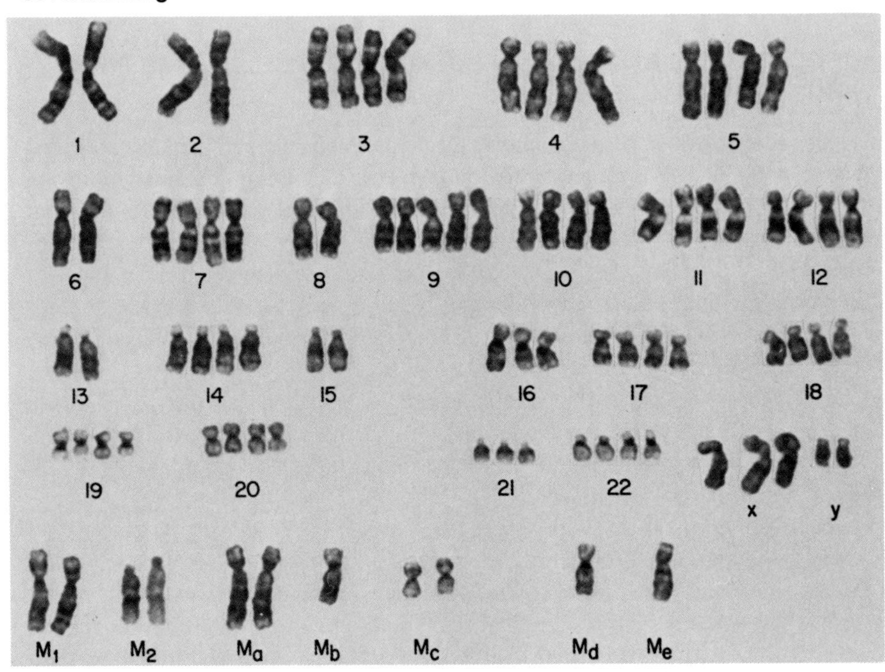

Figure 13

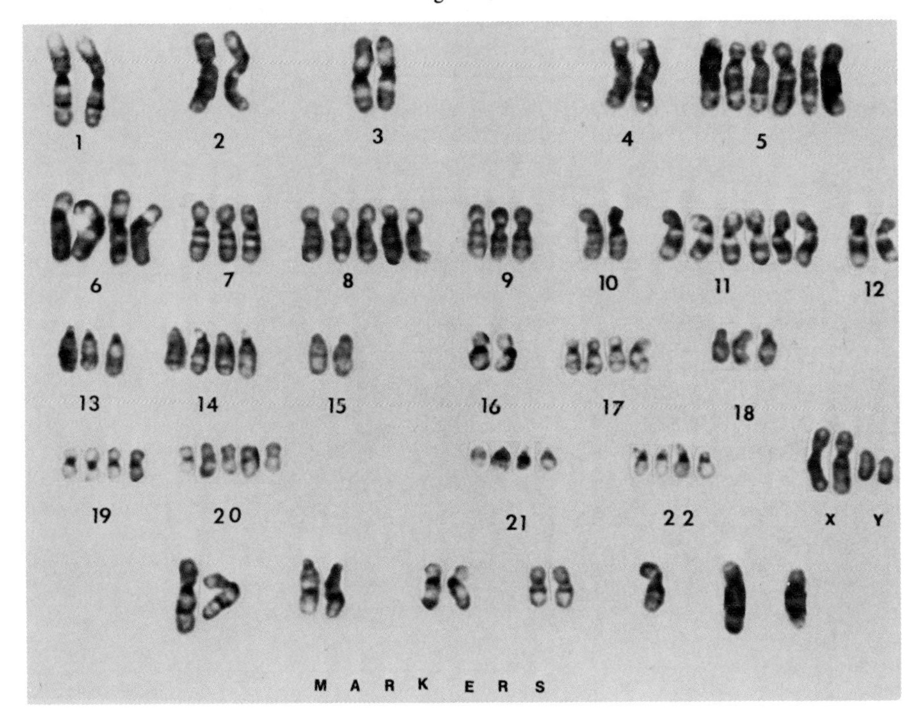

Figure 14

lines, including HeLa. The latter is of importance since the authenticity of other putative prostatic cancer lines has been disputed.

The necessity for performing very careful banding analysis on these cell lines is pointed to by observations obtained on line DU-145 of prostatic cancer origin. When originally published, a G-banded karyotype, as part of characterization of this new cell line, was included by the authors. They emphasized the presence of 3 marker chromosomes and rearranged Y chromosomes as peculiarities of the karyotypes of these cells. It appears that banding did not improve significantly upon the conventional karyotype presented by the same workers earlier [30]. However, when these cells were reexamined [31], a careful study of the karyotypes revealed that among the normal chromosomes presented by Stone et al [29] many were, in fact, markers. Noted also was the presence of two X chromosomes, as well as a Y chromosome with additional material on its long arm (Yq+). The high multiplicity of markers and their presence in all the metaphases examined indicated the clonal nature of the cells and implied that they can serve to monitor the identity of the cell line.

CONCLUSIONS

Taken in total, then, neither the DNA studies nor those based on karyotypic analyses of established cell lines have shed much light on any specific or nonrandom chromosome changes in prostatic cancer. To accomplish this, it will be necessary to utilize some of the newer techniques to examine prostatic tumors directly without resorting to long-term culture. Only on the basis of such analyses will it be possible to ascertain whether cancer of the prostate is characterized by nonrandom karyotypic changes. The fact that to date all established cell lines originating from prostatic cancer have been considerably hyperdiploid (Table I) points possibly to the fact that prostatic cancer cells with such high chromosome numbers are more likely to survive and proliferate in vitro as compared to those cancers which are near diploid or hypodiploid. That prostatic tumors characterized by the latter ploidies exist is pointed to by DNA studies already published, and one hopes that direct chromosome analysis will confirm this contention.

Obviously, much remains to be learned about the normal structure and function of the chromatin and chromosomes of normal prostatic cells, particularly as reflected in the diversity of the cellular structure and function in this complicated gland, as well as the role played by the chromosomal changes in the genesis,

Figs. 13 and 14. G-banded karyotypes of cells of the LNaCP line from an established culture of a human prostatic carcinoma [36]. In each case the number of chromosomes exceeds 80 and is accompanied by a large number of markers, some of which could be identified as to their origin.

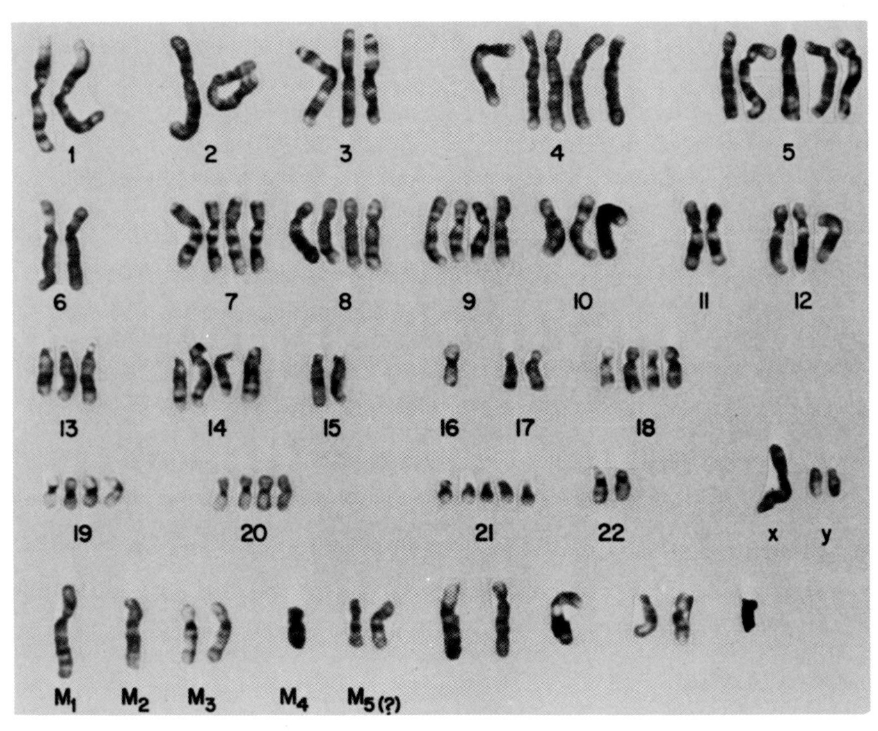

Figure 15

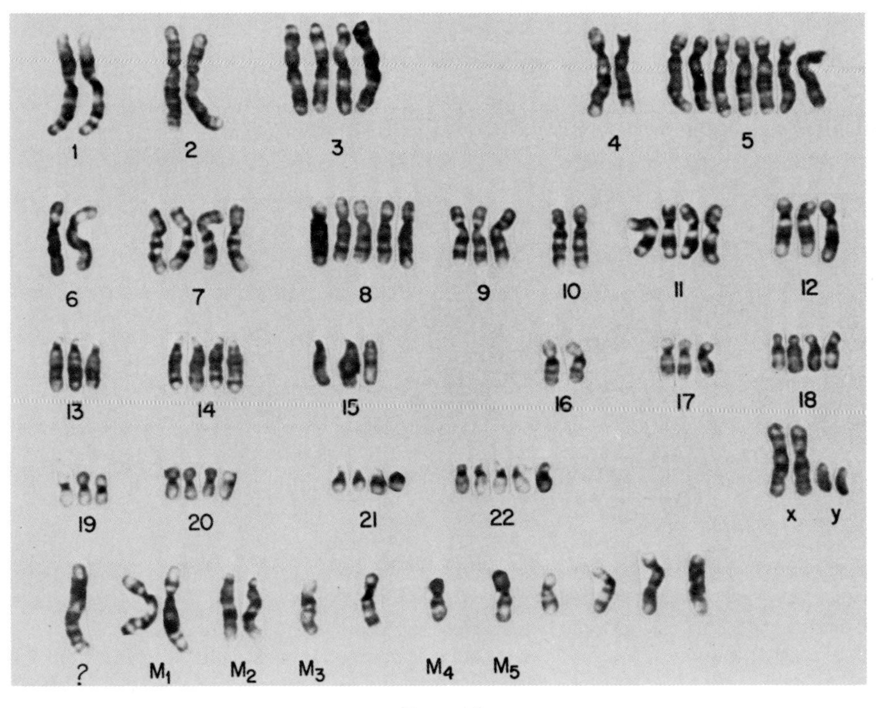

Figure 16

establishment, histology and, ultimately, biologic behavior, including response to therapy, of various prostatic cancers.

REFERENCES

1. Kornberg RD, Klug A: The Nucleosome. Sci Am 244: 52–64, 1981.
2. Chai LA, Sandberg AA: Evidence of nucleosomes in situ and their organization in chromatin and chromosomes of Chinese hamster cells. Cancer Genet Cytogenet 2: 361–380, 1980.
3. Sandberg AA: The Chromosomes in Human Cancer and Leukemia. New York: Elsevier North-Holland, Inc., 1980.
4. Coffey DS, Shimazaki J, Williams-Ashman HG: Polymerization of deoxyribonucleotides in relation to adrogen-induced prostatic growth. Arch Biochem Biophys 124: 184–198, 1968.
5. Vindeløv LL: Flow microfluorometric analysis of nuclear DNA in cells from solid tumors and cell suspensions. A new method for rapid isolation and staining of nuclei. Virchows Arch B Cell Pathol 24: 227–242, 1977.
6. Grattarola M, Zietz S, Lessin S, Desaive C, and Nicolini C: Early detection of micrometastases via flow microfluorimetry. Cancer Biochem Biophys 4: 13–18, 1979.
7. Collste LG, Devonec M, Darzynkiewcz Z, Traganos F, Sharpless TK, Whitmore WF Jr, Melamed MR: Bladder cancer diagnosis by flow cytometry. Correlation between cell samples from biopsy and bladder irrigation fluid. Cancer 45: 2389–2394, 1980.
8. Tribukait B, Gustafson H, Esposti P: Ploidy and proliferation in human bladder tumors as measured by flow-cytofluorometric DNA-analysis and its relations to histopathology and cytology. Cancer 43: 1742–1751, 1979.
9. Zank H, Krug H: Zytophotometrische DNS-Bestimmungen an Primärtumoren und Metastasen. Arch Geschwulstforsch 35: 343–359, 1970.
10. Böhm N, Sandritter W: DNA in human tumors: A cytophotometric study. Curr Topics Pathol 60: 151–219, 1975.
11. Frederiksen P, Thommesen P, Kjaer TB, Bichel P: Flow cytometric DNA analysis in fine needle aspiration biopsies from patients with prostatic lesions. Diagnostic value and relation to clinical stages. Acta Pathol Microbiol Scand Sect A 86: 461–464, 1978.
12. Bichel P, Frederiksen P, Kjaer T, Thommesen P, Vindeløv LL: Flow microfluorometry and transrectal fine-needle biopsy in the classification of human prostatic carcinoma. Cancer 40: 1206–1211, 1977.
13. Leistenschneider W, Nagel R: Nuclear-DNA analysis by scanning-single cell-photometry in prostatic cancer. Aktuel Urol 10: 353–358, 1979.
14. Atkin NB, Kay R: Prognostic significance of modal DNA value and other factors in malignant tumours, based on 1465 cases. Br J Cancer 40: 210–221, 1979.
15. Tavares AS, Costa J, Costa-Maia JC: Correlation between ploidy and prognosis in prostatic carcinoma. J Urol 109: 676–679, 1973.
16. Kjaer TB, Thommesen P, Frederiksen P, Bichel P: DNA content in cells aspirated from carcinoma of the prostate treated with oestrogenic compounds. Urol Res 7: 249–251, 1979.
17. Leistenschneider W, Nagel R: Estracyt therapy of advanced prostatic cancer with special reference to control of therapy with cytology and DNA cytophotometry. Eur Urol 6: 111–115, 1980.

Figs. 15 and 16. G-banded karyotypes of LNaCP cells from a tumor grown in a nude mouse. Though significant similarities exist with the karyotypes shown in Figures. 13 and 14, some of the markers differ as to their origin and differences exist in the distribution of the chromosomes in the various groups.

18. Sprenger E, Volk L, Michaelis WE: The significance of nuclear DNA-measurements in the diagnosis of prostatic carcinoma. Beitr Pathol 153: 370–378, 1974.
19. Sprenger E, Michaelis WE, Vogt-Schaden M, Otto C: The significance of DNA flow-through fluorescence cytophotometry for the diagnosis of prostate carcinoma. Beitr Pathol 159: 292–298, 1976.
20. Oshimura M, Sandberg AA: Isochromosome #17 in a prostatic cancer. J Urol 114: 249–250, 1975.
21. Sekine S: Cytogenetic observations in tumours of the urinary tract and male genitals. Jpn J Urol 67: 452–464, 1976.
22. Wake N, Slocum HK, Rustum YM, Matsui SI, Sandberg AA: Chromosomes and causation of human cancer and leukemia, XLIV. A method for chromosome analysis of solid tumors. Cancer Genet Cytogenet 3: 1–10, 1981.
23. Mark J, Dahlenfors R, Ekedahl C, Stenman G: The mixed salivary gland tumor—a usually benign human neoplasm frequently showing specific chromosomal abnormalities. Cancer Genet Cytogenet 2: 231–241, 1980.
24. Zankl H, Zang KD: Correlations between clinical and cytogenetical data in 180 human meningiomas. Cancer Genet Cytogenet 1: 351–356, 1980.
25. Sandberg AA: Chromosome markers and progression in bladder cancer. Cancer Res 97: 222–229, 1977.
26. Falor WH, Ward RM: Prognosis in early carcinoma of the bladder based on chromosomal analysis. J Urol 119: 44–48, 1978.
27. Buick RN, Stanisic TH, Fry SE, Salmon SE, Trent JM, Krasovich P: Development of an agar-methyl cellulose clonogenic assay for cells in transitional cell carcinoma of the human bladder. Cancer Res 39: 5051–5056, 1979.
28. Kusyk C, Edwards C, Arrighi F, Romsdahl M: Improved method for cytogenetic studies of solid tumors. J Natl Cancer Inst 63: 1199–1203, 1979.
29. Stone KR, Mickey DD, Wunderli H, Mickey GH, Paulson DF: Isolation of a human prostate carcinoma cell line (DU 145). Int J Cancer 21: 274–281, 1978.
30. Mickey DD, Stone KR, Wunderli H, Mickey GH, Vollmer RT, Paulson DF: Heterotransplantation of a human prostatic adenocarcinoma cell line in nude mice. Cancer Res 37: 4049–4058, 1977.
31. Nelson-Rees WA, Flandermeyer RR: Letter to the Editor: Cell line markers. Int J Cancer 21: 796–797, 1978.
32. Kaighn ME, Lechner JF, Babcock MS, Marnell M, Ohnuki Y, Narayan KS: The Pasadena cell lines. In Murphy GP (ed): "Models for Prostate Cancer." New York: Alan R. Liss, Inc., 1980, pp 85–109.
33. Kaighn ME, Narayan KS, Ohnuki Y, Lechner JF, Jones LW: Establishment and characterization of a human prostatic carcinoma cell line (PC-3). Invest Urol 17: 16–23, 1979.
34. Ohnuki Y, Marnell MM, Babcock MS, Lechner JF, Kaighn ME: Chromosomal analysis of human prostatic adenocarcinoma cell lines. Cancer Res 40: 524–534, 1980.
35. Lubaroff DM: HPC-36: An epithelial tissue culture line derived from human prostate adenocarcinoma. Natl Cancer Inst Monogr 49: 35–40, 1978.
36. Horoszewicz JS, Leong SS, Ming Chu T, Wajsman ZL, Friedman M, Papsidero L, Kim U, Chai LS, Kakati S, Arya SK, Sandberg AA: The LNCaP cell line—a new model for studies on human prostatic carcinoma. In Murphy GP (ed): "Models for Prostate Cancer." pp. 115–132, New York: Alan R. Liss, 1980, pp 115–132.
37. Williams RD: Human urologic cancer cell lines. Invest Urol 17: 359–363, 1980.
38. Mickey DD, Stone KR, Wunderli H, Mickey GM, Paulson DF: Characterization of a human prostate adenocarcinoma cell line (DU 145) as a monolayer culture and as a solid tumor in athymic mice. In Murphy GP (ed): "Models for Prostate Cancer." New York: Alan R. Liss, Inc., 1980, pp 67–84.

STROMAL-PARENCHYMAL INTERACTIONS

The Prostatic Cell: Structure and Function
Part A, pages 95–132

The Role of the Basal Lamina in Cell Attachment, Proliferation, and Differentiation. Tumor Cells vs Normal Cells

D. Gospodarowicz, D.K. Fujii, L. Giguere, N. Savion, J.-P. Tauber, and I. Vlodavsky

INTRODUCTION

Cell migration and growth in vivo are the result of a complex balance between cell-cell and cell-substrate interactions. Those forces which combine to modulate the cell shape may either permit or prevent cell proliferation and differentiation [1–5]. Following its original proposal by Grobstein [6], a role for cell-substrate interactions in the control of cell proliferation and morphogenesis has been demonstrated (for reviews see [7–10]). In the case of epithelial tissues with a high rate of cell turnover, such as the epidermis or the corneal epithelium, active cell proliferation is restricted to their basal layer, composed of tall and columnar cells. These cells are in close contact with a basal lamina. In contrast, cells in the upper layers, which have lost their ability to proliferate and gradually adopt a flattened configuration, are no longer in contact with the basal lamina. Thus, contact between the cells and their substrate rather than contact between cells could, in vivo, have a permissive influence on cell proliferation. Likewise, mammalian cells maintained under tissue culture conditions require, in order to proliferate and to express their normal phenotype, not only nutrients and growth factors [11, 12], but also an appropriate physical substratum upon which they can attach and spread (for reviews see [13, 14]). Recent investigations have suggested that, in vitro, cell-substratum interactions may play other roles in addition to cell anchorage [15–17]. The substrate (whether plastic in vitro or a basal lamina in vivo) upon which a cell rests can dictate its shape and may play a role in its response to serum factors [5, 10, 18]. Components of the basal lamina produced by cells have also been shown to be involved in cell differentiation and the control of gene expression [19–22], as well as in cell attachment [15–17]. Yaoi and Kanaseki [23], as well as Weiss et al [24], using microexudate carpets from chick or mouse embryo cells, have demonstrated a role for this material in cell proliferation. The substrate upon which cells rest in vitro could therefore be a decisive element in their proliferative response to various factors.

Identification of the components present within the basal lamina which could be involved in controlling cell proliferation either in vivo or in vitro has been made difficult mostly by its intricate nature. Because the in vitro reconstruction of the basal lamina from its isolated native components into the correct highly ordered structure that it represents would be a formidable task, we have taken advantage of the fact that cultured corneal endothelial cells have the ability to produce basal lamina in vitro which closely resembles the basement membrane upon which cells rest in vivo [25, 26].

COMPOSITION OF THE EXTRACELLULAR MATRIX PRODUCED BY CULTURED CORNEAL ENDOTHELIAL CELLS

Confluent cultures of corneal endothelial cells exhibit, as in vivo, an asymmetry of cell surfaces. While the apical cell surface is a nonthrombogenic surface to which platelets do not bind [25, 26], the basal cell surface is involved in the synthesis of highly thrombogenic basal lamina which, when examined by immunofluorescence, is composed of collagen type III and, to a lesser extent, of collagen type IV [14, 27]. Chemical analysis of the collagen types synthesized by bovine corneal endothelial cells has led to the conclusion that type III collagen is the major component both deposited in the extracellular matrix and secreted into the media [28]. The basement membrane collagens, types IV and V, are also found in each compartment, though the latter is associated preferentially with the cell matrix. The ratios of types I:III:IV + V collagens synthesized by corneal endothelial cells is 3:16:1 [28]. Associated with the ECM collagens are proteoglycans and glycosaminoglycans, composed mostly of heparan sulfate (90%) and chondroitin sulfate A and C (10%) [29]. Also present in large quantities are two glycoproteins which have been held responsible for cell attachment to the basal lamina. These are fibronectin and laminin [25, 30].

The presence of both laminin and collagen type IV, as well as that of fibronectin, in the extracellular matrix produced by cultured corneal endothelial cells has led to the conclusion that this matrix has the characteristics of a basement membrane [14, 30]. Indeed, previous studies have demonstrated that laminin is an antigen present within the lamina lucida portion of basement membranes produced by epithelia in vivo, while collagen type IV and fibronectin are localized to the lamina densa [31, 32].

The basal lamina produced by cultured corneal endothelial cells can be exposed easily by treating the cell monolayer which covers it with either detergents (0.5% Triton X-100 in PBS) or weak alkili (20 mM NH_4OH in water) and subsequent washing [33–36]. The basal lamina then appears as a uniform layer of amorphous material coating the entire plastic dish (Fig. 1) and provides the investigator with a tailor-made basal lamina which can further be used to study its biological properties, such as its ability to support cell attachment, migration, proliferation, and differentiation.

TUMOR CELLS

A central issue in tumor biology is the understanding of the interactions between tumor cells and their substratum, since this could throw some light on the need for stromal and fibroblastic support for carcinoma cell growth [37, 38]; on the ability of tumor cells to reorganize their local environment in order to invade [39, 40]; and on the mechanisms through which various artificial substrates that are introduced in vivo into the animal result in the production of malignant mesothelioma and fibrosarcoma [41]. We have therefore studied the interaction of tumor cells originating from solid tumors (human colon carcinoma and Ewing's sarcoma) with the ECM produced by cultured corneal endothelial cells. Both of these tumor cell types were chosen primarily because, although they are derived from solid tumors, they showed a poor ability to attach to tissue culture dishes and grow either as loosely attached aggregates or in suspension. In this respect, the Ewing's tumor, which represents the most common malignant bone tumor in children [42], is most interesting, since its origin has been controversial. In vivo, Ewing's tumor cells appear as small, closely apposed cells growing between corridors of connective tissue. This led Ewing [43] to consider them to be a myeloma derived from the endothelium. In contrast, when the same cells are grown on plastic, they adopt a totally different configuration and when viewed by electron microscopy resemble fibroblastic cells [44] rather than mesothelial cells. This sharp contrast between the morphological appearance of the cells in vivo and in vitro could be due to the substrate upon which they rest, as well as to other environmental factors.

Cell Morphology and Organization of Colon Carcinoma and Ewing's Sarcoma Cells When Maintained on ECM-Coated Dishes vs Plastic Dishes

Colon carcinoma cells seeded on plastic attach poorly to it and form tightly packed, ball-like cell aggregates (Figs. 2A, 3A–C). In contrast, cells

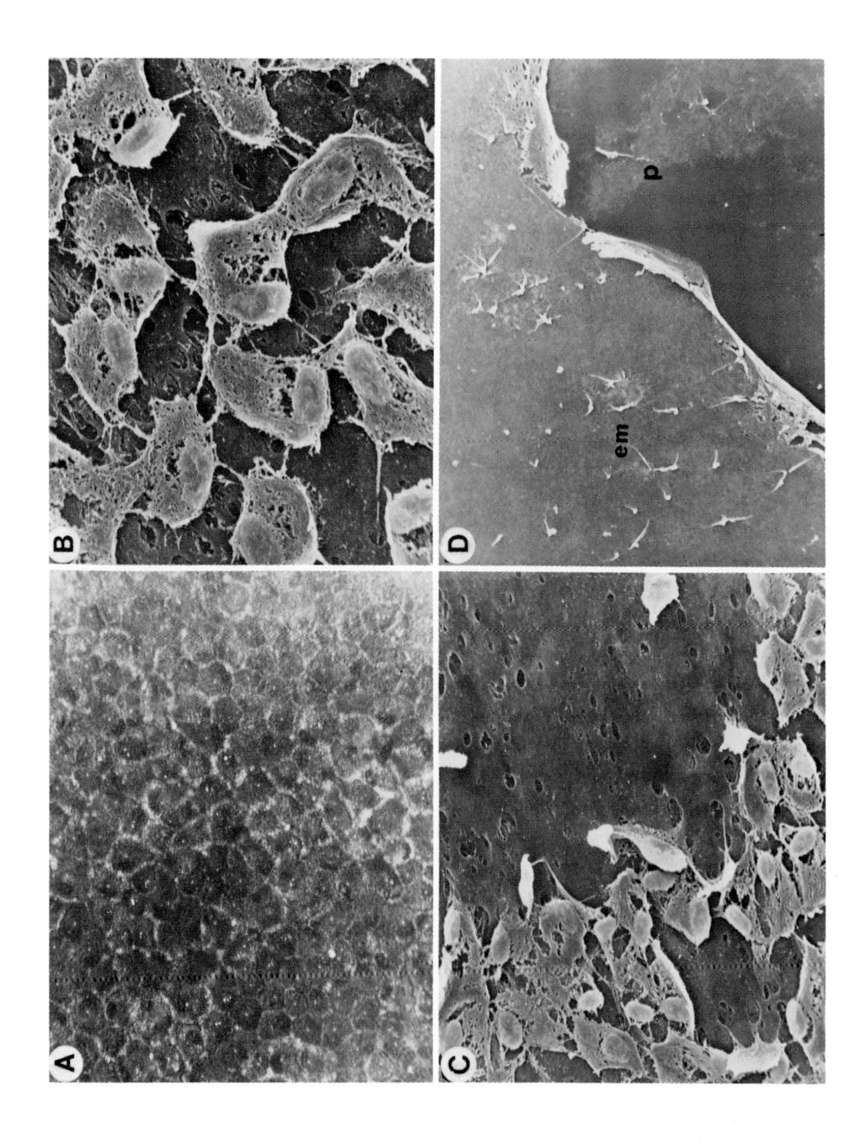
A
B
C
D
em
p

seeded on an ECM (Figs. 2B, C, 3D) adopt within 1–2 hours after seeding a flattened morphology, spreading out and showing no signs of cell aggregation. At confluence a monolayer composed of small and tightly packed cells that covered the entire area of the dish was observed (Fig. 3F–I). Although the cells did grow on top of one another late at confluence (Fig. 3F–I), the overgrowing cells rounded up and floated free into the medium probably because, unlike the cells underneath, they were prevented from attaching to the ECM. Upon dissociation of the cell layer and reseeding on plastic, the cells reaggregate, pile up, and proliferate to form large, multilayered clumps that may eventually cover the surface of the dish or float in the medium [45].

Similar morphological differences were observed with the Ewing's sarcoma cells grown on plastic versus an ECM [45] (Figs. 4, 5). Cell aggregates that are seeded on plastic adopt at either low (Figs. 4, 5A, B) or high cell density (Fig. 5C) the configuration of loosely attached aggregates of cells. In contrast, if the same cells are seeded either singly or as aggregates on dishes coated with an ECM, they spread and adopt a flattened morphology (Figs. 4, 5C). This could be observed both at a sparse density prior to the formation of cell-cell contacts (Fig. 5D) as well as at confluence, when an organized, non-overlapping cell monolayer is formed (Fig. 5F–H). The morphological configuration of confluent cultures was similar to that of a confluent vascular endothelial cell monolayer, thereby corroborating the initial impression of Ewing [43] with regard to the source of the disease.

Preliminary studies with human choroidal melanoma cells also demonstrate a striking morphological response to seeding on dishes coated with an ECM [45]. On plastic the cells appear as aggregates composed of spheroidal cells densely packed with dark melanin granules. In contrast, when the same cell aggregates are in contact with an ECM, extensive cell migration is observed and the cells adopt a flattened and spindly morphology characteristic of melanoma cells and show numerous and distinct cytoplasmic granules.

Fig. 1. Scanning electron microscopy of a monolayer of bovine corneal endothelial cells before and after exposure to Triton X-100. A monolayer composed of polygonal, highly flattened, and closely apposed cells can be seen in A (× 200). After the monolayer has been treated with Triton X-100, it is composed of nuclei and cytoskeletons which no longer attach firmly to the extracellular matrix. In some areas the extracellular matrix has been exposed (B, × 200). Washing the dishes with PBS removed the cytoskeleton and exposed the extracellular matrix present underneath the cells (C, × 200). The plate has been scratched with a needle to expose the plastic (P) to which the extracellular matrix (em) strongly adheres (D × 200).

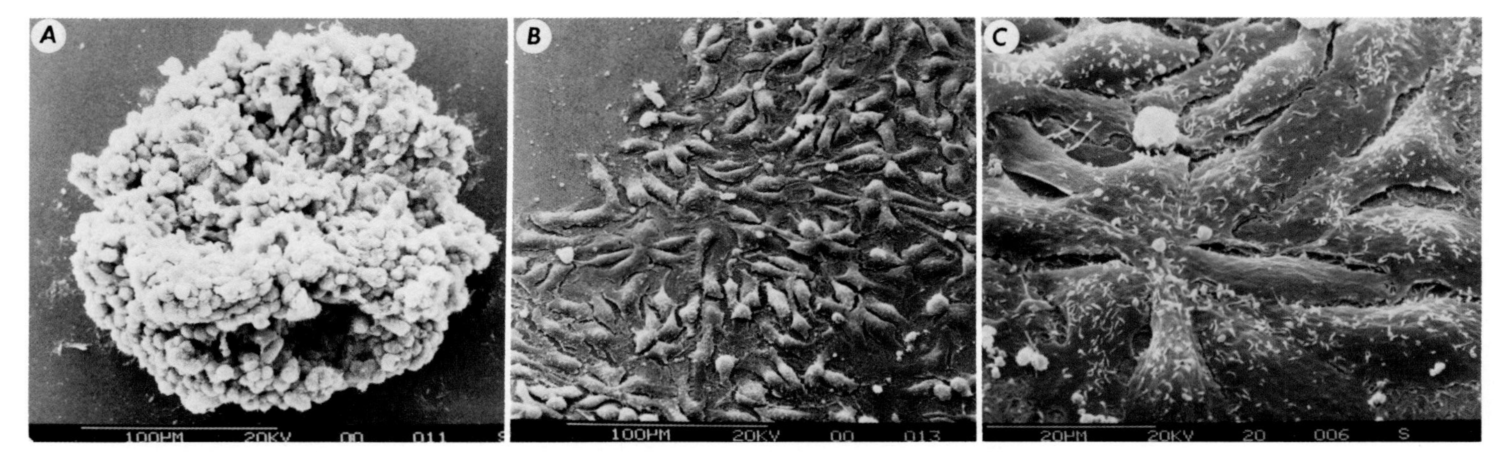

Fig. 2. Scanning electron microscopy of colon carcinoma cells maintained in tissue culture on either a plastic substratum (A) or an extracellular matrix (B, C). While on plastic cells grew as an aggregate of cells which did not adhere to the substratum (A), when maintained on ECM the cells flattened and grew as a monolayer (B, C).

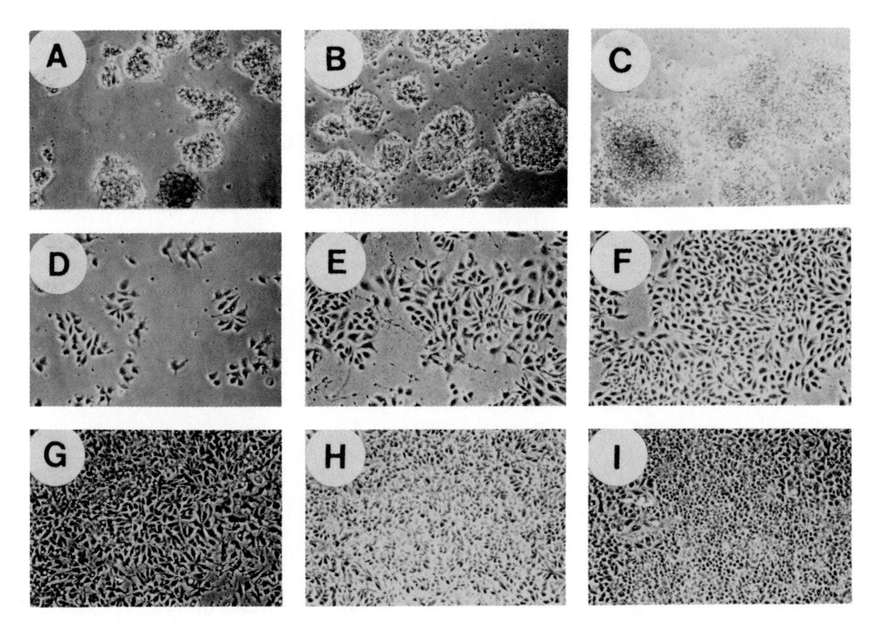

Fig. 3. Morphological appearance at different stages of cell growth and density of colon carcinoma cells maintained on plastic versus extracellular matrix. Stock cultures maintained on plastic tissue culture dishes were dissociated with STV and the cells seeded into plastic (A–C) or extracellular matrix-coated (D–I) dishes in DMEM (H-21) containing 10% fetal calf serum. Photographs were taken (phase contrast, X 100) starting on day one (A, D) and up to 10 days (C, I) after seeding in order to demonstrate the culture's morphological appearance at various cell densities. (A–C) Cells seeded on plastic. The cells form aggregates composed of small and spheroidal cells and proliferate as such to form large, multiple layered aggregates. Most of these aggregates are firmly attached to the tissue culture dish, but the percentage of floating cells (aggregates and single cells) increases when the cells reach confluence. (D–I) Cells seeded on extracellular matrix. Cell spreading and flattening and no signs of cell aggregation and overlapping can be seen at either a low (D–E) or high cell density (F, G). A layer of cuboildal and tightly packed cells is formed at confluence (H, I), but as the cells continue to proliferate areas of cell overlapping, and particularly shedding of single cells into the culture medium, are observed.

Time Course of Tumor Cell Attachment to Plastic Dishes vs Dishes Coated With an ECM

In the case of either colon carcinoma cells (Fig. 6A) or Ewing's (Fig. 6B), as many as 50–80% of the cells seeded on ECM attached firmly within 30 minutes, as compared to only about 5–10% of the cells on plastic. After 24 hours, no more than 35% of the seeded cells attached to plastic. In contrast, 70–90% of them attached firmly within the first hour of incubation to dishes coated with an ECM. The looser attachment of either the hepatocarcinoma or Ewing's cells to plastic than to ECM was easily demonstrated by subjecting the cultures to gentle pipetting. This released up to 95% of the

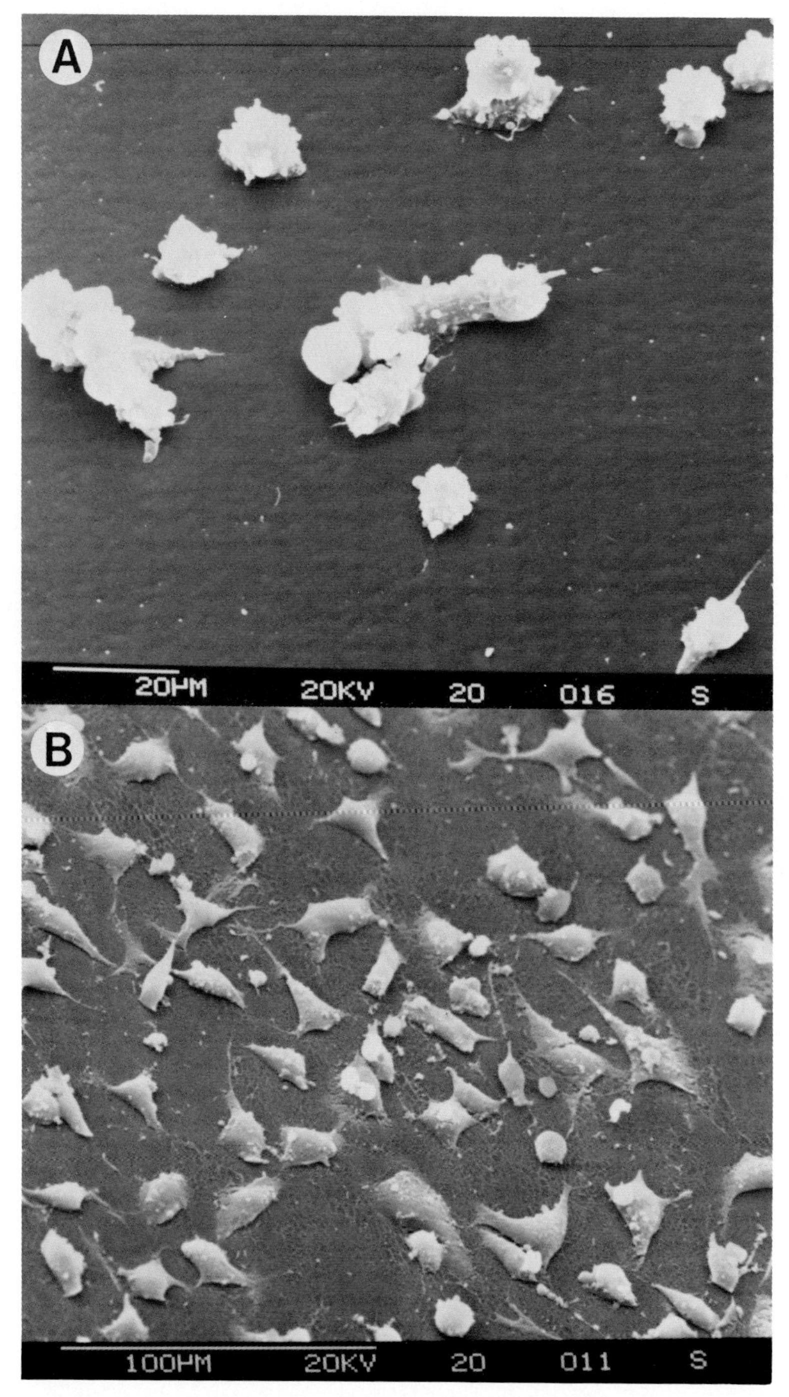

Fig. 4. Scanning electron microscopy of Ewing's sarcoma cells maintained in tissue culture on either a plastic substratum (A) or on an extracellular matrix (B). While on plastic cells adhered only loosely and stayed rounded (A), on ECM they flattened.

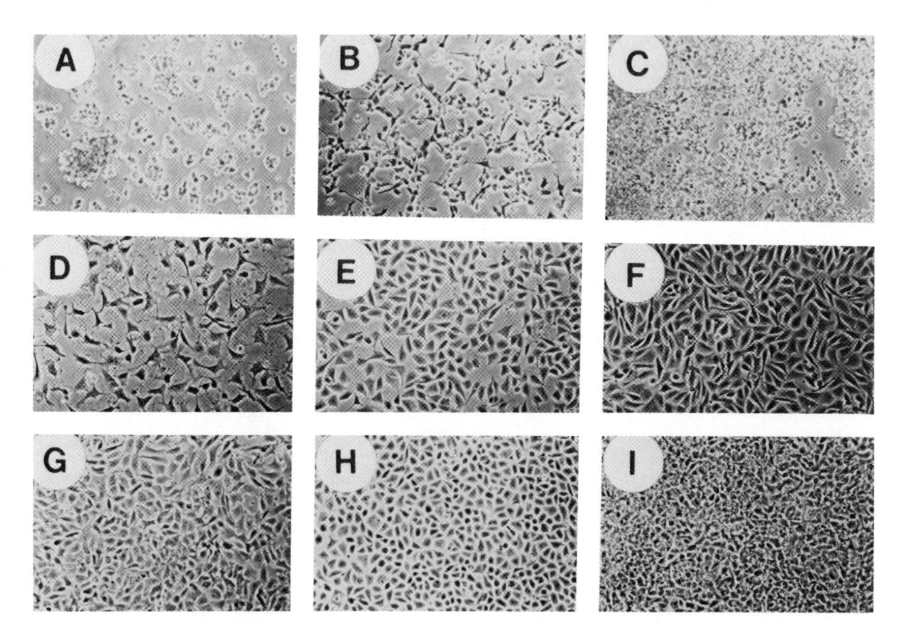

Fig. 5. Morphological appearance at different stages of cell growth and density of Ewing's sarcoma cells maintained on plastic versus extracellular matrix. Stock cultures maintained in plastic dishes were dissociated with STV and the cells seeded into plastic (A–C) or extracellular matrix-coated (D–I) dishes in DMEM (H-21) containing 10% calf serum. Photographs (phase contrast, × 100) were taken starting on day one (A, D) and up to 9 days (C, I) after seeding in order to demonstrate the culture's morphological appearance at both high and low cell densities. Loosely attached aggregates (A), as well as single spherical or elongated cells (B) that hardly contact each other can be seen at a sparse density 1–3 days after seeding. The elongated and firmly attached configuration was seldom or never observed in medium containing fibronectin-depleted rather than untreated calf serum. Cell aggregation and over growth is most prominent at higher cell densities (C) with a large proportion of cells floating in the medium. In contrast, cells on extracellular matrix are highly flattened and spread at either a sparse (D, E) or confluent (F–H) cell density, show no signs of cell aggregation and overlapping, and in some areas adopt the configuration of a highly organized and contact-inhibited cell monolayer (H). Late at confluence (7–9 days after seeding) cells start to grow on top of one another and become less spread (I).

cells grown on plastic, while no more than 5% of the cells cultured on the ECM were released. An even looser attachment of the Ewing cells could be observed at confluence, since in this case only a gentle shaking of cultures maintained on plastic was required to release the cells from the dish. Coating of plastic culture dishes with fibronectin (20 μg/ml) induced cell attachment in the case of Ewing's cells (albeit to a lesser extent than of ECM) (Fig. 6B) but had no effect on the colon carcinoma cells [45]. These results demonstrate that cells seeded on ECM adhere tenaciously to this substrate. In practical terms, this unique adhesive interaction may be advantageous

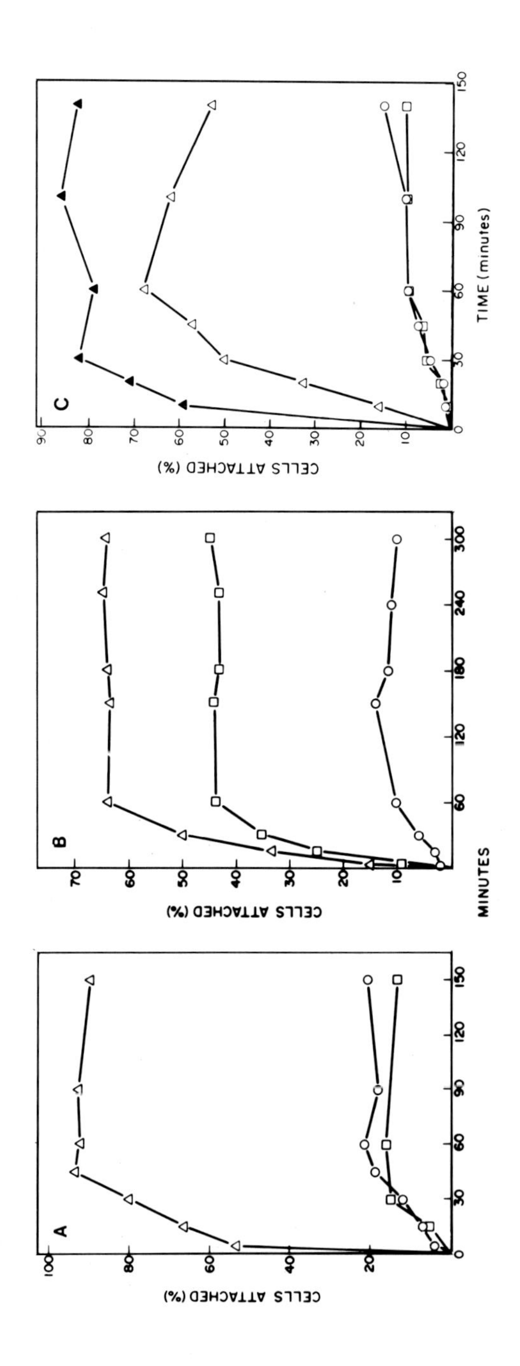
A
CELLS ATTACHED (%)
100
80
60
40
20
0
30
60
90
120
150
B
CELLS ATTACHED (%)
70
60
50
40
30
20
10
60
120
180
240
300
MINUTES
C
CELLS ATTACHED (%)
90
80
70
60
50
40
30
20
10
0
30
60
90
120
150
TIME (minutes)

for the culture of anchorage-dependent cells that fail to attach properly to currently available substrates and are not capable of producing an ECM in vitro.

The Respective Involvement of Laminin and Fibronectin in the Adhesion of Human Carcinoma and Sarcoma Cells

Since colon carcinoma cells show a strict requirement for ECM and do not adhere to dishes coated with fibronectin, while Ewing's sarcoma cells adhere and flatten almost equally well when seeded on ECM or dishes coated with purified fibronectin, it is possible that different adhesive proteins may mediate the attachment of sarcoma- and carcinoma-derived cells to extracellular matrices. The most likely candidates for mediating cell attachment are fibronectin [15, 46, 47] and laminin [32, 48]. Fibronectin has been shown to stimulate the adhesion of fibroblasts, but not of epidermal cells, to collagen type IV [15]. It could therefore mediate the attachment of sarcoma cells to their substrate. Studies on the in vivo distribution of

---

Fig. 6. Attachment of tumor cells as a function of time to plastic dishes versus dishes coated with an extracellular matrix or fibronectin. (A, B) Stock cultures of the colon carcinoma cells (A) and Ewing's sarcoma (B) cells were dissociated with STV and seeded (10^5 cells per 35-mm dish) in DMEM containing 10% fetal calf serum or 2.5% fibronectin-depleted serum, respectively, into plastic tissue culture dishes (○), dishes coated with fibronectin (20 μg fibronectin per dish) (□), and dishes coated with extracellular matrix (△). Non-attached cells were removed at various times by gentle pipetting and rinsing of the dishes (twice) with PBS. In the absence of such a treatment, some of the cells remained on the culture dish without showing signs of spreading or any firm attachment. These represent cells which were either left over after aspiration of the medium or which settled down on the tissue culture dish without changing their spherical morphology. The remaining attached cells were dissociated with STV and triplicate cultures counted with a Coulter counter. (C) Colon carcinoma cell stock cultures grown on ECM-coated dishes were dissociated into single cells by treatment with STV (0.5% trypsin, 0.02% EDTA). Two × 10^5 cells were then seeded on plastic tissue culture dishes (□), dishes coated with 10 μg per dish of affinity purified bovine plasma fibronectin (○), dishes coated with an ECM (▲), or dishes coated with vascular endothelial cell conditioned medium (△). To coat dishes with conditioned medium, plastic dishes were exposed to a medium (DMEM, H-16 supplemented with 10% calf serum) taken from vascular endothelial cells maintained for 8 days in culture (from the day of seeding until 3–4 days after reaching confluence). This medium was centrifuged (1500g × 5 minutes), incubated (14 hours, 37°C) with the dishes, and replaced with fresh medium prior to seeding the tumor cells. When a serum-free conditioned medium was used, it was collected 7–9 days after replacing the medium of subconfluent endothelial cultures with DMEM (H-16) containing no serum. Because the production and secretion of laminin by endothelial cells is greatly reduced when they reach confluence [30], medium conditioned by confluent cultures was not as active as medium conditioned by actively growing vascular endothelial cells. At various times after seeding carcinoma cells, unattached cells were removd by gentle pipetting and rinsing of the dishes (twice) with phosphate-buffered saline (PBS). The remaining firmly attached cells were dissociated with STV and duplicate cultures counted with a Coulter counter. The variations of different determinations did not exceed ± 10% of the mean.

laminin have shown that it was confined to lamina lucida region of basement membranes [32, 48] and was localized to cellular adhesion sites [49]. Recent studies on the attachment of epidermal cells in vitro (V.P. Terranova, personal communication) suggest that laminin is an adhesive factor for epithelial cells, it could therefore play the same role for carcinoma cells as that played by fibronectin for sarcoma cells.

Vascular endothelials cells maintained in culture secrete large amounts of fibronectin [50–52] and laminin [30], which can be found in both the extracellular matrix lying beneath the cell layer and the tissue culture medium. This medium can therefore provide a convenient source of soluble fibronectin as well as of laminin with which to study their respective involvements in promoting the attachment and flattening of carcinoma and sarcoma cells. We have therefore explored the effect of precoating plastic dishes with culture medium conditioned by bovine aortic vascular endothelial cells on the attachment and flattening of both human colon carcinoma (Fig. 6C) and Ewing's sarcoma cell lines.

When the time course of attachment of carcinoma cells to plastic or fibronectin-coated dishes was compared to that observed with dishes coated with ECM or preexposed to vascular endothelial cell conditioned medium, less than 30% of the cells seeded on plastic or fibronectin-coated dishes attached to these substrates, and no cell flattening was observed regardless of the time in culture (up to 10 days) and regardless of whether or not serum (10%) was present. In contrast, 70% and 80% of the seeded cells firmly attached and flattened within the first hour of incubation on dishes preexposed to endothelial conditioned medium or coated with ECM, respectively (Fig. 6C).

Preexposure of dishes to the endothelial cell conditioned medium (either serum-free or containing fibronectin-depleted calf serum) also induced the attachment of the Ewing's sarcoma cells. However, in this case and in contrast to carcinoma cells, coating of dishes with purified fibronectin was either more or as effective in promoting cell attachment and subsequent flattening [45].

The nature of the agents which mediate the attachment and flattening of the human carcinoma and Ewing's sarcoma cells to dishes preexposed to conditioned medium was analyzed by subjecting the endothelial cell conditioned medium to specific double immunoprecipitation with either rabbit anti-laminin [32] or anti-fibronectin antisera [50], followed by goat anti-rabbit IgG antiserum [53], and coating the dishes with either fibronectin-depleted or laminin-depleted conditioned medium [35]. As seen in Fig. 7B carcinoma cells no longer attached to dishes preexposed to conditioned medium from which laminin was removed by immunoprecipitation. On the other hand, immunoprecipitation of fibronectin (Fig. 7A) or collagen type

IV [53] by specific antibodies did not have any effect on the induction of attachment and flattening of carcinoma cells. In contrast, when the same immunoprecipitated fibronectin-free conditioned medium was used to coat dishes, a complete loss of attachment-promoting activity for Ewing's sarcoma cells was observed (Fig. 7D). The induced attachment and flattening of Ewing's cells was not affected by subjecting the conditioned medium to immunoprecipitation with anti-laminin (Fig. 7E), anti-collagen type IV (53), or non-immune rabbit serum (Fig. 7F) followed by coating the dishes. These results demonstrate that the human carcinoma- and sarcoma-derived cells show a specific response to different adhesive glycoproteins, such as laminin and fibronectin, respectively [53].

Since both laminin and fibronectin have been shown to be secreted underneath the endothelial cell layer and to be part of the ECM produced by these cells, they may function as conditioned medium does and may promote the tenacious attachment and rapid spreading of carcinoma- and sarcoma-derived cells to the underlying extracellular matrix [45]. The production of both laminin and fibronectin by vascular endothelial cells may therefore facilitate the arrest of blood-born metastatic cells [54] that produce little or no such adhesive glycoproteins [55, 56].

Tumor Cell Migration on ECM-Coated Dishes

Cell migration was studied qualitatively by seeding cell aggregates rather than single cells on plastic or ECM and observing the extent of cell migration out of the agregates. Cell migration was studied in most cases during the first 4 hours after seeding in order to minimize any possible effect of cell proliferation. Cell aggregates that were seeded into plastic dishes retained their previous morphology [45]. The Ewing sarcoma cells remained mostly in the form of floating and loosely packed cell aggregates, while the colon carcinoma cells remained as tightly packed aggregates, mostly attached to the substrate. In neither case and even after 10 days in culture did cells migrate out of the cell aggregates [45]. In contrast, seeding of the same cell aggregates on dishes coated with ECM was associated with spreading and migration of cells that could be observed within 5–15 minutes after seeding. Migratory activity was best observed in the cells located at the periphery of the aggregates [45]. Small aggregates flattened out in less than one hour, leading to the formation of colonies composed of flat and non-overlapping cells. Depending on the size of the initial aggregate, cell overlapping could be seen in the center of some of these colonies, but as time proceeded the cells reorganized and adopted a monolayer configuration [45]. Since cell migration is observed prior to cell proliferation, it can be regarded as a specific cellular response to the mere contact between cells and the ECM. This may reflect the preferential adhesion of the cells to the ECM compo-

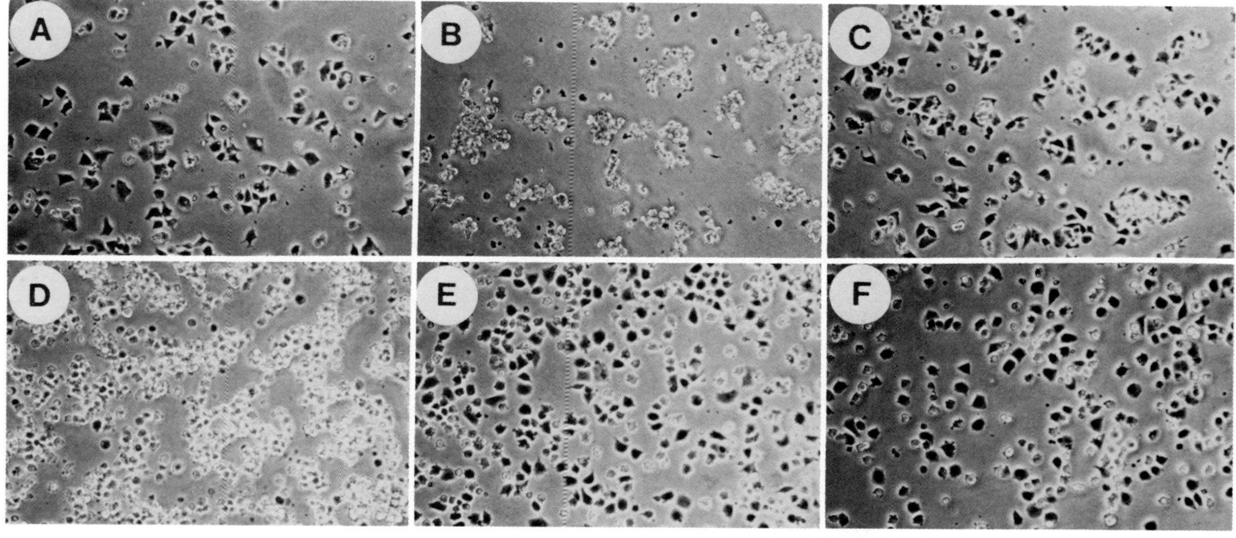

Fig. 7. Induction of tumor cell attachment promoted by coating dishes with vascular endothelial-cell conditioned medium from which fibronectin or laminin had been removed by double immunoprecipitation. One ml of vascular endothelial-cell conditioned medium was preincubated (1 hour, 37°C) with 10 μl of rabbit antisera against fibronectin (A, D), laminin (B, E), or with 10 μl of non-immune rabbit serum (C, F). Antibodies to laminin [38] and to bovine plasma fibronectin [41, 43] were the same as those previously used in studies already reported [38, 39, 41, 43]. The specificities of the antisera and lack of cross-reactivity between the various antigens have been established in these previous reports. The conditioned media were then incubated (2 hours, 37°C, followed by 14 hours at 4°C) with 30 μl of goat anti-rabbit IgG antiserum (35% ammonium sulphate cut), centrifuged (12,000g $\times$ 5 minutes), and the supernatant incubated in 35-mm tissue culture dishes for 12 hours at 37°C. The conditioned media were then removed and 2 ml of DMEM supplemented with 5% fibronectin-depleted calf serum and containing either 2×10^5 colon carcinoma cells (A–C) or Ewing's sarcoma cells (D–F) were then added to the dishes. Phase micrographs of cell attachment and spreading were taken 3 hours after seeding.

nents, whose force can overcome the adhesive forces between cells themselves and is much stronger than the adhesive forces between cells and plastic.

Effect of the ECM on Tumor Cell Growth

Normal human epithelial cells are difficult to grow using conventional culture techniques. This applies even to malignant cells of epithelial origin [57, 58], some of which, when maintained in culture, have an extremely long doubling time (10–20 days). Since cell shape has been shown to be a major factor in regulating cell growth [2, 18, 59], we have compared the growth rate of cells plated on plastic (spherical configuration) to that of cells plated on ECM which adopt a flattened morphology. Although differences in growth rate were observed, both the Ewing's and colon carcinoma cells proliferated in either configuration (Fig. 8A–C). This observation therefore demonstrated that cell adhesion to the ECM and the subsequent flattening imposed no restriction on their proliferation. On the contrary, when cells flattened out a stimulation of cell growth which depended on the cell type and culture conditions was observed. This stimulation was particularly evident with the colon carcinoma cells (Fig. 8A) which, when seeded on plastic, showed a lag period of 3–4 days before resuming a logarithmic growth rate (16-hour doubling time). In contrast, seeding of the same cells on ECM resulted in an active cell migration concomitant with a rapid resumption of proliferation, so that after 3–4 days the cell density of cultures maintained on an ECM was four- to tenfold higher than that of cultures maintained on plastic [45] (Fig. 8A).

Specific binding of EGF (2×10^4 receptor sites per cell) to colon carcinoma cells grown on either plastic or ECM was observed. When the effect of EGF on cell proliferation was studied, it was found to stimulate cell growth on plastic but had little or no effect with cells maintained on an ECM (Fig. 8A). This demonstrates that binding of a mitogen to a given cell type can, depending on the substrate, be followed or not by a mitogenic response. The likely explanation for such a difference in the response to EGF by cells maintained on plastic versus ECM is that cells in contact with the ECM are already induced, possibly via a change in cell shape, to express their full proliferative potential in response to serum components, thereby no longer requiring other stimuli. In contrast, cells on plastic, because they are free of such an extracellular dependent modulation, require an additional mitogenic stimulus in order to express fully their proliferative potential.

An increased growth rate of cells maintained on ECM was also observed with the Ewing's cells (Fig. 8B, C). Since these cells showed a very loose attachment to plastic, both attached and floating cells had to be counted in order to reach a meaningful conclusion regarding an effect on the total

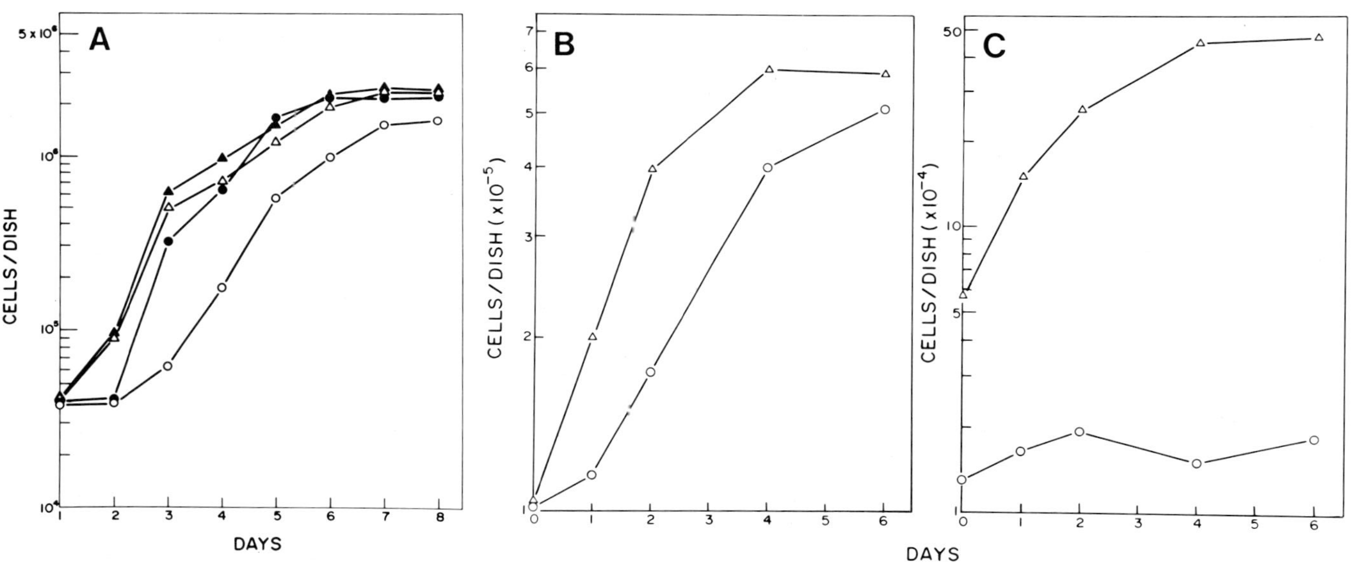

Fig. 8. A) Proliferation of hepatocarcinoma cells when maintained on plastic versus extracellular matrix and exposed or not to EGF. Cells (4×10^4) in 2 ml DMEM containing 10% fetal calf serum were seeded into each plastic (O) or extracellular matrix-coated (△) 35-mm dishes. EGF (10 ng/ml) was added every day to half of the uncoated (●) and extracellular matrix-coated (▲) dishes, and duplicate cultures were counted every day for both floating cells present in the tissue culture medium and attached cells dissociated with STV. The percentage of floating cells increased with time but did not exceed 20% of the total cell number. The curves represent the total number of cells (attached plus floating). B, C) Proliferation of Ewing's sarcoma cells when maintained on plastic versus extracellular matrix. Cells (10^5) in 2 ml DMEM containing 0.5% calf serum were seeded into each plastic (O) or extracellular matrix-coated (△) 35-mm dishes. Duplicate cultures were counted every day to determine the number of floating cells (present in the tissue culture medium) and of cells that are firmly attached (dissociated with STV). B) Total cell number (floating plus attached). C) Firmly attached cells. The number of firmly attached cells was higher than 80% of the total cell number found in dishes coated with extracellular matrix and lower than 10% of the total cell number obtained on plastic.

number of cells. When the cultures were maintained on ECM, the number of firmly attached and floating cells exceeded by two- to four-fold that of cultures maintained on plastic. This difference was only observed at low serum concentrations (0.5–1%) (Fig. 8B). In the case of Ewing's cells, therefore, the effect of the ECM on the rate of cell proliferation was mainly reflected in a lowering of the serum requirement of the cells and not so much in an imposition of a faster growth rate. The final cell density late at confluence was similar on plastic and ECM. If only the number of firmly attached cells was compared while the floating cells were ignored, active proliferation of the attached cells was observed only in dishes coated with an ECM. This resulted in a 10- to 50-fold higher final density of attached cells in cultures maintained on an ECM than on plastic (Fig. 8C). Although detachment of cells from the ECM was observed 3–5 days after they reached confluence, it could be prevented or delayed by changing the growth medium every other day. Similar studies with human choroidal melanoma cells have also demonstrated that cells maintained on an ECM proliferate rapidly [45]. This contrasts with a very slow rate of proliferation of these cells (12–18 days average doubling time) when maintained on plastic. Effects similar to those of the ECM as far as cell attachment and proliferation are concerned were not be observed when tumor cells were seeded on plastic dishes coated with purified preparations of collagen types I, III, or IV [45].

The above results therefore demonstrate that cultured tumor cells can proliferate when they are highly flattened and firmly attached to the substrate, as well as when they are either loosely attached or in suspension. Cell attachment to the ECM results in a stimulation of cell growth, which is best observed at a low cell density and with cells maintained in low serum concentrations.

Effect of ECM on the Attachment, Migration, Proliferation, and Differentiation of Nerve Cells

Nerve cells do not have the ability to produce an ECM in vivo and therefore rely on that produced by other tissues during the early steps of embryogenesis for both their migration and neurite outgrowth. This is shown by the very firm attachment of neurites and of their growth cones to the ECM in vivo. The interaction of nerve cells with a proper substrate could therefore be important insofar as nerve cell migration and differentiation are concerned. Likewise, a close contact with the ECM seems to be important in the control of nerve cell proliferation. In both the cortex and spinal cord, dividing nerve cells can only be found in close contact with the ECM which forms the inner lining of the cortex or which is located along the central cavity of the spinal cord. Following division, nerve cells can migrate to the outer part of the cortex or of the spinal cord and differentiate.

To study the interaction of nerve cells with the ECM, we first used as a model the PC-12 cell line, which is derived from a pheochromocytoma and has been shown to respond to nerve growth factor (NGF) by extending neurites on collagen-coated dishes. When the rate of firm attachment of PC 12 cells to plastic versus collagen- and ECM-coated dishes is compared, it was found to be 5% for plastic, 20% for collagen-coated dishes, and 80–85% for ECM-coated dishes in 24 hours [60]. Following their attachment to the ECM, the cells, which on either plastic or collagen substrata remained rounded, became flattened and began to emit fine neurites characterized by branching, varicosities, and growth cones (Fig. 9). This outgrowth of neurites is only temporary and by day 2 they start to regress unless NGF is present. In its presence, however, extensive thin neurite outgrowth can be seen, and apparent fasciculation of some neurites is observed [60]. In contrast, no neurites are extended by NGF-treated cells on plastic, and those cells on collagen-coated dishes extend thick, straight neurites poorly attached to the substrata at only a few points and with little branching or varicosities. Thus, ECM may be permissive for neurite outgrowth, and the trophic effects of NGF are necessary for long-term differentiation.

The ability of the ECM to support extensive cell differentiation is not the only biological effect of the ECM, since it can affect nerve cell migration and proliferation. While on plastic or collagen-coated dishes single cells will eventually aggregate and give rise to ball-like clumps of cells, single cells on ECM will grow as a monolayer of flattened cells. Only when cultures are kept for extended periods of time at confluence will cells eventually overgrow each other. Moreover, whereas the rate of proliferation of cells maintained on plastic is very slow, that of cultures maintained on ECM is faster and can be improved by the addition of EGF to the medium.

EFFECT OF ECM ON THE PROLIFERATION OF NORMAL CELLS MAINTAINED IN THE PRESENCE OF PLASMA

Culture of most cells in vitro requires the presence of serum [61]. Consequently, investigators have spent much effort in a search to identify the various factors in serum that stimulate cell growth in vitro. An important step in the search for serum growth factors has been the finding that one of the most potent mitogenic factors present in serum, baptized platelet-derived growth factor (PDGF), is in fact derived from platelets [62, 63].

Fig. 9. A–C) Phase contrast micrographs of unfixed PC12 cells cultured on extracellular matrix in the absence of NGF for 3 days (A), and in the presence of NGF for 3 days (B) and 13 days (C). D, E) Scanning electron micrographs of PC12 cells on extracellular matrix in the presence of NGF for 12 days. E) Arrows point to (1) a varicosity in a neurite; (2) the end of a neurite; (3) a branching point; and (4) fine projections extending from a neurite.

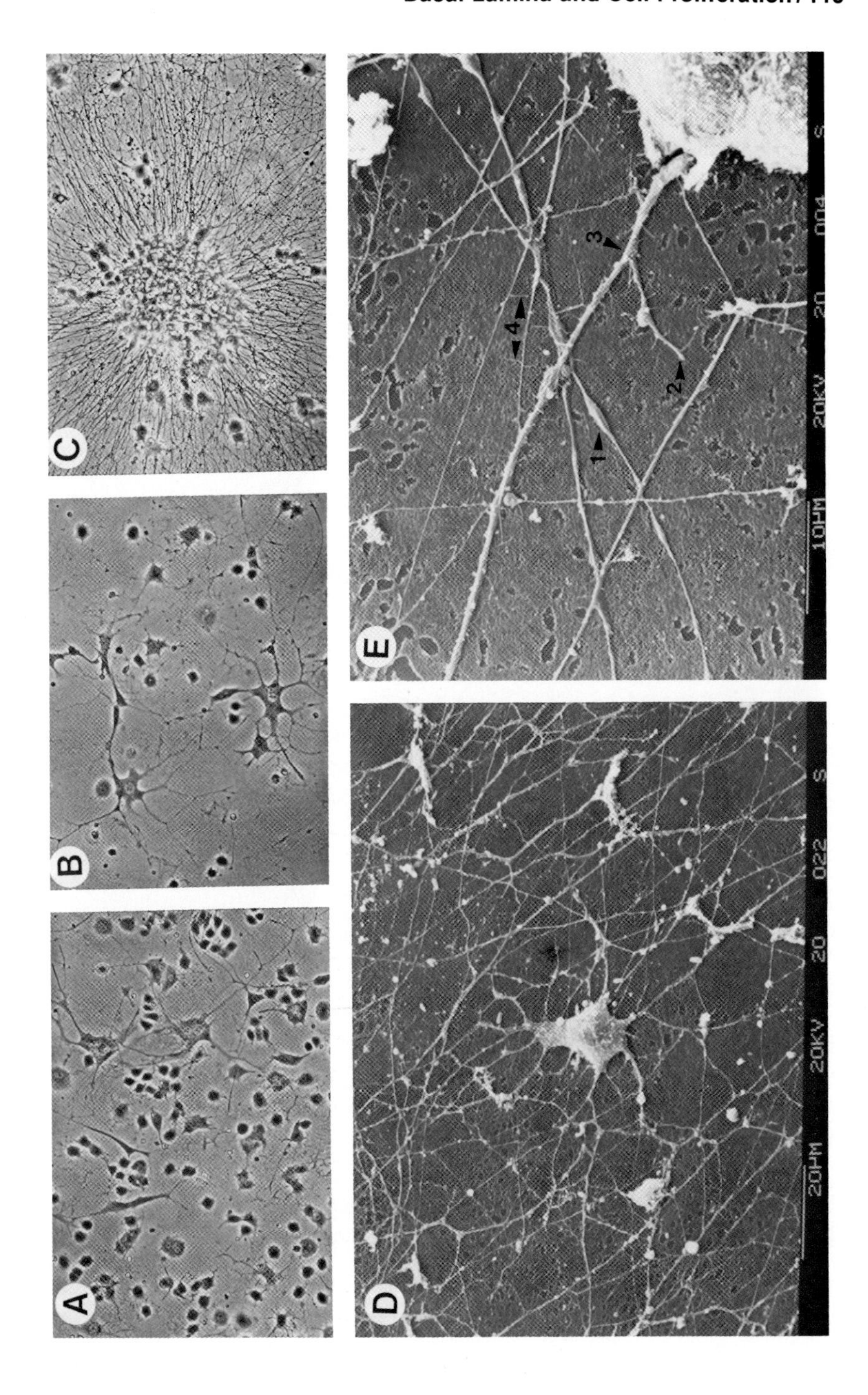
A
B
C
D
20HM 20KV 20 022 S
E
1
2
3
4
10HM 20KV 20 004 S

While plasma was unable to support the growth of aortic smooth muscle cells [64] or that of BALB/c 3T3 cells [65], serum made from the same pool of blood stimulated their proliferation. Addition of a platelet extract to cell-free plasma or that of PDGF restored the growth-promoting activity [64–66]. One could therefore conclude that one of the principal mitogens responsible for the induction of DNA synthesis present in whole blood serum is derived from platelets [65, 66]. However, all studies have thus far used cells maintained on plastic rather than on an ECM. This difference in the substrate upon which the cells are maintained could have prevented their response to factors present in plasma, thereby creating the difference in mitogenic activity between plasma and serum. To explore the possibility that the serum factors to which cells maintained on ECM become sensitive are also present in plasma, we have compared the mitogenic activity of plasma versus serum, using as target cells vascular smooth muscle cells (VSM) maintained on either plastic or an ECM [33].

VSM cells maintained on plastic proliferate in response to serum but not to plasma [33, 66]. In contrast, when cells were maintained on an ECM and exposed to either plasma or serum, they proliferated actively under both conditions and plasma was observed to be even more mitogenic for cells maintained on an ECM than was serum for cells maintained on plastic. When the growth rate and the final cell density of cultures maintained on an ECM and exposed to either plasma or serum were compared, they were found to be the same. When the final cell density of cultures maintained on an ECM was analyzed as a function of the serum or plasma concentration to which they were exposed, it was found to be a direct function of the serum or plasma concentration. It is therefore likely that the proliferation of vascular smooth muscle cells is controlled by factor(s) present in plasma and that the ECM has only a permissive role [33].

These results emphasize how drastically one can modify the proliferative response of a given cell type to serum factors by modifying the substrate upon which the cells are maintained [33]. It is possible that the lack of response of various cell types maintained under tissue culture conditions to plasma factors responsible in vivo for their proliferation and differentiation could be directly attributed to the artificial substrate, whether plastic or glass, upon which the cells rest and which limits their ability to produce an ECM.

Identification of Growth-Promoting Agents for Normal Cells When Maintained on an ECM Instead of Plastic

Vascular endothelial cells. Previous studies [67–69] have shown that vascular endothelial cell (VEC) cultures maintained on plastic and propagated in the presence of fibroblast growth factor (FGF) divide with an average doubling time of 18 hours when seeded at either a high (up to 1:1000) or low split ratio. Upon reaching confluence, the cells adopt a morphological configuration similar to that of the confluent culture from which they originated. In contrast, seeding of the same cells at a high split ratio in the absence of FGF results in a much longer doubling time (60–78 hours), and within a few passages cultures maintained in the absence of FGF exhibit, in addition to a much slower growth rate, morphological as well as structural alterations which mostly involved changes in the composition and distribution of the ECM [52, 70]. This raises the possibility that the ECM produced by these cells could have an effect on their ability to proliferate and to express their normal phenotype once confluent [14].

This is what was in fact observed when the growth of bovine VEC seeded at low density on plastic vs ECM was compared. Regardless of the initial cell density (sparse culture, 10 cells/mm^2, or clonal density, 1 cell/cm^2) at which they were seeded, cultures divided extremely rapidly when maintained on ECM-coated dishes [14, 34]. Addition of FGF to such cultures did not decrease their mean doubling time, which was already at a minimum (18–20 hours), nor did it result in a higher final cell density, which was already at a maximum (900–1000 cells/mm^2). One can therefore conclude that, while low density cell cultures maintained on plastic proliferate poorly and therefore require FGF in order to become confluent within a few days, when the cultures are maintained on ECM, they proliferate actively and no longer require FGF in order to become confluent. However, in either case (either maintained on plastic and exposed to FGF or maintained on an ECM), the rate of proliferation is a direct function of the serum or plasma concentration to which cultures are exposed. It is therefore likely that the effect of the ECM is more a permissive than a direct mitogenic effect, since cells still required serum or plasma in order to proliferate [14, 34]. Since VEC maintained on ECM now respond to plasma factor(s), one is led to wonder what the nature of such factor(s) is.

Among the plasma factors which could be held directly or indirectly responsible for the active proliferation of vascular endothelial cells are the high density lipoproteins (HDL), as well as the low density lipoproteins (LDL). Earlier studies have shown that both LDL and HDL can interact specifically with vascular endothelial cells [71–76], and others have shown that LDL could be mitogenic for vascular smooth muscle cells and dermal fibroblasts when added to lipoprotein-deficient serum (LPDS) [77–79] or to serum from abetalipoproteinemic subjects [80]. Likewise, in the case of cells which have a limited ability to make cholesterol de novo, or in the case of cells maintained in the presence of compounds such as compactin which totally inhibit their ability to make cholesterol, addition of LDL to the medium leads to resumption of cell proliferation [81]. In that case, LDL could act by providing an exogenous source of cholesterol to the cells, thereby obviating the block in cholesterol synthesis resulting from the presence of the inhibitor in the medium [81]. We have therefore compared the respective mitogenic activities of HDL and LDL on vascular endothelial cell cultures exposed to LPDS or to serum-free medium.

VEC maintained in the presence of medium supplemented with LPDS grow poorly [82]. Such cultures therefore require the presence of lipoproteins in order to proliferate optimally. Of the two classes of lipoproteins (HDL and LDL) which have been studied, HDL seems to be the major factor involved in the proliferation of vascular endothelial cells. This is due primarily to its lack of toxicity when added at high concentration, as well as to its lack of dependence on LPDS in order to exhibit its mitogenic properties [82].

LDL, unlike HDL, had a biphasic effect. Although mitogenic for vascular endothelial cells when added at low concentration, once physiological concentrations are reached it becomes toxic for the cells [82]. Moreover, and in contrast with HDL, the mitogenic effect of LDL was found to be a function of the LPDS concentration to which cultures were exposed. LDL at a concentration of 200 μg protein/ml did not stimulate cells to proliferate at an optimal growth-rate unless cultures were maintained in high (5%–10%) LPDS concentration. This mitogenic effect on the part of HDL, as opposed to the cytotoxic effect of LDL, was observed regardless of the density at which cultures were seeded (clonal or high density cultures). Therefore, HDL at physiological concentrations can replace serum or plasma. This is best exemplified by our observation that cells maintained in serum-free medium of ECM will proliferate at an optimal rate, provided that HDL is added together with transferrin (10 μg/ml) to the medium. In contrast, in the absence of LPDS, LDL concentrations as low as 80 μg protein/ml resulted in cell death and at 30 μg protein/ml had only a small mitogenic effect in comparison to that of HDL. The morphological appearance of VEC grown in the absence or presence of serum is shown in Fig. 10A–C.

The substrate upon which cultures were maintained was found to be of crucial importance if a mitogenic effect on the part of either HDL or LDL is to be observed. When maintained on plastic, cells exposed to LPDS did not survive and therefore could not respond to either lipoprotein [82]. In contrast, when maintained on ECM they survived quite well, thereby making it possible to observe the mitogenic effect of either HDL or LDL. This suggests that, in vivo, the integrity of the basement membrane upon which endothelial cells rest and migrate is an important factor in determining the cells' response to lipoproteins present in plasma [82].

Vascular smooth muscle (VSM) cells. Among the plasma components which could affect the proliferation of VSM cells are HDL and LDL, as well as somatomedin C, insulin, EGF, and FGF, since those agents have been shown to be mitogenic for a wide variety of cell types maintained under serum-free conditions [83] as well as for VSM cell cultures exposed to plasma [68, 84].

We have therefore compared the effects of the substrate (either ECM or plastic) on the proliferative response of low density VSM cell cultures exposed to a synthetic medium supplemented with these various factors. We were further encouraged to take this approach by previous observations [33] which indicated that VSM cells maintained on ECM-coated dishes have a much lower requirement for either serum or plasma in order to proliferate actively than when they are maintained on plastic. It is therefore possible that VSM cells, when maintained on ECM-coated dishes, could survive and still be responsive to plasma factors even when maintained in a well-defined synthetic medium unsupplemented with either plasma or serum [36]. Preliminary studies demonstrated that transferrin, which is the main iron-carrying protein in the bloodstream, must be present if any mitogenic response to plasma factors on the part of VSM cells seeded and maintained in total absence of serum is to be observed. It is likely that this absolute requirement for transferrin either reflects its role in delivering iron to the cells or its ability to detoxify the medium by removing toxic traces of metals [85].

When low density VSM cell cultures were maintained on ECM-coated dishes and exposed to a synthetic medium supplemented with transferrin (10 μg/ml), HDL (250 μg protein/ml), insulin (2 μg protein/ml) or somatomedin C (10 ng/ml), and FGF (100 ng/ml),or EGF (50 ng/ml), cells proliferated as actively as when they were exposed to optimal serum concentration. The single omission of HDL, insulin, or EGF resulted in a lower growth rate of the cultures, as well as in a lower final cell density. This indicates that all of these factors have an additive effect upon one another and must be present simultaneously in order to induce optimal cell growth. Neither EGF nor insulin, either singly or in combination, had a significant effect on cell growth. The morphological appearance of confluent cultures of VSM cultures grown in the absence or presence of serum is shown in Fig. 10E,F.

Since HDL, as well as insulin and EGF, are all normally present in plasma, these factors may reflect the plasma constituents involved in the control of the proliferation of VSM cells when such cells are maintained on ECM-coated dishes and exposed to plasma. The concentrations at which insulin was mitogenic are clearly pharmacological. However, since insulin can be replaced by somatomedin C, and since it is known to have a low affinity for somatomedin binding sites, it may be that the high concentrations of insulin required are due to its weak interaction with the somatomedin binding

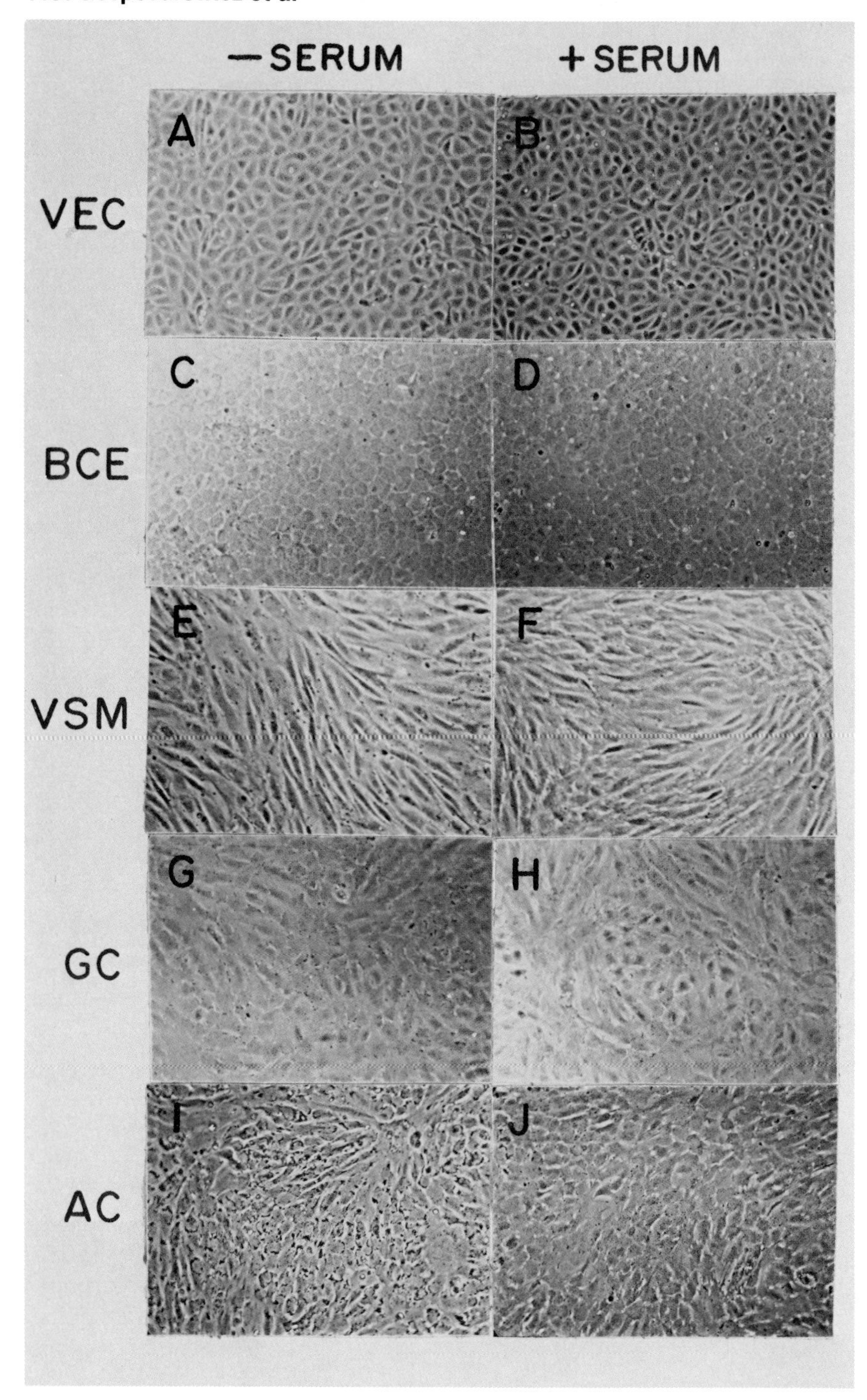
—SERUM
+SERUM
VEC
BCE
VSM
GC
AC
A
B
C
D
E
F
G
H
I
J

sites. If this is the case, the mitogenic activity of insulin on VSM cells is not directly mediated through its interaction with high affinity insulin binding sites but rather through its weak interaction with somatomedin C binding sites. In contrast, the effect of EGF, which was further documented by the identification on the cell surface of EGF receptor sites, is probably due to a direct interaction of EGF with the cells [36].

The use of a synthetic medium supplemented with transferrin, HDL, insulin, and EGF has allowed VSM cells not only to proliferate actively in the total absence of serum but also to be passaged repeatedly. This therefore makes realization of the goal of serial passage in a totally defined medium possible.

The substrate upon which VSM cells are maintained is an important factor in their response to the various factors to which they are exposed. When cells are maintained on plastic and exposed to a synthetic medium, they will not proliferate. The addition of FGF, which in previous studies [33–36] has been shown to replace the requirement for an ECM, will allow the cells to proliferate and to respond to either HDL or LDL. Yet, the life-spans of the cultures are far from impressive, since even when exposed to HDL and FGF cells senesce after undergoing 23 generations. In contrast, when cells are maintained on ECM-coated dishes, even when exposed to a synthetic medium unsupplemented with any factor, cultures had a life-span of 15 generations before senescing and, while the addition of FGF to the medium no longer has any effect on the life-span of the cultures, that of transferrin, HDL, insulin, and FGF or EGF will allow the cells to undergo 46 generations before senescing [36]. The effect of the ECM in delaying cell senescence is even more impressive if one considers the case of cells exposed to synthetic medium supplemented with optimal concentration of serum. While cultures maintained on plastic and exposed to serum can at best be maintained for 16 generations, those maintained on ECM have a life-span of 88 generations [36]. It may therefore be concluded that the ECM upon

---

Fig. 10. Morphological appearance of bovine vascular endothelial cells (VEC), corneal endothelial (BCE) cells, vascular smooth muscle (VSM) cells, granulosa cells (GC), and adrenal cortex (AC) cells grown in the total absence or in the presence of serum. VEC were grown in the presence of DMEM supplemented with (A): HDL (500 μg protein/ml) and transferrin (10 μg/ml) or (B): 10% calf serum. BCE cells were grown in the presence of DMEM supplemented with either (C): HDL (250 μg protein/ml), transferrin (10 μg protein/ml), insulin (2.5 μg/ml) and FGF (100 ng/ml), or (D): 10% fetal calf serum, 5% calf serum. VSM cells were grown in the presence of DMEM supplemented with (E): HDL (500 μg protein/ml), transferrin (10 μg protein/ml), insulin (2.5 μg protein/ml), and EGF (50 ng/ml), or (F): 10% bovine serum. GC were grown in F-12 supplemented with (G): insulin (1 μg/ml), FGF (100 ng/ml), and HDL (25 μg protein/ml), or (H): 10% calf serum. AC cells were grown in F-12 supplemented with (I): insulin (250 ng/ml), transferrin, (10 μg/ml), HDL (25 μg protein/ml), and FGF (100 ng/ml), or (J): 10% calf serum.

which VSM cells are maintained not only makes cells sensitive to factors present in plasma but also delays to a considerable extent the ultimate senescence of the cells when they are exposed to a synthetic medium supplemented either with well-defined factor(s) or with serum. Furthermore, since the life-span of the cultures exposed to serum is longer than that of cultures exposed to a combination of transferrin, HDL, insulin, and FGF or EGF, it is likely that there are other factor(s) present in serum which could delay their ultimate senescence in culture [36].

Corneal endothelial cells. The corneal endothelium forms the inner lining of the cornea. Like the vascular endothelium, this tissue consists of a single cell monolayer composed of highly flattened, closely apposed, and contact-inhibited cells endowed with a cell surface polarity. While the apical cell surface is a nonthrombogenic surface and is exposed to the aqueous humor, the basal cell surface is involved in the secretion of a highly thrombogenic basement membrane called Descemet's membrane, upon which it rests.

Previous studies have shown that both FGF and EGF can support the proliferation of bovine corneal endothelial (BCE) cells when maintained on plastic and exposed to serum [67, 86]. In contrast, when that same cell type is maintained on an ECM, neither FGF nor EGF is required in order to induce cell proliferation. Exposure to plasma or serum alone is enough to insure an optimal rate of proliferation of the cultures, regardless of the cell density at which cultures are seeded initially [27, 87]. Further analysis of the plasma factors involved in the control of proliferation of BCE cells demonstrated that these factors are similar to those supporting the proliferation of VSM cells and consist of transferrin (10 μg/ml), HDL (250 μg/ml) or EGF (20 ng/ml), and insulin (2.5 μg/ml). Using such a combination of factors, one can induce low-density BCE cultures to proliferate with a growth-rate similar to that observed when cells are exposed to optimal serum concentration (Fig. 10) [88] and thereby allow them to be passaged repeatedly at low cell density and in the total absence of serum. The morphological appearance of confluent cultures grown in the absence or presence of serum is shown in Fig. 10C, D. As with other cell types, the substrate upon which cells are maintained is crucial if such an effect on the part of transferrin, HDL, insulin, and FGF or EGF is to be observed, since cultures maintained on plastic will not proliferate when exposed to similar conditions (Fig. 11). Also in accord with observations with other cell types is the fact that the longevity of corneal endothelial cell cultures maintained in serum-free conditions and on ECM-coated dishes is greatly improved (Fig. 12). These conditions also result in a cell model which more closely mimics the in vivo situation, since in vivo the corneal endothelium is exposed to the aqueous

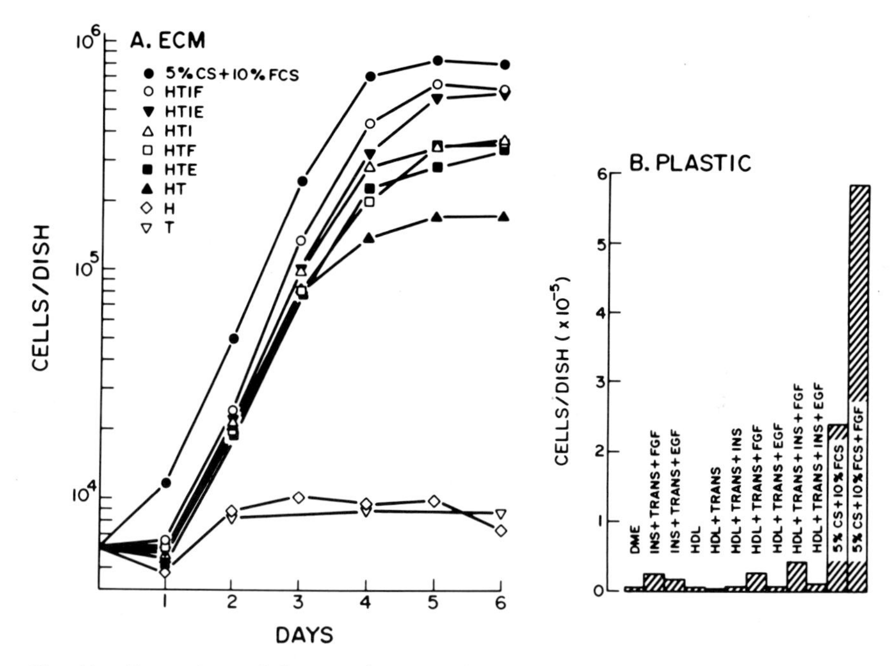

Fig. 11. Comparison of the growth-rate of low density bovine corneal endothelial cell cultures maintained on ECM-coated dishes and exposed to either DMEM supplemented with 5% calf serum, 10% fetal calf serum, or to medium supplemented with HDL, transferrin, insulin, and FGF or EGF, added either singly or in combination. B Same as A, except that cultures were maintained on plastic and that the final density of the cultures was compared after 6 days. A) Bovine corneal endothelial cells were seeded at 1×10^4 cells per 35-mm dish on ECM-coated dishes in the presence of DMEM supplemented with 5% calf serum (CS), 10% fetal calf serum (FCS, ●); HDL, transferrin, insulin, and FGF (HTIF, O); HDL, transferrin, insulin, and EGF (HTIE, ▼); HDL, transferrin, and insulin (HTI, △); HDL, transferrin, and FGF (HTF, □); HDL, transferrin, and EGF (HTE, ■); HDL and transferrin (HT, ▲); or HDL (H, ◇) and transferrin (T, ▽) alone. The concentration of HDL added was 500 μg protein/ml, transferrin was 10 μg/ml, insulin, FGF, and EGF were 5 μg/ml, 100 ng/ml, and 25 ng/ml, respectively. HDL and transferrin were added only once at day 0, while FGF was added every other day and insulin every 4 days. At daily intervals, triplicate plates representing each condition were trypsinized and counted. The standard deviation in the different determinations did not exceed 10% of the mean. B) Bovine corneal endothelial cells were seeded as described above, but on plastic instead of ECM-coated dishes. Cultures were exposed to DMEM supplemented with 5% calf serum, 10% fetal calf serum with or without FGF, or DMEM supplemented with 1) HDL, transferrin, insulin, and FGF or EGF, 2) HDL, transferrin with EGF, FGF, or insulin present, 3) HDL and transferrin, 4) HDL alone, 5) insulin, transferrin and FGF or EGF, and finally 6) DMEM alone. The final density of the cultures kept under various conditions was then compared after 6 days in culture. The concentrations and schedule of addition of transferrin, HDL, insulin, and FGF, or EGF were as in (A).

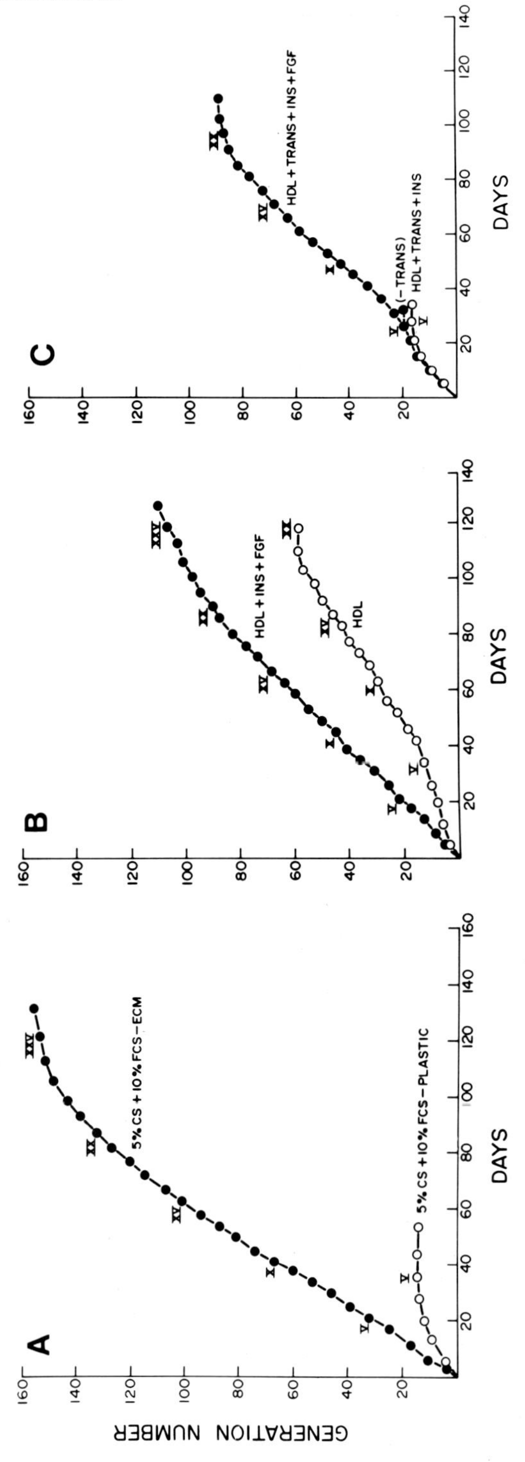
A
B
C
GENERATION NUMBER
DAYS
5% CS + 10% FCS – ECM
5% CS + 10% FCS – PLASTIC
HDL + INS + FGF
HDL
HDL + TRANS + INS + FGF
(– TRANS)
HDL + TRANS + INS

humor which, depending on the species considered, has a protein concentration that is only 0.1–1% that of plasma.

Granulosa and adrenal cortex cells. Both of these cell types in vivo have the ability to produce steroids. Earlier studies done on the control of proliferation of bovine granulosa cells have shown that this cell type, when maintained on plastic and exposed to optimal serum concentration, proliferates slowly or not at all [89]. The addition of either EGF or FGF to the media could trigger substantial cell proliferation, since low density cell cultures exposed to either mitogen can have an average doubling time as low as 18 hours [89]. Addition of either mitogen also delays the ultimate senescence of the cultures [89]. With adrenal cortex cells, on the other hand, although they do divide extremely slowly and rapidly senesce when maintained on plastic and exposed to serum, the addition of FGF, but not that of EGF, results in both a shortening of the average population doubling time and in the prevention of their precocious senescence in culture [90]. In contrast, maintaining either granulosa or adrenal cortex cells on an ECM renders the requirement for growth factors obsolete, and the addition of plasma alone is enough to insure an optimal growth rate of the cultures [35]. However, the plasma factor(s) to which granulosa and adrenal cortex cells respond when maintained on an ECM were found to be quite different from those to which endothelial or smooth muscle cells responded. In particular, HDL, which was shown to be mitogenic for endothelial or vascular smooth muscle cells over a wide range of concentrations was cytotoxic for granulosa cells when present at concentrations above 50 μg protein/ml. With adrenal

Fig. 12. A) Comparison of the effect of the substrate ECM versus plastic) upon which cells are maintained on the life span of bovine corneal endothelial cell cultures. Bovine corneal endothelial cells were maintained and passaged on plastic dishes (○) or on dishes coated with a ECM (●). Cultures were exposed to DMEM supplemented with 5% calf serum (CS), 10% fetal calf serum (FCS). B) Culture life span of bovine corneal endothelial cell cultures seeded in the presence of serum on ECM-coated dishes and exposed to DMEM supplemented with HDL alone (○) or HDL, insulin, and FGF (●). HDL (250 μg protein/ml) was added only once at each transfer, while FGF (100 ng/ml) was added every other day. Insulin (2 μg/ml) was added every fourth day. The number of generations was determined from the initial cell density 8 hours after seeding and the number of cells harvested at each transfer. Each point represents a single transfer. Roman numerals indicate the passage number. C) Life span of bovine corneal endothelial cell cultures seeded in the absence of serum on ECM-coated dishes. Cultures were exposed to DMEM supplemented with transferrin (10 μg/ml), HDL (500 μg/ml), and insulin (5 μg/ml) (○), or HDL, transferrin, insulin, and FGF (100 ng/ml) (●). Similar life spans were observed when cultures were passaged in the presence of EGF (50 ng/ml) instead of FGF (unpublished data). Schedule of addition of the various factors was as described. As soon as transferrin was omitted from the medium (-TRANS), cells stopped dividing and could no longer be passaged.

cortex cells, cytotoxicity was observed at a concentration above 30 μg protein/ml [91]. Insulin was observed to be the main mitogen for both granulosa and adrenal cortex cells [91, 92], and both cell types responded to concentrations as low as 30 ng/ml by proliferating actively, reaching a final cell density which was 60% that of cultures exposed to optimal serum or plasma concentrations. Addition of either EGF or FGF helped the cultures to reach a final cell density similar to that observed when cells were maintained in the presence of either plasma or serum. The morphological appearance of confluent granulosa and adrenal cell cultures grown in the absence or presence of serum is shown in Fig. 10 G,H and 10 I,J, respectively. As with other cell types, the importance of the substrate in supporting the proliferative response to insulin of both granulosa and adrenal cortex cells was demonstrated by the fact that such response could be observed only with cultures maintained on ECM-coated dishes but not with those maintained on plastic [91, 92].

Both of these cell types when cultured in the absence of serum and in the presence of insulin, HDL, and FGF were still capable of producing steroids in response to dibutyryl cyclic AMP. In the case of granulosa cells, exposure to FSH improved the ability of the cells to produce steroids, and in the case of adrenal cells exposure to ACTH also stimulated steroid production above its normal level. Addition of either LDL or HDL to the culture medium of confluent cultures grown in the absence of serum improved the ability of the cells to produce steroids [92].

Therefore, not only can one grow both adrenal cortex and granulosa cell cultures in a defined medium, but the differentiated properties of these cells are also preserved, as shown by their ability to respond to stimuli provided by their trophic hormones [92, 93].

NATURE OF THE ECM FACTORS INVOLVED IN CELL ATTACHMENT VS CELL PROLIFERATION

The intricate nature of the ECM is exemplified by the difficulties encountered in identifying its composition and by the complex interaction of its known components [13] (collagen, glycoproteins, proteoglycans, and glycosaminoglycans) which form a highly stable scaffolding upon which cells rest in vivo. Because the reconstitution of this unique structure from its known constituents would be a formidable task, we have examined the role that these components play in cell proliferation by indirect methods which rely on selective inactivation by chemical, enzymatic, or heat treatment of intact ECM. Although all of the treatments we have used are known to affect glycoproteins, and specifically proteoglycans, only three were effective in inactivating the ECM's ability to support cell proliferation. Exposure of ECM-coated dishes to 14M NH_4OH (pH 13.8), which results in the cleavage of proteoglycoproteins or glycopeptides at the O-glycosidic bond between the protein and carbohydrate moieties [94, 95] inhibited the rate of proliferation of vascular endothelial cells by 97%. Likewise, treatment of ECM-coated dishes with 4M Guanidine-HCl, which extracts up to 80% of the glycosaminoglycans, caused a 92% reduction in cell growth. Treatment of ECM-coated dishes with nitrous acid (HNO_2), which results in the degradation of heparin or heparin sulfate into sulfated disaccharides and non-sulfated oligosaccharides [96–99], affected cell proliferation by 90% and led to the release of $^{35}SO_4$-labeled macromolecules, 50% of which were disaccharides. Although the effect of HNO_2 on intact ECM is not known, its specific degradation of isolated heparan and heparan sulfate could indicate that it has a similar effect on ECM, and this may correlate with its adverse effect on the ability of the ECM to support cell growth. Chemical treatment of the ECM with a reducing agent such as dithiothreitol (from 0.1 mM to 100 mM), which has been reported to destroy the biological activity of platelet-derived growth factor completely, did not affect its ability to support growth, nor did treatment with sodium dodecyl sulfate (2%) or urea (2M or 8M). Specific enzymatic treatment of the ECM with collagenase, pepsin, trypsin, chymotrypsin, or neuraminidase did not inhibit cell proliferation. It is therefore doubtful that any of the substrates of these enzymes plays a direct role in cell proliferation. The lack of effect of either hyaluronidase or chondroitinase ABC, as well as the presence of chondroitinase-resistant material in extracts of ECM which affect cell proliferation, would tend to rule out a role for hyaluronic acid or chondroitin sulfates in the permissive effect of the ECM on cell proliferation [100].

The importance of cell shape in proliferation suggests that attachment factors present within the ECM which, because of their direct contact with the cell membrane, could modify cell shape, could also play a duel role in controlling cell proliferation.

To investigate the relationship between growth and attachment, we have compared the ability of vascular endothelial cells to attach to ECM following treatment by alkaline pH and heat. In the absence of serum, only 10% of the cells attach to plastic after one hour, and maximal cell attachment (40%) is not reached before 18 hours. In contrast, cells seeded on ECM-coated dishes rapidly attach and spread and most (90%) have attached by 1 hour. No significant difference is seen in the rate of cell attachment after treatment of the ECM at pH 13.8, which destroys 97% of the ability of the ECM to support cell proliferation. In fact, initial cell attachment (1 hour) was slightly enhanced by alkaline treatment. It therefore appears unlikely that the component of the ECM which is removed or destroyed by high pH treatment is involved in cell attachment [100].

In contrast to the results obtained after treatment of the ECM with alkaline pH, thermal treatment of the collagen bed, which results in its denaturation, had the opposite results. Treatment of the ECM at 70°C, which has no effect on cell proliferation, greatly reduces the rate of cell attachment. The rate of cell attachment is reduced even further after treatment of the ECM at 90°C, although cell growth is reduced by only 60%. This indicates that the ECM component(s) implicated in cell growth is probably distinct from those involved in cell attachment (100). Thermal disruptions of the ECM also revealed the importance of the spatial geometry of the ECM component responsible for cell proliferation [100]. The present study provides evidence regarding the nature of the components of the ECM which are responsible for conveying the permissive effect of the ECM on cell proliferation. It is likely that the active component is a sulphated glycoprotein or proteoglycan that is susceptible to extraction by 4M guanidine-HCl, is degraded by nitrous acid, and contains an O-glycosidic bond and glucosamine and/or galactosamine. Its resistance to hyaluronidase and chondroitinase ABD suggests that neither hyaluronic acid nor chondroitin sulfates are involved. Identification of the active component, however, must await a detailed analysis of the ECM and of the material extracted from the ECM under conditions which inhibit cell proliferation. Although cell attachment and proliferation appear to be separate processes mediated through different mechanisms, the role of the component of the ECM responsible for cell proliferation and cell differentiation has yet to be examined. It is well known that cell proliferation precedes many differentiated steps during embryogenesis, and numerous extracellular matrix components have been shown to the ECM which is active in cell proliferation to the alkaline-labile component of demineralized bone matrix described by Reddi and Huggins [101, 102] as inducing differentiation of fibroblasts. It may very well be that it will turn out to be calcium, which, in the form of microcrystalline precipitate, has been shown to be as good a commitment factor as FGF or PDGF [103, 104]. In that regard, it is of interest to note that, in vivo, basement membranes in all types of organs are rich in calcium deposits which are bound to the numerous cationic groups present within the GAGs and proteoglycans, particularly in heparan sulfate. The ability of basement membrane to accumulate calcium is reflected by its ability to stain with alizarin red and may represent an evolutionary mechanism through which the commitment factors are automatically incorporated into the substrate upon which cells will migrate, proliferate, and differentiate.

CONCLUSION

The ways in which the ECM exerts its permissive effect on cell proliferation can only be the object of speculation. One possible effect is to modify the cell shape in order to make it responsive to factor(s) to which the cells do not respond unless they adopt an appropriate shape. Recently, Folkman and Moscona [18], using vascular endothelial cells maintained on tissue culture dishes coated with an agent which modifies the adhesiveness of the cells to the dish, were able to control precisely the cellular shape in morphologies ranging from highly flattened to almost spheroidal. When the extent of cell spreading was correlated with DNA synthesis or cell growth, it was found to be highly coupled. Whereas highly flattened cells responded to serum factors, spheroidal cells no longer responded and intermediate degrees of response could be observed, depending on how flattened the cells were. Likewise, with corneal epithelial cells, changes in cell shape which depend on the substrate upon which the cells are maintained correspond to drastically altered sensitivities of the cells to EGF vs FGF [4, 5]. An attractive hypothesis proposed by Yaoi and Kanaseki [23] is that the ECM could play a key role in mitosis and facilitate cytokinesis. This hypothesis was based on their observation that, while both high- and low-density cultures maintained on ECM exhibit a high rate of DNA synthesis and a high mitotic index, only high-density cultures maintained on plastic have both a high rate of DNA synthesis and a high mitotic index. In contrast, low-density cultures maintained on plastic, although they have a high rate of DNA synthesis, have a low mitotic index, thus suggesting that cells do not enter into mitosis. It is therefore likely that, while plastic provides a foreign substrate upon which cells can attach tenaciously and spread in a vain attempt to phagocytose it, the ECM provides a natural substrate that the cells recognize and upon which they can undergo their characteristic changes in morphology (rounding up) occurring at mitosis. These morphological changes probably reflect the rearrangement of the cellular cytoskeleton, so that cells can go through the cleavage steps, giving rise to two progeny cells instead of undergoing endomitosis.

ACKNOWLEDGMENTS

This work was supported by grants from the NIH (HL 20197 and 32678, EY 02186, and HD 11082). The authors wish to thank Mr. Harvey Scodel for his invaluable assistance in the preparation of this manuscript.

REFERENCES

1. Thompson D: In Bonner JT (ed): "On Growth and Form," Oxford: Cambridge University Press, 1961, pp 1–64.
2. Maroudas NG: Chemical and mechanical requirements for fibroblast adhesion. Nature 244:353–354, 1973.
3. Folkman J: In Gallo RC (ed): "Recent Advances in Cancer Research: Cell Biology, Molecular Biology, and Tumor Virology," Cleveland: CRC, vol 1, 1977, pp 119–130.

4. Gospodarowicz D, Greenburg G, Birdwell CR: Determination of cellular shape by the extracellular matrix and its correlation with the control of cellular growth. Cancer Res 38:4155–4171, 1978.
5. Gospodarowicz D, Vlodavsky I, Greenburg G, and Johnson LK: Cellular shape is determined by the extracellular matrix and is responsible for the control of cellular growth and function. In Ross R, Sato G (eds): "Hormones and Cell Culture." Cold Spring Harbor Conferences on Cell Proliferation, New York: Cold Spring Harbor Press, vol 6, 1979, pp 561–592.
6. Grobstein CJ: Inductive interaction in the development of the mouse metanephros. J Exp Zool 130:319–340, 1955.
7. Grobstein C: Mechanisms of organogenetic tissue interaction. Cancer Inst Monogr 26:279–299, 1967.
8. Grobstein C: Developmental role of intercellular matrix: retrospective and prospective. In Slavkin HC, Grenlich RC (eds): "Extracellular Matrix Influences on Gene Expression." New York: Academic Press, 1975, pp 9–16, 804–814.
9. Kratochwil K: Tissue interaction during embryonic development. In Tarin D (ed): "General Properties in Tissue Interaction in Carcinogenesis." New York: Academic Press, 1972, pp 1–48.
10. Wessels NK: Substrate and nutrient effects upon epidermal basal cell orientation and proliferation. Proc Natl Acad Sci USA 52:252–259, 1964.
11. Holley RW, Kiernan JA: Contact inhibition of cell division in 3T3 cells. Proc Natl Acad Sci USA 60:300–304, 1968.
12. Temin HM, Pierson RW, Dulak NC: The role of serum in the control of multiplication of avian and mammalian cells in culture. In Rothblat GH, Cristofalo J (eds): "Growth, Nutrition and Metabolism of Cells in Culture." New York: Academic Press, 1972, pp 49–81.
13. Bornstein P, Sage H: Structurally distinct collagen types. Ann Rev Biochem 49:957–1003, 1980.
14. Gospodarowicz D, Tauber J-P: Growth factors and extracellular matrix. Endocrine Rev 1:201–227, 1980.
15. Murray JC, Stingl G, Kleinman HK, Martin GR, Kidwell WR: Epidermal cells adhere preferentially to type IV (basement membrane) collagen. J Cell Biol 80:197–202, 1979.
16. Rollins BJ, Culp LA: Preliminary characterization of the proteoglycans in the substrate adhesion sites of normal and virus-transformed murine cells. Biochemistry 18:5621–5629, 1979.
17. Wicha MS, Liotta LA, Garbisa, Kidwell WR: Basement membrane collagen requirements for attachment and growth of mammary epithelium. Exp Cell Res 124:181–190, 1979.
18. Folkman J, Moscona A: Role of cell shape in growth control. Nature 273:345–349, 1978.
19. Hay ED: Interaction between the cell surface and extracellular matrix in corneal development. In Lash JW, Burger MM (eds): "Cell and Tissue Interaction." New York: Raven Press, 1977, pp 115–137.
20. Sun TT, Green H: Cultured epithelial cells of cornea, conjunctiva, and skin: Absence of marked intrinsic difference in their differentiated state. Nature 269:489–492, 1977.
21. Bernfield MR: The cell periphery in morphogenesis. In Litlefield JW, de Grouchy J (eds): "Birth Defects, Excerpta Medica, Int. Congress Series 432" Amsterdam, New York, Oxford: Elsevier, North Holland, 1978, pp 111–125.
22. Yang J, Richards J, Bowman P, Guzman R, Eham J, McCormick K, Hamamoto S, Pitelka D, Nandi S: Substained growth and three-dimensional organization of primary mammary tumor. Proc Natl Acad Sci USA 76:3401–3405, 1979.
23. Yaoi Y, Kanaseki T: Role of microexudate carpet in cell division. Nature 237:283–285, 1972.

24. Weiss L, Poste G, Mackearnin A, Willett K: Growth of mammalian cells on substrates coated with cellular microexudates. Effect on cell growth at low population densities. J Cell Biol 64:135–145, 1975.
25. Gospodarowicz D, Greenburg G, Vlodavsky I, Alvarado J, Johnson LK: The identification and localization of fibronectin in cultured corneal endothelial cells: cell surface polarity and physiological implications. Exp Eye Res 29:485–509, 1979.
26. Gospodarowicz D, Vlodavsky I, Greenburg G, Alvarado J, Johnson, LK: Studies on atherogenesis and corneal transplantation using cultured vascular and corneal endothelia. Rec Progr Hormone Res 35:375–448, 1979.
27. Gospodarowicz D, Vlodavsky I, Savion N: The role of fibroblast growth factor and the extracellular matrix in the control of proliferation and differentiation of corneal endothelial cells. Vision Res 21:87–103, 1981.
28. Tseng SC, Savion N, Gospodarowicz D, Stern R: Characterization of collagens synthesized by bovine corneal endothelial cell cultures. J Biol Chem 256:3361–3365, 1981.
29. Gospodarowicz D, Fujii DK: The extracellular matrix and the control of cell proliferation and differentiation. In Scott WA, Werner R, Schultz J (eds): "Cellular Responses to Molecular Modulators." Miami Winter Symposia, vol 18, 1981 (in press).
30. Gospodarowicz D, Greenburg G, Foidart JM, Savion N: The production and localization of laminin in cultured vascular and corneal endothelial cells. J Cell Physiol 107:173–183, 1981.
31. Foidart JM, Reddi AH: Immunofluorescent localization of type IV collagen and laminin during endochondral bone differentiation and regulation by pituitary growth hormone. Dev Biol 75:130–136.
32. Foidart JM, Bere EW, Yaar M, Rennard WI, Gullino M, Martin GR, Katz SI: Distribution and immunoelectron microscopic localization of laminin, a noncollagenous basement membrane glycoprotein. Lab Invest 42:336–342, 1980.
33. Gospodarowicz D CR Ill: Do plasma and serum have different abilities to promote cell growth? Proc Natl Acad Sci USA 77:2726–2730, 1980.
34. Gospodarowicz D CR Ill: The extracellular matrix and the control of proliferation of vascular endothelial cells. J Clin Invest 65:1351–1364, 1980.
35. Gospodarowicz D, Delgado D, Vlodavsky I: Permissive effect of the extracellular matrix on cell proliferation in vitro. Proc Natl Acad Sci USA 77:4094–4098, 1980.
36. Gospodarowicz D, Hirabayashi K, Giguere L, Tauber JP: Factors controlling the proliferative rate, final cell density, and life span of bovine vascular smooth muscle cells in culture. J Cell Biol 1981, 89:568–578, 1981.
37. Aaronson SA, Todaro GJ, Freeman AE: Human sarcoma cells in culture. Exp Cell Res 61:1–5, 1970.
38. Leighton J: Contributions of tissue culture studies to an understanding of the biology of cancer: a review. Cancer Res 17:929–935, 1957.
39. Liotta LA, Abe S, Robey PG, Martin GR: Preferential digestion of basement membrane collagen by an enzyme derived from a metastatic murine tumor. Proc Natl Acad Sci USA 76:2268–2272, 1979.
40. Rifkin DB, Loeb JN, Moore G, Reich E: Properties of plasminogen activators formed by neoplastic human cell cultures. J Exp Med 139:1317–1328, 1974.
41. Thomassen MJ, Buoen LC, Brand KG: Foreign-body tumorigenesis: Number distribution, and cell density of preneoplastic clones. J Natl Cancer Inst 54:203–207, 1975.
42. Nesbit ME: A Cancer Journal for Clinicians 26:174–183, 1976.
43. Ewing J: Diffuse endothelioma of bone. Proc NY Pathol Soc 21:17–24, 1921.
44. Howe-Jensen K, Priori E, Dmochowoki L: Studies on ultrastructure of Ewing's sarcoma and bone. Cancer 29:280–286, 1972.

45. Vlodavsky I, Lui G-M, Gospodarowicz D: Morphological appearance, growth behavior and migratory activity of human tumor cells maintained on extracellular matrix versus plastic. Cell 19:607–616, 1980.
46. Klebe RJ: Isolation of a collagen-dependent cell attachment factor. Nature 250:248–251, 1974.
47. Yamada KM, Olden K: Fibronectins — adhesive glycoproteins of cell surface and blood. Nature 275:179–184, 1978.
48. Timpl R, Rode H, Gehran-Robey P, Rennard SI, Foidart J-M, Martin GR: Laminin — a glycoprotein from basement membrane. J Biol Chem 254:9933–9937, 1979.
49. Alitalo K, Kurkinen M, Vaheri A, Krieg T, Timpl R: Extracellular matrix components synthesized by human amniotic epithelial cells in culture. Cell 19:1053–1062, 1980.
50. Birdwell CR, Gospodarowicz D, Nicolson G: Identification, localization, and role of fibronectin in cultured bovine endothelial cells. Proc Natl Acad Sci USA 75:3272–3277, 1978.
51. Jaffe EA, Mosher DF: Synthesis of fibronectin by cultured human endothelial cells. J Exp Med 147:1779–1791, 1978.
52. Vlodavsky I, Johnson LK, Greenburg G, Gospodarowicz D: Vascular endothelial cells maintained in the absence of fibroblast growth factor undergo structural and functional alterations that are incompatible with their in vivo differentiated properties. J Cell Biol 83:468–486, 1979.
53. Vlodavsky I, Gospodarowicz D: Respective involvement of laminin and fibronectin in the adhesion of human carcinoma and sarcoma cells. Nature 289:304–306, 1981.
54. Kramer RH, Nicolson GL: Interactions of tumor cells with vascular endothelial cell monolayers: A model for metastatic invasion. Proc Natl Acad Sci USA 76:5704–5708, 1979.
55. Smith HS, Riggs JL, Mosesson MW: Production of fibronectin by human epithelial cells in culture. Cancer Res 39:4138–4142, 1979.
56. Gospodarowicz D, Vlodavsky I: The role of the extracellular matrix and growth factors in the control of proliferation of anchorage-dependent cells. In: "Progress in Cancer Research and Therapy," New York: Raven Press 1981 (in press).
57. Owens RB: Selective cultivation of mammalian epithelial cells. In: "Methods in Cell Biology." vol 14, 1976, pp 341–373.
58. Rafferty KA: Epithelial cells: Growth in culture of normal and neoplastic forms. Adv Cancer Res 21:249–272, 1975.
59. Maroudas NG, O'Neill CH, Stanton MF: Fibroblast anchorage in carcinogenesis by fibres. Lancet 1:807–809, 1973.
60. Fujii DK, Massoglia S, Gospodarowicz D: Cell 1981 (submitted).
61. Carrel AJ: On the permanent life of tissue outside the organism. Exp Med 15:516–536, 1912.
62. Balk SD: Calcium as a regulator of the proliferation of normal, but not of transformed, chicken fibroblasts in a plasma-containing medium. Proc Natl Acad Sci USA 68:271–275 1971.
63. Balk SD, Whitfield JF, Youdale T, Braun AC: Roles of calcium, serum, plasma, and folic acid in the control of proliferation of normal and rous sarcoma. Proc Natl Acad Sci USA 70:675–679, 1973.
64. Ross R, Glomset J, Kariya B, Harker L: A platelet dependent serum factor that stimulates the proliferation of arterial smooth muscle cells in vitro. Proc Natl Acad Sci USA 71:1207–1210, 1974.
65. Kohler N, Lipton A: Platelets as a source of fibroblast growth-promoting activity. Exp Cell Res 87:297–301, 1974.

66. Ross R, Vogel A: The platelet-derived growth factor. Cell 14:203–301, 1978,
67. Gospodarowicz D, Greenburg G, Bialecki H, Zetter B: Factors involved in the modulation of cell proliferation in vivo and in vitro: the role of fibroblast and epidermal growth factors in the proliferative response of mammalian cells. In Vitro 14:85–118, 1978.
68. Gospodarowicz D, Moran JS, Braun D: Control of proliferation of bovine vascular endothelial cells. J Cell Physiol 91:377–385, 1977.
69. Gospodarowicz D, Moran JS, Braun D, Birdwell CR: Clonal growth of bovine endothelial cells in tissue culture: fibroblast growth factor as a survival agent. Proc Natl Acad Sci USA 73:4120–4124, 1976.
70. Greenburg G, Vlodavsky I, Foidart J-M, Gospodarowicz, D: Conditioned medium from endothelial cell cultures can restore the normal phenotypic expression of vascular endothelium maintained in vitro in the absence of fibroblast growth factor. J Cell Physiol 103:333–347, 1980.
71. Fielding PE, Vlodavsky I, Gospodarowicz D, Fielding CJ: Effect of contact inhibition on the regulation of cholesterol metabolism in cultured vascular endothelial cells. J Biol Chem 244:749–755, 1979.
72. Reckless JPD, Weinstein DB, Steinberg D: Lipoprotein and cholesterol metabolism in rabbit arterial endothelial cells in culture. Biochim Biophys Acta 529:475–487, 1978.
73. Stein O, Stein Y: High density lipoproteins reduce the uptake of low density lipoproteins by human endothelial cells in culture. Biochim Biophys Acta 23:563–568, 1976.
74. Tauber J-P, Vlodavsky I, Goldminz D, Gospodarowicz D: Up regulation in vascular endothelial cells of high density lipoprotein receptor sites induced by 25 hydroxycholesterol. Europ J Biochem 1982 (in press).
75. Tauber J-P, Goldminz D, Vlodavsky I, Gospodarowicz D: The interactions of the high density lipoproteins with cultured vascular endothelial cells. Europ J Biochem 1982 (in press).
76. Vlodavsky I, Fielding PE, Fielding CJ, Gospodarowicz D: Role of contact inhibition in the regulation of receptor mediated uptake of low density lipoprotein in cultured vascular endothelial cells. Proc Natl Acad Sci USA 75:356–360, 1978.
77. Brown G, Mahely R, Assmann G: Swine aortic smooth muscle in tissue culture – some effects of purified swine lipoproteins on cell growth and morphology. Circ Res 39:415–424, 1976.
78. Fischer-Dzoga K, Fraser R, Wissler RW: Aortic smooth muscle cells: 1. Effect of lipoprotein fractions of hyperlipemic serum and lymph. Exp Mol Pathol 24:346–359, 1976.
79. Ross R, Glomset JA: Atherosclerosis and the arterial smooth muscle cell. Science 180:1332–1339, 1973.
80. Layman DL, Jelen BJ, Illingworth DR: Inability of serum from A betalipoproteinemic subjects to stimulate proliferation of human smooth muscle cells and dermal fibroblasts in vitro. Proc Natl Acad Sci USA 77:1511–1515, 1980.
81. Goldstein JL, Helgeson JAS, Brown MS: Inhibition of cholesterol synthesis with compactin renders growth of cultured cells dependent on the low density lipoprotein receptor. J Biol Chem 254:5403–5409, 1979.
82. Tauber J-P, Cheng J, Gospodarowicz D: The effect of high and low density lipoproteins on the proliferation of vascular endothelial cells. J Clin Invest 66:696–708, 1980.
83. Bottenstein J, Hayashi I, Hutchings S, Masui H, Mather J, McClure D, Ohasa S, Rizzino A, Sato G, Serrero G, Wolfe R, Wu R: The growth of cells in serum-free hormone-supplemented media. Meth Enzymol 58:94–109, 1978.
84. Gospodarowicz D, Mescher AL, Birdwell CR: Control of cellular proliferation by the fibroblast and epidermal growth factors. In: "Gene Expression and Regulation in Cultured Cells," Third Decennial Review Conference, National Cancer Institute Monographs, no. 48, pp 109–130, 1978.

85. Barnes D, Sato G: Serum-free cell culture: a unifying approach. Cell 22:649–655, 1980.
86. Gospodarowicz D, Mescher AL, Birdwell CR: Stimulation of corneal endothelial cell proliferation in vitro by fibroblast and epidermal growth factors. Exp Eye Res 25:75–89, 1977.
87. Gospodarowicz D, Ill CR: The extracellular matrix and the control of proliferation of corneal endothelial and lens epithelial cells. Exp Eye Res 31:181-199, 1980.
88. Giguere L, Cheng J, Gospodarowicz D: Factors involved in the control of proliferation of bovine corneal endothelial cells maintained in serum-free medium. J Cell Physiol 1982 (in press).
89. Gospodarowicz D, Ill CR, Birdwell CR: Effects of fibroblast and epidermal growth factors on ovarian cell proliferation in vitro: I. characterization of the response of granulosa cells to FGF and EGF. Endocrinology 100:1108–1120, 1977.
90. Gospodarowicz D, Ill CR, Hornsby PJ, Gill GN: Control of bovine adrenal cortical cell proliferation by fibroblast growth factor. Lack of effect of epidermal growth factor. Endocrinology 100:1080–1089, 1977.
91. Gospodarowicz D, Cheng J, Ill CR: Endocrinology, 1981 (in press).
92. Savion N, Lui G-M, Laherty R, Gospodarowicz D: Factors controlling proliferation and progesterone production by bovine granulosa cells in serum-free medium. Endocrinology,1981 (in press).
93. Savion N, Gospodarowicz D: Factors controlling the proliferation and phenotypic expression of cultured bovine granulosa cells. In Mahesh VB (ed): Developments in Endocrinology, vol 12, "Functional Correlates of Hormone Receptors in Reproduction." New York: Elsevier, North-Holland, pp 437–461.
94. Anderson B, Hoffman P, Meyer K: The O-Serine linkage in peptide of chondroitin 4- or 6-sulfate. J Biol Chem 240:156–167, 1965.
95. Marshall RD, Neuberger A: Structural analysis of the carbohydrate groups of glycoproteins. In Gottschalk A (ed): "Glycoproteins," part A, 1972, pp 322–336.
96. Cifonelli JA: Reaction of heparitin sulfate with nitrous acid. Carbohydr Res 8:233–242, 1968.
97. Kosher RA, Searls RL: Sulfated mucopolysaccharide synthesis during the development of rana pipiens. Dev Biol 32:50–68, 1973.
98. Castellani AA, Balduinia D, Brovelli A: In Balazs E (ed): "Chemistry and Molecular Biology of the Intercellular Matrix." vol 2, 1970, pp 921–928.
99. Lindahl V, Roden L: Carbohydrate-peptide linkages in proteoglycans of animal, plant, and bacterial origin. In Gottschalk A (ed): "Glycoproteins," part A, 1972, pp 491–515.
100. Gospodarowicz D, Greenburg G: Growth control of mammalian cells. Growth factors and extracellular matrix. In: "The Biology of Normal Human Growth." Proceedings of the First Karolinska Institute Nobel Conference. New York: Raven Press, 1981 pp 1–21.
101. Reddi AH, Huggins CB: Obligatory transformation of fibroblasts by bone matrix in rats fed sucrose ration. Proc Soc Exp Biol Med 145:475–486, 1974.
102. Reddi AH: Collagen and cell differentiation. In Remachadran GN, Reddi AH (eds): "Biochemistry of Collagen." 1976, pp 449–477.
103. Stiles CD, Capne GT, Scher CD, Antoniades HM, Van Wyk JJ, Pledger WJ: Dual control of cell growth by somatomedins and platelet-derived growth factor. Proc Natl Acad Sci USA 76:1279–1283, 1979.
104. Dulbecco R, Elkington J: Induction of growth in resting fibroblastic cell cultures by Ca^{++}. Proc Natl Acad Sci USA 72:1584–1588, 1975.

The Prostatic Cell: Structure and Function
Part A, pages 133–136

Preliminary Studies of the Hormonal Control of Male Accessory Sex Organ Epithelial Collagen

A. Mariotti and M. Mawhinney

INTRODUCTION

Prostatic fibromuscular stroma is important in normal and neoplastic growth of the organ [1, 2]. While various studies have determined the fibromuscular stroma to be a potential target tissue for both androgen and estrogen [3–14], the functional significance and hormonal control of specific stromal components remain to be defined. Our studies were designed to define the action of androgen on collagen levels in rat ventral prostate and seminal vesicle and, by using the guinea pig seminal vesicle epithelium and smooth muscle preparations, to determine if the action of androgen involves changes in epithelium and/or smooth muscle collagen.

METHODS AND MATERIALS

Wistar rats, purchased from Hilltop Labs (Scottdale, PA) and guinea pigs, purchased from Ancare (Manhasset, NY) were housed in the animal quarters with standard light regimens and food rations. Rat castrations were performed via the scrotal route under ether anesthesia, while guinea pigs were castrated under barbiturate anesthesia.

Dihydrotestosterone (DHT, 10 mg/kg, Sigma Chemical Co.) and estradiol benzoate (E_2B, 0.01 mg/kg, Sigma Chemical Co.) were prepared in peanut oil, mixed continually on a magnetic stirrer, and injected daily subcutaneously in a volume of 0.1–0.2 ml.

Animals were sacrificed by cervical dislocation. Rat ventral prostate lobes were freed of external fascia, weighed, wrapped in aluminum foil, and frozen in liquid nitrogen. Rat seminal vesicles were separated from the anterior prostates, freed of luminal secretions, weighed, wrapped in aluminum foil, and frozen in liquid nitrogen. Guinea pig seminal vesicles were excised and separated into epithelium and smooth muscle fractions as previously described [15]. All tissue samples were stored at –20°C in air-tight plastic containers prior to assay. Quantification of DNA was performed on these tissues according to methods previously described [16], with the exception that the procedures for RNA recovery and measurement were not utilized. Collagen was measured according to the procedure outlined by Kivirikko et al [17].

RESULTS

Castration of adult rats caused reductions in ventral prostate and seminal vesicle wet weight, DNA content, and collagen content (Table I). Maintenance of castrates with DHT prevented any significant reductions in these three parameters (Table I).

Through the use of the guinea pig seminal vesicle, the effects of castration and androgen maintenance on male accessory sex organ epithelium and muscle were discerned (Table II). Two weeks following the castrations of adult guinea pigs, there was a 63% reduction in epithelial wet weight, while DNA and collagen contents were reduced 38% and 36%, respectively. Maintenance of castrates with DHT caused supra-normal epithelial growth, but DNA and collagen contents were maintained within the normal range. In marked contrast to the epithelium, castration reduced muscle wet weight, while DNA and collagen contents were unchanged. As expected, maintenance of castrates with DHT sustained muscle weights and had no effect on DNA or collagen.

TABLE I. The effect of castration and androgen maintenance on adult rat ventral prostate and seminal vesicle

	Organ weight (mg)		DNA content (μg/organ)		Collagen content (μg/organ)	
Ventral prostate						
Sham	(6)	538 ± 20	(3)	980 ± 68	(6)	392 ± 51
Castrate	(11)	37.1 ± 2.6[a]	(8)	211 ± 22[a]	(9)	162 ± 9.9[a]
DHT	(10)	646 ± 31	(16)	1035 ± 76	(13)	427 ± 44
Seminal vesicle						
Sham	(6)	337 ± 10	(6)	717 ± 88	(6)	974 ± 54
Castrate	(11)	87.1 ± 4.4[a]	(6)	456 ± 19[a]	(9)	445 ± 65[a]
DHT	(6)	453 ± 82	(19)	2451 ± 54	(17)	994 ± 54

Animals were castrated and treated daily with oil or dihydrotestosterone (DHT, 10 mg/kg) for two weeks. Data are expressed as mean ± SEM, and numbers in parentheses indicate number of individual observations.

[a]Significantly less than corresponding value in sham and DHT-treated group.

TABLE II. The effect of castration and androgen maintenance on adult guinea pig seminal vesicle epithelium and muscle

	Organ weight (mg/100 gm body weight)	DNA content (μg/organ)	Collagen content (μg/organ)
SVE			
Sham	37.9 ± 3.7	2193.7 ± 139.9	103.5 ± 4.9
Castrate	14.1 ± 1.2[a]	1343.8 ± 90.1[a]	65.1 ± 5.6[a]
DHT	49.8 ± 2.6	2366.8 ± 157.8	104.8 ± 6.3
SVM			
Sham	71.5 ± 3.4	639.7 ± 50.8	758.7 ± 42.6
Castrate	53.9 ± 3.4[a]	664.4 ± 21.8	855.8 ± 136.2
DHT	86.8 ± 5.4	687.4 ± 15.4	875.0 ± 71.7

Animals were castrated and either treated daily with oil or dihydrotestosterone (DHT, 10 mg/kg) for two weeks. Data are expressed as mean ± SEM of 4–10 observations.
[a]Significantly less than corresponding value in sham and DHT-treated group.

DISCUSSION

Previous studies have shown the fibromuscular stroma of male accessory sex organs to be a target tissue for both androgen and estrogen. Our preliminary studies confirmed Müntzing's [13] observation of the castration-induced reduction in ventral prostate collagen and extended these observations to show that the androgen sensitive collagens of the adult male accessory sex organs are confined to the epithelium. Interestingly, the hormone-induced changes in epithelial DNA/collagen ratio were constant. Only future experiments will determine if such a relationship is observed under all conditions of normal growth and whether cause and effect relationships exist between changes in epithelial collagen(s) and changes in epithelial cells.

REFERENCES

1. Cunha GR: Stromal induction and specification of morphogenesis and cytodifferentiation of the epithelia of the Mullerian ducts and urogenital sinus during development of the uterus and vagina in mice. J Exp Zool 196: 361–370,1976.
2. McNeal JE: Origin and evolution of benign prostatic enlargement. Invest Urol 15: 340–345,1978.
3. Mawhinney MG, Schwartz FL, Thomas JA, Belis JA, Lloyd JW: Androgen assimilation by the epithelium and muscle of the guinea pig seminal vesicle. J Pharmacol Exp Ther 188: 324–335,1974.
4. Schwartz FL, Mawhinney MG: Quantification of endogenous testosterone and dihydrotestosterone and their possible intracellular determinants in various tissues of the male guinea pig. J Steroid Biochem 8: 805–814,1977.
5. Belis JA, Blume CD, Mawhinney MG: Androgen and estrogen binding in male guinea pig accessory sex organs. Endocrinology 101: 726–740,1977.

6. Blume CD, Mawhinney MG: Estrophilic molecules in the male guinea pig. J Steroid Biochem 9: 515–525,1978.
7. Sirret DAN, Cowan SK, Janeczko AE, Grant JK, Glen ES: Prostatic tissue distribution of 17 β-hydroxy-5α-androstan-3-one and of androgen receptors in benign hyperplasia. J Steroid Biochem 13: 723--728,1980.
8. Cowan RA, Cook B, Cowan SK, Sirett DAN, Wallace AM: Testosterone 5α-reductase and the accumulation of dihydrotestosterone in benign prostatic hyperplasia. J Steroid Biochem 11: 609–613,1979.
9. Wilkin RP, Bruchovsky N, Shnitka TK, Rennie PS, Comeau TL: Stromal 5α-reductase activity is elevated in benign prostatic hyperplasia. Acta Endocrinol 94: 284–288,1980.
10. Bashirelahi N, Young J, Sanefugi H, Trump B: Androgen and estrogen receptor distribution in epithelial and stromal cells of human prostate. Fed Proc 37: 244,1978.
11. Leav I, Merk F, Ofner P, Goodrich G, Kwan P, Stein B, Sar M, Stumpf W: Biopotentiality of response to sex hormones by the prostate of castrated or hypophysectomized dogs. Am J Pathol 93: 69–92,1978.
12. DeKlerk DP, Coffey DS: Quantitative determination of prostatic epithelial and stromal hyperplasia by a new technique, biomorphometrics. Invest Urol 16: 240–245,1978.
13. Müntzing J: Androgen and collagen as growth regulators of the rat ventral prostate. The Prostate 1: 71–78, 1980.
14. Neubauer BL, Mawhinney MG: Actions of androgen and estrogen on guinea pig seminal vesicle epithelium and muscle. Endocrinology 108: 680–687,1980.
15. Levey HA, Szego CM: Metabolic characteristics of the guinea pig seminal vesicle. Am J Physiol 182: 507–512,1955.
16. Schneider WC: Determination of nucleic acids in tissues by pentose analysis. In Colowick S, Kaplan N (eds): "Methods in Enzymology," New York: Academic Press, vol. 3, 1957, pp 680–683.
17. Kivirikko KI, Laitinen O, Prockop DJ: Modifications of a specific assay for hydroxyproline in urine. Anal Biochem 19: 249–255,1967.

The Prostatic Cell: Structure and Function
Part A, pages 137–144

Collagen Synthesis and Breakdown in the Rat Ventral Prostate

J. Müntzing

INTRODUCTION

The importance of the fibromuscular stroma in prostate physiology is becoming increasingly clear. Embryologic studies have shown that the stroma has a crucial role in the differentiation of the epithelium in the developing prostate [1, 2]. Prostatic epithelium separated from the stroma has a very limited growth potential [3, 4]. The activity of 5α-reductase has been shown to be located predominantly in the stroma [5, 6]. It has also been proposed that the prostatic stroma is responsible for the growth limitation of the prostate [3, 7].

The component in the fibromuscular stroma responsible for the growth limitation could be the collagenous fibers. These fibers form the framework within the border of which the prostate can atrophy or grow dependent on the degree of androgen stimulation. Collagenous fibers have the mechanical strength to resist an enlargement of the growing prostate beyond a certain size [8]. This would result in a crowding of the prostatic epithelial cells forcing them to adopt a cell shape shown to be associated with a decrease in DNA synthesis and further proliferation [9].

The likelihood for the stromal collagen to function as a growth restraint for the prostate appeared to be reduced when it was shown that the prostatic collagen was as dependent on androgen as the epithelial cells [10, 11]. However, there seemed to be a possible explanation as to why the collagen content was reduced after orchiectomy and restored to normal by exogenous androgen while at the same time being able to function as a growth restraint for the prostate. This possible explanation was discussed recently, and a working hypothesis for the growth control of the prostate was proposed [10]. In the present communication this hypothesis is elaborated further, and experimental results supporting the hypothesis are presented.

WORKING HYPOTHESIS

The events at an androgen-induced regeneration of the atrophied prostate of orchiectomized rats start with a stimulation of the epithelial cells to division and secretion and with a stimulation of the fibroblasts in the stroma to produce collagen. The proliferation rate of the epithelial cells is more rapid than collagen synthesis. This leads to a gradual crowding of the epithelial cells forcing them to become high and cylindric. Such a cell shape is associated with decreased DNA synthesis and proliferation [9]. This would lead to a reduction of the growth rate of the prostate. The rate-limiting process in prostatic growth would be the secretion rate of collagen. Although the proliferation of the epithelial cells is hampered, their secretory activity is unimpaired. This leads to a gradual distension of the acini. This may in turn lead to a gradually increasing retrograde leakage into the stroma of a hypothetic collagenolytic enzyme secreted from the epithelial cells. Such retrograde leakage has been demonstrated for other prostatic enzymes such as acid phosphatase [12–14]. The collagenolytic enzyme leaked into the stroma starts to digest the collagen. As a consequence there is a gradually reduced net increase of prostatic collagen in spite of an unaltered high secretion of collagen from the fibroblasts. When a steady state between collagen production and breakdown is reached the prostate has reached its maximal size. This size can be increased only when the number of collagen-producing cells in the stroma is increased as a consequence of increasing age or of tissue damage and subsequent repair.

The situation at steady state when the prostate has reached its maximal size is illustrated by Figure 1. The fibroblast in the stroma is stimulated by androgen to produce collagen. This new collagen would have given the epithelial cells the necessary room for cell multiplication. At the same time, however, the epithelial cells are stimulated by the androgen to secrete a collagenolytic enzyme which through retrograde leakage digests as much collagen as is produced. Therefore, there are no cell divisions in the epithelium, but the gland size remains constant. There should be a fairly rapid turnover of the collagen.

After orchiectomy there would be no collagen synthesized by the fibroblasts in the stroma as they are not stimulated by androgen. At the same time there would be very little or no retrograde leakage of the collagenolytic enzyme as the secretion from the epithelial cells ceases. There should be a very low turnover of collagen in the atrophied prostate of orchiectomized animals.

In the regenerating prostate of orchiectomized androgen-treated animals the fibroblasts are stimulated to synthesize collagen. Although there is a secretion of the collagenolytic enzyme, only a little leaks retrograde, at least initially. This prostate should be characterized by a high collagen synthesis and a relatively low degradation resulting in a net increase of collagen.

This hypothesis would be supported if it could be shown that there was a collagenolytic enzyme in the prostate. Further support would be obtained if the

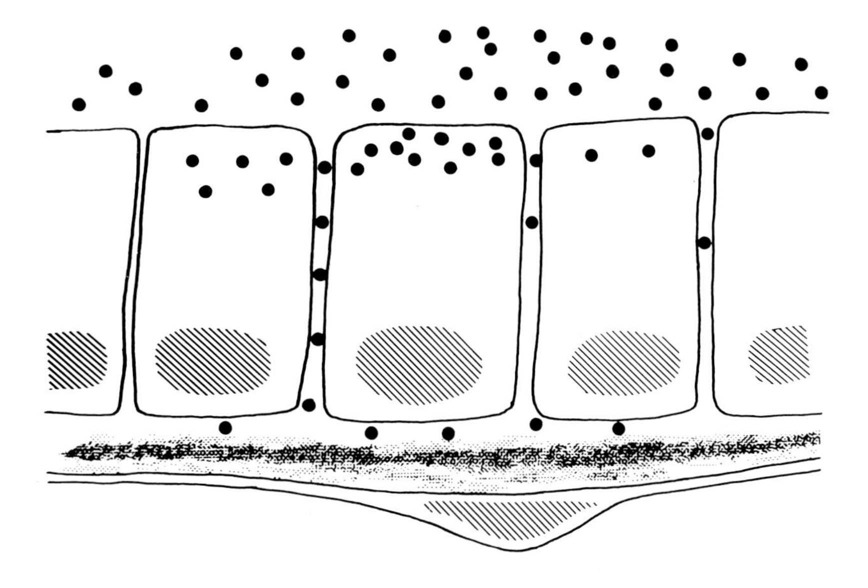

● Collagenase secreted from the epithelial cells

▧ Collagen produced by the fibroblasts.

Fig. 1. Epithelium and stroma in the fully developed rat ventral prostate. Androgen stimulates the fibroblasts to production of collagen which would have given the androgen-stimulated epithelial cells the necessary room for multiplication. The increase of collagen is counteracted by a breakdown of collagen through the action of a collagenolytic enzyme secreted from the epithelial cells. No cell divisions can occur in the epithelium in spite of the androgen stimulation and the gland size remains constant.

prostatic collagen turnover could be analyzed in intact, in orchiectomized, and in orchiectomized androgen-treated rats with the results found to be as proposed above. The results of such experiments are presented in this communication.

MATERIALS AND METHODS

The Collagenolytic Enzyme in the Prostate

The ventral prostates from six male Wistar SPF rats weighing 250–300 gm were dissected and weighed. Each prostate was homogenized in ice-cold TRIS-buffer, pH 3.5, containing Ca^{++}. The low pH was chosen based on results from pilot experiments and on results demonstrating that pH 3.5 was the optimum for the collagenolytic enzyme in the rat uterus [15]. The greater part of the homogenates were transferred to ice-cold incubation flasks and were then incubated at 37°C. Samples of the homogenates were taken before incubation and after incubation for 1, 2, and 4 hours. The remaining part of the homogenates was incubated at 0°C for 4 hours. After removal the samples were centrifuged. The centrifugates were hydrolysed with hydrochloric acid and the content of hydroxyproline, which is a way of estimating the content of collagen [16], was determined [16, 17].

The Collagen Turnover in the Prostate

Sixteen intact rats were divided at random into four groups. The animals were injected intravenously with 50 μCi of proline, L-[2,3-^{3}H], with a specific activity of 23.7 Ci/mmole (New England Nuclear). Proline is used for synthesis of proteins in general but especially for synthesis of collagen, in which proline is converted to hydroxyproline [8]. One, 2, 4, and 24 hours after injection the groups of animals were sacrificed. The radioactivity concentration in various organs including one lobe of the ventral prostate was analyzed. The other lobe of the ventral prostate was homogenized in ice-cold TRIS-buffer, pH 7.0, containing Ca^{++}. The prostatic collagenases and peptidases were destroyed by rapidly heating the homogenates to 95°C. Samples of the homogenates, which contained tritiated proteins including tritiated collagen, were then incubated for 2 hours at 37°C with and without the addition of an excess of highly purified bacterial collagenase essentially free of nonspecific protease activity (BDH Chemicals Ltd, Poole, England). After incubation the incubates were centrifuged and the radioactivity liberated by collagenase was calculated.

Similar experiments were performed using 1) rats which had been orchiectomized 14 days prior to the experiment; 2) rats which had been orchiectomized 21 days prior to the experiment and had received an injection of testosterone hexyloxyphenylpropionate, 100 mg/kg, 7 days prior to the experiment; and 3) intact rats which had received an injection of the testosterone ester 14 days prior to the experiment.

RESULTS

The Collagenolytic Enzyme in the Prostate

Incubation at 37°C of homogenates of the rat ventral prostate resulted in a gradual solubilisation of the prostatic collagen. Table I shows that there is gradually less collagen—as reflected by hydroxyproline—in the centrifugates. The enzymatic character of this solubilization of collagen is suggested by the unchanged amount of collagen in the centrifugates of the samples incubated at 0°C. Thus, these results indicate a high likelihood for the existence of a prostatic collagenolytic enzyme.

TABLE I. Hydroxyproline (HP) remaining undissolved after incubation of homogenates of rat ventral prostate

Incubation (hr)	Incubation temperature (°C)	Amount of HP, μg/mg of prostate after centrifugation of incubated homogenate
0	—	0.36 ± 0.02
1	37	0.33 ± 0.02
2	37	0.29 ± 0.03
4	37	0.20 ± 0.04
4	0	0.35 ± 0.03

The Collagen Turnover in the Prostate

In intact animals there was a high incorporation of tritiated proline into collagen already 1 hour after injection of the radiolabeled precursor (Table II). The radioactivity in collagen is approximately 25% of all the radioactivity in the prostate 1 hour after injection. There was a fairly rapid decrease of tritium-labeled collagen in the prostate of intact animals. There was no such decrease of the other radiolabeled proteins in the ventral prostate. The half-life of the radioactive collagen in the ventral prostate of intact rats is 12.8 hours. This result is in accord with the hypothesis which predicted a rapid turnover of prostatic collagen in intact rats.

The results from the intact animals contrast with the results from the orchiectomized animals. Here there was very little incorporation of tritiated proline into collagen. The little radioactivity that was incorporated was not diminished at all in 24 hours. Also this result is in accord with the aforementioned hypothesis. There is no androgenic stimulation of the fibroblasts to synthetize collagen, and there is no retrograde leakage of prostatic collagenases secreted from the epithelial cells and thus no collagen digestion.

When orchiectomized animals had been subjected to 7 days of androgen treatment, the prostate had started to regenerate. In those animals in which the prostate still was only one third of the normal size, collagen synthesis was fairly high. What is especially notable is the slow decrease of radiolabeled collagen. The half-life of the radiolabeled collagen is 23.5, hours which is practically twice as long as in intact animals. The difference is highly significant statistically. This result is also in accord with the hypothesis. In the regenerating prostate the fibroblasts are stimulated to synthesize collagen. The epithelial cells may synthesize and secrete the collagenolytic enzyme, but there is only little retrograde leakage. This means that the collagen breakdown is low as indicated by the long half-life for the radiolabeled collagen.

TABLE II. Incorporation of ^{3}H-proline in collagen of the rat ventral prostate

Hours after injection of ^{3}H-proline	^{3}H Liberated by collagenase, % of given dose per gm of ventral prostate			
	Intact animals	Orchiectomized animals	Orchiectomized androgen-treated animals	Intact androgen-treated animals
1	0.155 ± 0.019	0.014 ± 0.001	0.110 ± 0.010	0.153 ± 0.013
2	0.148 ± 0.018	0.009 ± 0.002	0.098 ± 0.016	0.124 ± 0.013
4	0.105 ± 0.018	0.012 ± 0.002	0.086 ± 0.010	0.092 ± 0.015
24	0.042 ± 0.005	0.013 ± 0.001	0.052 ± 0.007	0.040 ± 0.006

In the intact, androgen-treated animals there was a high rate of incorporation of tritiated proline into prostatic collagen and also a rapid decrease of radiolabeled collagen. The half-life is 12.8 hours, which is exactly the same value as in the intact untreated animals. Again, this result is in accord with the hypothesis. Obviously exogenous androgen did not increase collagen synthesis above the level already induced by the endogenous androgens.

DISCUSSION

The experimental results presented here provide support for the hypothesis that prostatic size is regulated by a feedback system resulting in a balance between collagen production and collagen breakdown in the prostate. Further support for the hypothesis may be given by a histochemical study of the basal membrane in the prostate of intact and of orchiectomized animals [18]. In that study it was shown that the basal membrane was much less dense in intact animals than in orchiectomized animals. This could be a morphologic correlate to the difference in collagen turnover in the prostate of intact and of orchiectomized animals.

So far the present studies have been restricted to the rat ventral prostate, and little is known about the collagen content and collagen turnover in other androgen-dependent organs or in the prostate of other species. However, if the hypothesis presented here is applicable also to the human prostate, it may contribute to an understanding of the role of the stroma in prostatic disease. In this context it should be mentioned that stromal induction or local stromal growth appears to be causal for the development of prostatic hyperplasia in man [19, 20]. It seems probable that an increased knowledge of the stromal-epithelial interaction in the prostate would give us the possibility of developing completely new methods of influencing the carcinomatous and noncarcinomatous growth of the prostate.

CONCLUSIONS

In the fully grown rat, ventral prostate collagen synthesis from the fibroblasts is stimulated by androgen. As no accumulation of collagen occurs, the collagen synthesis is balanced by a breakdown of collagen. The breakdown appears to be caused by a collagenolytic enzyme secreted from the epithelial cells. The unaltered content of collagen constitutes a physical barrier for the epithelial cells. This barrier leads to a crowding of the epithelial cells, and the crowding leads to a cessation of DNA synthesis in spite of a continuous androgen stimulation of the epithelial cells. Thus, prostatic size in intact animals appears to be determined by the content of collagen.

ACKNOWLEDGMENTS

The skillful technical assistance by Ms Inger Persson is gratefully acknowledged.

REFERENCES

1. Cunha GR: Epithelial-stromal interactions in development of the urogenital tract. Int Rev Cytol 47:137–194, 1977.
2. Cunha GR, Lung B: The importance of stroma in morphogenesis and functional activity of urogenital epithelium. In Vitro 15:50–71, 1979.
3. Franks LM, Riddle PN, Carbonell AW, Gey GO: A comparative study of the ultrastructure and lack of growth capacity of adult human prostate epithelium mechanically separated from its stroma. J Pathol 100:113–119, 1970.
4. Stone KR, Stone MP, Paulson DF: In vitro cultivation of prostatic epithelium. Invest Urol 14:79–82, 1976.
5. Cowan RA, Cowan SK, Grant JK, Elder HY: Biochemical investigations of separated epithelium and stroma from benign hyperplastic prostatic issue. J Endocrinol 74:111–120, 1977.
6. Wilkin RP, Bruchovsky N, Shnitka TK, Rennie PS, Comeau TL: Stromal 5α-reductase activity is elevated in benign prostatic hyperplasia. Acta Endocrinol (Kbh) 94:284–288, 1980.
7. Müntzing J, Liljekvist J, Murphy GP: Chalones and stroma as possible growth-limiting factors in the rat ventral prostate. Invest Urol 16:399–402, 1979.
8. Bailey AJ: The nature of collagen. In Florkin M, Stotz EH (eds): "Comparative Biochemistry." Amsterdam, London, New York: Elsevier, vol 26B, 1968, p 297.
9. Folkman J, Moscona M: Role of cell shape in growth. Nature 273:345–349, 1978.
10. Müntzing J: Androgen and collagen as growth regulators of the rat ventral prostate. The Prostate 1:71–78, 1980.
11. Mariotti A, Thornton M, Mawhinney M: Actions of androgen and estrogen on collagen levels in male accessary sex organs. Endocrinol, 1981 (in press).
12. Reiner L, Rutenburg AM, Seligman AM: Acid phosphatase activity in human neoplasms. Cancer 10:563–576, 1957.
13. Müntzing J, Nilsson T: Enzyme activity and distribution in the hyperplastic and cancerous human prostate. Scand J Urol Nephrol 6:107–111, 1972.
14. Wajsman Z, Chu TM: Detection and diagnosis of prostatic cancer. In Murphy GP (ed): "Prostatic Cancer." Littleton: PSG Publishing Co, 1979, p 111.
15. Woessner JF: Catabolism of collagen and non-collagen protein in the rat uterus during post-partum involution. Biochem J 83:304–314, 1962.
16. Neuman RE, Logan MA: The determination of hydroxyproline. J Biol Chem 184:299–306, 1950.
17. Leach AA: Notes on a modification of the Neuman and Logan method for the determination of the hydroxyproline. Biochem J 74:70–71, 1960.
18. Arcadi JA: Role of the ground substance in atrophy of normal and malignant prostatic issue following estrogen administration and orchiectomy. J Clin Endocrinol Metab 14:1113–1125, 1954.
19. Pradhan BK, Chandra K: Morphogenesis of nodular hyperplasia–prostate. J Urol 113:210–213, 1975.
20. McNeal JE: Origin and evolution of benign prostatic enlargement. Invest Urol 15:340–345, 1978.

The Prostatic Cell: Structure and Function
Part A, pages 145–159

Physiology of Castration-Induced Regression in Rat Prostate

Chung Lee

INTRODUCTION

It is well known that the prostate is dependent on the presence of testicular hormones for maintenance of its structural and functional integrity [1, 2]. Withdrawal of this hormonal support, as by orchiectomy, results in dramatic metabolic changes leading to a rapid rate of tissue involution in the prostate. The nature of histologic changes associated with prostatic involution has been documented in considerable detail [3–5]. Biochemically, prostatic regression has been associated with an overall decline of metabolic activities [6–8]. DNA synthesis in the prostate of rats ceases soon after orchiectomy [9]. Rates of tissue respiration and protein synthesis in the prostate decrease drastically by castration. As a consequence, biochemical constituents, such as DNA, RNA, and protein contents, decrease rapidly in a regressing prostate.

Thus, it would appear that castration-induced prostatic involution seems to be a simple biologic phenomenon which is the direct result of the cessation or slowing down of the anabolic activities in the prostatic tissue in the absence of testicular hormones. The requirement of an active metabolic process for tissue atrophy in a regressing prostate was first postulated by Bruchovsky and associates [10] in 1975. This concept was developed based on the observation that the rapid rate of cell loss in a regressing prostate could not be accounted for by a normal cell turnover rate which was only 8% in 3 days.

In an attempt to identify the active metabolic component during tissue involution, we studied various metabolic events associated with castration-induced regression in the rat prostate. This report summarizes our findings.

MATERIALS AND METHODS

Adult male Sprague Dawley rats, weighing 275–325 gm were used in this study. They were orchiectomized transcrotally under ether anesthesia. At different intervals following orchiectomy, animals were sacrificed by decapitation and the prostates were dissected and weighed. Tissue protein contents were measured according to the method of Lowry [11]; and contents of DNA and RNA were determined by the procedure recommended by Munro and Fleck [12].

In Vitro ^{3}H-Leucine Incorporation by Prostatic Tissue [13]

Upon removal from the animals, ventral prostates were placed in a petri dish containing medium 199 (GIBCO, Grand Island, NY) and cut with a scalpel into 2-mm^3 pieces. The tissue pieces (20–30 mg) were transferred into a 25-ml Erlenmeyer culture flask containing 4 ml of medium 199 which was supplemented with 2 μCi of 4,5-^{3}H-leucine (57.4 Ci/mmole, New England Nuclear, Boston, MA). The mixture was incubated at 37°C for 1 hour under an atmosphere of 95% O_2 and 5% CO_2. After the incubation, the reaction was stopped by adding into the incubation mixture 4 ml of 10% trichloroacetic acid. The radioactivity in the protein fraction of the incubated tissue was measured by liquid scintillation counting and was expressed in cpm per mg protein per hour.

In Vivo ^{3}H-Leucine Release From Prostatic Protein [14]

The rate of protein degradation was studied using a pulse labeling technique by intravenously injecting physiologic saline solution containing ^{3}H-leucine (15 μCi/100 gm body weight) in animals 1 day prior to orchiectomy. Intact control animals received sham operation. The amount of radioactivity remaining in the protein fraction of the prostate was expressed in cpm/prostate.

In Vitro ^{3}H-Uridine Incorporation by Prostatic Tissue [13]

Prostatic tissues were cut into 2-mm^3 pieces and incubated in 4 ml of medium 199 containing 4 μCi of 5,6-^{3}H-uridine (37.6 Ci/mmole, New England Nuclear) plus 0.4 mg of unlabeled uridine (Sigma Chemical Co., St. Louis, MO) at 37°C for 1 hour under 95% O_2 and 5% CO_2. The reaction was stopped by adding into the incubation mixture 4 ml of 0.2 N perchloric acid. The radioactivity in the RNA fraction was expressed in cpm per μg RNA or per μg DNA.

Determination of Acid Ribonuclease in Rat Prostate [15]

The activity of acid ribonuclease in the prostate was measured according to the method of Takahashi [16] with minor modifications. Briefly, the prostatic tissue was homogenized in saline solution containing 0.1% Triton X-100. The supernatant fraction of this homogenate was then incubated in sodium acetate buffer, pH 4.5, containing water-soluble RNA as the substrate. The incubation was carried at 37°C for 15 minutes in a shaker-incubator. The reaction was stopped by 25% perchloric acid containing 0.75% uranyl acetate. An increase in 0.001 in absorbance at 260 nm was defined as 1 unit (U) of enzyme activity. And the activity was expressed in U/mg protein.

Determination of Cathepsin D in Rat Prostate [17]

Cathepsin D activity was measured according to the method of Anson [18] as modified by Ferguson et al [19]. Briefly, tissue homogenates were incubated in sodium acetate buffer, pH 3.7, containing 2.5% of double crystallized bovine hemoglobin (Sigma Chemical Co.) at 39°C for 30 minutes in a shaker-incubator. The reaction was stopped by adding 10% trichloroacetic acid. One unit of cathepsin D was defined as an increment of 0.001 absorbance at 280 nm. Results were expressed in units per mg tissue, per mg protein, or per μg DNA.

Administration of Actinomycin D, Cycloheximide, and Chloroquine to Rats [15, 17, 20]

Actinomycin D (Cosmegen, Merk, Sharp, and Dohme, West Point, PA) was injected into animals subcutaneously at a dose of 50 μg per rat in 0.2 ml of sterile saline. Cycloheximide (Sigma Chemical Co.) was administered as subcutaneous injections at 100 μg per 100 gm body weight. Treatments of actinoymcin D or cycloheximide began on the day of orchiectomy and continued daily for 4 more days. The control animals received injections of saline solution. Rats were sacrificed 24 hours after the last injection and the ventral prostates were dissected and weighed.

Chloroquine phosphate (Winthrop Laboratories, New York, NY) was dissolved in distilled water and was given to animals by gastric tube at a dose of 75 mg per kg body weight for 4 consecutive days beginning 1 day before orchiectomy. The control animals received an equal amount of water. Rats were sacrificed 7 days after orchiectomy and the ventral prostates were removed and weighed.

Statistical Analysis [21]

All numeric values were expressed in mean ± SEM. Analysis of variance test and Duncan's multiple range test were employed to compare the differences in values resulting from different treatments in each experiment.

RESULTS

Figure 1 summarizes the results on the wet weight, protein, RNA, and DNA content of the three lobes of the prostate at different intervals following orchiectomy [22]. The DNA content in these lobes decreased at a slower rate than did the wet weight, RNA, and protein. This relationship indicates that there is a loss in cell number as well as in cell volume. Another interesting observation is that the three lobes regressed at different rates; the ventral prostate regressed the most rapidly while the dorsal prostate the least. Basically, the pattern of prostatic regression can be defined by three stages [8]. The first stage is 0–2 days

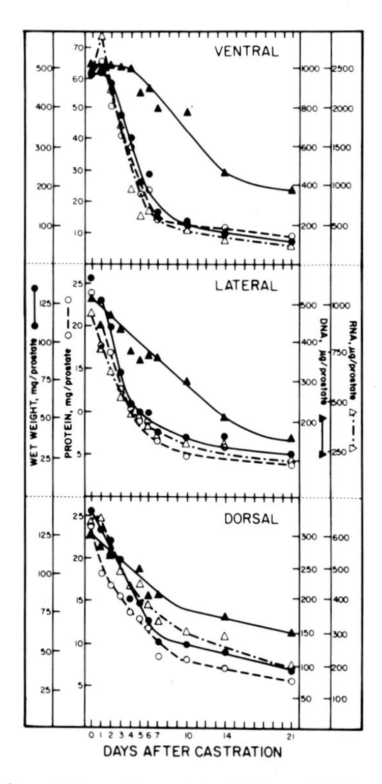

Fig. 1. Changes in prostatic weights and in protein, RNA, and DNA contents in the ventral, lateral, and dorsal lobes of the prostate in rats at different intervals postcastration. Each point represents the average value of at least five observations.

postcastration, during which the wet weight and gross chemical constituents were within the normal ranges. At 3–6 days, the second stage, prostatic weights, protein, and RNA contents decreased rapidly. In the ventral prostate, for example, the daily loss of wet weight averaged 100 mg. The period after day 7 is the third stage during which the rate of decline in the above parameters slowed markedly. The ventral prostate was used in the following experiments because, among the three lobes, it showed the most extensive rate of involution.

Protein Synthesis and Degradation in Regressing Prostate [13, 14]

The rate of protein synthesis in the regressing prostate, as indicated by the rate of in vitro incorporation of ^{3}H-leucine, is presented in Figure 2. The prostate in the intact, sham-operated animals maintained a constant rate of protein synthesis while that in the orchiectomized rats declined steadily. However, in view of the rapid rate of protein loss in the regressing prostate, this gradual decline

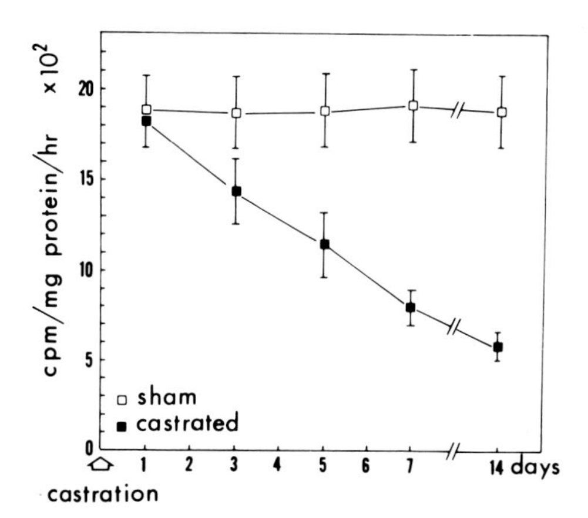

Fig. 2. Incorporation of ^{3}H-leucine into the protein fraction by the prostatic tissues after 1-hour incubation in medium 199 containing ^{3}H-leucine. Each point is the average of six observations. The vertical bars denote standard deviation.

in protein synthesis does not seem to be able to account for a loss of about 12 mg of protein per day.

The pattern of protein degradation in the regressing prostate is studied by measuring the amount of radioactivity remaining in the prostate following a pulse labeling of ^{3}H-leucine. The rationale and experimental measures justifying the use of this pulse-labeling procedure have been described by Bockrath [23]. Figure 3 shows that, during the first 6 days postcastration, the prostates of castrated animals lost more labeled proteins than those of the intact animals. The decay curves could be converted to straight lines on a logarithmic scale. The half-life thus calculated for the castrated rat prostate is 1.8 days; for the intact rat prostate it is 3.4 days, and the difference is statistically significant. The observation of the excess loss of prostatic protein in castrated rats is further confirmed by a reduction in protein loss following testosterone replacement therapy to the castrated animals. Therefore, it is concluded that the accelerated rate of protein loss during the period of rapid tissue involution is a combined effect of a reduced rate of protein synthesis and an increased rate of protein degradation.

^{3}H-Uridine Incorporation in Regressing Prostate [13]

Figure 4 shows that the rate of ^{3}H-uridine incorporation into the RNA fraction of the ventral prostate increased following castration. Autoradiographic studies have demonstrated that the radiosensitive granules were over the nuclei of prostatic epithelial cells. However, this apparent increase in the specific activity of RNA is probably due to a marked reduction in the total RNA content in the regressing prostate because when the same data were expressed on the basis of

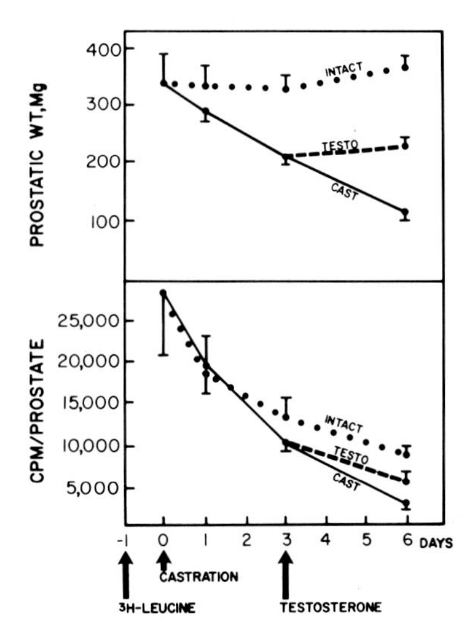

Fig. 3. Changes in prostatic weight and in total radioactivity in the prostatic protein following a pulse injection ^{3}H-leucine one day prior to castration. Intact animals received sham operation. Testosterone was given as a subcutaneous implant of silastic capsule containing 2 cm of crystalline testosterone. Each point is the average of at least three observations. The vertical bars denote standard error.

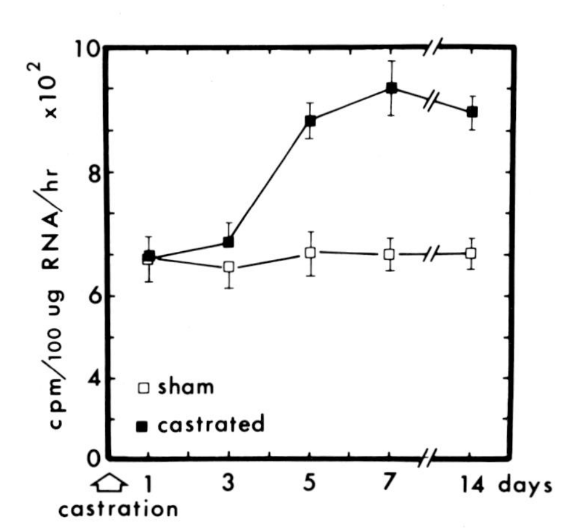

Fig. 4. Incorporation of ^{3}H-uridine into the RNA fraction of the rat prostate after 1-hour incubation in medium 199 containing ^{3}H-uridine. Each point is the average of eight observations. The vertical bars denote standard error of the mean.

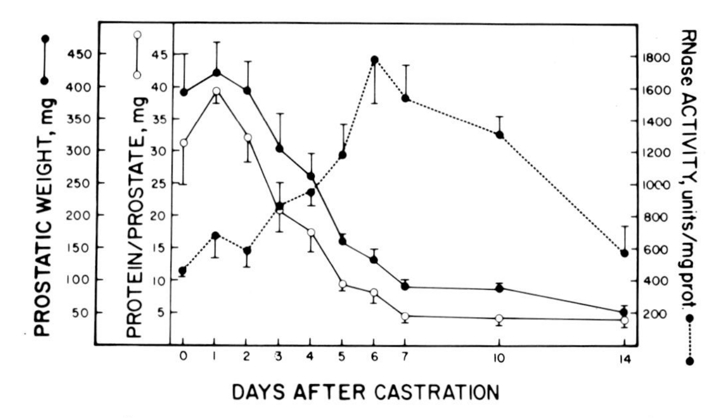

Fig. 5. Temporal changes in wet weight, protein, and acid ribonuclease activity of the ventral prostate in rats at different intervals postcastration. The unit of the enzyme is defined in Materials and Methods. Points on each date represent the average of five observations. The vertical bars denote standard error of the mean.

DNA content, the rate of incorporation in the regressing prostate was lower than that in the unregressed tissue. Nevertheless, over a period of 14 days postcastration, this value was maintained at 67–88% of the control values, while the wet weight and the rate of ^{3}H-leucine incorporation reduced to 11% and 20%, respectively. Therefore, the relative rate of synthesis of RNA seems greater compared to other metabolic processes in the regressing prostate.

Acid Ribonuclease in Regressing Prostate [15]

The observation that an active RNA synthesis occurs coupled with a rapid decrease in the total RNA content in the regressing prostate suggested that cellular apparatus capable of rapid RNA destruction must be responsible for this net result. Figure 5 illustrates the activity of acid ribonuclease in the rat prostate at different intervals following castration. The specific activity (U/mg protein) was relatively low in the prostate of noncastrated rats. The enzyme activity increased after castration, reached a maximal level between 5–7 days, and decreased afterward to the precastration level by 14 days. Thus, the occurrence of an elevated activity of acid ribonuclease coincided with the period of a rapid decline in the total RNA content in the regressing prostate.

Cathepsin D in Regressing Prostate [17]

Table I shows the cathepsin D activity in the prostate and in the liver of intact and 7-day castrated rats. Castration resulted in an increase in activities of cathepsin D in the prostate but not in the liver. In another study [24], activities of cathepsin D in the prostate exhibited a pattern of change similar to that of acid

TABLE I. Effect of orchiectomy on the activity of cathepsin D in the rat prostate and liver

	Intact rats	7-Day castrated rats
Body weight (gm)	338 ± 3 (7)	329 ± 2 (50)
Prostate weight (mg)	495 ± 24 (7)[a]	119 ± 5 (50)
Cathepsin D in prostate		
per mg of tissue	0.84 ± 0.32 (7)[a]	7.63 ± 0.74 (20)
per mg of protein	14.3 ± 6.0 (7)[a]	80.7 ± 10.7 (10)
per μg of DNA	0.45 ± 0.17 (7)[a]	3.74 ± 0.58 (10)
Cathepsin D in liver		
per mg of tissue	10.1 ± 0.94 (4)	8.8 ± 0.85 (5)

Values are mean ± SEM (number of observations).
[a]Value is significantly different from that of 7-day castrated rats ($P < 0.01$).

ribonuclease following castration of the animals. Thus, elevated activities of cathepsin D also coincided with the period of rapid prostatic regression.

Partial Inhibition of Castration-Induced Prostatic Regression by Actinomycin D and Cycloheximide [15, 24]

Table II shows the effect of treatment with actinomycin D on the prostatic weights and serum levels of testosterone in castrated rats, intact rats, and castrated testosterone-treated rats. Actinomycin D caused a reduction of prostatic weights in both intact animals and castrated testosterone-treated animals but caused a partial inhibition of prostatic involution in castrated rats. Although serum testosterone levels were suppressed by actinomycin D in the intact animals, the castrated testosterone-treated animals had the same serum levels of testosterone in the actinomycin-injected group as in the water-injected controls. This observation demonstrates that the dose of actinomycin D was effective in inhibiting the prostatic anabolic activities which is probably also responsible for the inhibition of prostatic involution. This concept is further supported by the observation that actinomycin D administration suppressed in otherwise elevated activities of acid ribonuclease and cathepsin D (Table III).

The effect of cycloheximide on the prostatic weights of castrated rats is shown in Table IV. Like the action of actinomycin D, cycloheximide also partially inhibited the castration-induced regression of the rat prostate.

Partial Inhibition of Castration-Induced Prostatic Regression by Chloroquine [17]

Table V shows that chloroquine feeding resulted in an inhibition of prostatic involution by 17.6%. The concentrations of RNA, DNA, and protein in the

TABLE II. Effect of treatment with actinomycin D (Act-D) for 5 days on the prostatic weight and serum testosterone levels in castrated, intact, and castrated testosterone-treated rats

	Number of rats	Prostatic weight (gm)	Serum testosterone (ng/100 ml)
Castrated rats			
water group	5	118 ± 20[b]	19 ± 9
Act-D group[a]	5	191 ± 28	20 ± 14
Intact sham-operated rats			
water group	5	440 ± 26[c]	332 ± 15[c]
Act-D group[a]	4	270 ± 19	38 ± 3
Castrated testosterone-treated rats			
water group	5	490 ± 21[c]	418 ± 21
Act-D group[a]	5	310 ± 25	416 ± 58

Values are mean ± SEM.

[a]Actinomycin D was given daily for 5 days at 50 μg/day. In the castrated rats and sham-operated rats, the drug treatment started on the day of surgery. In the castrated testosterone-treated rats, a silastic capsule containing 4 cm of crystalline testosterone was implanted to each rat immediately following orchiectomy. Actinomycin D treatment started 3 weeks later.

[b]Value is significantly different from that of the Act-D group ($P < 0.05$).

[c]Value is significantly different from that of the Act-D group ($P < 0.01$).

TABLE III. Effect of actinomycin D on the wet weight, acid ribonuclease, and cathepsin D in the prostate of castrated rats

	Number of rats	Prostatic weight (gm)	Acid ribonuclease (U/mg protein)	Cathepsin D (U/mg protein)
Water group	5	154 ± 14[a]	1120 ± 45[a]	17.7 ± 1.3[a]
Act-D group	4	212 ± 18	390 ± 28	10.7 ± 1.3

Subcutaneous injection of actinomycin D (50 μg/day) or water were given for 5 days, beginning on the day of orchiectomy.

Values are mean ± SEM.

[a]Value is significantly different from that of the Act-D group ($P < 0.01$).

prostate were similar in both the chloroquine-treated group and the water-fed controls. The greater prostatic weight in the chloroquine-treated animals was thus attributable to a greater number of cells rather than a similar number of larger cells. Furthermore, the cathepsin D activity in the prostate of chloroquine-treated animals was three times greater than that of the water-fed control animals. The observation of an elevated cathepsin D activity by chloroquine feeding was substantiated by the results of electron microscopic studies. Figure 6 shows the

TABLE IV. Effect of cycloheximide on castration-induced prostatic regression in rats

	Number of rats	Prostate (mg)
Intact, sham-operated rats, saline injected	5	202 ± 27
5-Day postcastrated rats, saline injected	5	63 ± 7
5-Day postcastrated rats, cycloheximide injected	10	101 ± 6

Cycloheximide (100 μg/100 gm/body weight/0.2 ml/day) or saline injection were given subcutaneously for 5 days beginning on the day of castration or sham operation.
Values are mean ± SEM and are significantly different from one another (P < 0.01).

TABLE V. Effect of chloroquine feeding to castrated rats on wet weight and cathepsin D activity in the prostate

	Water-treated group	Chloroquine-treated group
Prostate weight (mg)	119 ± 5 (50)[a]	140 ± 5 (51)
mg protein/gm of tissue	77 ± 4 (19)	71 ± 4 (20)
mg RNA/gm of tissue	3.9 ± 0.3 (10)	3.6 ± 0.3 (10)
mg DNA/gm of tissue	2.6 ± 0.2 (19)	2.6 ± 0.2 (20)
Cathepsin D, U/mg protein	80.7 ± 11 (10)[a]	242.8 ± 30 (10)

Chloroquine phosphate was suspended in distilled water and administered to animals by gastric tube at a dose of 75 mg/kg body weight. Control animals received equal amounts of distilled water. The drug was given daily for 5 days beginning one day prior to castration. All animals were sacrificed 7 days postcastration, and ventral prostates were removed for analysis.
Values are mean ± SEM (number of observations).
[a]Value is significantly different from that in the chloroquine-treated group (P < 0.01).

electron microscopy of prostatic cells in chloroquine-treated (Fig. 6A) and in water fed (Fig. 6B) animals. The most significant difference between these two tissues is the size and number of the dense bodies or lysosomes. The prostates from chloroquine-treated animals had more and larger dense bodies than those in the water-fed controls.

DISCUSSION

In considering the phenomenon of tissue involution or tissue growth, the following relationship holds true:

$$\text{Synthesis} > \text{Degradation} \rightarrow \text{Tissue growth}$$
$$\text{Synthesis} = \text{Degradation} \rightarrow \text{Tissue maintenance}$$
$$\text{Synthesis} < \text{Degradation} \rightarrow \text{Tissue involution}$$

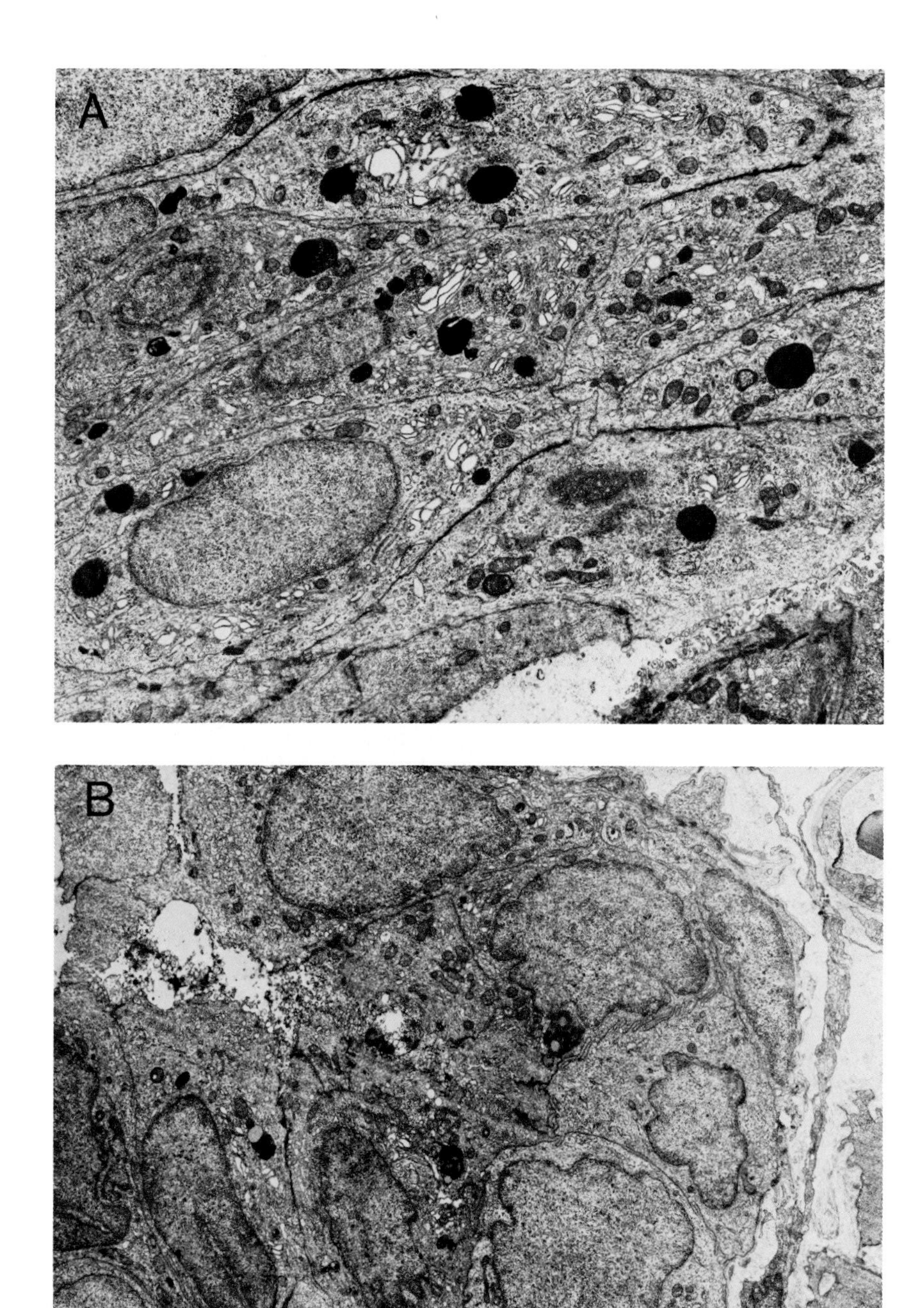

Fig. 6. Electron microscopy of prostatic epithelial cells in 7-day castrated rats treated with chloroquine (A) or with water (B). Note the difference in the number and size of the dense bodies. ×3800.

Therefore, it is reasonable to state that both processes of degradation and synthesis play equally important roles in tissue growth as well as in tissue involution. It is obvious that, while some of the synthetic processes are contributing to tissue growth, others are eventually contributing to the degradative process. The synthesis of degradative enzymes, for example, qualifies for the latter category.

Results of our present study support the above view and a hypothetical relationship between the processes of synthesis and degradation can be postulated. Figure 7 depicts that, during the period of active prostatic regression, a decreased rate of protein synthesis coupled with an increased rate of protein degradation leads to a rapid loss of prostatic protein. Our observations of elevated activities of acid ribonuclease and cathepsin D and those of increased rates of release of leucine from the protein fraction of the regressing prostates provide evidence to support the concept of the existence of an increased rate of degradation during the period of active tissue involution.

We further postulate that the increased rate of degradation during prostatic regression is, at least in part, attributable to increased rates of an active synthesis. Couch and Anderson [25] could not explain a higher template activity in the prostatic chromatin of 3-day castrated rats than that in the intact animals. Again, our observations of a relative active uridine incorporation and the partial inhibition of prostatic involution by actinomycin D or cycloheximide provide supportive evidence to indicate that active synthetic processes are required to achieve the maximal rate of tissue involution. In this connection, the process of protein synthesis in a prostate can be divided into two components. One component is represented by those processes leading to protein accumulation and tissue growth and is probably reduced to a minimal activity in a regressing prostate. The other component results in synthesis of proteins responsible for tissue involution and

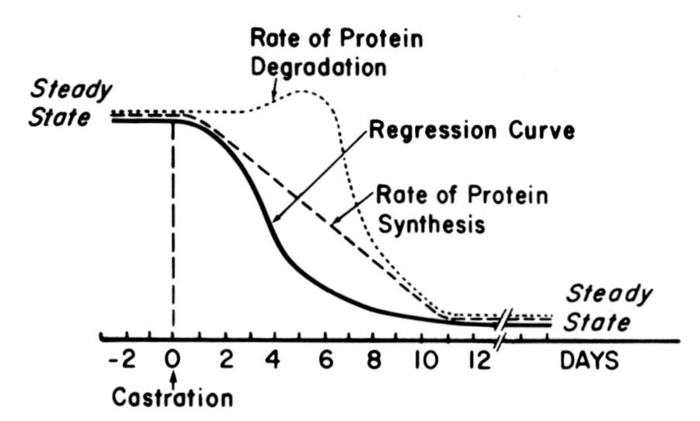

Fig. 7. A hypothetical presentation of metabolic events associated with castration-induced regression in the rat prostate. Two levels of the steady state represent the equal degrees of degradation and synthesis in the prostate before castration and after regression reaches completion. During the period of active tissue involution (days 2–6) the regression curve is the combined effect of an increased rate of degradation and a decreased rate of synthesis.

is probably more active than usual in a regressing prostate. Thus, during prostatic involution, a selection process seems to be in operation to permit the synthesis of a few species of proteins but not others for the purpose of facilitating tissue degradation.

The observation of a partial inhibition of prostatic involution by chloroquine feeding offers further insight into the mechanism of this regression phenomenon. Unlike the effect of actinomycin D which inhibits prostatic regression by suppressing the level of degradative enzymes, chloroquine inhibits regression despite causing an accumulation of degradative enzymes in the tissue. Histologic studies by Brandes [4] and Helminen and Ericsson [26] indicate that prostatic involution is largely attributable to bulk degradation by lysosomes. Assuming that lysosomal enzymes are consumed during digestion of the substrate, an increase in stability of lysosomal membrane by chloroquine renders the cellular constituents unavailable for lysosomal enzymes to digest, thereby leading to an elevated enzyme activity. These lines of reasoning are supported by an increase in the number and size of dense bodies in the prostate of chloroquine-treated animals.

In conclusion, it is clear that the sequence of events during prostatic involution can be described by the identifiable stages and illustrated in Figure 8. A successful achievement of tissue involution requires the involvement of all of these steps. Upon receiving the signal of androgen withdrawal, the prostatic cells undergo a series of preparations which reduce the processes that would lead to tissue growth and increase the processes that would lead to tissue involution. Associated with this process is the synthesis of degradative enzymes. If synthesis of these enzymes is blocked by agents like actinomycin D or cycloheximide, activities of enzymes would be reduced and tissue involution would be retarded. Furthermore, if the mechanism of protein synthesis is permitted to proceed but the enzymes are prevented from interacting with the cellular substrate by agents like chloroquine, prostatic involution would also be inhibited, resulting in a tissue accumulation of these enzymes.

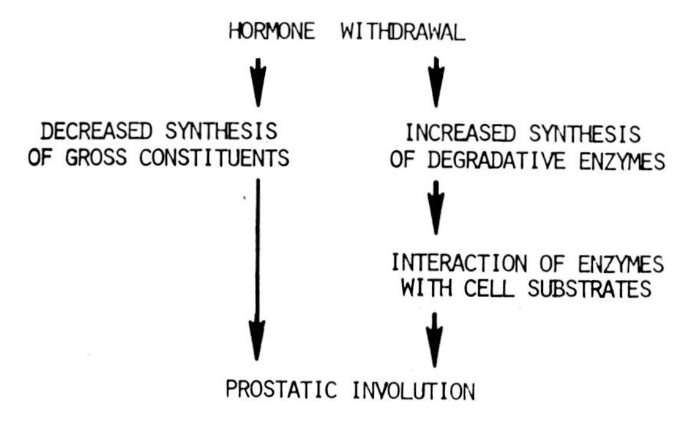

Fig. 8. Identifiable metabolic events associated with castration-induced regression in rat prostate.

It should be pointed out that this diagram represents only a tentative hypothesis. It is expected that this scheme will be revised as new information is generated. At the present state, it appears that the process of castration-induced regression in the rat prostate involves an active catabolic process which results from an active synthetic process and that these processes are modifiable by nonhormonal agents.

ACKNOWLEDGMENTS

The author would like to thank Dr. John T. Grayhack for his encouragement and support of this work and especially for his critical comments on this manuscript.

This study is supported by NIH grant HD 11611, by the Edwin and Lucy Kretschmer Fund of Northwestern University Medical School, and by a grant from the Grainger Foundation.

REFERENCES

1. Butler WWS, Schade AL: The effect of castration and androgen replacement on the nucleic acid composition, metabolism and enzymatic capacity of the rat ventral prostate. Endocrinology 63:271–279, 1958.
2. Ofner P: Effects and metabolism of hormones in normal and neoplastic prostatic tissue. Vit Horm 26:237–291, 1968.
3. Moore CR, Price D, Gallagner TF: Rat prostate cytology as a testis-hormone indicator and the prevention of castration changes by testis-extract injection. Am J Anat 45:71–98, 1930.
4. Brandes D: The fine structure and histochemistry of prostatic glands in relation of sex hormones. Int Rev Cytol 20:207–276, 1966.
5. MacKenzie AR, Hall T, Lo MC, Whitmore WF: Influence of castration and sex hormones on size, histology, and zinc content of canine prostate. J Urol 89:864–874, 1963.
6. Huggins C: The prostatic secretion. Harvey Lectures 42:148–193, 1947.
7. Williams-Ashman HG, Liao S, Hancock RL, Jurkowitz L, Silverman DA: Testicular hormones and the synthesis of ribonucleic acids and proteins in the prostatic gland. Rec Prog Horm Res 20:247–292, 1964.
8. Lesser B, Bruchovsky N: Effect of duration of period after castration on the response of the rat ventral prostate to androgen. Biochem J 149:429–431, 1974.
9. Sufrin G, Coffey DS: A new model for studying the effect of drugs on prostatic growth. I. Antiandrogens and DNA synthesis. Invest Urol 11:45–54, 1973.
10. Bruchovsky N, Lesser B, VanDoorn E, Craven S: Hormonal effects on cell proliferation in rat prostate. Vit Horm 33:61–102, 1975.
11. Lowry OH, Rosebrough NJ, Farr AL, and Randall RJ: Protein measurement with the Folin phenol reagent. J Biol Chem 193:265–275, 1951.
12. Munro HN, Fleck A: The determination of nucleic acids. Meth Biochem Analysis 14:113–176, 1966.
13. Stanisic T, Sadlowski R, Lee C, Grayhack JT: Elevated rate of ^{3}H-uridine incorporation in regressing rat ventral prostate. Invest Urol 16:15–18, 1978.
14. Lee C, Kolbusz WE, Diamond CA: Protein synthesis and degradation in regressing rat prostate. Twelfth Annual Meeting of the Society for the Study of Reproduction, Quebec City, Canada. August 21–24, 1979.
15. Engel G, Lee C, Grayhack JT: Acid ribonuclease in rat prostate during castration-induced involution. Biol Reprod 22:827–831, 1980.

16. Takahashi K: The structure and function of ribonuclease T_1. Chromatographic purification and properties of ribonuclease T_1. J Biol Chem 49:1–10, 1961.
17. Sharer WC, Lee C, Grayhack JT: Partial inhibition of castration-induced involution in rat prostate by chloroquine. A preliminary observation. Invest Urol 17:135–137, 1979.
18. Anson ML: The estimation of pepsin, trypsin, papain, and cathepsin with hemoglobin. J Gen Physiol 22:79–89, 1938.
19. Ferguson JB, Andrews JR, Voynick IM, Fruton JS: The specificity of cathepsin D. J Biol Chem 248:6701–6708, 1973.
20. Stanisic T, Sadlowski R, Lee C, Grayhack JT: Partial inhibition of castration induced ventral prostate regression with actinomycin D and cycloheximide. Invest Urol 16:19–22, 1978.
21. Steel RED, Torrie JH: Principles and Procedures of Statistics. New York: McGraw-Hill, 1960.
22. Lee C, Anderson R, Zuk A, Holland JM: Differing rates of regression in three lobes of rat prostate following orchiectomy. Fifth Annual Meeting for the American Society of Andrology, Chicago, Illinois. March 11–14, 1980.
23. Bockrath JM: Incorporation and release of tritiated leucine in rat prostate during castration-induced involution. Seventy-sixth Annual Meeting of the American Urological Association, Boston, Massachusetts, May 10–14, 1981.
24. Tanabe E, Grayhack JT: Activities of cathepsin D in rat prostate during castration-induced involution. Thirteenth Annual Meeting of the Society for the Study of Reproduction, Ann Arbor, Michigan, August 12–15, 1980.
25. Couch RM, Anderson KM: Rat ventral prostate chromatin. Effect of androgens on its chemical composition, physical properties, and template activity. Biochemistry 12:3114–3121, 1973.
26. Helminen HJ, Ericsson JLE: Ultrastructural studies on prostatic involution in the rat. Mechanism of autophagy in epithelial cells, with special reference to rough-surfaced endoplasmic reticulum. J Ultrastruct Res 36:708–724, 1971.

The Prostatic Cell: Structure and Function
Part A, pages 161–175

Partial Characterization of Stromal and Epithelial Forms of 5α-Reductase in Human Prostate

N. Bruchovsky, M.G. McLoughlin, P.S. Rennie, and M.P. To

Using tissue recombinant experiments, Cuhna and co-workers [1–3] and Lasnitzki and Mizuno [4–6] have demonstrated that the mesenchyme is essential for both the in vivo and in vitro morphogenesis of rodent prostate. McNeal has speculated that the inductive potential of the mesenchyme may be re-expressed in adult life during the evolution of benign prostatic hyperplasia (BPH) [7,8] in male human beings. The influence of the mesenchyme on normal and abnormal prostatic growth hinges in part on the ability of such tissue to form dihydrotestosterone owing to the presence of 5α-reductase [9–11]. This trait is especially pronounced in hyman prostate where the bulk of the enzyme is localized in stroma [9,11]; indeed, the relevance of mesenchymal processes in the pathogenesis of BPH is underlined by the recent finding of Wilkin et al [12] that stromal 5α-reductase activity is abnormally high in BPH. It has been inferred that this change may predispose the hyperplastic prostate to an increased rate of testosterone metabolism and thereby contribute to the inordinate accumulation of dihydrotestosterone characteristic of benign enlargement [13].

To gain more insight into the significance of 5α-reductase in BPH we studied several kinetic parameters of the enzymes associated with stroma and epithelium. Our evidence is compatible with the existence of at least two separate forms of 5α-reductase and suggests that the epithelial form is very active under physiological conditions even though it represents only a small fraction of total enzyme activity in prostate.

MATERIALS AND METHODS

Tissue Specimens

Normal prostates were obtained either at autopsy 2–15 hours after death or from brain-dead kidney donors. The age range of this group was 17–71 years. Hyperplastic prostates were obtained within 1 hour of suprapubic or retropubic extirpation. The age of the patients with BPH ranged from 53–90 years. Carcinomatous tissue was obtained at the time of radical prostatectomy. The age range of the cancer patients was 59–73 years. In each instance the diagnosis was confirmed by pathological examination. Studies on malignant tissue were confined to well-differentiated carcinoma.

Separation of Stroma and Epithelium

All procedures were performed at 4°C. The tissue (< 2 gm) was minced with scissors and forced through a stainless steel wire screen (30 mesh, 0.55 mm grid) with a Teflon pestle. The epithelial fraction was collected in a final volume of 10 ml by intermittently percolating 10 mM-TES buffer, pH 7.0, containing 0.5 mM-mercaptoethanol and 0.05 M NaCl (TES buffer) through the tissue pulp. After the epithelial fraction was collected, the remaining stromal fraction retained on the screen was washed with a further 20 ml of TES buffer until its appearance was white. The stroma was then homogenized in 1–2 ml of TES buffer with a Brinkman Polytron homogenizer unit equipped with a PT 10 probe. A 10-second homogenization at maximum power setting was repeated three times with a 1-minute cooling period between each homogenization. The tissue suspensions were then homogenized manually in a Dounce apparatus with 25 strokes of a loosely fitting pestle A. The protein concentration of the final homogenates was determined with the Bio-rad Protein Assay (Bio-Rad Laboratories, Mississauga, Ontario, Canada) with bovine gamma globulin as standard, and the homogenates were diluted with TES buffer to a concentration of about 300 μg/ml.

Incubation Conditions

In a final volume of 2 ml, the incubation mixtures contained: 1.6 ml homogenate, 2–100 nM [1,2-^{3}H] testosterone, and an NADPH-generating system started with 1×10^{-6}–5×10^{-3} M NADP. The samples were then incubated at 37°C in an oscillating water bath for intervals ranging from 5–60 minutes. Full details of this procedure are given in reference [13].

Estimation of 5α-reductase activity was based on the percentage formation of dihydrotestosterone and 3α(β)-androstanediol from testosterone.

Extraction of Steroids

At the end of incubation, 5 volumes of chloroform: methanol (2:1, vol/vol) were added to each sample. Tubes were stoppered and agitated on a rotary shaker for 20 minutes at 500 rpm. Phase separation was accomplished by centrifugation at 400g for 10 minutes after which the upper aqueous phase was removed. The lower phase was further extracted with 1 volume upper phase solvent (chloroform:methanol:water, 3:48:47, by vol), equal to the volume of aqueous phase removed. This cycle was repeated once more prior to thin-layer chromatography. Recovery of steroids was monitored by counting the radioactivity and was always close to 100%.

Thin-Layer Chromatography

Resolution of testosterone, dihydrotestosterone and 3α(β)-androstanediol was achieved on a Macherey-Nagel precoated polygram Sil-G-Hy thin layer chromatography plates (Brinkmann Instruments, Toronto, Ontario, Canada). A portion of each extract corresponding to 50,000 dpm was supplemented with 10 μg each of the appropriate standards and applied to the plate as a single spot. The plates were developed once in dichloromethane:ether (4:1), sprayed with a solution of 0.05% (wt/vol) 2′,3,4′, 5,7-pentahydroxyflavone in methanol (Morin, Merck, Brinkmann), and warmed briefly at 100°C. After the positions of the standards had been noted under UV light, the silica gel was transferred in sections to counting vials. Methanol (1 ml) and 9 ml of 0.4% diphenyloxazole in toluene were added to each vial and the samples were assayed for radioactivity. About 90% of the radioactivity applied to the thin-layer chromatography plate was recovered.

Radioimmunoassay

Homogenates of whole tissue, stroma, and epithelium were extracted with a 10% (vol/vol) ethylacetate:hexane. The organic phase of the extract was chromatographed on Al_2O_3 [14], and the fractions containing dihydrotestosterone were pooled. The amount of dihydrotestosterone recovered was measured by radioimmunoassay using a rabbit antiserum. Information concerning the sensitivity, accuracy and precision of the assay has been published elsewhere [11].

Assay of Acid Phosphatase

Tissue was separated into stroma and epithelium in the usual manner but using 0.05 M Na acetate buffer, pH 4.8. The two fractions were subjected to two cycles of rapid freeze-thawing and centrifuged at 1,000g for 10 minutes. The supernatant from each fraction was decanted and assayed for acid phosphatase using an ACA Analytical Test Pack, Du Pont Instruments, Wilmington, DE.

Assay of Hydroxyproline

Separated tissue was centrifuged at 1,000g for 10 minutes and each pellet, containing about 40 mg tissue protein, was hydrolyzed in concentrated HCl for 24 hours at 100°C in a sealed ampoule. The samples were then freeze-dried and resuspended in 0.5 ml of TES buffer. An aliquot (20 μl) was then analyzed on a Beckman single column amino acid analyzer.

Radioactive Materials

[1,2-^{3}H] Testosterone (40 Ci/mmole) was purchased from New England Nuclear Corporation (Boston, MA). Purity was checked by thin-layer chromatography and the steroid was considered acceptable only if it was 95–100% pure.

In preparation for incubation radioactive steroid in benzene:ethanol (9:1, vol/vol) was dried under N_2, dissolved in a small amount of ethanol, and diluted with TES buffer so that the final concentration was 100 pmole/40 μl.

Liquid Scintillation Counting

Radioactivity was counted in a Beckman LS-7500 liquid scintillation system using a diphenyloxazole/toluene solution which contained 4 gm diphenyloxazole/liter toluene with added methanol (10%, vol/vol). The counting efficiency as determined by external standardization was about 48%. All data obtained as cpm were converted to dpm.

Other Analytical Procedures

DNA was measured by the method of Burton [15] using calf thymus DNA as standard.

Chemicals and Reagents

The reagents used to prepare buffers and other solutions were purchased from Sigma Chemical Company, St. Louis, MO, and were of the highest purity available. Steroids were obtained from Steraloids, Pawling, NY. The supplier of the dihydrotestosterone anti-serum (DT 3-154) was Endocrine Sciences, Tarzana, CA. Deionized glass-distilled water was used in making up all solutions.

RESULTS

Morphology of Stroma and Epithelium

The histological appearance of the stroma is shown in Figure 1A and that of the epithelium in Figure 1B. The former consists of spindle shaped fibromuscular cells and collagen, while the latter is made up of sheets of densely packed cuboidal cells with round, darkly staining nuclei.

Purity of Stromal and Epithelial Fractions

From a detailed microscopic analysis of separated stromal and epithelial fractions from 10 different prostates, it was established that the purity of stroma was virtually 100% in all cases; in contrast the purity of the epithelium ranged from

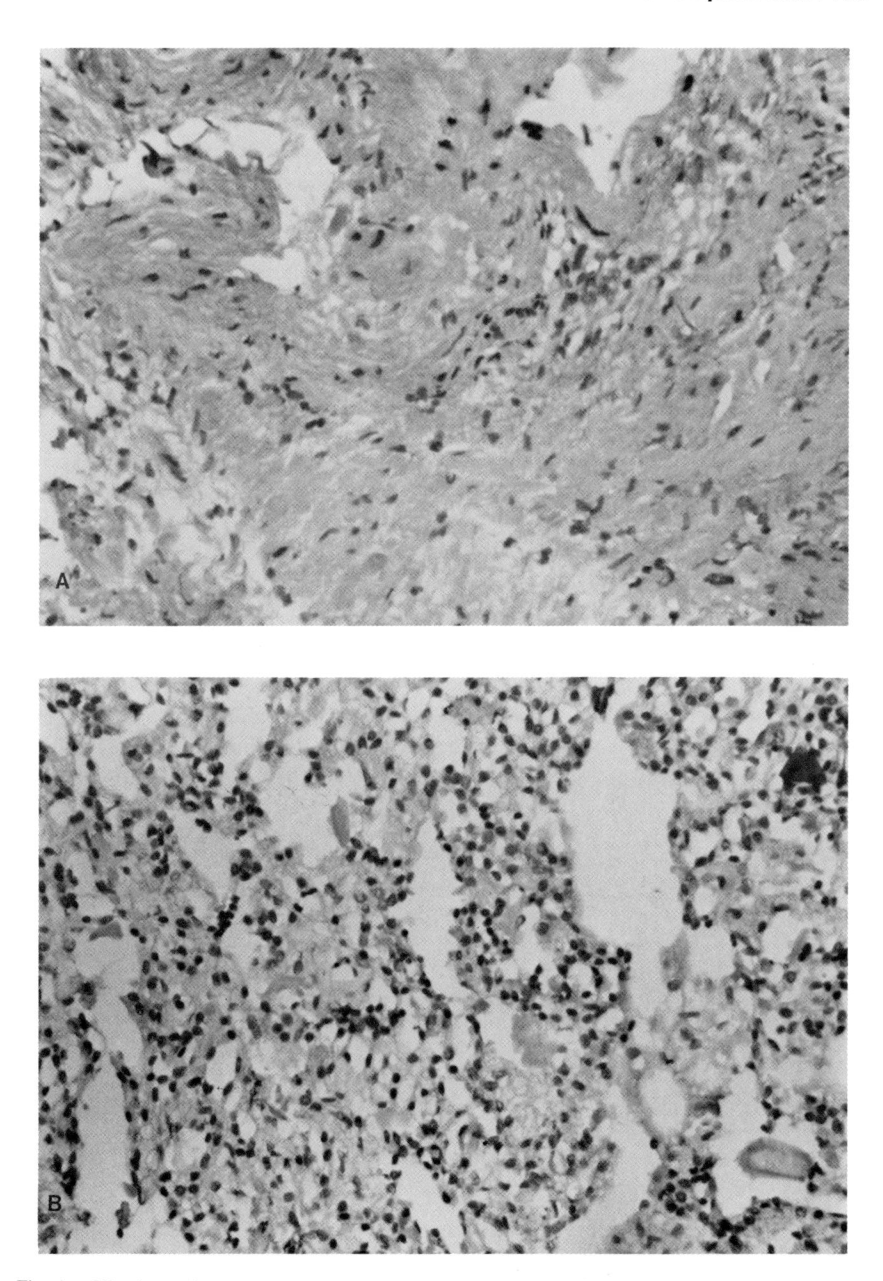

Fig. 1. Histology of prostatic stroma and epithelium. Separated stroma and epithelium were fixed in 10% formaldehyde, stained with hematoxylin and eosin, and examined by light microscopy. A) Stroma. B) Epithelium. × 360.

50–100% owing to contamination by stromal debris. About 40% of the whole tissue DNA and protein was recovered in the stromal fraction [11].

The results of an analysis of acid phosphatase activity in stroma and epithelium, listed in Table I, indicate that most of the activity is associated with the epithelial fraction as might be expected. The small amount of activity associated with stroma would be consistent with a degree of contamination of stroma by epithelial components, ranging from 4–25%. Since it is not known how much basal acid phosphatase activity is associated with purified stroma, part of the activity detected in stroma may represent endogenous enzyme.

The results presented in Figure 2 indicate that virtually no hydroxyproline is recovered in the separated epithelium. Thus the apparent contamination of the separated epithelium by stromal components appears to be less than suggested by histological criteria.

Requirements for the Metabolism of Testosterone in Stroma and Epithelium

Concentration of co-factors. Experiments were performed to establish conditions under which the activity of 5α-reductase was greatest. When the metabolism of testosterone was studied at pH 7.0 in the presence of increasing concentrations of NADP as a component of an NADPH-generating system, the results shown in Figure 3 were obtained. The activity of 5α-reductase is highest in the presence of an NADPH-generating system containing 10^{-3} M NADP both in stroma and epithelium. At higher concentrations a marked inhibitory affect is observed.

Effect of pH. The activities of 5α-reductase in stroma and epithelium were measured over a pH range of 4.0–9.0. As shown by the results in Figure 4, maximum enzyme activity is observed between pH 5.5 and pH 7.0. There is no

TABLE I. Acid phosphatase activity in stroma and epithelium

		Specific activity (IU/mg protein)	
Tissue	Condition	Stroma	Epithelium
1	BPH	16,000	403,000
2	BPH	2,000	51,000
3	BPH	21,000	73,000
4	BPH	12,000	37,000
5	Carcinoma	300	5,000
6	Carcinoma	300	3,000

Tissue was separated mechanically into stromal and epithelial fractions, and the acid phosphatase activity was measured as described in Materials and Methods.

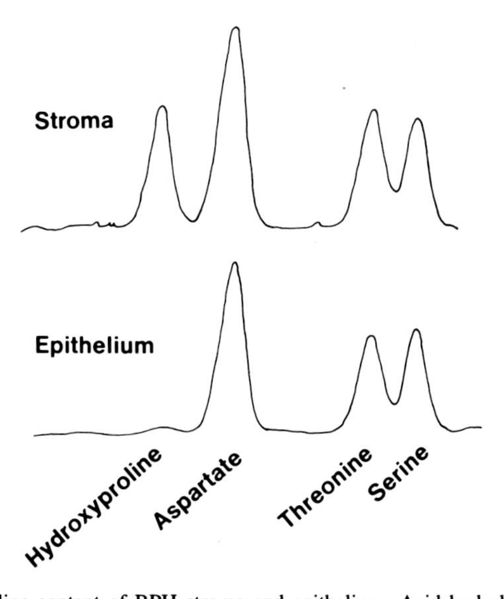

Fig. 2. Hydroxyproline content of BPH stroma and epithelium. Acid hydrolyzed tissue samples (equivalent to 1.6 mg protein) were applied to a Beckman single column amino acid analyzer. Details of sample preparation are described in Materials and Methods. The height of the hydroxyproline peak in the stromal preparation is almost 30 times that in the epithelial preparation.

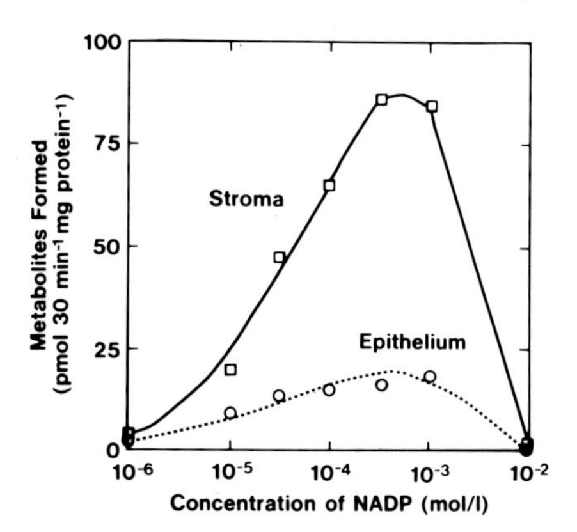

Fig. 3. Effect of NADP concentration of 5α-reductase activity. In a final volume of 2 ml TES buffer, pH 7.0, the incubation mixture contained 500 μg tissue protein, 50 nM-[1,2-^{3}H] testosterone, and an NADPH generating system consisting of 5 mM-glucose 6-phosphate, 0.5 unit glucose 6-phosphate dehydrogenase, and 1×10^{-6}–5×10^{-3} M-NADP. Samples were incubated at 37°C for 30 minutes. Metabolites formed: stroma, □; epithelium, ○.

apparent difference in the pH maximum for 5α-reductase activities in stroma and epithelium.

Concentration of protein and time of incubation. The effect of protein concentration on the rate of testosterone metabolism is illustrated by the results in Figure 5. The increase in 5α-reductase activity is linear over the range of epithelial protein concentrations tested; in contrast the activity is slightly inhibited at stromal protein concentrations above 1.0 mg/sample. Because of the latter observation, the amount of protein in all incubation mixtures was adjusted to be below this limit.

In the presence of an NADPH-generating system, 50 nM androgen and approximately 500 μg of stromal or epithelial protein, the metabolism of testosterone increased linearly with the time for at least 30 minutes (Fig. 6).

Effect of testosterone concentration. The activities of stromal and epithelial 5α-reductase were measured in the presence of increasing concentrations of testosterone. As shown by the results in Figure 7, a constant rate of metabolism is achieved with epithelial protein in the presence of 50 nM testosterone; in contrast, the rate of metabolism with stromal protein begins to plateau only when the concentration of testosterone is above 50 nM. A Lineweaver-Burk plot of these data is given in Figure 8, and the values obtained for Km and Vmax are presented in Table II. The mean Vmax of the stromal 5α-reductase at 598 ± 112 pmole/30 min/mg protein is 13-fold greater than that of the epithelial enzyme at 47 ± 14 pmole/30 min/mg protein. Similarly the stromal 5α-reductase is characterized by a mean Km which is ninefold larger than that of the epithelial form of the enzyme, 195 ± 44 nmole/liter vs 21 ± 4 nmole/liter.

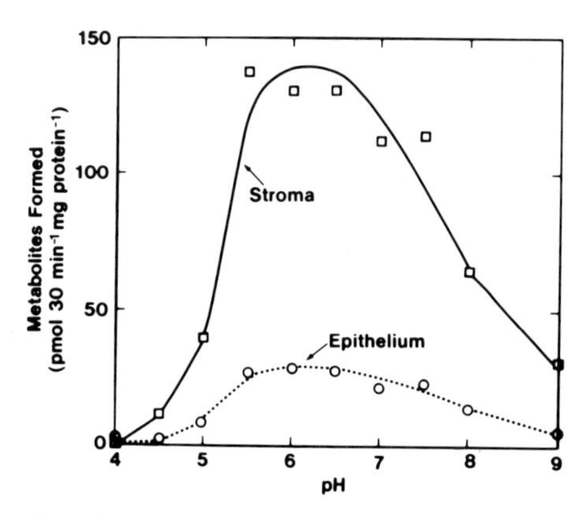

Fig. 4. Effect of pH on 5α-reductase activity. Conditions were the same as described in the Figure 3 legend except for the concentration of NADP used, 5×10^{-4}M. The incubation mixtures were adjusted with 0.1 N NaOH or 0.5 M Na acetate buffer to obtain the desired pH. Metabolites formed: stroma, □; epithelium, ○.

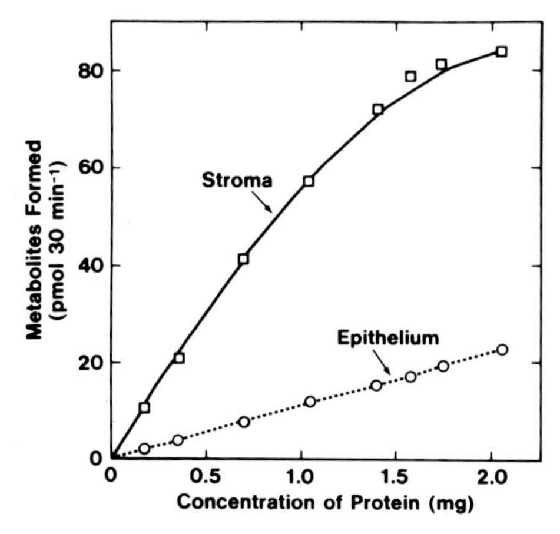

Fig. 5. Effect of protein concentration on 5α-reductase activity. In a final volume of 2 ml TES buffer, pH 7.0, the incubation mixture contained 100–2000 μg tissue protein, 50 nM-[1,2-^{3}H] testosterone, and an NADPH generating system started with 5 × 10^{-4} M NADP. Samples were incubated at 37° C for 30 minutes. Metabolities formed: stroma, □; epithelium, ○.

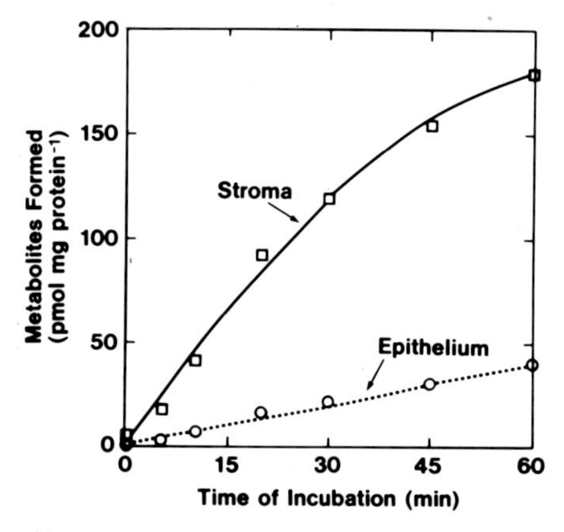

Fig. 6. Effect of time of incubation on 5α-reductase activity. Conditions were essentially the same as described in the Figure 5 legend. The protein concentration was 500 μg/2 ml, and the time of incubation varied from 0–60 minutes. Metabolities formed: stroma, □; epithelium, ○.

The bulk of the 5α-reductase activity in hyperplastic prostate is associated with stroma. However, the fact that the Km of the epithelial enzyme is close to the physiological level of testosterone in the blood (10–20 nM [16]) implies that the epithelial form of the enzyme may be more active than the stromal form, the latter being characterized by a Km which falls well outside the normal circulating concentration of testosterone. In examining the potential consequences of the difference in Km values, we measured the concentration of dihydrotestosterone

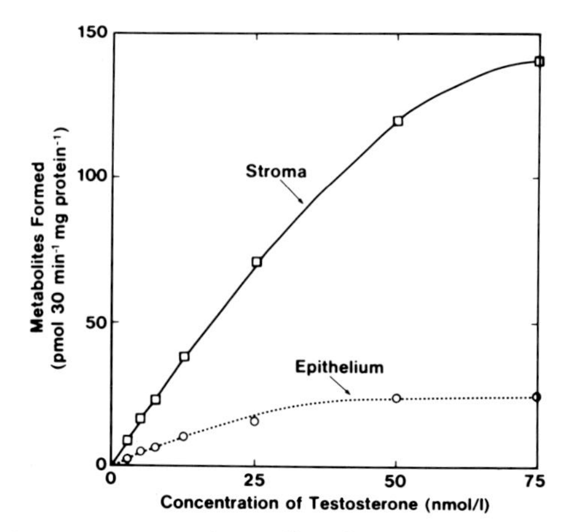

Fig. 7. Effect of testosterone concentration on 5α-reductase activity. Conditions were essentially the same as described on the Figure 5 legend. The protein concentration was 500 μg/2 ml, and the concentration of testosterone varied from 2.5–75 nmole/1. Metabolites formed: stroma, □; epithelium, ○.

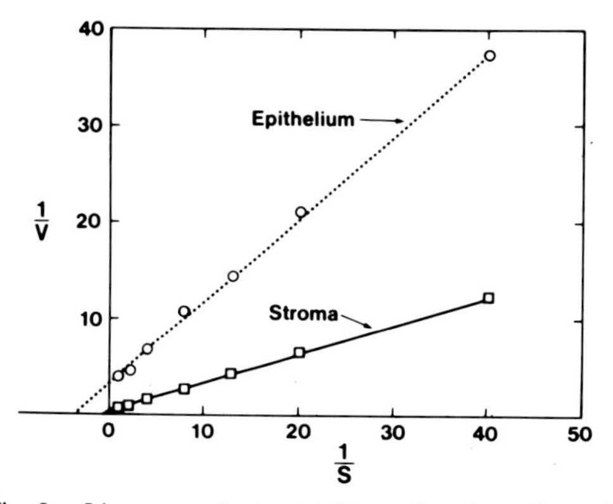

Fig. 8. Lineweaver-Burk plot. Data taken from Figure 7.

TABLE II. Kinetic parameters of 5α-reductase in stroma and epithelium

Tissue	Condition	Vmax (pmole/30 min/mg protein)		Km (nmole/liter)	
		Stroma	Epithelium	Stroma	Epithelium
1	BPH	378	31	114	27
2	BPH	746	35	266	14
3	BPH	669	76	206	23
Mean ± SEM		598 ± 112	47 ± 14	195 ± 44	21 ± 4

Conditions for incubation were as described in the Figure 7 legend. Vmax and Km parameters were obtained from a Lineweaver-Burk plot of each set of data.

in stroma and epithelium by radioimmunoassay. The preliminary observations recorded in Table III suggest that BPH stroma and epithelium are both characterized by an above normal level of dihydrotestosterone. More importantly, the concentration appears to be highest in epithelium giving a trend towards an elevatated epithelial:stromal ratio of the concentration of dihydrotestosterone as might be predicted on the basis of relative Km values. This finding is consistent with an active process of testosterone metabolism in the epithelial cells.

Stromal Versus Epithelial Localization of 5α-Reductase

Since the Vmax estimates presented in Table II suggested that the specific activity of 5α-reductase in BPH stroma greatly exceeds that of the epithelial enzyme, we attempted to confirm this point by measuring the specific activities of 5α-reductase in a larger number of biopsy specimens using a single-point assay. To conform as closely as possible to the physiological state, the comparative studies were carried out in the presence of 50 nM testosterone. Although this concentration is slightly below the optimum for measuring 5α-reductase activity, it approaches the upper limit of the concentration of androgen found in the hyperplastic human prostate [17]. Data on the specific activities of the stromal and epithelial forms of 5α-reductase are presented in Table IV. Consistent with the results above (Table II), the specific activity of the 5α-reductase was uniformly higher in the stromal than in the epithelial fractions of all prostates examined. Comparing stromal fractions alone, it is clear that the mean specific activity of 5α-reductase in BPH stroma at 91.0 ± 10.3 pmole/30 min/mg protein

TABLE III. Concentration of dihydrotestosterone in stroma and epithelium

	Concentration of dihydrotestosterone (pmole/mg DNA)		
Tissue	Stroma	Epithelium	Ratio E/S
Normal			
1	4.3	4.9	1.1
2	3.0	3.5	1.2
BPH			
1	5.4	7.1	1.3
2	11.8	20.0	1.7
3	6.4	9.1	1.4
4	6.0	9.0	1.5
Carcinoma			
1	5.6	5.1	0.9
2	5.9	15.0	2.5

The concentration of dihydrotestosterone was measured in separated stroma and epithelium by radioimmunoassay as described in Materials and Methods. Dividing the concentration in epithelium by that in stroma gives the E/S ratio.

TABLE IV. 5α-Reductase activities in stroma and epithelium

Tissue	Enzyme activity (metabolites formed, pmole/30 min/mg protein)	
	Stroma	Epithelium
Normal	30.1 ± 5.3(4)	11.3 ± 3.0(4)
BPH	91.0 ± 10.3(12)	14.9 ± 2.5(12)
Carcinoma	12.4 ± (2)	3.7 ± (2)

In a final volume of 2 ml TES buffer, pH 7.0, the incubation mixture contained 500 μg protein from stromal or epithelial homogenate, 50 nM-[1,2-^{3}H] testosterone; and an NADPH-generating system started with 5×10^{-4} M-NADP. Samples were incubated at 37°C for 30 minutes.

is significantly greater than the corresponding value in normal stroma, 30.1 ± 5.3 pmole/30 min/mg protein (Student's t test $p < 0.05$). Stroma from carcinomatous prostate, on the other hand, is relatively poor in 5α-reductase activity.

The data in Table V indicate that the localization of 5α-reductase is predominantly in stroma irrespective of the normal or abnormal condition of the prostate. Moreover, the proportion of 5α-reductase activity associated with BPH stroma at 82.6 ± 2.0% relative to the normal value of 64.1 ± 7.2% is significantly elevated (Student's t test, $p < 0.05$).

Subcellular Localization of 5α-Reductase Activity in BPH Tissue

Various subcellular fractions of stroma and epithelium were isolated by centrifugation and analyzed for 5α-reductase activity in the presence of 50 nM testosterone. As shown by the data in Table VI the specific activity of 5α-reductase is highest in the mitochondrial and microsomal fractions from both stroma and epithelium. The lowest specific activity is observed in the cytosol fraction. Despite the elevated activity associated with the mitochondrial and microsomal fractions, when the total activity is estimated the bulk of the enzyme activity is recovered in the nuclear fraction. This effect is more pronounced with stromal than epithelial organelles. Since a negligible amount is recovered in the cytosol fraction, the major part of the enzyme is clearly membrane-bound.

DISCUSSION

The first indication that testosterone was not directly involved in the pathogenesis of benign prostatic hyperplasia was the finding that the concentration of dihydrotestosterone was grossly elevated in both human [18] and canine [19] hyperplastic tissue. This initial line of evidence has since been strengthened by the observation that canine BPH can be induced by dihydrotestosterone and that both the spontaneous and induced forms are associated with an increased net formation of dihydrotestosterone [20–22].

TABLE V. Stromal versus epithelial localization of 5α-reductase activity

Tissue	% Total enzyme activity in stroma
Normal	64.1 ± 7.2(4)
BPH	82.6 ± 2.0(12)
Carcinoma	71.0 ± (2)

Homogenates of stroma and epithelium were analyzed for activity of 5α-reductase as described in the legend to Table IV. Total enzyme activity was determined on the basis of the combined protein content of the stromal and epithelial fractions. The percentage of the total enzyme activity of each fraction was then calculated. Values are presented as the mean ± SEM. The number of prostates examined is shown in parentheses.

TABLE VI. Subcellular localization of 5α-reductase activity in BPH tissue

	Specific activity (pmole/30 min/mg protein)		Total activity (pmole/30 min/fraction)	
	Stroma	Epithelium	Stroma	Epithelium
Homogenate	44	10	74	23
Crude nuclei	41	14	430	81
Mitochondria	120	29	120	64
Microsomes	120	42	120	69
Cytosol	4	<1	43	9

Homogenates of stroma and epithelium were centrifuged at 1000g for 10 minutes to yield a pellet of crude nuclei. The 1000g supernatant was centrifuged at 10,000g for 30 minutes to yield a pellet of mitochondria. Lastly the 10,000g supernatant was centrifuged in a Beckman Spinco ultracentrifuge at 100,000g for 60 minutes to yield a pellet of microsomes and a cytosol supernatant. The pellet fractions were resuspended in TES buffer, pH 7.0 and analyzed for 5α-reductase activity as described in the legend to Table IV. Total enzyme activity was calculated as specific activity × total protein in fraction.

The mechanism by which dihydrotestosterone is accumulated by BPH tissue has not been defined but at least three lines of evidence suggest that 5α-reductase is involved: First, the amount of 5α-reductase activity in whole-tissue homogenates of BPH is increased threefold above normal [13]; second, the enzyme is largely localized in the stromal compartment not only in normal and carcinomatous tissue, but also in BPH specimens (Table V, references [9,12]; third, BPH is characterized by an increased amount of stromal 5α-reductase activity (Table IV). These observations are in accord with McNeal's hypothesis that the human prostate stroma contains an inductive mechanism which initiates the hyperplastic process [7,8].

The kinetics of androgen production in turnover are apparently quite different in BPH and carcinoma. While both tissues are characterized by a high concentration of dihydrotestosterone [11,23], stromal 5α-reductase activity is grossly elevated in BPH but is abnormally low in malignant tissue (Table IV). The observation that the stromal and epithelial forms of 5α-reductase are characterized by different Km values (Table II) suggests the following explanation for the paradoxical elevation of the concentration of dihydrotestosterone in carcinoma.

Although the majority of the 5α-reductase activity in human prostate is localized in stroma, the epithelial form of the enzyme cannot be overlooked since its Km is considerably smaller than that of the stromal form. This property seems to assure that the epithelial enzyme will be active under physiological conditions and is consistent with our finding that the epithelium contains as much if not more dihydrotestosterone than the stroma (Table III). If the 5α-reductase in carcinomatous tissue happens to be characterized by a small Km, similar in magnitude to the Km for BPH epithelial enzyme, conversion of testosterone to dihydrotestosterone would proceed efficiently despite the decrease in bulk enzyme activity associated with malignancy (Table IV). Net accumulation of dihydrotestosterone would not be unexpected even under conditions of therapy, such as castration and the administration of diethylstilbestrol, which occasionally fail to eliminate dihydrotestosterone from the neoplastic cell [23].

ACKNOWLEDGMENTS

We thank Cynthia Wells for typing the manuscript. Dr. T K. Shnitka and Dr. H. Pontifex performed the histological and pathological examinations of the experimental tissues. We sincerely appreciate their critical evaluation and many helpful discussions.

REFERENCES

1. Cunha GR, Lung B: The importance of stroma in morphogenesis and functional activity of urogential epithelium. In Vitro 15:50–71, 1979.
2. Cunha GR: Experimental analysis of male accessory sex gland development. In Spring-Mills E, Hafez ESE (eds): "Male Accessory Sex Glands." Amsterdam: Elsevier/North Holland Biomedical Press, 1980, pp 39–59.
3. Cunha GR, Lung B, Reese B: Glandular epithelial induction by embryonic mesenchyme in adult bladder epithelium of BALB/C mice. Invest Urol 17:302–304, 1980.
4. Lasnitzki I, Mizuno T: Induction of the rat prostate gland by androgens in organ culture. J Endocrinol 74:47–55, 1977.
5. Lasnitzki I, Mizuno T: Role of the mesenchyme in the induction of the rat prostate gland by androgens in organ culture. J Endocrinol 82:171–178, 1979.
6. Lasnitzki I, Mizuno T: Prostate induction: interaction of epithelium and mesenchyme from normal wild-type mice and androgen-insensitive mice with testicular feminization. J Endocrinol 85:423–428, 1980.
7. McNeal JE: Origin and evolution of benign prostatic enlargement. Invest Urol 15:340–345, 1978.
8. McNeal JE: New morphologic findings relevant to the origin and evolution of carcinoma of the prostate and BPH. In Coffey DS, Isaacs JT (eds): "Prostate Cancer." Geneva: UICC Technical Report Series 48:24–37, 1979.

9. Cowan RA, Cowan SK, Grant JK, Elder HY: Biochemical investigations of separated epithelium and stroma from benign hyperplastic prostatic tissue. J Endocrinol 74:111–120, 1977.
10. Bard DR, Lasnitzki I, Mizuno T: Metabolism of testosterone by the epithelium and mesenchyme of the rat urogenital sinus. J Endocrinol 83:211–218, 1979.
11. Bruchovsky N, Rennie PS, Wilkin RP: New aspects of androgen action in prostatic cells: stromal localization of 5α-reductase, nuclear abundance of androstanolone and binding of receptor to linker deoxyribonucleic acid. In Schröder FH, de Voogt HJ (eds): "Steroid Receptors, Metabolism and Prostatic Cancer." Amsterdam: Excerpta Medica, pp 57–76, 1980.
12. Wilkin RP, Bruchovsky N, Shnitka TK, Rennie PS, Comeau TL: Stromal 5α-reductase activity is elevated in benign prostatic hyperplasia. Acta Endocrinol (Kbh) 94:284–288, 1980.
13. Bruchovsky N, Lieskovsky G: Increased ratio of 5α-reductase: 3α-(β)-hydroxysteroid dehydrogenase activities in the hyperplastic human prostate. J Endocrinol 80:289–301, 1979.
14. Furuyama S, Mayes P, Nugent CA: A radioimmunoassay for plasma testosterone. Steroids 16:415–428, 1970.
15. Burton K: A study of the conditions and mechanisms of the diphenylamine reaction for the colorimetric estimation of deoxyribonucleic acid. Biochem J 62:315–323, 1956.
16. Bruchovsky N, Lesser B, Van Doorn E, Craven S: Hormonal effects on cell proliferation in rat prostate. Vit Horm 33:61–102, 1975.
17. Habib FK, Lee SR, Stitch SR, Smith PH: Androgen levels in the plasma and prostatic tissues of patients with benign hypertrophy and carcinoma of the prostate. J Endocrinol 71:99–107, 1976.
18. Siiteri P, Wilson JD: Dihydrotestosterone in prostatic hypertrophy. I. The formation and content of dihydrotestosterone in the hypertrophic prostate of man. J Clin Invest 49:1737–1745, 1970.
19. Gloyna R, Siiteri PK, Wilson JD: Dihydrotestosterone in prostatic hypertrophy. II. The formation and content of dihydrotestosterone in the hypertrophic canine prostate and the effect of dihydrotestosterone on prostate growth in the dog. J Clin Invest 49:1746–1753, 1970.
20. DeKlerk DP, Coffey DS, Ewing LL, McDermott IR, Reiner WG, Robinson CH, Scott WW, Strandberg JD, Talalay P, Walsh PC, Wheaton LG, Zirkin BR: Comparison of spontaneous and experimentally induced canine prostatic hyperplasia. J Clin Invest 64:842–849, 1979.
21. Moore RJ, Gazak JM, Quebbeman JF, Wilson JD: Concentration of dihydrotestosterone and 3α-androstanediol in naturally occurring and androgen-induced prostatic hyperplasia in the dog. J Clin Invest 64:1003–1010, 1979.
22. Isaacs JT, Coffey DS: Changes in dihydrotestosterone metabolism associated with the development of canine benign prostatic hyperplasia. Endocrinology 108:445–453, 1980.
23. Geller J, Albert J, Loza D: Steroid levels in cancer of the prostate-markers of tumour differentiation and adequacy of anti-androgen therapy. J Steroid Biochem 11:631–636, 1979.

The Prostatic Cell: Structure and Function
Part A, pages 177–203

Tissue Interactions in Prostate Development: Roles of Sex Steroids

Leland W.K. Chung, Neil G. Anderson, Blake Lee Neubauer, Gerald R. Cunha, Timothy C. Thompson, and Audrey K. Rocco

INTRODUCTION

Recent studies on transplantable prostatic tumors [1,2], prostatic cancer cells grown in tissue culture [3,4], surgical specimens of human prostate [5,6], and the growth of human prostate in nude mice [7] have significantly contributed to our understanding of prostatic cancer cells. Results of these studies have also revealed a large number of differences between normal and cancerous tissues. However, because of the lack of suitable animal models, little attention has been paid to analyzing the developmental processes that might lead to the orderly progression of normal prostatic cells into prostatic neoplasia. To approach this problem, we focused on the roles of sex steroids on the development of prostate cancer in susceptible Nb (Noble) rats. There is strong evidence to suggest that sex steroids may be involved in the etiology of prostatic cancer. For example prostatic cancer of dorsolateral lobe can be induced in Nb rats by long-term testosterone or testosterone plus estrone administration [8]. The absence of benign prostatic hyperplasia and prostatic cancer in man castrated prepubertally also suggests the roles of sex steroids during early life which may be an important determinant for the development of latent prostatic neoplasia [9]. The other feature of prostatic cancer is tissue heterogeneity. For example, prostatic cancer derived from Nb rats can be subcoloned into androgen-dependent, estrogen-dependent, and autonomous tumor lines [10,11]. Human prostatic cancer may arise from limited foci, but progresses at vastly different rates. To answer these questions, it is therefore essential to elucidate the mechanisms by which sex steroids or other factors may regulate cellular proliferation and differentiation. Recently, we have established a model system utilizing stroma from embryonic urogenital sinus and epithelium from *adult* mouse bladder and observed the biochemical events that are associated with prostatic morphogenesis [12]. This model system is employed in the present communication to investigate the roles of stroma and epithelium during androgen induction. The importance of stroma as the primary target cells for androgen action during prostatic morphogenesis is emphasized. Furthermore, the possible utilization of this system for analyzing human prostatic neoplastic development will be discussed.

MATERIALS AND METHODS

Animals and Treatments

All Nb rats (Charles River, a gift from NCI, Frederick, MD) were weaned at the age of 24 days. They were treated immediately with testosterone propionate (TP, 0.6 mg/day), 17β-estradiol dipropionate (E_2P_2, 0.08 mg/day), or the combination of both TP and E_2P_2 (0.6 mg/day and 0.08 mg/day, respectively) in the form of Sialastic implants (Dupont). Daily doses of TP and/or E_2P_2 equal the average release rates which were calculated by weighing a large number of initial implants and the residual implants at the time of hormonal replacement. Animals were treated continuously with these hormones for an accumulated period of 6–8 months. Morphological and biochemical alterations of the ventral and dorsolateral prostates were examined.

In experiments where functional activity of stroma and epithelium interactions was tested, urogenital sinuses dissected from 16-day-old wild-type mouse embryos (C57/6, Jackson Laboratories), and urinary bladders excised from adult outbred Tfm/Y mice (a gift from Dr. S. Ohno), were used as sources for clean stroma and epithelia, respectively. Urogenital sinus mesenchyme and Tfm/Y bladder epithelium were obtained following tryptic separation of these organs by procedures previously established by Cunha and co-workers [12]. Wild-type urogenital sinus mesenchyme was associated with the Tfm/Y bladder epithelium ($UGM^{+/+}$ + $BLE^{Tfm/y}$ recombinants) and grown overnight at 37°C on a solidified agar medium composed of 0.4% agar in Eagle's basal medium supplemented with 10% fetal calf serum, 1% L-glutamine, and 50 units/ml of penicillin–streptomycin. Following overnight culture to allow the tissues to firmly adhere to each other, the recombinants were grafted under the kidney capsules of male athymic nude mice. The cleanness of separation of the epithelial and mesenchymal components was examined by growing these tissues separately in male hosts; clean separation is evident by complete absence of morphogenesis (see below).

Morphological Examination

Ventral and dorsolateral prostates of Nb rats. Tissues freshly excised from the male hosts were immediately frozen in liquid nitrogen. Frozen sections of these tissues were serially sectioned at 6 μ thickness and stained with hematoxylin and eosin.

Tissue recombinations. Following one month of in vivo growth, some of the hosts were sacrificed and the grafts processed for histological analysis. Other hosts were castrated via the scrotal route, for 7 to 10 days in order to allow for regression of androgen-dependent tissues. The hosts were divided into two groups: 1) Hosts injected subcutaneously for 3 days with TP (0.2 mg/day), and 2) hosts injected subcutaneously with TP (0.2 mg/day) plus the antiandrogen, cyproterone acetate (CA) (4 mg/day). This dose of CA was previously demonstrated to completely abolish TP-induced DNA synthesis in rat prostate [13]. Specimens of host bladder, host prostate, and the tissue recombinants from these two treatment groups were examined histologically. For histological analysis specimens were fixed in Bouin's fluid, embedded in paraffin, and serially sectioned at 6 μ. Slides were prepared and stained with hematoxylin and eosin.

Biochemical Examination

High-pressure liquid chromatographic (HPLC) studies of testosterone metabolism. We have recently developed a one-step HPLC system which will allow us to analyze several major testosterone metabolites in both intact rat and mouse tissue minces and in separated stroma and epithelium from rat prostates. Detailed analytical procedures were published elsewhere [14]. In brief, minced prostates (60–87 μg DNA) or tissue recombinants ($UGM^{+/+}$ and $BLE^{+/+}$, 20–35 μg DNA) were incubated in 0.5 ml Kreb's Ringer phosphate buffer (pH 7.4) containing [1, 2, 6, 7, 16, 17-^{3}H] testosterone (New England Nuclear) at a final concentration of 0.5 μM and a final specific activity of 0.8 Ci/mmole. For separated stroma and prostatic tubules (epithelium), testosterone metabolism was studied in tissue homogenate fortified with NADPH (1 mM, Boeringer). The incubations were carried out in glass culture tubes, sealed with polypropylene caps on a Labquake shaker (Lab Industries) in an incubator at 37°C. At timed intervals, the incubations were terminated with the addition of 2.5 ml freshly opened anesthesia-grade diethyl ether. Successive extractions of the aqueous phase were performed with an additional 2.5 ml ether and 2.5 ml redistilled spectrophotometric grade ethyl acetate:n-hexane (1:9) (Fisher Scientific). These organic extracts were pooled, taken to dryness under vacuum at 50°C, and subsequently redissolved in 140 μl of the following reference steroids: androstenedione (10^{-5}M), testosterone (10^{-5}M), androstanedione (10^{-2}M), dihydrotestosterone (10^{-2}M), and androsterone (10^{-2}M) in HPLC grade methanol (Fisher).

Testosterone and its metabolites were separated on an HPLC system (ALTEX) utilizing a C-18 ultrasphere ODS reverse-phase column which was eluted with an isocratic mobile phase of filtered (45 μm) tetrahydrofuran:methanol:H_2O (20:40:40). Fractions corresponding to steroid reference standards, as determined by either UV absorption or retention times of radiolabeled standards (3α- and

3β-androstanediols, Amersham Corporation), were collected into 7.0 ml scintillation vials using an automatic fraction collector. The samples were dried under vacuum at 50°C, 5 ml of Maxifluor scintillation cocktail (J.T. Baker Chemical Co.) was added, and samples were counted on a Beckman LS-3133P scintillation counter (Beckman Instruments). The counting efficiency for [^{3}H] was approximately 60%.

The identity of various steroids was confirmed by their respective retention time on HPLC and their co-crystallization with unlabeled steroid reference standards [15]. Samples of steroids separated by HPLC were added to 50 mg of the appropriate carrier steroid, reconstituted in benzene:ethanol (9:1), and the mixtures were crystallized from various solvent systems (see below). The identity and radiohomogeneity of each steroid was established by successive crystallizations to constant specific activity.

Photoaffinity labeling of prostatic cytosol with 8-azido-cyclic AMP (8-Az-cAMP). Fresh prostatic tissues were homogenized in 5 vol. (w/v) of 0.32 M sucrose. Tissue cytosols were obtained by ultracentrifugation of the tissue homogenate at 105,000 g for one hour. Twenty μl of the cytosol, mixed with 1 μl MES buffer (0.5 M 4-morpholinethane sulfonic acid, pH 6.5), were incubated in the dark at 37°C for 30 minutes with 5 μl of 8-azido-cAMP (final concentration of 150 nM, 42 Ci/mmole, International Chemical and Nuclear, Inc.) in the presence or absence of 1 μl of unlabeled cAMP (final concentration of 45 μM). The mixtures were exposed to UV light (254 nm) for 7 minutes at a distance of 8 cm to initiate photoaffinity binding. The reaction was terminated by the addition of SDS buffer. Aliquots of the mixtures (15–50 μg of protein) were subjected to one-dimensional SDS polyacrylamide gel electrophoresis in the presence of appropriate protein reference standards [16].

Cytosolic androgen receptor in rat prostate and kidney of testicular feminized (Tfm/y) and control (Ta/y) male mice: Effects of sodium molybdate. Ventral and dorsolateral prostates from intact control and sex steroids-treated Nb rats or kidneys from intact testicular feminized (Tfm/y) or control (Ta/y) mice were homogenized in TED buffer (10 mM Tris-HCl, 1 mM EDTA, and 1.5 mM dithiothreitol) at a ratio of 1:10 either in the presence or absence of 10 mM sodium molybdate. Cytosols were isolated by ultracentrifugation of the tissue homogenates at 105,000 g for one hour. Aliquots of 100 μl of cytosol were incubated with TED buffer containing 17α-methyl-[^{3}H]-trienolone (R-1881, 87 Ci/mmole, 0.125 to 10 nM) in the presence or absence of the unlabeled competing ligand R-1881 (1 μM). The incubation proceeded in ice for 18 hours. Bound and free ligand were determined after the addition of 0.6 ml of TED buffer containing dextran-coated charcoal (0.0033% T-70 dextran and 0.25% activated charcoal). Data were analyzed by the Scatchard method [17].

Determination of the rate of DNA synthesis in mouse bladder, mouse prostate, and tissue recombinations. Male hosts bearing $UGM^{+/+}$ + $BLE^{+/+}$ recombinants for four weeks were castrated for 7 to 10 days and then treated with TP (0.2 mg/day) for an accumulated period of 24–120 hours. Some animals were also treated with TP plus CA (4 mg/day) for 72 hours. Mice were sacrificed at various times by cervical dislocation, and the tissue recombinants, host bladder, and host prostate were surgically dissected and minced with fine scissors at 2°C. Aliquots of the minced tissues (15–75 mg) were transferred onto glass vials containing 2 ml of Kreb's Ringer phosphate buffer and [^{3}H]-thymidine (400 mCi/mmole, 1.0×10^{-5}M). The minced specimens were incubated at 37°C for 30 minutes in a Dubanoff metabolic shaker. At the end of incubation, 5 ml of ice-chilled Kreb's Ringer phosphate buffer containing unlabeled thymidine (1×10^{-4}M) was added to the incubation mixture, and the tissues were resuspended and immediately centrifuged. Tissue pellets were washed a second time with the same buffer. The washed tissue pellets were then stored at –20°C prior to DNA extraction, determination [18], and scintillation counting as described previously [19]. Rate of DNA synthesis was expressed as specific activity (cpm/μg DNA/30 min). Under these experimental conditions, it was established that the rate of DNA synthesis is linear with the tissue weights and the incubation times.

Two-dimensional polyacrylamide gel electrophoretic analysis of ^{35}S-methionine-labeled total cellular proteins from mouse bladder, mouse prostate, and tissue recombinants. The optimal conditions for labeling total tissue proteins with ^{35}S-methionine have been established earlier in this laboratory [20]. Hosts bearing $UGM^{+/+}$ + $BLE^{Tfm/y}$ recombinants for four weeks were castrated for seven days to allow the regression of androgen-dependent organs and then were given a single injection of TP (0.2 mg), which in 24 hours maximally stimulates de novo protein synthesis [19]. Hosts were then killed and their urinary bladders, prostates, and tissue recombinants (15–75 mg) were isolated, minced, and incubated in 2 ml of Kreb's Ringer phosphate buffer (pH 7.4) containing ^{35}S-methionine (2.3 Ci/mmole, 1×10^{-5}M) for one hour. The incorporation of ^{35}S-methionine was terminated by the addition of 5 ml ice-cold Kreb's Ringer phosphate buffer containing unlabeled methionine (1×10^{-4}M). Tissue suspensions were centrifuged at 10,000g for 2 minutes at 2°C. The recovered tissue pellets were washed once more with 5 ml of the above Kreb's Ringer phosphate buffer containing unlabeled methionine. Tissue pellets were homogenized in 3 volumes of lysis buffer (9.5 M urea, 2% [w/v] NP-40, and 2% [w/v] ampholines consisting of 1.6% [w/v] pH range 5–7 and 0.4% [w/v] pH range 3–10) in a glass homogenizer equipped with a Teflon pestle. Aliquots of the homogenate (30–50 μl) were used for two-dimensional polyacrylamide gel electrophoretic analysis [21]. In brief, the tissue homogenates saturated with additional urea crystals were loaded onto first-dimensional isoelectric focusing (IEF) disc gels (3.6% [w/v] acrylamide, 2 × 110 mm). The gel was run at 400 V for 16 hours and then at 800 V for 1 hour. The gel was extruded and equilibrated immediately with sodium dodecyl sulfate (SDS) buffer (10% [v/v] glycerol, 5% [v/v] β-mercaptoethanol, 2.3% [w/v] SDS, and 0.0625 M Tris-HCl, pH 6.8) in a test tube for 1–2 hours with gentle shaking. The equilibrated gels were then loaded onto second-dimensional SDS slab gels (7.5% [w/v] acrylamide, 13 × 15 cm) and were electrophoresed vertically toward the anode (16 mA/gel). Electrophoresis was terminated when the tracking dye, bromophenol blue, was 1 cm from the bottom of the gel. The gels were then equilibrated with destaining buffer (10% isopropanol in 7% acetic acid) for 1 hour and impregnated with [^{3}H]-Enhancer (NEN, Boston, MA) for one additional hour. Following thorough rinsing with distilled water for 1 hour the gels were dried onto filter paper. Autoradiography was accomplished by exposing the gels to x-ray film (Cronex-4, Kodak, Rochester, NY) at –80°C for 3–7 days. The apparent protein molecular weights and the isoelectric points on the gels were estimated by using standard proteins of known molecular weights (bovine serum albumin 68K, glutamate dehydrogenase 53K, ovalbumin 43K, aldolase 40K, chemotrypsin 25K) and measuring directly the pH of the IEF gel, respectively.

Separation of stroma and epithelium from rat prostates. Rat prostatic epithelial and stromal components were separated by limited enzymatic digestion followed by Percoll gradient centrifugation as described by Nandi and co-workers on the mammary glands [22]. Rat prostates (3–5 gm) were minced finely with a razor blade and resuspended in 50 ml of Hank's balanced salt solution (HBSS) containing 0.1% collagenase (Worthington Biochemical Corp.) and 0.1% hyaluronidase (Sigma Chem. Co.). Tissue suspensions were swirled gently in a gyratory shaker which was placed in an incubator at 37°C for 90 minutes. The resulting tissue suspensions were filtered through one layer of Nytex-150 and the filtrate collected. Cells in the filtrate were washed twice with 10 ml HBSS and layered on top of a preformed Percoll gradient (39% w/v) as described by Yang et al [23]. Distinct stroma cell bands were collected and their identity was further confirmed by standard tissue culture techniques. Prostatic epithelial cells were collected by further incubating prostatic tubules with 0.5% pronase (Sigma Chem. Co.) for 30 minutes. The resulting tissue suspensions were again filtered through one layer of Nytex-150. The retarded fraction contained prostatic tubules and were enriched predominately with epithelium as evidenced by its histological appearance.

Other analytical procedures. Total tissue protein was determined by the method of Lowry et al [24], with bovine serum albumin as the reference standard. DNA content was determined by a fluorometric method [25], with calf thymus DNA as the reference standard.

RESULTS

Progression of prostatic adenocarcinoma was studied in Nb rats. In this study, attempts were made to define morphological and biochemical changes during sex steroid-induced prostatic carcinogenesis. The histology of VP and DLP was compared between untreated controls and the long-term hormone-treated groups (Fig. 1 A–H). Long-term TP treatment induced cystic degeneration of the glandular structures in VP, probably as a result of increased luminal pressure (Fig. 1B). The effects of TP on DLP, however, were less obvious. Selective areas of atrophic epithelium and hyperplasia were noted (Fig. 1F). E_2P_2 alone significantly stimulated stromal proliferation and retarded both VP and DLP development (Fig. 1C, G). Small acini with immature glandular development similar to prostate isolated from rats castrated at birth were easily detectable [26]. TP plus E_2P_2 treatment also enhanced stromal proliferation in both VP and DLP. Epithelial squamous metaplasia was apparent. In addition, this treatment regimen also resulted in many areas of intense lymphocytic infiltration in both VP and DLP (Fig. 1D, H).

Studies on photoaffinity labeling of different forms of protein kinases by [^{32}P]-8-azido-cAMP revealed marked differences between VP and DLP with respect to their sensitivity toward sex steroids. Three major 8-azido-cAMP labeled proteins, 59K, 51K, and 43K daltons, were detected in the cytosols of both VP and DLP isolated from untreated control rats (Fig. 2, 3). Treatment of rats with TP, E_2P_2, or both altered the quantitative distribution of protein kinases in VP cytosol (Fig. 2). However, when TP was administered, either alone or in combination with E_2P_2, it almost completely abolished the binding of DLP cytosol to this photoaffinity probe (Fig. 3). E_2P_2 treatment alone did not alter the qualitative pattern of protein kinases in the DLP. Quantitative differences of 8-azido-cAMP binding were noted between hormone-dependent, independent, and anaplastic Dunning tumors [49].

To relate morphological changes of the prostate with testosterone metabolic patterns, a new one-step HPLC system was developed (Fig. 4). Identity of testosterone and its major metabolites was determined by retention time on HPLC and recrystallization to constant specific activities under three solvent-pair conditions (Table I). The metabolism of testosterone by tissue minces was compared between VP and DLP which were isolated from rats treated with different hormonal regimens (Table II). As compared to untreated controls, TP significantly enhanced testosterone metabolism in the VP but not the DLP. Under these assay conditions, the major metabolites formed were dihydrotestosterone (DHT) and androsterone. DHT formation in untreated DLP was 2.5-fold that of the VP. E_2P_2 treatment alone inhibited testosterone metabolism, and a 2 to 12-fold reduction in DHT and androsterone formation was detected. TP plus E_2P_2 treatment, on the other hand, reduced DHT formation without altering androsterone production. Since TP plus E_2P_2 treatment significantly enhanced stromal prolif-

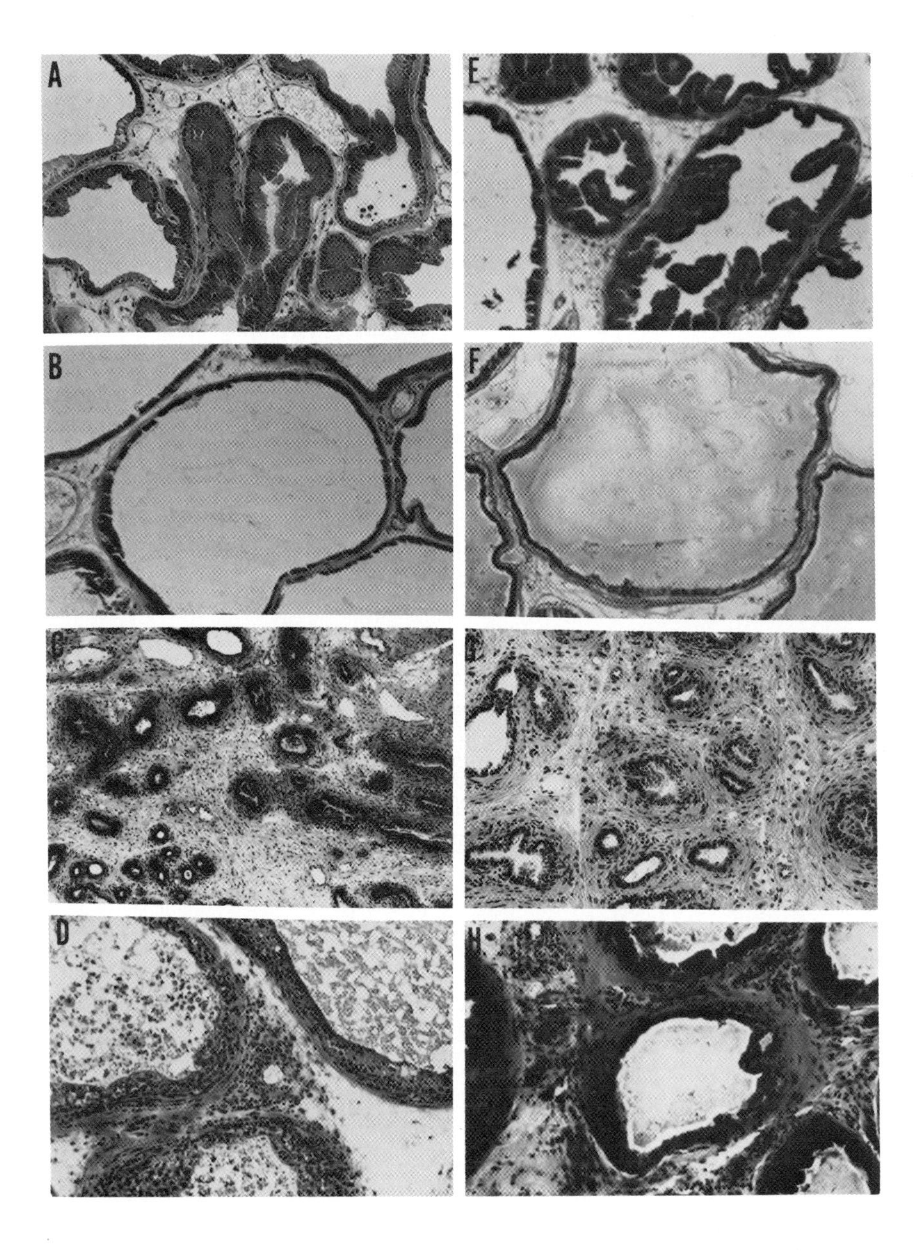

Fig. 1. Histology of ventral (A–D) and dorsolateral (E–H) prostates isolated from untreated (A and E), TP (B and F), E_2P_2 (C and G), or TP plus E_2P_2-treated (D and H) rats. 250 ×.

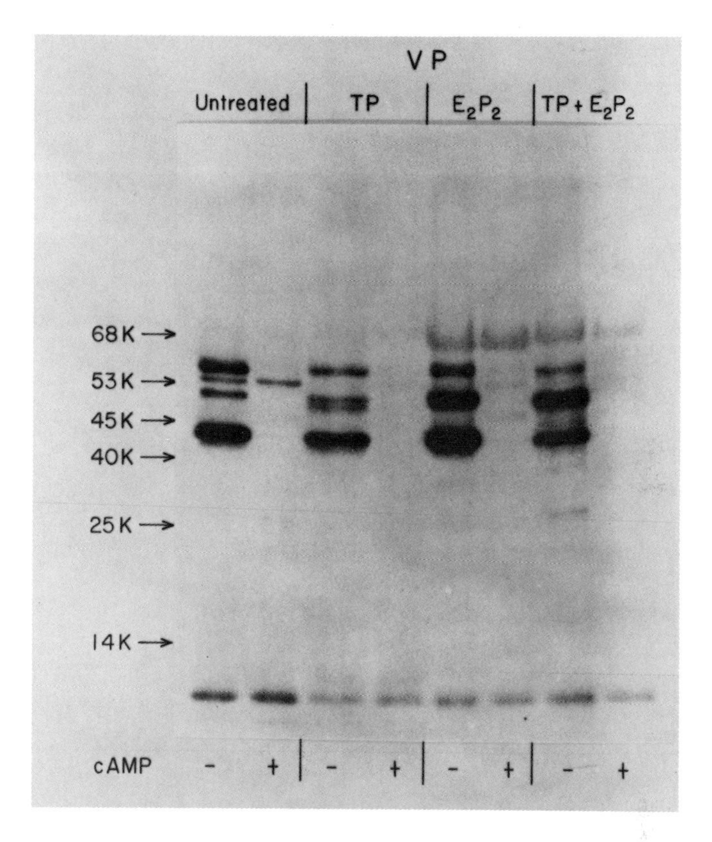

Fig. 2. Photoaffinity labeling of regulatory subunits of cAMP-dependent protein kinases in rat ventral prostatic cytosol.

eration in both VP and DLP, the question of possible compartmentalization of steroid-metabolizing enzymes in either the stromal or epithelial compartment was raised. Experiments utilizing highly enriched epithelial and stromal components isolated from VP and DLP of untreated rats for testosterone metabolism revealed that the epithelium isolated from DLP converted testosterone to DHT at a rate of five times that of the VP (Fig. 5A, B). Unlike that of the human prostate, rat prostatic epithelial cells were more active than the stromal cells in metabolizing testosterone (Fig. 5A–D).

We have also examined the cytosolic androgen receptor contents (R-1881 binding) in VP and DLP isolated from untreated and hormone-treated Nb rats. Table III shows that, as compared to the untreated controls, TP administered either alone or in combination with E_2P_2 markedly reduced the total number of specific cytosolic androgen receptor sites while enhancing markedly the binding

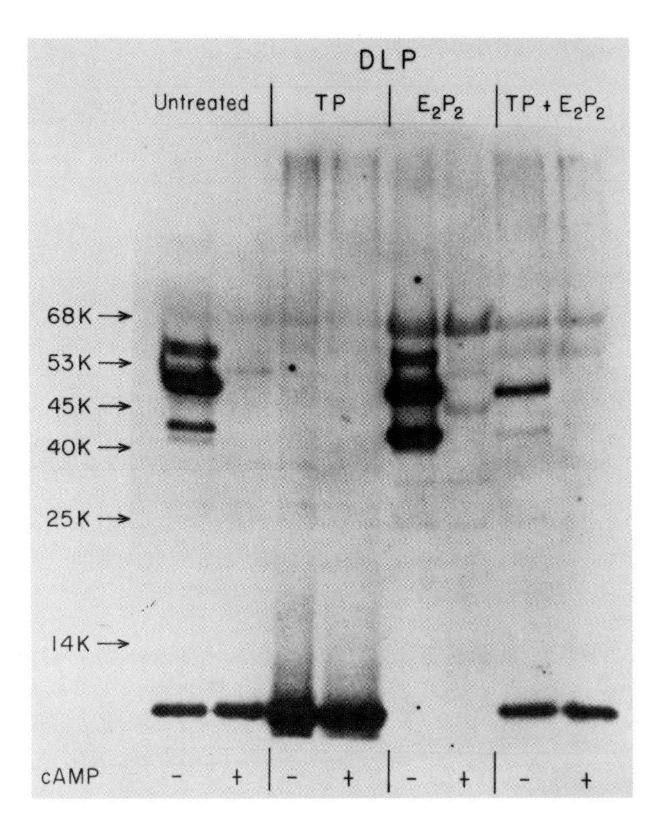

Fig. 3. Photoaffinity labeling of regulatory subunits of cAMP-dependent protein kinases in rat dorsolateral prostatic cytosol.

affinity. A much lower level of high-affinity cytosolic androgen receptor was detected in the cytosolic fraction of the DLP. These regimens of hormonal treatment totally abolished the high-affinity binding sites in the DLP.

The other approach to determine the importance of tissue interactions during prostatic development is to investigate the inductive potential of stroma in tissue recombinants. This system was established previously by Cunha and his associates [12] who found that normal prostatic morphogenesis occurs as a result of an interaction between adult urothelium and embryonic urogenital sinus mesenchyme. The mesenchyme induces and specifies the morphological and functional characteristics of the epithelium. In this communication, additional data are provided to suggest that the stromal cells are the actual targets for androgen actions during prostatic development.

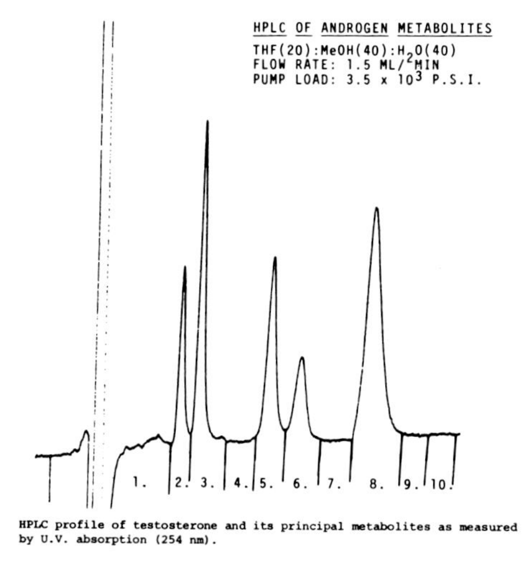

HPLC profile of testosterone and its principal metabolites as measured by U.V. absorption (254 nm).

Area	Steroid	Retention Times
1	unknown polar metabolites	< 5 min
2	androstenedione	5 min, 45 sec
3	testosterone	6 min, 30 sec
4	3β-androstanediol*	7 min, 30 sec
5	androstanedione	9 min
6	dihydrotestosterone	10 min
7	3α-androstanediol*	11 min, 45 sec
8	androsterone	12 min, 45 sec
9	unknown**	13 → 14 min
10	unknown**	14 → 15 min

* Determined by use of radiolabelled steroid.

** Comprises < 1% of total radioactivity.

Fig. 4. High-pressure liquid chromatographic (HPLC) separation of testosterone and its metabolites.

Figure 6A shows that grafts of isolated urogenital sinus mesenchyme (UGM) alone failed to develop into prostatic morphology suggesting the cleanness of the isolated mesenchyme. However, the heterotypic recombinants consisting of $UGM^{+/+}$ + $BLE^{Tfm/y}$ (adult bladder epithelium isolated from Tfm/y mouse) developed normal prostatic morphology suggesting the direct inductive influence of UGM upon the Tfm epithelium (Fig. 6B). The induced prostatic morphology obviously responded to androgen-induced growth (Fig. 6C, D) and cyproterone acetate-induced atrophy (Fig. 6E) similar to that expected of the host prostate.

To establish that these heterotypic recombinants ($UGM^{+/+}$ + $BLE^{Tfm/y}$) indeed behave as prostate, we have further examined the following biochemical parameters: DNA synthesis and its inhibition by the antiandrogen, cyproterone acetate, total tissue protein, and steroid metabolism profiles. Similar to that

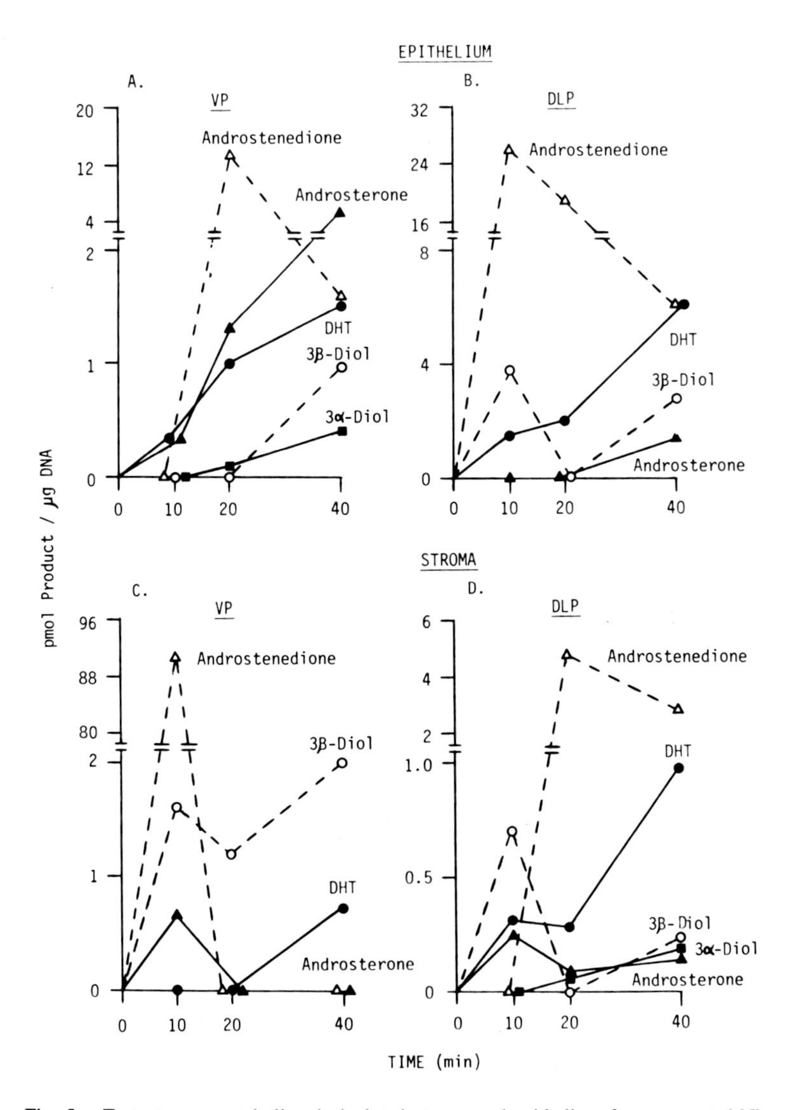

Fig. 5. Testosterone metabolism in isolated stroma and epithelium from untreated Nb rats.

observed in rats [27], prostate isolated from castrated mice responded to TP-induced DNA synthesis with a peak rate of [^{3}H]-thymidine incorporation into tissue DNA occurring at 72 hours following TP administration (Table IV). In contrast, mouse urinary bladder, a non-target organ for androgen, failed to exhibit TP-induced DNA synthesis. The tissue recombinant responded to TP-induced DNA synthesis similar to that observed in the host prostate (Table IV). Moreover,

TABLE I. Crystallization to constant specific activity of radioactive metabolites isolated by HPLC from two incubations of mouse prostate/bladder with [^{3}H]-testosterone

Area number	Steroid	Sequence of solvent pairs	Specific activity (dpm/mg) after recrystallization							% Initial radioactivity present in last recrystallization
				First		Second		Third		
			Start	C_1	M_1	C_2	M_2	C_3	M_3	
2	Δ^4-androstenedione	a,b,c	916	795	1632	834	1020	838	858	93
3	testosterone	a,b,c	12574	11826	11738	12258	12166	12382	12250	98
4	5α-androstane-3β, 17β-diol* (3β-androstandediol)	a,d,e	33	28	1339	29	28	29	24	88
5	5α-androstanedione*	a,b,c	85	63	221	31	46	36	40	42
6	dihydrotestosterone	a,d,e	6563	6185	5932	6266	5521	6366	5660	97
7	5α-androstane-3α, 17β-diol (3α-androstanediol)	a,d,e	720	705	578	621	552	574	543	80
8	androsterone*	a,b,c	42	33	102	21	28	29	25	69

Solvents: (a) acetone: H_20; (b) acetone: n-Hexane; (c) ethylacetate: n-Hexane; (d) chloroform: n-Hexane; (e) ethylacetate: cyclohexane; C: crystals; M: mother liquor.

*Isolated from bladder.

this TP-induced DNA synthesis in the host prostate and the tissue recombinant was sensitive to antagonism by cyproterone acetate (Fig. 7). In contrast, however, DNA synthesis in the host urinary bladder was totally insensitive to similar antiandrogenic antagonism.

Total cell proteins labeled with ^{35}S-methionine were compared between host prostate and host bladder (Figs. 8, 9). As expected, the intensity of overall labeling of proteins in host prostate was greater than that of the bladder. In

TABLE II. Testosterone metabolism by minced ventral (VP) and dorsolateral (DLP) prostates isolated from untreated and TP-, E_2P_2-, or TP plus E_2P_2-treated rats

	Percentage of testosterone							
	VP				DLP			
Metabolites	Untreated	TP	E_2P_2[a]	TP + E_2P_2	Untreated	TP	E_2P_2[a]	TP + E_2P_2
Unknown polar metabolites	2.3	3.1	0.7	2.4	3.6	3.4	0.8	2.8
Androstenedione	2.5	2.1	1.5	2.2	2.1	2.7	1.9	2.3
Testosterone	78.0	49.8	92.3	72.8	66.6	77.3	92.8	80.6
5α-Androstane-3β,17β-diol	1.1	0.9	0.5	1.0	1.1	1.2	0.5	0.9
Androstanedione	0.5	0.9	0.5	1.0	1.5	1.4	0.5	0.8
Dihydrotestosterone	4.1	17.6	2.7	1.7	10.6	6.2	2.0	0.9
5α-Androstane-3α,17β-diol	0.9	1.1	0.4	0.9	1.2	1.1	0.3	0.5
Androsterone	10.0	23.7	1.2	16.7	12.3	5.7	1.0	10.3
Column wash	0.6	1.0	0.2	0.9	1.1	1.0	0.2	0.9

[^{3}H]Testosterone (5 nmole; 5.0 μCi) was incubated with minced tissue (60 to 87 μg DNA per assay) and Kreb's Ringer Phosphate buffer, pH 7.4, in total incubation volumes of 1.0 ml. Reference steroids were added to the sample extracts, separated by HPLC, and the radioactivity measured.
[a]E_2P_2 treated animal was 4 months of age; all other animals were 6–8 months of age.

TABLE III. Scatchard analysis of androgen receptor in ventral (VP) and dorsolateral (DLP) prostates: Effects of long term sex steroids treatment

	VP		DLP	
	Kd (nM)	fmole/mg	Kd (nM)	fmole/mg
Untreated	0.41	39.1	0.7	0.6
TP	0.19	3.9	—	nil
TP + E_2P_2	0.03	0.9	—	nil

addition, there were numerous qualitative and quantitative differences noted in these two tissues. For example, proteins in region P-1 to P-7 were associated with prostate whereas proteins in region B-1 to B-3 were bladder-specific. $UGM^{+/+}$ + $BLE^{Tfm/y}$ recombinant exhibited protein synthetic profiles almost identical to those of the prostate (Fig. 10). Protein spots indicative of bladder phenotype were not expressed in the tissue recombinant.

Since prostate and bladder exhibited differences in testosterone metabolism, an attempt was made to compare the metabolism of testosterone between host prostate, host bladder, and $UGM^{+/+}$ + $BLE^{+/+}$ recombinants in vitro (Table V). With the exception of 3β-androstanediol and androsterone formation, all

TABLE IV. Time courses for androgen-induced DNA synthesis in host prostate, host bladder, and tissue recombinants comprised of $UGM^{+/+}$ + $BLE^{+/+}$

	Rate of DNA Synthesis[a] (cpm/μg DNA/30 min)			
Tissue type	0	48 hr	72 hr	120 hr
Host prostate	96 (1.0)	323 (3.4)	662 (6.9)	242 (2.5)
Host bladder	205 (1.0)	262 (1.3)	253 (1.2)	232 (1.1)
$UGM^{+/+}$ + $BLE^{+/+}$	—	225 (2.3)	481 (5.0)	155 (1.6)

[a]Male hosts carrying tissue recombinants were castrated for 10 days and then treated with TP (0.2 mg/day) for 0, 2, 3, and 5 days. Host prostate, host bladder, and tissue recombinants were harvested and incubated with Krebs Ringer phosphate buffer (pH 7.4) containing (^{3}H)-thymidine (400 mCi/nmole, 1×10^{-5}) for 30 minutes at 37°C according to Methods. Rate of DNA synthesis were calculated at each time point. Numbers in the parentheses indicate the ratios against 0 time samples. In case of $UGM^{+/+}$ plus $BLE^{+/+}$, 0 time host prostate was used for tabulation. Data represent the average of two determinations with differences between determination less than 10%.

TABLE V. ^{3}H-testosterone metabolic profiles in host bladder, $UGM^{+/+}$ + $BLE^{+/+}$, and host prostate

Steroid	Bladder	$UGM^{+/+}$ + $BLE^{+/+}$ (% of testosterone metabolites[a])	Prostate
Δ^4-androstenedione	18.3 ± 2.4	2.6 ± 1.6	23.5 ± 9.2
3β-androstanediol	10.0 ± 4.2	13.4 ± 4.2	2.1 ± 0.8
5α-androstanedione	10.7 ± 2.8	3.6 ± 1.4	1.7 ± 0.9
dihydrotestosterone	18.8 ± 2.3	26.6 ± 6.4	26.7 ± 5.3
3α-androstanediol	9.0 ± 3.5	16.6 ± 1.9	20.8 ± 5.7
androsterone	23.0 ± 6.8	17.6 ± 4.8	5.6 ± 0.5
unknown polar metabolites	5.7 ± 1.7	19.8 ± 10.4	17.6 ± 5.9

[a]Values represent percent mean ± SE of at least six experiments.

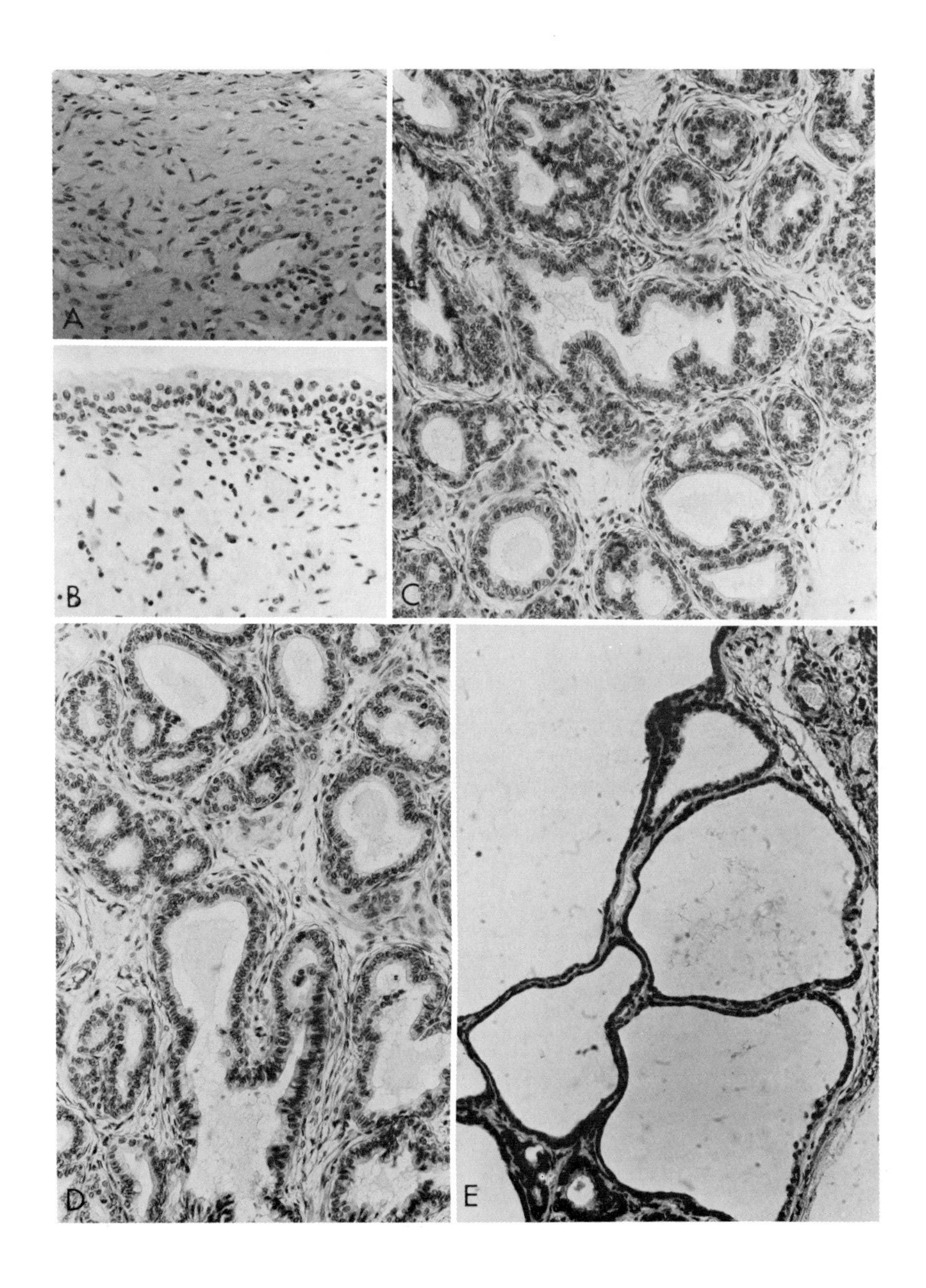
A
B
C
D
E

other testosterone metabolites formed in the tissue recombinants were similar to those of the host prostate. The incompleteness of expressing the prostatic metabolic enzyme profile suggests that the tissue recombinant retained, at least partially, the bladder phenotype.

If bladder epithelium from testicular feminized mice expressed prostate phenotype, the question was whether or not the urothelium from testicular-feminized mice can express androgen receptor activity. Unfortunately, tissue recombinants are small and thus made the direct determination of androgen receptor difficult. Alternatively, we posed the question as to whether testicular-feminized mice may express androgen receptor activity under special assay conditions. We chose the assay condition that contained sodium molybdate in the assay buffer. Previously it has been shown that sodium molybdate stabilizes glucocorticoid [28], estrogen [29], progesterone [30], and androgen [31] receptors. Figure 11 shows that kidney cytosol isolated from wild-type (Ta/y) contained androgen receptor with a kd of 1.7 nM. In contrast, kidney cytosol isolated from testicular-feminized mice contained no detectable high-affinity androgen receptor. The addition of sodium molybdate to the assay medium restored the Tfm/y cytosolic androgen receptor to a level that is comparable, with respect to both total number of binding sites and the kd, to that of the wild-type. Sodium molybdate, however, further enhanced the affinity and total number of specific binding sites in the wild-type.

DISCUSSION

Two developmental models were utilized in the present study to examine the progression of normal and abnormal prostate development. In the Nb rat model, sex steroids are known to induce prostatic adenocarcinoma in the dorsolateral

---

Fig. 6. All grafts were grown for four weeks in male hosts. A) A graft of urogenital sinus mesenchyme from a 16-day-old mouse embryo. The mesenchymal cells have formed a mass of fibromuscular cells. Note the absence of any epithelial structures which indicates that the tryptic separation was effective. 250 ×. B) A homotypic recombinant of bladder stroma and epithelium from an adult mouse. The urothelium has differentiated normally. 250 ×. C) A heterotypic recombinant of wild-type urogenital sinus mesenchyme from a 16-day-old mouse embryo associated with adult Tfm/y bladder epithelium. Prostatic morphogenesis has been induced in the urothelium. Note the secretory product within the acini. 250 ×. D) A $UGM^{+/+}$ + BLE^{Tfm} recombinant as in C. The recombinant was grown for one month in an intact male host which was then castrated for seven days and subsequently given testosterone propionate (TP) (0.2 mg/day) for three days. Secretory activity (tall cellular height and secretory product) has been reestablished following administration of the androgen. 250 ×. E) A $UGM^{+/+}$ + BLE^{Tfm} recombinant subjected to identical growth conditions as in D with the exception that following castration the host was injected with TP (0.2 mg/day) and cyproterme acetate (4 mg/day). The antiandrogen has prevented TP restoration of the glandular acini. 250 ×.

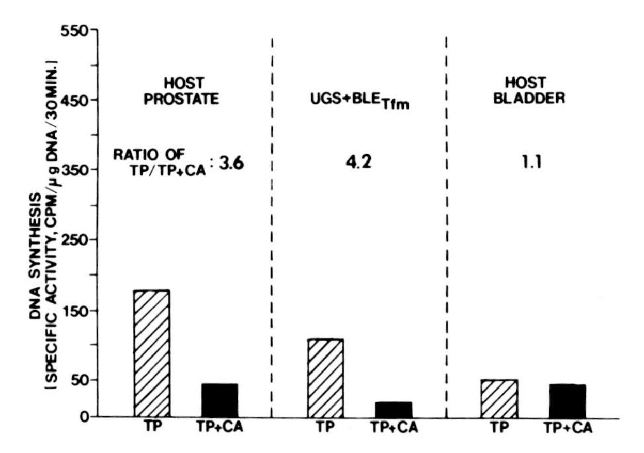

Fig. 7. DNA synthesis in mouse prostate, mouse bladder, and tissue recombinants consisting of epithelium isolated from Tfm/y mouse bladder and mouse urogenital sinus mesenchyme. Rate of DNA synthesis was determined at 72 hours after TP (testosterone propionate) or TP + CA (cyproterone acetate) treatment.

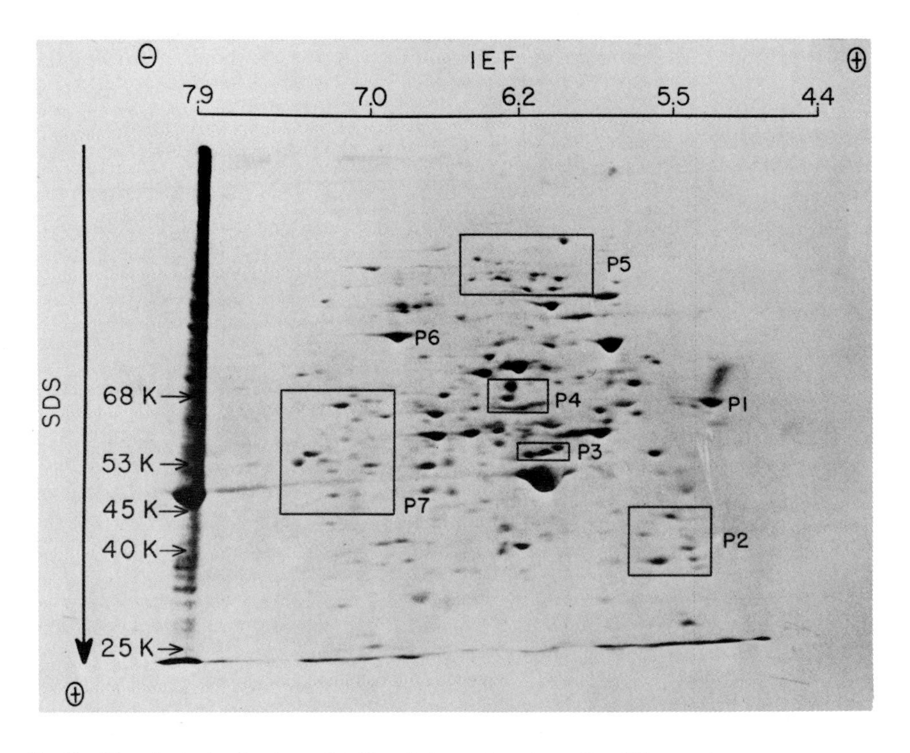

Fig. 8. Two-dimensional polyacrylamide gel electrophoretic profile of ^{35}S-methionine-labeled proteins isolated from mouse prostate.

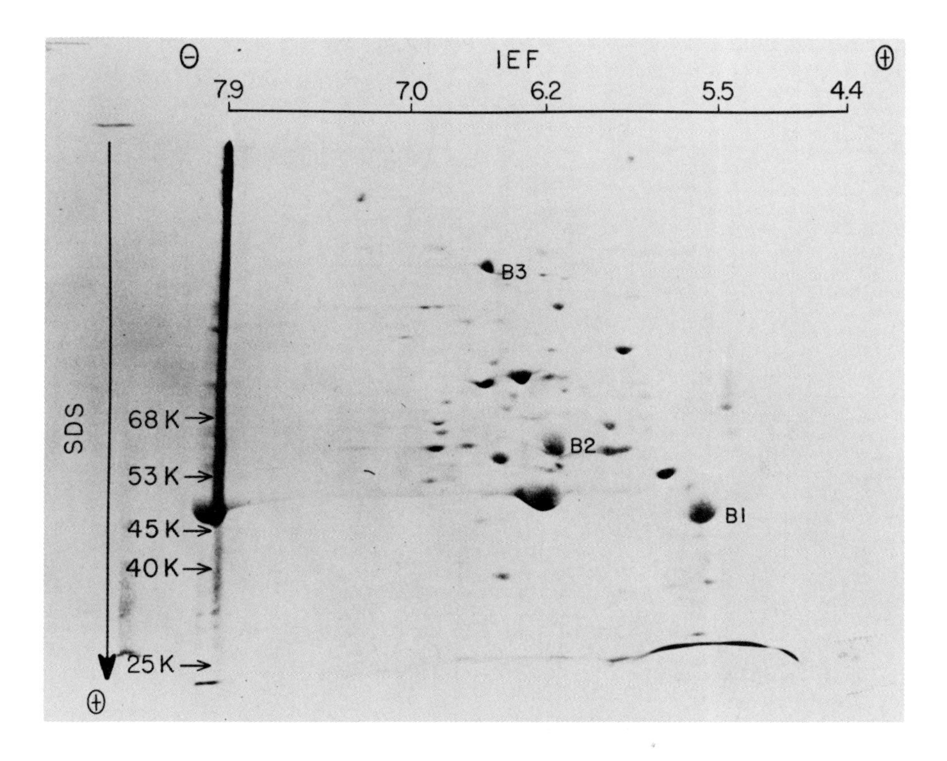

Fig. 9. Two-dimensional polyacrylamide gel electrophoretic profile of ^{35}S-methionine-labeled proteins isolated from mouse bladder.

lobe [8]. A number of morphological and biochemical changes were observed in the gland during a long-term sex steroid administration. Some of these changes are lobular-specific and sex steroid-dependent. For example, TP and/or E_2P_2 induced only qualitative changes of 8-azido-cAMP binding to VP cytosol whereas the binding of this photoaffinity ligand to DLP cytosol is almost completely abolished in TP and TP plus E_2P_2 but not in E_2P_2-treated rats. These differential effects of TP and TP plus E_2P_2 on DLP coincide with the observation that only these hormonal regimens caused prostate adenocarcinoma in DLP [8]. Thus, the binding of 8-azido-cAMP to prostatic tissue cytosol may be utilized as a marker for monitoring sex steroid-induced prostatic cancer in Nb rats. Eight-azido-cAMP has been demonstrated previously to bind the regulatory subunits of cAMP-dependent protein kinases [32]. The binding observed at 59K and 51K corresponds to Type II and I protein kinase regulatory subunits, respectively, based on DEAE column chromatography [33], autophosphorylation, and one- and two-dimensional polyacrylamide gel analysis [34].

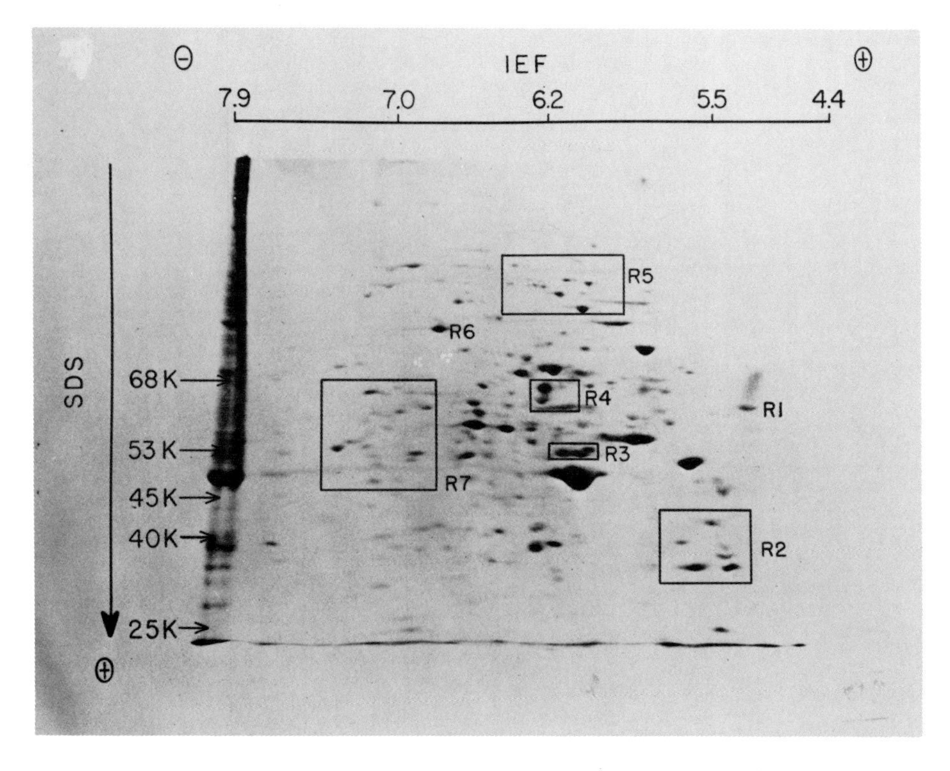

Fig. 10. Two-dimensional polyacrylamide gel electrophoretic profile of ^{35}S-methionine-labeled proteins isolated from tissue recombinants consisting of mouse urogenital sinus mesenchyme and Tfm/y mouse bladder epithelium.

Analysis of the rate of testosterone metabolism by epithelial and stromal-enriched populations revealed that the DLP epithelium is about fivefold more active than VP epithelium in converting testosterone into DHT. Whether this high rate of DHT formation in DLP may relate to its exquisite sensitivity toward the development of either hormonal-induced [8] or spontaneously-derived [35] prostatic adenocarcinomas in rats is not known. Higher than normal levels of DHT were reported in canine benign hyperplasia prostate and in human benign prostatic hyperplasia and in prostatic adenocarcinoma tissues [36]. In addition, long-term sex steroid treatments also caused certain specific histological changes of the prostate. At present, it is difficult to associate any of these histological changes with the development of latent prostatic adenocarcinoma. Similarly, marked changes in cytosolic androgen receptor and its kinetic properties were also observed and the significance of these modifications in relation to sex steroid-induced prostatic adenocarcinoma development in DLP is not clear.

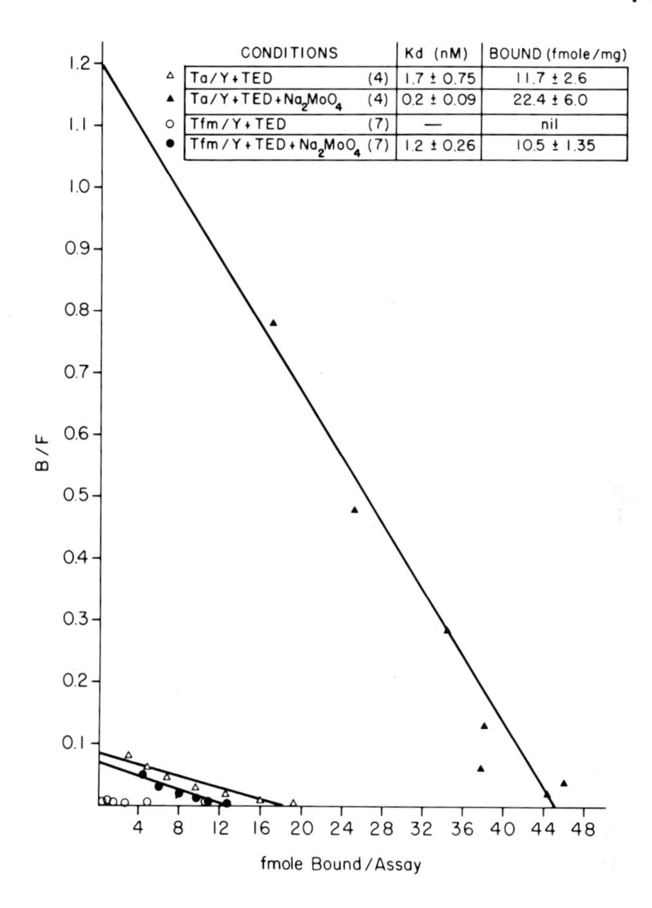

Fig. 11. Scatchard analysis of androgen receptor present in kidney cytosol isolated from control (Ta/y) and Tfm/y mice: Effects of sodium molybdate.

The second developmental model involves the study of interactions of isolated embryonic mesenchyme and adult epithelium. In addition to previous morphological and histochemical demonstrations of the positive induction of adult urothelium by UGM to express prostatic phenotypes, the present study further documents that with the exception of a few steroid-metabolizing enzymes, the adult urothelium expressed functional prostatic activities which include the responsiveness of the $UGM^{+/+}$ + $BLE^{Tfm/y}$ to TP-induced DNA synthesis, inhibition of this DNA synthesis by the antiandrogen, cyproterone acetate and total cell protein profiles as analyzed by two-dimensional polyacrylamide gel electrophoresis. More importantly, the present study demonstrates the role of stroma in eliciting androgen action, ie, directive induction of adult urothelium to participate

TABLE VI. Examples of homo- and heterologous recombination of mesenchyme and epithelium and the developmental consequences of such interaction

Sources of epithelium and mesenchyme	Developmental consequences	Nature of interaction	References
Within species			
Embryonic salivary gland mesenchyme and embryonic salivary gland epithelium	Branching morphogenesis	Extracellular matrix	[41]
Wolflian bud epithelium and metanephrogenic mesenchyme	Kidney tubule formation	Direct cell contact	[42]
Embryonic mesenchyme of different sources and pancreatic epithelium	DNA synthesis, cytodifferentiation and morphogenesis	Mesenchymal factor interacts with cell surface	[43]
Urogenital sinus mesenchyme and bladder epithelium	Prostatic morphology and function	Not tested	[44]

Between species			
Mouse molar mesenchyme and chick limb bud epithelium	Tooth development, enamel or mesenchymal-specific collagen synthesis	Close cell contact	[45,46]
Mouse flank skin mesenchyme and chick corneal anterior epithelium	Feather formation	Not tested	[47]
Mouse urogenital sinus mesenchyme and adult human vaginal epithelium	Maintenance of morphology	Not tested	[48]
Mouse urogenital sinus mesenchyme and fetal human bladder epithelium	Epithelium outgrowth resembles prostatic bud	Not tested	[48]

in prostatic morphogenesis and expression of biochemical functions. This is consistent with our previous observation that the tissue recombinant consisting of $UGM^{Tfm/y}$ + $BLE^{+/+}$ failed to elicite this same androgen action [12]. The participation of adult urothelium from Tfm/y in these androgen-induced processes suggest the possible induction of androgen receptor in adult urothelium through close stromal-epithelial interactions. Attempts to demonstrate the presence of androgen receptor in the kidney cytosol of Tfm/y mice were achieved by the addition of sodium molybdate to the assay medium. However, a more direct demonstration of the presence of androgen receptor in the stromal-induced urothelium by autoradiographic and biochemical (using rat tissues) analyses is currently in progress.

The demonstration of directive influences of urogenital sinus stroma on the phenotypic expression of *adult* urothelium under androgenic environment is remarkable when considering many other inductive systems in developmental biology which generally involve tissue interactions between embryonic tissues (Table VI). In general, tissue interactions are not only required for normal embryonic morphogenesis and cytodifferentiation but also for the maintenance of normal epithelial morphology and function in adulthood. Disruptive or defective stromal-epithelial interactions have been suggested as causative factors in the development of neoplasia [37,38]. In view of the tissue interaction systems depicted in Table VI, several common features emerge. First, stromal-epithelial interactions can take place within or between species and organs. This suggests that the developmental potential of somatic cells are conserved through evolution. Second, the responsiveness of adult bladder epithelium to the inductive influences from urogenital sinus stroma may suggest the pluripotency of these cells. Alternatively, the development of bladder cells is closely related to that of the prostatic cells. Third, adult and fetal human epithelial cells can be maintained as tissue recombinants in nude mice. Epithelial cells alone generally will not survive under these same culture conditions. Obviously, experiments leading to the understanding of the basic mechanisms underlying tissue and cell interactions are essential before any knowledge can be gained from the biological processes, such as abnormal cell proliferation, differentiation, invasion, and metastasis. Utilizing tissue interaction models, one can also study the interactions between normal and abnormal tissues. The elegant demonstration of complete reversal of tumorigenicity under embryonic environments by Pierce [39] and Mintz [40] further illustrated the potential of modifying growth conditions which ultimately may influence the fate of tumor cells. Additional studies and understanding of these basic developmental processes may shed light on future therapy for the treatment of prostatic cancer in man.

ACKNOWLEDGMENTS

The excellent technical assistance of Ms Karen Breitweiser and secretarial assistance of Ms Pamela Lingenfelter are gratefully appreciated. This study is supported by PHS grant CA-27418 and AM-25266.

REFERENCES

1. Smolev J, Heston W, Scott WW, Coffey DS: Characterization of the Dunning R-3327H prostatic adenocarcinoma: An appropriate animal model for prostatic cancer. Cancer Treat Rep 61:273–287, 1977.
2. Pollard M, Luckert PH: Transplantable metastasized prostate adenocarcinoma in rats. J Natl Cancer Inst 54:643–649, 1975.
3. Kaighn ME, Lechner JF, Narayan KS, Jones LW: Prostatic carcinoma: Tissue culture cell lines. Natl Cancer Inst Monogr 49:17–21, 1978.
4. Webber MM: Growth and maintenance of normal prostatic epithelium in vitro—a human cell model. In Murphy GP (ed): New York: Alan R. Liss, Inc., 1980, pp 181–216.
5. Menon M, Tananis CE, Hicks LL, Hawkins EF, McLoughlin MG, Walsh PC: Characterization of binding of potent synthetic androgen, methyltrienolone to human tissues. J Clin Invest 61:150–162, 1978.
6. Shain SA, Boesel RW, Lamm DL, Radwin HM: Characterization of unoccupied and occupied androgen binding components of the hyperplastic human prostate. Steroid 21:541–556, 1978.
7. Hoehn W, Foebsis AC, Schroeder FH: Human prostatic adenocarcinoma: Some characterization of a serially transplanted line in nude mice PC-82. The Prostate 1:94–104, 1980.
8. Noble RL: The development of prostatic adenocarcinoma in the NB rat following prolonged sex hormone administration. Cancer Res 17:1929–1933, 1977.
9. Moore RA: Benign hypertrophy and carcinoma of the prostate. In Twombly G, Packs G (eds): "Endocrinology of Neoplastic Diseases." London, New York: Oxford Univ Press, 1947, pp 194–212.
10. Noble RL: Production of NB rat carcinoma of the dorsal prostate and response of estrogen-dependent transplants to sex hormones and tamoxifen. Cancer Res 40:3547–3550, 1980.
11. Noble RL: Development of androgen-stimulated transplants of NB rat carcinoma of the dorsal prostate and their response to sex hormones and tamoxifen. Cancer Res 40:3551–3554, 1980.
12. Cunha GR, Chung LWK, Shannon JM, Reese BA: Stromal-epithelial interactions in sex differentiation. Biol Reprod 22:19–42, 1980.
13. Coffey DS: The effects of androgen on DNA and RNA synthesis in sex accessory tissue. In David Brandes (ed): "Male Accessory Sex Organs," New York: Academic Press, 1974, pp 307–328.
14. Neubauer BL, Anderson NG, Cunha GR, Towell JF, Chung LWK: A new isocratic HPLC system for the measurement of in vitro testosterone metabolism in tissue recombinants composed of adult mouse urinary bladder epithelium and urogenital sinus mesenchyme. Proc West Pharmacol Soc 24:289–293, 1981.
15. Gloyna RE, Wilson JD: A comparative study of the conversion of testosterone to 17β-hydroxy-5α-androstan-3-one (dihydrotestosterone) by prostate and epididymis. J Clin Endocrinol 29:970–977, 1969.

16. Laemmli UK: Cleavage of structure proteins during the assembly of the head of bacteriophage T4. Nature 227:680–685, 1970.
17. Scatchard G: The attraction of protein for small molecules and ions. Ann NY Acad Sci 51:660–672, 1949.
18. Burton K: Determination of DNA concentration with diphenylamine. Meth Enzymol 12B:163–166, 1968.
19. Chung LWK, Coffey DS: Biochemical characterizations of prostatic nuclei II. Relationship between DNA synthesis and protein synthesis. Biochim Biophys Acta 247:584–596, 1971.
20. Anderson NG, Rocco AK, Chung LWK: Progression of prostatic adenocarcinoma in NB rats. J Supramolec Struct & Cell Biochem Suppl 5:223, 1981.
21. O'Farrell PH: High resolution two-dimensional electrophoresis of proteins. J Biol Chem 250:4007–4021, 1975.
22. Yang J, Guzman R, Richards J, Nandi S: Primary culture of mouse mammary tumor epithelial cells embedded in collagen gels. In Vitro 16:502–506, 1980.
23. Yang J, Guzman R, Richards J, Jentoft V, DeVault MR, Wellings SR, Nandi S: Primary culture of human mammary epithelial cells embedded in collagen gels. J Natl Cancer Inst 65:337–343, 1980.
24. Lowry OH, Rosebrough NJ, Farr AL, Randall RJ: Protein measurement with the folin phenol reagent. J Biol Chem 193:265–275, 1951.
25. Hinegardner RT: An improved fluorometric assay for DNA. Analyt Biochem. 39:197–201, 1971.
26. Chung LWK, MacFadden DK: Sex steroid imprinting and prostatic growth. Invest Urol 17:337–342, 1980.
27. Coffey DS, Shimazaki J, Williams-Ashman HG: Polymerization of deoxyribonucleotides in relation to androgen-induced prostatic growth. Arch Biochem Biophys 124:184–198, 1968.
28. Leach KL, Dahmer MK, Hammond ND, Sando JJ, Pratt WB: Molybdate inhibition of glucocorticoid receptor inactivation and transformation. J Biol Chem 254:11884–11890, 1979.
29. Shyamala G, Leonard L: Inhibition of mouse uterine estrogen receptor activation by sodium molybdate. Fed Proc 39:2133, 1980.
30. Bevins CL, Bashirelahi N: Stabilization of 8 S progesterone receptor from human prostate in the presence of molybdate ion. Cancer Res 40:2234–2239, 1980.
31. Gaubert CM, Tremblay RR, Dúbe JY: Effect of sodium molybdate on cytosolic androgen receptors in rat prostate. J Steroid Biochem 13:931–937, 1980.
32. Cho-Chung YS: Cyclic AMP and its receptor protein in tumor growth regulation in vivo. Adv Cyclic Nucleotide Res 10:163–177, 1979.
33. Malkinson AM, Butley MS: Alteration in cyclic adenosine 3′:5′-monophosphate-dependent protein kinases during normal and neoplastic lung development. Cancer Res 41:1334–1341, 1981.
34. Breitweiser K, Butley MS, Malkinson AM, Chung LWK: Photoaffinity labeling differences between hormone-dependent and independent prostatic adenocarcinoma cells to 8-azido-CAMP. Cancer Res (in preparation).
35. Dunning WF: Prostatic cancer in the rat. Natl Cancer Inst Monog 12:351–370, 1963.
36. Coffey DS, Isaacs JT: Prostatic Cancer. Report No. 9 VICC Technical Report Series. Geneva, Vol. 48. 1979, pp 1–289.
37. Tarin D: Tissue interactions in carcinogenesis. New York, London: Academic Press, 1972, pp 1–483.
38. McNeal JE: Development and comparative anatomy of the prostate. In Grayhack JT, Wilson JD, Sherbenski MJ (eds): "Benign Prostatic Hyperplasia." 1976, pp 1–9.

39. Pierce GB, Pantazis GC, Caldwell JE, Wells RS: Embryologic control of malignancy. J Supramolec Struct & Cell Biochem Supp 5:156, 1981.
40. Mintz B: Gene expression in neoplasia and differentiation. Harvey Lect. Sem. 71. New York, London: Academic Press, 1978, pp 193–245.
41. Bernfield MR, Banerjee SD: Acid mucopolysaccharide (glycosaminoglycan) at the epithelial-mesenchymal interface of mouse embryo salivary glands. J Cell Biol 52:664–673, 1972.
42. Sáxen L: Mechanism of morphogenetic tissue interactions: the message of transfilter experiments. In McKinnell RG, DiBerardino MA, Blumenfeld M, Bergad (eds): "Differentiation and Neoplasia." Berlin-Heidelberg: Springer-Verlag 1980, pp 147–154.
43. Levine S, Pictet R, Rutler WJ: Control of cell proliferation and cytodifferentiation by a factor reacting with cell surface. Nature 246:49–52, 1973.
44. Cunha GR, Lung B, Reese B: Glandular epithelial induction by embryonic mesenchyme in adult bladder epithelium of BALB/c mice. Invest Urol 17:302–304, 1980.
45. Kollar EJ, Fisher C: Tooth induction in chick epithelium: expression of quiescent genes for enamel synthesis. Science 207:993–995, 1980.
46. Hata RI, Slavkin HC: De novo induction of gene product during heterologous epithelial-mesenchyme interactions in vitro. Proc Natl Acad Sci USA 75:2790–2794, 1978.
47. Coulombre JL, Coutombre AJ: Metaplastic induction of scales and feathers in the corneal anterior epithelium of the chick embryo. Dev Biol 25:464–478, 1971.
48. Cunha GR, Shannon JM, Neubauer BL, Sawyer LM, Fujii H, Taguchi O, Chung LWK: Mesenchymal-epithelial interactions in sex differentiation (in press).
49. Chung LWK, Thompson TC, Breitweiser, K: Sensitive biochemical methods to distinguish hormone dependent and independent Dunning tumors of prostatic origin. Proc West Pharmacol Soc 24:305–310, 1981.

PROSTATIC SECRETIONS

The Prostatic Cell: Structure and Function
Part A, pages 207-224

Polyamines and Prostatic Function

Diane Haddock Russell

INTRODUCTION

For those of us interested in the definition of the functional significance of polyamine biosynthesis and accumulation, studies of these events in the prostate have historical significance. While Leeuwenhoek [1] was studying the microscopic properties of human semen, he found that, upon setting, a crystalline substance precipitated which he referred to as "semenstuf." Rosenheim [2] later identified this substance as spermine phosphate in both seminal fluid and testes. Spermine is now known to be a product secreted into the seminal plasma by the ventral prostate [3]. Its concentration in human semen is 10–15 mM, whereas the other known naturally occurring polyamine, spermidine, is almost nondetectable. Possible biochemical mechanisms of action of polyamines in seminal fluid have been extensively studied and reviewed [3–5]. One postulated mechanism of action for polyamines in seminal fluid is to serve as substrates for transglutaminase (EC 2.3.2.13) to facilitate cross linking of proteins involved in clot formation [5]. This would facilitate the formation of a copulation plug and aid in fertilization by facilitating high sperm concentration and retention in the vagina. Folk et al [6] have demonstrated N^1- and N^8-(γ-glutamyl)spermidine, N^1,N^8-bis-(γ-glutamyl)spermidine, N^1-(γ-glutamyl)spermine, and N^1,N^{12}-bis(γ-glutamyl)-spermine after proteolytic digestion of rat vesicular secretion proteins that have been incubated with coagulating gland extracts. Further, several proteins in the seminal clot and in the clot liquor had covalently bound polyamines and upon proteolytic digestion release γ-glutamyl polyamine derivatives [5].

There is substantial evidence that polyamine biosynthesis and accumulation constitute mandatory steps for organ growth [7–10]. Ornithine decarboxylase (EC 4.1.1.17, ODC), the initial and rate-limiting enzyme in the polyamine biosynthetic pathway, is rapidly induced in response to a variety of growth-promoting stimuli such as trophic hormones, steroid hormones, mitogens, partial hepatectomy, growth factors, etc [11]. In both normal and transformed cells as well as tissues, a major route of induction of ODC is via a cyclic AMP-mediated cascade of events [12]. This cascade includes the activation of cyclic AMP-dependent protein kinase (EC 2.7.1.37) and the phosphorylation of nonhistone chromosomal proteins related to the synthesis of new messenger RNA specific to ODC [13,14].

There are two other major categories of hormones that induce ODC by a mechanism independent of cyclic AMP-dependent protein kinase (Table I). Steroid hormones are known to have cytoplasmic receptors that migrate into the nucleus and apparently can interact with the gene sites for the production of messenger RNA for ODC [15–20]. Another class of hormones that induces ODC by an unknown mechanism are the so-called "coated pit" hormones [12]. These hormones result in a rapid decrease in the cyclic AMP concentrations, presumably due to the endocytosis of a membrane fragment which also contains adenylate cyclase [21]. Hormones currently classified in this category include insulin (thought to affect every tissue of the body), epidermal growth factor, nerve growth factor, and human chorion gonadatropin [21]. Although the second messenger for this class of hormones is unknown, these hormones induce ODC activity in a variety of cell lines and tissues [22–29]. Although studies of prostatic ODC induction have focused on the steriod hormone testosterone, studies we present in this paper implicate cyclic AMP-mediated trophic hormone(s), and it is likely that insulin would affect this induction were it to be studied [30]. A general schematic model of the transcriptional regulation of ODC activity by polypeptide trophic hormones and steroid hormones is presented in Figure 1. Consistent effects of all three classes of hormones are the transcriptional induction of ODC and the tight coupling of polyamine and ribosomal RNA accumulation [7–10]. Extensive evidence suggests that this coordinate synthesis is a result of posttranslational modification(s) of ODC and its ability to then act as an initiation

TABLE I. Categories of hormones related to the mechanisms of action

Categories	Mechanism
Trophic hormones	Hormones with membrane receptors which result in the activation of adenylate cyclase, cyclic AMP synthesis, activation of cyclic AMP-dependent protein kinase(s), and translocation to the nucleus to alter transcription.
Steroid hormones	Hormones which bind to cytoplasmic receptors followed by transfer of the receptor complex to the nucleus to alter transcription.
"Coated pit" hormones	Hormones with membrane receptors not coupled to adenylate cyclase activation. Receptors migrate to coated pits and undergo endocytosis, presumably for down regulation of receptors. The mechanism of action is unknown.

factor of RNA polymerase I, the rate-limiting enzyme in ribosomal RNA synthesis [10,31–33].

This paper will deal mainly with intracellular mechanisms related to multihormone regulation of polyamine biosynthesis in the prostate but also will discuss the implications of protein-conjugated polyamines in tissues and seminal fluid and of urinary acetyl polyamine concentrations as a function of disease activity, using prostate carcinoma as an example.

MATERIALS AND METHODS

Materials

L-[1-^{14}C]ornithine monohydrochloride (5 mCi/mmole), [γ-^{32}P]ATP (5 Ci/mmole), and Omnifluor were obtained from New England Nuclear, Boston, MA. Unlabeled ATP was obtained from Grand Island Biological Co., Grand Island, NY. Trihydroaminomethane (Trizma), 5α-dihydrotestosterone (5α-androstan-17β-ol-3-one), 1,2-propanediol (propylene glycol), and phenylmethylsulfonyl fluoride were obtained from Sigma Chemical Co., St. Louis, MO. 3-Isobutyl-1-methylxanthine and cyclic adenosine 3′,5′-monophosphate were purchased from Calbiochem, San Diego, CA. DEAE-cellulose (Cellex-D, 0.51 mEq/gm) was obtained from Bio-Rad Laboratories, Richmond, CA.

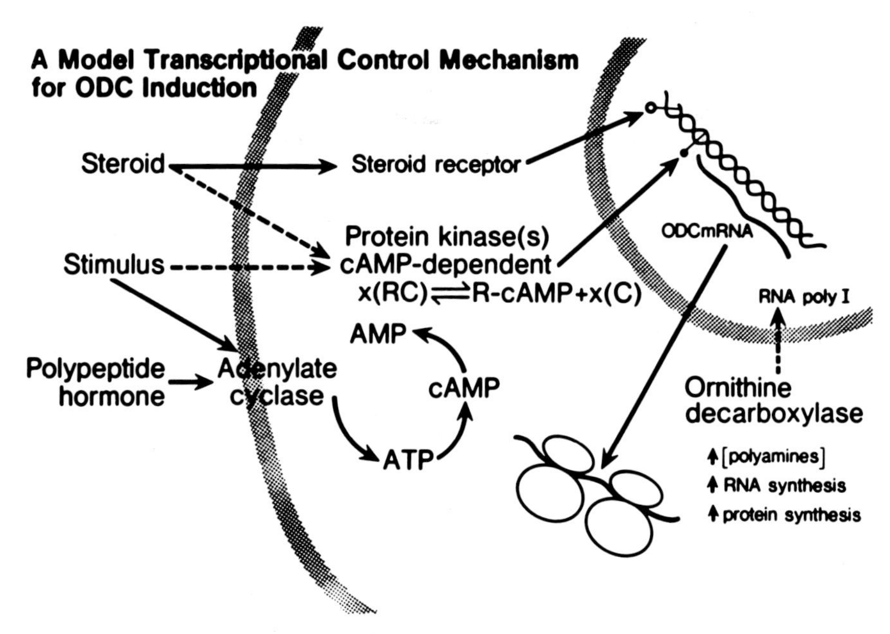

Fig. 1. Schematic model of the transcriptional regulation of ornithine decarboxylase (ODC) activity by polypeptide trophic hormones and steroid hormones.

Animal Procedures

For studies of cyclic AMP-dependent protein kinase and ODC in the prostate, animals to be castrated and their weight-matched controls were obtained from Hilltop, Chatsworth, CA. Bilateral orchiectomy was performed via the scrotal route under light ether anesthesia, and animals were killed by cervical dislocation up to 7 days postoperatively. Bilaterally adrenalectomized animals, hypophysectomized animals, and age-matched controls were purchased from Zivic-Miller, Allison Park, PA. Adrenalectomized animals were maintained on drinking water containing 0.9% saline. These animals were routinely killed 8 days postoperatively as were the hypophysectomized animals.

5-α-Dihydrotestosterone was dissolved in warmed propylene glycol (500 μg/200 μl) and injected subcutaneously at a dose level of 500 μg/100 gm of body weight; control animals received the injection vehicle alone. Injections were performed at 24-hour intervals. Animal procedures were generally carried out at the same time each day to avoid diurnal variations in experimental parameters. Tissues for analysis were removed rapidly and frozen on dry ice. Analysis was performed on pooled tissues from 3 or 4 animals.

Determination of ODC Activity

ODC activity was measured in tissue supernatants as described previously with minor exceptions [34]. Cell or tissue samples were homogenized with a Polytron (Brinkman) in 4 volumes of buffer consisting of 0.05 M sodium-potassium phosphate, pH 7.2, 0.1 mM EDTA, and 1 mM dithiothreitol. Samples were centrifuged at 20,000g for 15 minutes at 4°C, and the supernatants were used as the source of enzyme activity. Aliquots of the supernatants were incubated in 15-ml tapered centrifuged tubes fitted with Kontes rubber stoppers and center wells in a total volume of 200 μl at 37°C in the presence of 0.25 mM L-[1-^{14}C]-ornithine and 50 μM pyridoxal phosphate. The assay was terminated after 30 minutes by the addition of 0.5 ml 1 M citric acid and the $^{14}CO_2$ evolved was collected on 3 MM Whatman filter paper present in the center well spotted with 20 μl of NCS (Amersham) and counted in Omnifluor-toluene.

Determination of Cyclic AMP-Dependent Protein Kinase Activity

The degree of activation of the cyclic AMP-dependent protein kinases represents the relative proportion of the protein kinase present as a holoenzyme compared to that present as free catalytic subunit and is determined by assaying the supernatant kinase activity in the presence and absence of saturating amounts of cyclic AMP as previously described [35–37]. Protein kinase activity was determined as described by Huang and Robinson [38] in a total volume of 75 μl containing 20 mM sodium phosphate, pH 6.8, 0.5 mM 3-isobutyl-1-methylxanthine, 5 mM NaF, 10 mM $MgCl_2$, 50 μg F_2b histone, ± 10 μM cyclic

AMP, 0.1 mM ATP, and 1 μCi [γ-^{32}P]ATP. The reaction was initiated by the addition of ATP and allowed to proceed at 30°C for 8 minutes for column fractions and 2 minutes for cytosol samples. ^{32}P Incorporation was linear with respect to both time and kinase concentration under these conditions.

DEAE-Cellulose Chromatography of Type I and Type II Cyclic AMP-Dependent Protein Kinase

Frozen tissue (20–40 mg) was homogenized at 4°C in 1 ml of 5 mM Tris-HCl, pH 7.5, containing 0.2 mM EDTA and 3 mM NaF. Homogenates were centrifuged at 10,000g for 5 minutes and 0.7 ml of the resulting supernatant applied to a DEAE-cellulose column (0.7 × 14 cm) previously equilibrated with the above buffer. Protein concentration was assessed by the method of Bradford [39] to ensure that corresponding amounts of protein were present in each supernatant. Columns were washed with 50 ml buffer and the kinases eluted with a linear gradient of 0–0.35 M NaCl in equilibration buffer, total volume 30 ml. One-ml fractions were collected, and 50-μl aliquots were assayed for protein kinase activity. To assess the recovery rate, the cyclic AMP-dependent protein kinase activity in a 10-μl aliquot of the supernatant also was determined. After chromatography, 70–90% of the supernatant kinase activity was recovered consistently. The determination of recovery includes a factor to compensate for salt inhibition of kinase activity in the eluted peaks. This inhibition was determined to be 39% for type I and 52% for type II by comparing the activity of pooled peak fractions before and after dialysis to remove the NaCl. Specific activity of the isozymes was calculated for the total kinase activity (pmole/min) eluted in respective peaks (corrected for salt inhibition) on the basis of the original supernatant protein applied to the column. The changes in the specific activity were taken to represent changes in total relative tissue pool sizes.

Cation Exchange Analysis Procedure for Polyamines

Analyzer. A Durrum D-500 amino acid analyzer (Dionex Corp, Sunnyvale, CA) equipped with a fluorescence detector assembly with a 2-mm path length flow cell was used for polyamine analyses. All sample functions, including injection and peak area analysis, were accomplished by a PDP8/M computer (Digital Equipment Co, Maynard MA). As many as 80 sample cartridges can be loaded for automatic analysis and injection.

Resin. The column contained a Durrum cation exchange resin, divinyl benzene polystyrene polymer, 16% cross linkage, with a bead diameter of 10 ± 1 μm, packed to a height of 11.5 cm in a stainless steel column with a 1.7-mm internal diameter.

Buffers. The stock buffer solution (Buffer 3R) consisted of 2.4 M potassium chloride (KCl), 0.09 M potassium citrate and 5 ml of thiodiglycol per liter of double-deionized distilled water. The pH was adjusted to 5.6 with concentrated hydrochloric acid. For Buffer 2R, stock buffer was diluted to 1.9 M KCl and 0.07 M potassium citrate. For Buffer 2L, stock buffer was diluted 1/2 and contained 1.2 M KCl and 0.035 M potassium citrate per liter. For Buffer 1L, stock buffer was diluted 1/5 and contained 0.5 M KCl and 0.02 M potassium citrate per liter. Buffers were filtered through a Millipore filter (47-mm diameter, 0.45-μmole pore size) before use.

Fluorescent reagent. O-Phthalaldehyde, obtained from Aldrich Chemical Co (San Leandro, CA), was prepared in the following manner. One liter of borate buffer, pH 10.4, was prepared by adding 25 gm of KOH to 800 ml deionized water. Boric acid was added to the KOH solution until the pH was 10.4 ± 0.1. Deionized water was added to adjust the volume to 1 liter. The following chemicals were then added to the borate buffer: 4.5 ml of 2-mercaptoethanol (Sigma), 3 ml of BRIJ 30% solution (Pierce Chemical Co, Rockford, IL) and 5.8 gm of KSCN (Sigma). The O-phthalaldehyde crystals were dissolved in 20 ml of glass-distilled methyl alcohol, and this mixture was added to the buffer solution and stirred gently. The solution was purged with nitrogen for 10 minutes in the amino acid analyzer reagent reservoir.

Elution program. Elution and separation of the polyamines was accomplished in 62.5 minutes utilizing a four-buffer system as previously described [40,41]. As little as 20 pmoles of each polyamine could be accurately detected.

RESULTS AND DISCUSSION

Polyamine Concentrations in Normal and Hyperplastic Human Prostate

Prostatic hyperplasia is difficult to study since normal age-matched controls cannot be obtained. In fact, prostatic hyperplasia is essentially a characteristic of aging. However, we have attempted to evaluate the alterations of polyamine profiles as compared to 22- to 36-year-old accident victims [41]. Normal prostatic tissue was obtained from kidney donors and from young males after accidental deaths. Tissue was obtained by open surgery without the use of a coagulant or irrigating fluid. The specimen was examined histologically, and only those of mixed hyperplasia (glandular and stromal) were used in the study. A marked increase in the spermine concentration was the most consistent finding (Tables II, III). The mean value increased from 24.4 to 56.8 nmole/mg protein. Hyperplastic prostate actually had a decreased putrescine concentration although neither putrescine nor spermidine was significantly elevated in the benign hyperplastic prostate.

TABLE II. Polyamines in normal (I to V) and hyperplastic (1 to 23) tissue samples of the human prostate

Patient	Age	Putrescine	Spermidine (nmole/mg protein)	Spermine	Spermidine/spermine ratio
I	22	10.5	4.9	34.8	0.14
II	36	11.8	4.5	23.9	0.19
III	28	6.4	3.5	27.1	0.13
IV	21	3.8	2.7	28.8	0.09
V	33	0.2	1.0	7.4	0.13
1	70	5.2	9.8	89.6	0.11
2	48	8.6	6.8	82.7	0.08
3	71	3.4	3.4	53.3	0.06
4	74	2.8	5.7	45.4	0.13
5	73	1.3	2.6	44.2	0.05
6	67	0.3	2.1	36.7	0.05
7	75	4.9	7.8	63.8	0.12
8	72	2.5	5.4	81.9	0.06
		3.1[a]	4.5	80.2	0.06
9	73	1.5	3.9	35.1	0.11
10	64	2.3	4.1	30.8	0.13
11	63	1.2	6.5	105.4	0.06
12	64	1.0	3.7	31.2	0.13
13	69	6.9	4.1	63.3	0.06
14	65	1.7	10.0	102.8	0.10
15	66	3.8	4.5	61.0	0.07
16	72	7.1	3.7	31.9	0.12
17	71	9.5	4.7	58.9	0.07
18	72	1.1	5.5	59.7	0.09
19	60	1.8	2.1	34.3	0.06
20	70	4.9	3.1	31.7	0.10
		2.8[a]	3.6	29.9	0.12
21	72	2.1	5.1	67.7	0.08
22	72	2.1	2.4	39.5	0.06
23	70	2.8	5.9	54.7	0.11

Patients I and II were explanted during kidney transplantation; patients II to V were explanted within 6 hours following death by accident. Tissue samples of patients with benign hyperplasia of the prostate were immediately stored at –30°. Data reproduced by permission from Cancer Research [41].

[a]Intratissue control.

Alterations in the Amounts of Type I Cyclic AMP-Dependent Protein Kinase and ODC Activity in the Ventral Prostate in Response to Castration

Tbe involvement of cyclic nucleotides in the action of steroid hormones has been less clear than the involvement in response to trophic hormones. Singhal

TABLE III. Tissue level of polyamines in normal and benign hyperplastic prostate

	Putrescine	Spermidine (nmole/mg protein)	Spermine
Prostate			
normal	6.53 ± 4.70	3.31 ± 1.57	24.40 ± 10.29
pathological (BHP)	3.42 ± 2.55	4.89 ± 2.10	56.76 ± 23.02[a]

The results were analyzed by paired and unpaired Student's t test. Data are expressed as the mean ± SD. Reproduced by permission from Cancer Research [41].
[a]Significantly different from mean of controls ($P < 0.005$).

et al [42] have accumulated a considerable body of evidence that exogenous cyclic AMP can exert extromimetic or andromimetic effects in vivo, that the absolute levels of cyclic AMP and its rate of biosynthesis are dependent on the gonadal status of the animal, and that methylxanthines, potent inhibitors of cyclic AMP phosphodiesterases, can potentiate steroid-induced responses. They have shown also that adenylate cyclase (EC 4.6.1.) activity, cyclic AMP levels, and polyamine levels decrease in the ventral prostate of the rat after antiandrogen administration.

Other events involved in the trophic response also are altered by androgens. Wilson and Ahmed [43] demonstrated that the androgenic status of the animal can have profound effects on the phosphorylation of nuclear proteins by [^{32}P]ATP in the rat ventral prostate. Liao and Fang [44] have shown that nucleolar RNA polymerase is selectively enhanced by androgens.

We have previously demonstrated that specifically type I cyclic AMP-dependent protein kinase is involved in the transcriptional induction of ODC. For instance, the amount of type I cyclic AMP-dependent protein kinase increased in rat heart in response to isoproterenol-induced hypertrophy [35], and specific activation of type I cyclic AMP-dependent protein kinase precedes peak induction of ODC in G_1 of cell cycle in synchronized Chinese hamster ovary cells [45,46]. ODC induction in mitogen-stimulated lymphocytes also is related to the specific activation of type I cyclic AMP-dependent protein kinase even though human lymphocytes contain equal amounts of type I and type II activity [47,48]. Therefore, we studied the relationship of type I cyclic AMP-dependent protein kinase in the hormonally manipulated rat prostate.

The ventral prostate exhibits a high activity of ODC under normal conditions [15,49–51]. However, in response to castration, the amount of ODC falls markedly to about 25% of control level within 1 day and to 10% of control level within 3 days (Fig. 2). During this same time period, there is a marked reduction specifically in type I cyclic AMP-dependent protein kinase in the ventral prostate. This level drops to essentially 60% of control level within 3 days and does not decline further by 7 days of castration (Fig. 3). Table IV demonstrates that

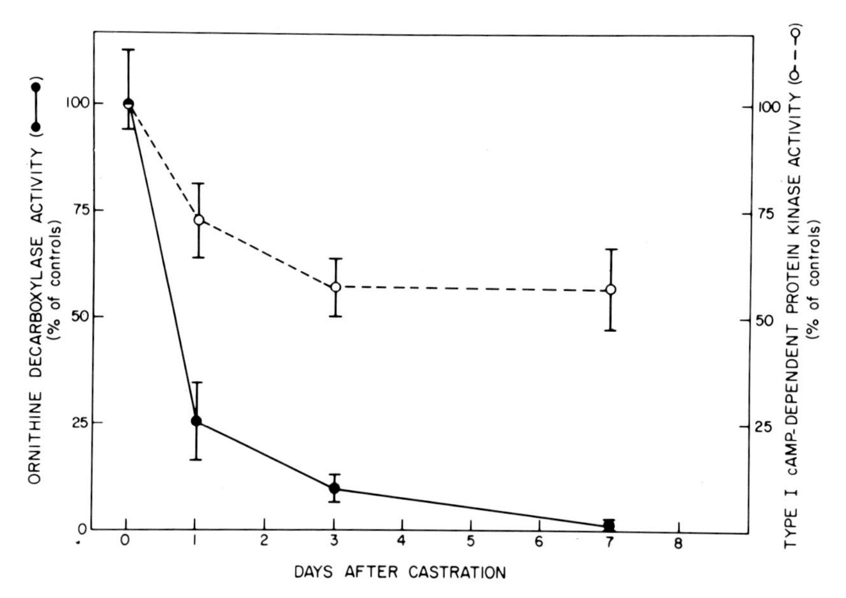

Fig. 2. Rapid decline in ornithine decarboxylase activity and the amount of type I cyclic AMP-dependent protein kinase activity in the prostate in response to castration. Enzymes are assayed as described in Materials and Methods. Each point represents the mean ± SEM of at least 10 separate rats with duplicate determinations of each enzyme assay. Reproduced by permission from Pergamon Press, Ltd [11].

castrated rats maintained on dihydrotestosterone for 3 days showed no significant difference in the amount of prostatic type I protein kinase activity compared to intact controls. A maintenance dose of dihydrotestosterone administered immediately after castration actually increased type I and type II activities to values greater than observed in tissues from control animals. However, 3 days of daily injection of dihydrotestosterone given to 3-day castrates increased only type I protein kinase activity from 48% to 93% of type I activity in intact animals and did not increase the amount of type II protein kinase activity [30].

We determined the time necessary for ODC activity to return to control values in the castrated prostate in response to dihydrotestosterone therapy (Fig. 4). There was a significant increase in ODC activity in the castrated ventral prostate within 12 hours of the injection of dihydrotestosterone. Injections of dihydrotestosterone at 24 and 48 hours maintained the level of ODC at or near control level.

Dihydrotestosterone Required to Maintain Type I Cyclic AMP-Dependent Protein Kinase Isozyme in the Castrated Prostate

In the intact prostate, ODC activity can be enhanced by administration of aminophylline, a phosphodiesterase inhibitor which leads to the rapid accumu-

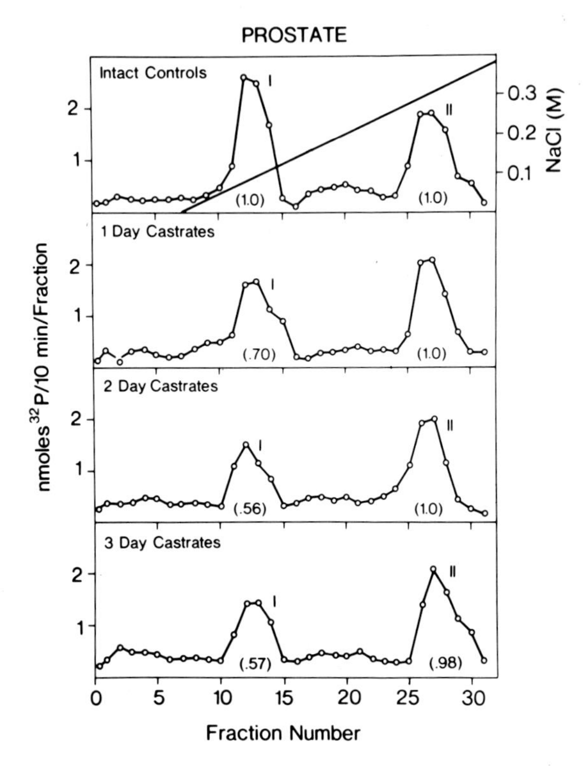

Fig. 3. Representative elution profiles after DEAE-cellulose chromatography of type I and type II cyclic AMP-dependent protein kinases of the ventral prostate. Chromatography was performed on sham-operated controls and at 1, 2, and 3 days after castration. Ten separate columns were run for each time point. Each column run was comprised of pooled tissue from 3 or 4 rats. The variation of chromatographs was less than 10%. Reproduced from Proceedings of the National Academy of Sciences USA [30].

lation of cyclic AMP (Fig. 5). Within 4 hours of injection, ODC activity was threefold above the control value. However, in the ventral prostate after 3 days of castration, the injection of aminophylline was not able to induce ODC activity and it remained near a nondetectable level. We suggest that the inability to stimulate ODC activity in the castrated rat prostate is directly related to the decrease in the total amount of type I cyclic AMP-dependent protein kinase activity. This is substantiated not only by the rapid decline in both ODC activity and the amount of type I cyclic AMP-dependent protein kinase activity in the prostate in response to castration, but also by the parallel reaccumulation of type I protein kinase activity and the ability to reestablish the normal high activity of ODC in the prostate in response to steroid maintenance.

TABLE IV. Effect of dihydrotestosterone (DHT) maintenance on type I and type II protein kinase of the ventral prostate

Treatment	Percent of intact control protein kinase activity	
	Type I	Type II
Intact	100	100
3-Day castration	57[a]	102
Castration maintained on DHT 3 days	110	98
3-Day castration and DHT 3 days	103	99

Animals were castrated via the scrotal route under light ether anesthesia. One group was allowed to regress for 3 days prior to subcutaneous injections of 5α-dihydrotestosterone (DHT) daily for 3 days until sacrifice (500 mg/200 ml propylene glycol/100 gm body weight). The other group was placed on maintenance injections of DHT for 3 days starting at the time of operation. Upon sacrifice, the protein kinase isozyme profiles in the ventral prostate of the two groups were compared after DEAE-cellulose chromatography. Ten determinations of tissues from 3 to 4 rats each were assayed. Data reproduced by permission from Pergamon Press, Ltd [11].
[a]Data differ from intact ($P < 0.001$).

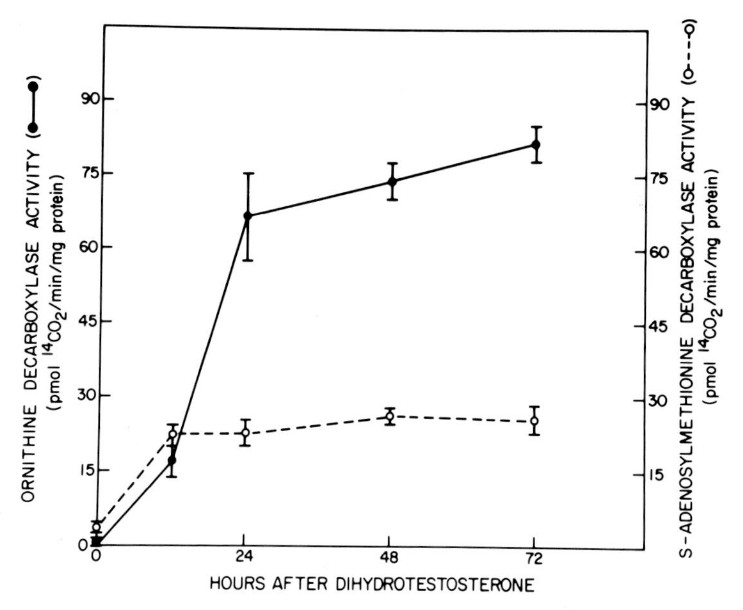

Fig. 4. The ability of dihydrotestosterone to reestablish intact prostate levels of ornithine decarboxylase activity and S-adenosyl-L-methionine decarboxylase activity. Zero time on the abscissa represents the level of enzyme activity in rats castrated for 3 days. Dihydrotestosterone (500 μg/100 gm body weight) was administered at zero, 24, and 48 hours. Each value represents the mean ± SEM of at least 5 separate rats with duplicate determinations of enzyme activity. Reproduced by permission from Pergamon Press, Ltd [11].

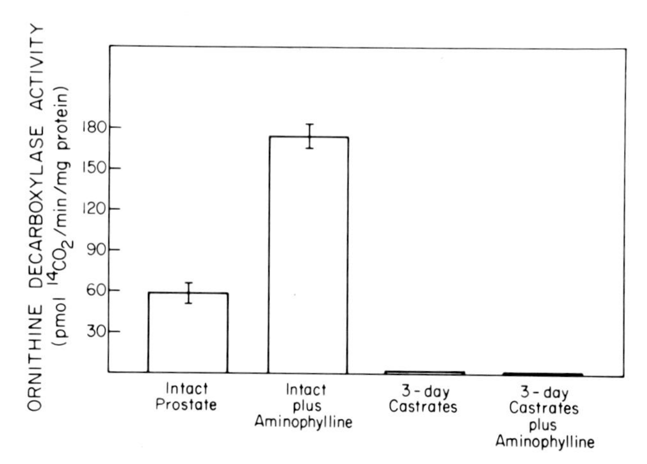

Fig. 5. Induction of ornithine decarboxylase activity in the intact prostate in response to aminophylline (200 μmole/kg) compared to the same response in the prostate of the 3-day castrate. Ornithine decarboxylase activity was assessed at 4 hours after the injection of aminophylline, the time of maximal induction. Each value represents the mean ± SEM of at least 5 separate rats with duplicate determinations of enzyme activity. Reproduced by permission from Pergamon Press, Ltd [11].

Significance of Polyamine Conjugates in Extracellular Fluids

It was reported in 1971 [52] that patients with metastatic cancer excreted elevated amounts of conjugated polyamines in their urine. Based on animal studies of tumor growth and regression [10], a model was proposed to summarize the potential roles of polyamines as biochemical markers of human tumor cell growth and tumor cell death (Fig. 6). It has been established in my laboratory [10,53] and substantiated by various other laboratories [54] that the increased pretreatment level of spermidine in the urine of patients with cancer compared with the level in normal individuals reflects spontaneous tumor cell loss. After initiation of chemotherapy or radiation therapy, a greater than twofold rise in spermidine within 24 to 48 hours predicts partial or complete responses of the tumor to treatment with a high degree of accuracy. Putrescine levels in urine prior to chemotherapy reflect the proliferative compartment of the tumor, whereas putrescine levels after chemotherapy reflect recruitment of tumor cells in the proliferative compartment as well as repopulation of normal bone marrow cells [10,55,56]. In a study of patients with carcinoma of the prostate, Fair et al [57] reported that increased urinary spermidine correlated with the histological grading of the tumor. Durie et al [56] have found that the absolute urinary level of spermidine is a function of disease activity. However, Chaisiri et al [58], using a radioimmunoassay technique for measuring plasma spermidine, were not able

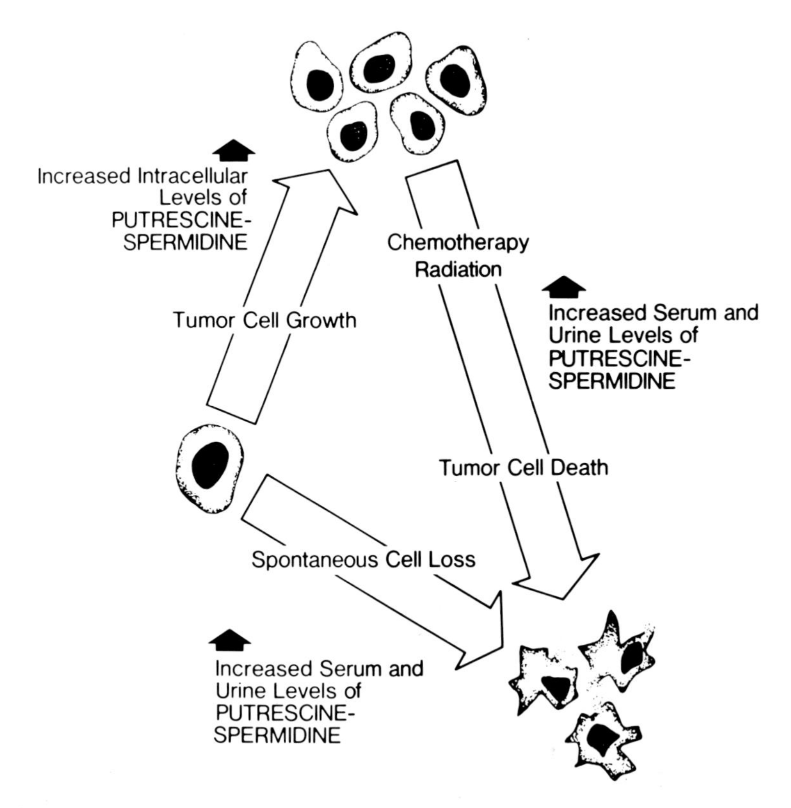

Fig. 6. A model of polyamines as biochemical markers of tumor cell growth and tumor cell death. Reproduced by permission from The Lancet [55].

to correlate plasma levels with clinical stage or metastatic status of the patients. This may be due to rapid clearance from the plasma.

The polyamine conjugates present in the urine of normals and cancer patients which upon hydrolysis produce the parent compounds have been shown to be acetyl derivatives [59–61]. Derivatives so far identified are N^1-acetylspermidine, N^8-acetylspermine, and N-acetylputrescine. It also has been reported that treatment with carbon tetrachloride which causes massive necrosis of rat liver produces increased acetylation of spermidine [62]. Now that methods for the separation and quantitation of the acetyl derivatives of the polyamines are available [63,64], it will be important to assess whether cell loss and cell growth factors can be better interpreted by assessing the amount of each individual acetyl derivative.

Possible Significance of γ-Glutamyl Polyamine Derivatives in Cells and in Seminal Fluid

Recent reports have implicated the polyamines as physiological substrates for transglutaminase. Folk et al [6] and Williams-Ashman et al [65] have demonstrated the presence of γ-glutamyl putrescine and γ-glutamyl spermidine derivatives in cells and in seminal fluid. After the mitogenic stimulation of human lymphocytes, Folk et al [6] isolated a protein fraction labeled with [^{3}H]-putrescine which, upon digestion, yielded γ-glutamyl putrescine. We have detected protein-conjugated putrescine in salt-extracted protein fractions of nucleoli and nuclei of calf and rat liver [66] and recently in nuclei and nucleoli of prostate (unpublished data). Further, we have found that maximal nuclear levels of conjugated putrescine 12-fold above controls were present 8 hours after partial hepatectomy in rat liver and were concomitant with increased transglutaminase activity previously reported at 8 hours [67]. To date, all intracellular conjugates identified have been monoglutamyl derivatives whereas, as previously discussed in the Introduction, both mono- and bis-derivatives were present in seminal fluid and were generated by proteolysis of vesicular secretion proteins [6].

The ability to detect protein conjugates of putrescine, spermidine, and spermine selectively in salt-extracted protein fractions of nuclei and nucleoli suggests that transamidation of proteins by the action of transglutaminase may be important in the regulation of genetic transcription. It would appear that intracellular conjugation is not involved in cross linking of proteins since bis-derivatives have not been detected, although further work is required to fully elucidate the general nature of these conjugates in physiological systems. There are two recent reviews by Williams-Ashman and co-workers [5,65] which deal with the possible roles of transglutaminases in mammalian reproductive tissues and fluids. They have demonstrated unique forms of transglutaminases in rat liver coagulating gland and its secretion and in the dorsal lateral prostate but not in the ventral lobe of the gland. It is possible that an understanding of transglutaminase-mediated polyamine conjugation may help to further unravel the profound effects of selective polyamines on the regulation of macromolecular synthesis.

CONCLUSIONS

We have demonstrated a marked alteration in the spermine concentration of the human benign hyperplastic prostate. Because the enzymes in the polyamine biosynthetic pathway are regulated by multiple trophic, steroid, and coated-pit hormones, this would suggest altered hormonal states with age which favor spermine accumulation.

Studies of protein kinase alterations and ODC activity in the intact prostate and after castration link steroid action to the ability of the steroid hormone to affect the concentration of type I cyclic AMP-dependent protein kinase activity.

The ability of steroid-responsive tissues to respond to a cyclic AMP-mediated hormone is dependent upon the amount of type I cyclic AMP-dependent protein kinase activity within the tissue. This demonstrates the importance of the interaction and circulating concentrations of different classes of hormones, ie, trophic, steroid and coated-pit hormones, in relation to the final physiological response.

Urinary levels of acetylputrescine and acetylspermidine are indicative of disease activity in cancer patients including prostatic carcinomas and increases in these derivatives after therapy prescribe tumor growth fraction and tumor cell kill with a high degree of accuracy.

The recent demonstration of γ-glutamyl polyamine derivatives in growth systems (PHA-stimulated lymphocytes) and in seminal fluid and their possible formation by transglutaminases suggests regulatory roles related to protein cross-linking reactions and perhaps genetic transcription. Protein-polyamine conjugates were isolated from nuclear calf liver, rat liver, and prostate preparations. In regenerating rat liver, nuclear protein-putrescine conjugates parallel increased nuclear transglutaminase activity.

ACKNOWLEDGMENTS

This work was supported by USPHS research grant CA-14783 from the National Cancer Institute.

REFERENCES

1. Leeuwenhoek A: Observationes D. Anthonii Lewenhoeck de Natis e semin genitali Aminalculus. Phil Trans R Soc Lond 12: 1040–1043, 1978.
2. Rosenheim O: The isolation of spermine phosphate from semen and testis. Biochem J 18: 1253–1263, 1924.
3. Williams-Ashman HG, Pegg AE, Lockwood DH: Mechanisms and regulation of polyamine and putrescine biosynthesis in male genital glands and other tissues of mammals. Adv Enzyme Regul 7: 291–323, 1969.
4. Williams-Ashman HG, Corti A, Sheth AR: Formation and functions of aliphatic polyamines in the prostate gland and its secretions. In Goland M (ed): "Normal and Abnormal Growth of the Prostate." Springfield: Thomas, 1975, pp 222–239.
5. Williams-Ashman HG, Canellakis ZN: Transglutaminase-mediated covalent attachment of polyamines to proteins: Mechanisms and potential physiological significance. Physiol Chem Phys 12: 457–470, 1980.
6. Folk JE, Park MH, Chung SI, Schrode J, Lester EP, Cooper HL: Polyamines as physiological substrates for transglutaminases. J Biol Chem 255: 3695–3700, 1980.
7. Cohen SS: "Introduction to the Polyamines." New Jersey: Englewood Cliffs, Prentice-Hall, 1971.
8. Russell DH: Polyamines in growth—normal and neoplastic. In Russell DH (ed): "Polyamines in Normal and Neoplastic Growth." New York: Raven Press, 1973, pp 1–13.
9. Bachrach U: "Function of the Naturally Occurring Polyamines." New York: Academic Press, 1973.
10. Russell DH, Durie BGM: "Polyamines as Markers of Normal and Malignant Growth." New York: Raven Press, 1978.

11. Russell DH, Haddox MK: Cyclic AMP-mediated induction of ornithine decarboxylase in normal and neoplastic growth. Adv. Enzyme Regul 17: 61–87, 1979.
12. Russell DH: Ornithine decarboxylase: Transcriptional induction by trophic hormones via a cAMP and cAMP-dependent protein kinase pathway. In Morris D, Marton LJ (eds): "Polyamines in Biology and Medicine." New York: Marcel Dekker, 1981, pp 105–121.
13. Jungmann RA, Russell DH: Cyclic AMP, cyclic AMP-dependent protein kinase, and the regulation of gene expression. Life Sci 20: 1787–1798, 1977.
14. Russell DH, Byus CV, Manen CA: Proposed model of major sequential biochemical events of a trophic response. Life Sci 19: 1297–1306, 1976.
15. Pegg AE, Williams-Ashman HG: Biosynthesis of putrescine in the prostate gland of the rat. Biochem J 108: 533–539, 1968.
16. Russell DH, Taylor RL: Polyamine synthesis and accumulation in the castrated rat uterus after estradiol 17-β stimulation. Endocrinology 88: 1397–1403, 1971.
17. Kaye AM, Icekson I, Lindner HR: Stimulation by estrogens of ornithine and S-adenosylmethionine decarboxylases in the immature rat uterus. Biochim Biophys Acta 252: 150–159, 1971.
18. Piik K, Rajamäki P, Guha SK: Jänne J: Regulation of L-ornithine decarboxylase and S-adenosyl-L-methionine decarboxylase in rat ventral prostate and seminal vesicle. Biochem J 168: 379–385, 1977.
19. Barkai U, Kraicer PF: Definition of period of induction of deciduoma in the rat using ornithine decarboxylase as a marker of growth onset. Int J Fertil 23: 106–111, 1978.
20. Wyatt GR, Rothaus K, Lawler D, Herbst EJ: Ornithine decarboxylase and polyamines in silkmoth pupal tissues: Effects of ecdysone and injury. Biochim Biophys Acta 304: 482–494, 1973.
21. Goldstein JL, Anderson RGW, Brown MS: Coated pits, coated vesicles and receptor-mediated endocytosis. Nature 179: 679–685, 1979.
22. Stastny M, Cohen S: The stimulation of ornithine decarboxylase activity in testes of the neonatal mouse. Biochim Biophys Acta 261: 177–180, 1972.
23. Haselbacher GK, Humbel RE: Stimulation of ornithine decarboxylase activity in chick fibroblasts by non-suppressible insulin-like activity (NSILA), insulin and serum. J Cell Physiol 88: 239–246, 1976.
24. Grillo MA, Bedino S: Stimulation by insulin of chicken liver ornithine decarboxylase. Int J Biochem 8: 711–713, 1977.
25. Aisbitt RPG, Barry JM: Stimulation by insulin of ornithine decarboxylase activity in cultured mammary tissue. Biochim Biophys Acta 320: 610–616, 1973.
26. Lewis ME, Lakshmanan J, Nagaiah K, MacDonnell PC, Guroff G: Nerve growth factor increases activity of ornithine decarboxylase in rat brain. Proc Natl Acad Sci USA 75: 1021–1023, 1978.
27. Hatanaka H, Otten U, Thoenen H: Nerve growth factor-mediated selective induction of ornithine decarboxylase in rat pheochromocytoma; a cyclic AMP-independent process. FEBS Lett 92: 313–316, 1978.
28. Feldman EJ, Aures D, Grossman MI: Epidermal growth factor stimulates ornithine decarboxylase activity in the digestive tract of mouse. Proc Soc Exp Biol Med 159: 400–402, 1978.
29. DiPasquale A, White D, McGuire J: Epidermal growth factor stimulates putrescine transport and ornithine decarboxylase activity in cultivated human fibroblasts. Exp Cell Res 116: 317–323, 1978.
30. Fuller DJM Byus CV, Russell DH: Specific regulation by steroid hormones of the amount of type I cyclic AMP-dependent protein kinase holoenzyme. Proc Natl Acad Sci USA 75: 223–227, 1978.
31. Manen CA, Russell DH: Ornithine decarboxylase may function as an initiation factor for RNA polymerase I. Science 195: 505–506, 1977.

32. Manen CA, Russell DH: Regulation of RNA polymerase I activity by ornithine decarboxylase. Biochem Pharmacol 26: 2379–2384, 1977.
33. Russell DH: Posttranslational modification of ornithine decarboxylase by its product putrescine. Biochem Biophys Res Commun 99:1167–1172, 1981.
34. Russell D, Snyder SH: Amine synthesis in rapidly growing tissues: Ornithine decarboxylase activity in regenerating rat liver, chick embryo, and various tumors. Proc Natl Acad Sci USA 60: 1420–1427, 1968.
35. Byus CV, Costa M, Sipes IG, Brodie BB, Russell DH: Activation of cyclic AMP-dependent protein kinase and induction of ornithine decarboxylase as early events in the induction of mixed-function oxygenases. Proc Natl Acad Sci USA 73: 1241–1245, 1976.
36. Corbin JD, Keely SL, Park CR: The distribution and dissociation of cyclic adenosine 3′:5′-monophosphate-dependent protein kinases in adipose, cardiac and other tissues. J Biol Chem 250: 218–225, 1975.
37. Mao CC, Guidotti A: Simultaneous isolation of adenosine 3′,5′-cyclic monophosphate (cAMP) and guanosine 3′,5′-cyclic monophosphate (cGMP) in small tissue samples. Anal Biochem 59: 63–68, 1974.
38. Huang KP, Robinson JC: A rapid and sensitive assay method for protein kinase. Anal Biochem 72: 593–599, 1976.
39. Bradford MM: A rapid and sensitive method for the quantitation of microgram quantities of protein utilizing the principle of protein-dye binding. Anal Biochem 72: 248–254, 1976.
40. Russell DH, Russell SD: Relative usefulness of measuring polyamines in serum, plasma, and urine as biochemical markers of cancer. Clin Chem 21: 860–863, 1975.
41. Dunzendorfer U, Russell DH: Altered polyamine profiles in prostatic hyperplasia and in kidney tumors. Cancer Res 38: 2321–2324, 1978.
42. Singhal RL, Tsang BK, Sutherland DJB: Regulation of cyclic nucleotide and prostaglandin metabolism in sex steroid-dependent cells. In Singhel RL, Thomas JA (eds): "Advances in Sex Hormone Research." Baltimore: University Park Press, 1976, pp 325–424.
43. Wilson MJ, Ahmed K: Enzymic characteristics and effects of testosterone treatment on nucleolar and chromatin-associated histone phosphokinase activity of rat ventral prostate. Exp Cell Res 106: 151–157, 1977.
44. Liao S, Fang S: Receptor-proteins for androgens and the mode of action of androgens on gene transcription in ventral prostate. Vitamins and Hormones 27: 17–90, 1969.
45. Fuller DJM, Gerner EW, Russell DH: Polyamine biosynthesis and accumulation during the G_1 to S phase transition. J Cell Physiol 93: 81–88, 1977.
46. Costa M, Gerner EW, Russell DH: Cell cycle-specific activity of type I and type II cyclic adenosine 3′:5′-monophosphate-dependent protein kinases in Chinese hamster ovary cells. J Biol Chem 251: 3313–3319, 1976.
47. Byus CV, Klimpel GR, Lucas DO, Russell DH: Type I and type II cyclic AMP-dependent protein kinase as opposite effectors of lymphocyte mitogenesis. Nature 268: 63–64, 1977.
48. Byus CV, Klimpel GR, Lucas DO, Russell DH: Ornithine decarboxylase induction in mitogen-stimulated lymphocytes is related to the specific activation of type I adenosine cyclic 3′,5′-monophosphate-dependent protein kinase. Mol Pharmacol 14: 431–441, 1978.
49. Fuller DJM, Donaldson LJ, Thomas GH: Ornithine decarboxylase activity and [^{125}I]iododeoxyuridine incorporation in rat prostate. Biochem J 150: 557–559, 1975.
50. Jänne J, Williams-Ashman HG: On the purification of L-ornithine decarboxylase from rat prostate and effects of thiol compounds on the enzyme. J Biol Chem 246: 1725–1732, 1971.
51. Pegg AE, Williams-Ashman HG: Rapid effects of testosterone on prostatic polyamine-synthesizing enzyme systems. Biochem J 109: 32–33, 1968.
52. Russell DH: Increased polyamine concentrations in the urine of human cancer patients. Nature 233: 144–145, 1971.

53. Russell DH: Clinical relevance of polyamines as biochemical markers of tumor kinetics: A review. Clin Chem 23: 22–27, 1977.
54. Bachrach U: Polyamines as chemical markers of malignancy. Ital J Biochem 25: 77–93, 1976.
55. Russell DH, Durie BGM, Salmon SE: Polyamines as predictors of success and failure in cancer chemotherapy. Lancet II: 797–799, 1975.
56. Durie BGM, Salmon SE, Russell DH: Polyamines as markers of response and disease activity in cancer chemotherapy. Cancer Res 37: 214–221, 1977.
57. Fair WR, Wehner N, Brorsson U: Urinary polyamine levels in the diagnosis of carcinoma of the prostate. J Urol 114: 88–92, 1975.
58. Chaisiri P, Harper ME, Blamey RW, Peeling WB, Griffiths K: Plasma spermidine concentrations in patients with tumors of the breast or prostate or testis. Clin Chim Acta 104: 367–375, 1980.
59. Nakajima T, Zack JF, Wolfgram F: N-Monacetylspermidine as a normal constituent of urine. Biochim Biophys Acta 184: 651–652, 1969.
60. Tsuji M, Nakajima T, Sano I: Putrescine, spermidine, N-acetylspermidine and spermine in the urine of patients with leukaemias and tumors. Clin Chem Acta 59: 161–167, 1975.
61. Abdel-Monem MM, Ohno K: Polyamine metabolism III: Urinary acetyl polyamines in human cancer. J Pharm Sci 67: 1671–1673, 1978.
62. Matsui I, Pegg AE: Increase in acetylation of spermidine in rat liver extracts brought about by treatment with carbon tetrachloride. Biochem Biophys Res Commun 92: 1009–1015, 1980.
63. Prussak CE, Russell DH: Acetylation of spermidine in Chinese hamster ovary cells. Biochem Biophys Res Commun 97: 1450–1458, 1980.
64. Seiler N, Knödgen B: Determination of the naturally occurring monoacetyl derivatives of di- and polyamines. J Chromatogr 164: 155–168, 1979.
65. Williams-Ashman HG, Beil RE, Wilson J, Hawkins M, Grayhack J, Zunamon A, Weinstein NK: Transglutaminases in mammalian reproductive tissues and fluids: Relation to polyamine metabolism and semen coagulation. Adv Enzyme Regul 18: 239–258, 1980.
66. Haddox MK, Russell DH: Polyamines are conjugated to nucleolar proteins. Fed Proc 39: 643, 1980.
67. Haddox MK, Russell DH: Increased nuclear conjugated polyamines and transglutaminase during liver regeneration. Proc Natl Acad Sci USA 78:1712–1716, 1981.

The Prostatic Cell: Structure and Function
Part A, pages 225–230

A Proposed Physiological Role of Prostaglandin $F_{2\alpha}$ in Prostatic Function

Wells E. Farnsworth

INTRODUCTION

Grayhack and co-workers [1] gave us the first inkling that prolactin synergizes with testosterone in the support of prostatic growth. Lawrence and Landau [2] provided the hint that the mode of action of the lactogen might be to increase the affinity of the prostate for the androgen. The first primitive corroboration of this idea came from our laboratory in Buffalo. We were able to show at the Tenovus Workshop on Prostate Cancer in 1970 [3] that moderate levels of sheep prolactin (oPr) or human placental lactogen (HPL) caused up to a 30% increase in binding of ^{3}H-testosterone to human benign hyperplastic prostate slices which had predominantly stromal hyperplasia. Adenomatous tissue, with a predominance of epithelial hyperplasia, appeared resistant to the effect of lactogen. Of course, this work was done before anyone except students of transcortin and sex hormone binding globulin (SHBG) knew anything about Scatchard plots. It was before people had found that prostatic stroma also responds to androgen and has, as well, sensitivity to estrogens [4]. Finally, it was not yet known that 5-α-reductase activity resides almost exclusively in the stroma [5].

During the past decade, many conflicting reports have been published about prolactin and the prostate. Lasnitzki [6] has explained these different findings by showing that physiological doses do increase the biological effectiveness of androgen but doses which are a thousandfold the normal serum prolactin level are inhibitory [7,8].

Involvement of prolactin adds a conflicting third dimension to the use of estrogens as antiandrogens: While estrogens do inhibit androgen secretion and do, by increasing the SHBG binding capacity, limit the level of unbound androgen, they also cause a significant rise in serum prolactin concentration. This increase in lactogen, as stated above, increases the capacity of the prostate to take up free testosterone. With more efficient uptake, the pool of free steroid in the serum is more depleted. By mass action, this results in the provision of more steroid being dissociated from the SHBG. Perhaps this explains the finding of Farnsworth and Brown [9] that cancer tissue, presumably bathed by a richer serum prolactin concentration than in BPH [10], is better able to concentrate androgen. An additional or alternative explanation of the cancer tissue's greater concentration of androgen may be the tissue's higher SHBG concentration [11], which rises in parallel with the estrogen-evoked increase in plasma SHBG capacity. If this intracellular SHBG is not an artifact of homogenization [12], it could contribute the extra steroid binding capacity of the plasma SHBG and provide an intracellular pool of androgen upon which the cytosolic receptors could draw.

Almost no one has examined the involvement of prostaglandins in the steroid binding process. I want to relate what we have learned about prostaglandin in the prostate because it seems to help explain a lot of the findings about prolactin action.

MATERIAL AND METHODS

All of the experimental work discussed in this report has been described in earlier, referenced publications.

RESULTS

Just after my preliminary experiments with prolactin, I learned that prostaglandin $F_{2\alpha}$ ($PGF_{2\alpha}$) causes luteolysis, the destruction of the corpus luteum [13]. Since prolactin is generally credited with providing luteotrophic support of the corpus luteum, I wondered if $PGF_{2\alpha}$ could be used to block the effect of prolactin on androgen binding. In collaboration with Dr. John Wilks at Upjohn and with generous gifts of $PGF_{2\alpha}$ by Dr. John Pike of the same company, we found that addition of low concentrations of $PGF_{2\alpha}$ to the incubation medium in the absence of exogenous prolactin caused *not decreased* but *increased* androgen binding to prostate minces [14]. In addition, just as we had found with prolactin, the predominantly stromal tissue was more responsive than the predominantly epithelial tissue. Not only was the stroma more responsive but it was the main site of accumulation of endogenous $PGF_{2\alpha}$. We reached this conclusion based on our morphometric studies [15] which showed the marker enzyme, beta-glucuronidase, to be restricted to prostate epithelium. Since $PGF_{2\alpha}$ concentration in prostate tissue specimens varied inversely with glucuronidase activity, the prostaglandin appears to be in the nonepithelial, ie, stromal tissue.

These findings suggested that prostaglandin might be a mediator of prolactin action. Rillema [16] was later to show that several prostaglandins exert a prolactin-like effect in the stimulation of RNA and casein synthesis in mouse mammary gland explants. Recently, Dave and Knazek [17] have seen that PGI_2 (prostacyclin) can duplicate the action of prolactin in inducing additional prolactin receptors in mouse liver membranes. PGI_2 has a 2-minute half life and the 6-

keto metabolite is inactive. To do the experiment, the investigators had to add new PGI_2 continuously.

If, indeed, $PGF_{2\alpha}$ is mediator of prolactin action, several questions need to be answered:

1) How does prolactin influence $PGF_{2\alpha}$ levels?

   a) By increasing $PGF_{2\alpha}$ receptors?
   b) By increasing $PGF_{2\alpha}$ synthesis?

Also:

2) Since Kledzik et al [18], and most recently, Boesel and Shain [19] show that the androgen level determines the prolactin receptor concentration in prostate tissue, will the androgen also affect $PGF_{2\alpha}$ receptors and/or levels?

Receptors. Cavanaugh and Farnsworth [20] first addressed the question of $PGF_{2\alpha}$ receptors. Plasma membranes, isolated from surgical specimens of BPH, were incubated with ^{3}H-$PGF_{2\alpha}$ and varying concentrations of testosterone and/or human placental lactogen. HPL was used because this was the only human lactogen abundantly available at the time of the study. Nonspecific binding was corrected for by adding 10^{-6}M $PGF_{2\alpha}$ to matched vessels.

The presence of testosterone at 10^{-8}M to 10^{-10}M increased $PGF_{2\alpha}$ binding significantly as did a concentration of 1 μg/ml of HPL. The much more potent human pituitary prolactin (hPr), at a dose of only 60 pg/ml, was also effective. This level of hPr is one thirtieth the normal minimal concentration of hPr in male serum. When testosterone and HPL were added together, they seemed to get in each other's way.

If endogenous testosterone was stripped off the tissue by treatment with an antibody against testosterone, the 10^{-8}M testosterone + endogenous prolactin could increase $PGF_{2\alpha}$ binding somewhat, but little more than it did in unstripped preparations. In contrast, when endogenous human prolactin was stripped off without disturbing the endogenous androgen, the affinity of the samples for $PGF_{2\alpha}$ was increased about ten-fold. As increased concentrations of exogenous hPr were added back, binding of $PGF_{2\alpha}$ decreased. Apparently, the optimal dose is very low. This was similar to Rillema's finding [16] with his mammary gland explants. It is interesting that when both ligands were stripped off, a) the effect of adding testosterone alone was increased; b) the effect of HPL, in the absence of endogenous testosterone, was partially antagonistic to $PGF_{2\alpha}$ binding; c) HPL displayed limited effectiveness when 10^{-8}M testosterone was also present.

It appears, therefore, that lactogen will increase $PGF_{2\alpha}$ binding in the presence of some testosterone but the receptors can become saturated by excess steroid or protein hormone. This resembles our in vivo experience with prolactin and androgens [21].

If a bolus of ^{3}H-testosterone is administered to patients with low and high hPr concentrations, far more steroid is incorporated into the prostates of the high hPr group. However, if the incorporation of androgen per unit of plasma prolactin is plotted *vs* the plasma prolactin concentration, it is seen that the unit effectiveness of hPr falls as its concentration increases. Presumably, the prolactin receptors become saturated so that they are relatively insensitive to the hPr. Androgen receptors can also become saturated so that the level of incorporation reaches a plateau as the androgen concentration in the plasma increases. It follows that depletion of serum prolactin should reduce androgen uptake into the prostate. Dr. Gonder and I [22] have found clinical remissions in a majority of the prostate cancer patients we have treated with inhibitors of prolactin secretion such as L-Dopa or Sinemet. Likewise, Jacobi et al [23] have obtained clinical remissions after inhibiting pituitary output of hPr with bromocriptine and have shown that, with prolactin depletion, prostatic uptake of testosterone is diminished.

Origin of $PGF_{2\alpha}$. $PGF_{2\alpha}$, like all prostaglandins, arises from an unsaturated, 20-carbon fatty acid, arachidonic acid. To find out if the human prostate can synthesize prostaglandin, Cavanaugh and Farnsworth [24] incubated minced prostate tissue, obtained at suprapubic prostatectomy, with ^{3}H-arachidonic acid in the presence of $10^{-7}M$ testosterone alone, 100 μg/ml HPL alone, or a combination of HPL with $10^{-7}M$ testosterone. $PGF_{2\alpha}$ was isolated from an extract of the incubation medium by thin layer chromatography and its identity confirmed by Dr. Hebe Greizerstein and Caryn Wojtowicz by GC-mass spectroscopy. Neither the steroid alone nor the peptide hormone alone was very effective, but $10^{-7}M$ testosterone plus 50 μg/ml HPL evoked a dramatic rise in $PGF_{2\alpha}$ production. It was disconcerting to see that, as the HPL concentrations was raised, $PGF_{2\alpha}$ synthesis fell off.

Was this a toxic effect of higher concentrations or were we saturating the receptors? Neither: The $PGF_{2\alpha}$ was being further metabolized.

$PGF_{2\alpha}$ is a fairly labile compound and undergoes rapid metabolism. That this was happening here was shown by using ^{3}H-PGF_{2}-α as substrate and examining the effects of androgen and HPL on the metabolites.

Exogenous testosterone was moderately effective at stimulating conversion of $PGF_{2\alpha}$ to metabolites. With all three levels of testosterone alone, the most abundant product was dihydroketo-$PGF_{2\alpha}$. This requires action of the enzymes prostaglandin dehydrogenase, to oxidize the 15-hydroxyl to a carbonyl, and δ-13-reductase, to reduce the 13,14-double bond. Probably 15-reductase, which re-reduces the 15-carbonyl to 15-OH, is limited in its activity since the yield of dihydro-$PGF_{2\alpha}$ was relatively small.

The effects of 50 μg/ml and 100 μm/ml of HPL were somewhat greater than those with $10^{-7}M$ testosterone. Optimal synergism was seen with a combination of $10^{-9}M$ testosterone and 100 μg/ml HPL. This was confirmed by the finding of comparable responses to 10^{-7}M testosterone plus 100 μg/ml HPL by tissue which had been stripped of both endogenous ligands.

One might postulate that 13,14-dihydro-15-keto- $PGF_{2\alpha}$ is the real mediator of prostate. The following experiment may help decide this:

The effect of indomethacin. Indomethacin is generally accepted as an inhibitor of prostaglandin synthesis from arachidonic acid. Addition of low doses of the drug to suspensions of minced prostate in medium containing ^{3}H-arachidonate did, in fact, produce a small but significant reduction in the disappearance of the substrate. On the other hand, doses of 20 μM or 200 μM indomethacin caused very substantial utilization of the arachidonate. When we examined the yield of products, we saw that the 0.2-μM dose did diminish $PGF_{2\alpha}$ and its metabolites. The same was true with the 2-μM dose. Indomethacin at a dose of 20 μM or 200 μM caused a massive accumulation of 15-keto $PGF_{2\alpha}$, the immediate precursor of the 13,14-dihydro-15-keto-$PGF_{2\alpha}$ we had seen before.

Since indomethacin is an inhibitor of prostaglandin action and, in the prostate, can stop $PGF_{2\alpha}$ metabolism just before the formation of dihydroketo-$PGF_{2\alpha}$, perhaps, as suggested, the dihydroketo-$PGF_{2\alpha}$ is the active mediator of prolactin action. Alternatively, perhaps 13,14-reduction of the 15-keto-$PGF_{2\alpha}$ is coupled to the biological activity of $PGF_{2\alpha}$ and maybe of prolactin. Remember the finding of Dave and Knazek [17] with PGI_2.

Will dihydroketo-$PGF_{2\alpha}$ increase testosterone binding, duplicating the effect of prolactin and $PGF_{2\alpha}$? Will indomethacin inhibit the action of prolactin? Will other prostaglandins duplicate the action of $PGF_{2\alpha}$? If so, which will be most effective?

Right now we are trying to find out.

REFERENCES

1. Grayhack, J T, Bunce P L, Kearns J W, and Scott W W: Influence of the pituitary on prostatic response to androgen. Bull Johns Hopk Hosp 96: 154–163, 1955.
2. Lawrence A M, and Laudau R L: Impaired ventral prostate affinity for testosterone in hypophysectomized rat. Endocrinology 77: 1119–1125, 1965.
3. Farnsworth W E: The normal prostate and its endocrine control. In Griffiths K, Pierrepoint C G (eds): "Some Aspects of the Aetiology and Biochemistry of Prostatic Cancer." Cardiff: A.O.A. Publishing, 1970, pp 3–15.
4. Bartsch G, Oberholzer M, Rohr H P: The effect of antiestrogen, antiandrogen and the prolactin inhibitor, 2-bromo-α-ergocriptine on the stromal tissue of human benign prostatic hyperplasia. Invest Urol 18: 308–312, 1981.
5. Wilkin R P, Bruchovsky N, Shnitka T K, Rennie P S, Comeau T L: Stromal 5-α-reductase activity is elevated in benign prostatic hyperplasia. Acta Endocrinol 94: 284–288, 1980.
6. Rillema J A: Activation of casein synthesis by prolactins plus spermidine in mammary gland explants of mice. Biochem Biophys Res Commun 70: 45–49, 1976.
7. Manandhar M S P, Thomas J A: Effect of prolactin on the metabolism of androgens by the rat ventral prostate in vitro. Invest Urol 14: 20–22, 1976.

8. Helmerich D, Altwein J E: Effect of prolactin and the anti-prolactin bromocriptine on the testosterone uptake and metabolism in androgen-sensitive and insensitive canine organs. Urol Res 1: 101–105, 1976.
9. Farnsworth W E, Brown J R: Androgen of the human prostate. Endocrine Res Commun 3: 105–117, 1976.
10. Rolandi E, Pescatore D, Milesi G M, Giberti C, Saania A, Barreca T: Evaluation of LH, FSH, TSH, Prl and GH secretion in patients suffering from prostatic neoplasms. Acta Endocrinol (Kbl.) 95: 23–26, 1980.
11. Krieg M, Grobe I, Voigt K D Alternähr E, Klosterhalfen H: Human prostatic carcinoma: significant differences in its androgen binding and metabolism compared to the human benign prostatic hypertrophy. Acta Endocrinol (Kbl.) 88: 397–407, 1978.
12. Bordin S, Petra R H: Immunocytochemical localization of the sex steroid-binding protein of plasma in tissues of the adult monkey *Macaca nemestrina*. Proc Natl Acad USA 77: 5678–5682, 1980.
13. Gibori G, and Keyes P L: Luteotropic role of estrogen in early pregnancy in the rat. Endocrinology 106: 1584–1588, 1980.
14. Farnsworth W E, Wilks J W: Prostaglandin $F_{2\alpha}$ and human prostatic affinity for testosterone. Prostaglandins 9: 67–74, 1975.
15. Farnsworth W E, Montes M: Derivation and determination of a human prostatic epithelial index. Arch Androl 2: 85–88, 1979.
16. Rillema J A: Activation of casein synthesis by prostaglandins plus spermidine in mammary gland explants of mice. Biochem Biophys Res Commun 70: 45–49, 1976.
17. Dave J R, Knazek R A: Prostaglandin I_1 modifies both prolactin binding capacity and fluidity of mouse liver membranes. Proc Natl Acad Sci USA 77: 6597–6600, 1980.
18. Kledzik G S, Marshall S, Campbell G A, Gelato M, Meites J: Effect of castration, testosterone, estradiol, and prolactin on specific prolactin-binding activity on the ventral prostate of male rats. Endocrinology 98: 373–379, 1976.
19. Boesel R W, Shain S A: Aging in the AXC rat: androgen regulation of prostate prolactin receptors. J Androl 1: 269–276, 1980.
20. Cavanaugh A H, Farnsworth W E: Receptor sites on human prostate tissue for prostaglandin $F_{2\alpha}$. Life Sci 21: 83–92, 1977.
21. Farnsworth W E, Slaunwhite W R, Jr, Sharma M, Oseko F, Brown J R, Gonder M J, Cartagena R: Interaction of prolactin and testosterone in the human prostate. Urol Res 9: 79–88, 1981.
22. Farnsworth W E, Gonder M J: Prolactin and prostate cancer. Urology 10: 33–34, 1977.
23. Jacobi G H, Sinterhauf K, Kurth K H, Altwein J E: Bromocriptine and prostatic carcinoma: plasma kinetics, production and tissue uptake ^{3}H-testosterone in vivo. J Urol 119: 240–243, 1978.
24. Cavanaugh A H, Farnsworth W E, Greizerstain H B, Wojtowicz C: The influence of testosterone and lactogen on synthesis and metabolism of prostaglandin $F_{2\alpha}$ by the human prostate. Life Sci 26: 29–34, 1980.
25. Cavanaugh A H, Farnsworth W E, Greizerstein H B, Wojtowicz C: A novel effect of indomethacin on prostaglandin $F_{2\alpha}$ synthesis and metabolism by the human prostate. Life Sci 26: 19–28, 1980.

The Prostatic Cell: Structure and Function
Part A, pages 231–246

Evaluation of Prostatic Fluid in Prostatic Pathology

John T. Grayhack and Chung Lee

The challenge to identify accurately the high probability of pathologic changes in internal organs by an evaluation of body fluids has been a long-standing one in medicine. Interest in the cellular components and biochemical substances secreted into the urine has been widespread among medical practitioners and scientists, including urologists. However, attempts to utilize an evaluation of the fluid expressed from the prostate by digital massage to assist in identifying prostatic disease states have been very limited. The expressed fluid has usually been evaluated by microscopic and biochemical analysis and by bacterial culture techniques. Although it is our purpose to discuss primarily the results of biochemical studies of the prostatic fluid, the observations with regard to microscopic studies and bacterial culture deserve brief consideration. In this selective summary, the data obtained from the recent evaluation of our experiences will be utilized where possible. More extensive reviews are available in the reference articles.

MICROSCOPIC ANALYSIS

Examination of the prostatic fluid obtained from the urethral meatus by digital compression of the prostate has been utilized to assess the probability of inflammatory changes in the prostate for many years. The fluid normally has a characteristic opalescent gross appearance. Microscopic examination to identify cells, particles, and organisms has usually been carried out with a dry high-power magnification (450 ×) of the prostatic fluid on a glass slide covered by a coverslip. Our observations employing this technique indicate that 30 of 31 patients without evidence of urologic disease averaged less than two white blood cells per high-power field (WBC/hpf); 76 of 88 patients (88%) with noninflammatory urologic disease had less than 10 WBC/hpf [1]. Our data, along with those of Blacklock [2] and Anderson [3], support the concept that clinically significant inflammation is probably present in the prostate when the fluid contains 10 or more WBC/hpf. Normal prostatic fluid also contains phospholipid particles that are identifiable microscopically; the impression that these are decreased in inflammation is based on clinical observation, but has not been carefully documented. The presence of spermatozoa, large translucent plaques, or ropy material indicates that the fluid is contaminated by secretion of other accessory sex organs.

Microscopic examination of expressed prostatic fluid may also yield evidence of specific significant pathology. Identification of the unusual presence of Trichomonas vaginalis as a probable cause of prostatitis usually depends on this examination, although culture techniques are available to assist in identifying this organism [4, 5]. Stained fluid specimens are useful in demonstrating bacteria, but are not commonly employed for this purpose. Cytologic evaluation of prostatic fluid has been utilized with limited success to identify the presence of prostatic carcinoma. A recent report indicates that examination of the post-prostatic massage urine is more likely to permit recognition of cellular evidence that a carcinoma of the prostate is present than examination of the prostatic fluid directly [6]. The frequency with which localized carcinoma can be recognized by this technique is not well established. Although little persistent enthusiasm has been generated for their use, periodic re-evaluation of cytologic studies of the fluid would seem indicated, particularly if new techniques to identify individuals with high risk of malignancy become available.

BACTERIAL STUDIES

Bacteriological assessment of prostatic fluid has been attempted by utilization of stained smears in the past but relies almost entirely on culture techniques at present. The procedure proposed by Meares and Stamey [7] to localize bacteria to the prostate consists of collecting the first voided (VB1) and midstream (VB2) urines for culture followed by collection of prostatic fluid obtained by massage (EPF) and a final voided specimen (VB3). The relative colony counts of pathogenic bacteria are essential to evaluating the probability of their presence in the prostate.

Attempts to identify bacterial infection localized to the prostate by the procedures described are usually confined to patients with persistent or recurrent systemic or local symptoms and signs of prostatic inflammation or urinary tract infection. Purposeful prostatic massage is not commonly carried out in the presence of acute prostatitis; the clinical findings combined with those on urine culture are usually accepted in making this diagnosis. Since the majority of patients with increased numbers of white blood cells in the prostatic fluid do not have identifiable bacterial prostatitis and since bacterial prosatitis often manifests itself by causing recurrent urinary tract infection despite limited numbers of bacteria in the prostatic fluid and equivocal clinical changes in the prostate, proper collection of specimens for bacteriologic study is essential. Usually, repeated consistent observations are necessary to establish a diagnosis of chronic bacterial prostatitis. These techniques can identify a small number of individuals with a chronic bacterial infection of the prostate. As sophisticated bacteriologic techniques become more readily available, they undoubtedly will be utilized to study specimens collected by the technique described in an effort to identify specific causes for the large group of patients with prostate inflammation for which no etiology is recognized at this time.

BIOCHEMICAL ANALYSIS

Efforts to identify characteristic biochemical or physical changes in prostatic fluid composition associated with disease states in man have been based largely on the knowledge that the prostatic secretion is merocrine and apocrine in nature [8] and the presumption based on limited observations that its composition is likely to reflect the metabolic status of the prostatic epithelial cell [9–12]. Recently, these efforts have produced interesting observations. Results of analysis of enzymes, proteins, polyamines, cholesterol, citric acid, and zinc concentration and of changes in pH and specific gravity deserve consideration.

Enzymes

The observations with regard to lactic dehydrogenase (LDH) and acid phosphatase have provided the most interesting data regarding changes in enzyme concentrations. Both enzymes show a progressive decrease in mean concentration in prostatic fluid with increasing age [13, 14]. Interest in determining the relative concentration of LDH isoenzymes was stimulated by the increase in LDH-5 as compared to LDH-1 noted in tissue and tissue extracts of carcinoma of the prostate as compared to benign prostatic hyperplasia (BPH) [15, 16] and by the discovery that histologically benign tissue in a prostate gland with carcinoma commonly also demonstrated this relative increase in LDH-5 concentration [17]. Our observations [18, 19] of the concentrations of the LDH isoenzymes in prostatic fluid continue to indicate a shift from a predominance of LDH-1 in men 45 years of age and under without evidence of prostatic inflammation to a predominance of LDH-5 in men with carcinoma, BPH, and prostatic inflammation. Table I presents the mean LDH-5/LDH-1 ratios for all the observations in prostatic fluid from men with histologically verified carcinoma or BPH. The group of men with BPH were subdivided into two groups; namely, those with histologic evidence of prostatitis or with 10 or more WBC/hpf in the prostatic fluid on microscopic examination, designated as BPH with WBC, and those judged to lack evidence of significant inflammation, designated as BPH. Using these observations, the mean LDH-5/LDH-1 ratio is significantly greater ($P < 0.01$) in patients with a histologically verified diagnosis of carcinoma than in men with BPH without inflammation or our designated normal group. The LDH-

5/LDH-1 ratio of men with BPH with evidence of inflammation is not statistically different from men with carcinoma. Men with histologically verified BPH have a mean LDH-5/LDH-1 ratio of 2.07 ± 0.1362 as compared to a ratio of 0.715 ± 0.0547 in the men 45 years of age and under ($P < 0.01$). The findings regarding LDH-5/LDH-1 cited were not altered when the mean for the mean values of each individual studied was calculated (Table II). When the means for the lowest recorded LDH-5/LDH-1 ratio observed in any individual are calculated, the difference between the means for carcinoma and BPH without inflammation or normal males persists. In this instance, the mean for patients with carcinoma exceeds the mean for all other groups. The mean of our designated normal group continues to be significantly less than the mean for all other groups including BPH ($P < 0.05$).

The individual LDH-5/LDH-1 values observed are less than 2 in over 95% of the designated normal males whether the mean of the observations or the lowest observed ratio for each individual is considered. The ratio of less than 2 is noted in over 95% of those normal men whether or not prostatic fluid specimens containing red blood cells or sperm are included or excluded from consideration. If prostatic fluid specimens contaminated by red blood cells and sperm are excluded, the mean of observed LDH-5/LDH-1 ratios for individual patients equals or exceeds 2 in 83% (73%) of patients with cancer, 33% (32%) of patients with BPH without inflammation, and 70% (70%) of patients with BPH with WBC. The lowest observed individual LDH-5/LDH-1 ratio is 2 or over in 69% (60%) of patients with cancer, 15% (14%) of patients with BPH without inflammation, and 35% (34%) of patients with BPH with WBC. (The numbers in parentheses indicate the percentages for the various groups if the ratios observed in prostatic fluid specimens containing red blood cells or sperm are included in the calculations.) Our preliminary observations indicate that the percentages cited for patients with malignancy did not vary appreciably with the stage of the disease [20].

Quantitative and histochemical evaluation of acid phosphatase content of benign and malignant prostatic tissue has demonstrated a reduced concentration of this enzyme in carcinoma of the prostate [21]. Kent et al [22] found that the means of the concentration of acid phosphatase per ml in the prostatic fluid of men with Stage C and Stage D carcinoma of the prostate were significantly lower than the means of acid phosphatase concentration observed in normal men, men with chronic prostatitis and nonmalignant disease, and men with BPH. In our observations, we have evaluated the changes in the concentration of the acid phosphatase per gram of protein equivalent. The term "protein equivalent" is utilized because the protein concentration was determined by absorption of the diluted uncentrifuged prostatic fluid at 280 nm; the protein concentration determined by this procedure does not correspond with that observed with the Lowry method. The mean acid phosphatase concentration determined enzymatically

TABLE I. Mean of all observed prostatic fluid LDH-5/LDH-1 ratios

Patient groups	No.	Mean	SE
Cancer (92)	171	5.85	± 0.5779
BPH (117)	379	2.07	± 0.1362
BPH + WBC (76)	261	8.19	± 2.7421
Normal (228)	264	0.715	± 0.0547

Mean of all our observations as of 1/15/81 of LDH-5/LDH-1 ratio in prostatic fluid from patients with histologically verified carcinoma of the prostate and benign prostatic hyperplasia. Patients with benign prostatic hyperplasia were subdivided into those with 10 or more WBC/hpf on microscopic examination of the prostatic fluid or with a histologic diagnosis of prostatitis and those without evidence of inflammation. Men 45 years of age and under without evidence of prostatic inflammation were designated normal males. A group of 296 males with an unconfirmed clinical diagnosis of abacterial or bacterial prostatitis had a mean LDH-5/LDH-1 ratio of 3.288 ± 0.2348 with a total of 482 observations. The number in parentheses equals the number of individuals studied.

TABLE II. Mean of individual mean prostatic fluid LDH-5/LDH-1 ratio

Patient groups	Mean	SE
Cancer (92)	5.912	± 0.7574
BPH (117)	2.010	± 0.1927
BPH + WBC (76)	6.073	± 1.1939
Normal (228)	.693	± 0.0567

Mean of mean LDH-5/LDH-1 ratio in prostatic fluid from each patient studied as of 1/15/81. Mean of means for patients designated as having prostatitis (296) was 3.125 ± 0.2816. The number in parentheses equals the number of individuals studied.

[23] or by radioimmunoassay was significantly lower in the prostatic fluid of patients with carcinoma than in those with histologically identified BPH with or without evidence of inflammation, patients with a clinical diagnosis of prostatitis, or normal men. When individual values of acid phosphatase determined enzymatically were evaluated, 10 of 14 patients with carcinoma had less than 100 units per gram of protein equivalent. Only 1 of 43 patients with BPH and 2 of 59 patients with clinical prostatitis had concentrations of acid phosphatase at this low level [23].

Proteins

Attempts to identify differences in the protein content of prostatic fluid obtained from normal or pathologic prostates were initiated by Nylander [24]. By employing paper electrophoresis, he demonstrated that prostatic fluid obtained from a normal prostate was separable into three fractions corresponding to the alpha, beta, and gamma globulin of the blood. The alpha globulin fraction was increased in fluid obtained from patients with BPH and from two individuals with carcinoma; the gamma globulin fraction was increased in patients with chronic prostatitis. Using agar gel electrophoresis, Soanes et al [25] found that the prostatic fluid from patients with chronic prostatitis often had patterns of protein migration that varied from normal, but these patterns were not consistent. Using acrylamide gel electrophoresis, Resnick and Stubbs [26] were unable to identify a difference in protein fractions in the prostatic fluid of men with BPH or carcinoma. Denis et al [15] utilized extracts obtained by in vitro manual compression of benign and malignant glands for evaluation by agar gel electrophoresis and identified an increase in the concentration of the slowest fraction corresponding to gamma globulin in fluid obtained from carcinoma of the prostate. Neither Resnick and Stubbs [26] nor Soanes et al [25] found a change in total protein concentration in relation to prostatic pathology, tending to confirm the discrepancy we observed in prostatic fluid between protein determinations by the Lowry method and by calculation of protein concentration based on absorption observed at 280 nm.

Observations of specific proteins in the prostatic fluid of patients with normal or diseased prostate glands are of particular interest. Several years after Chodirker and Tomasi [27] demonstrated immunoglobulin in prostate fluid, Gray et al [28] noted a significant increase in the concentration of IgA, IgG, and IgM in prostatic fluid of patients with prostatitis compared to normal controls. Shah [29] noted an indefinite trend to increased levels of IgA in prostatic fluid of patients with BPH and early carcinoma. Our limited observation [30] showed no statistically significant difference in prostatic fluid levels of IgA, IgM, and IgG in relation to prostatic disease, although IgA and IgM tended to have a higher concentration in prostatic fluid of patients with prostatitis, BPH, and cancer, and IgG tended to have a higher concentration in patients with cancer.

The observations regarding protein concentration in the prostatic fluid that are of particular interest concern the complement C_3 and C_4 and transferrin. The concentration of these three specific proteins has been found to be significantly increased in prostatic fluid in men with carcinoma of the prostate compared to fluid from men with BPH or prostatitis [30]. Since the specimen available for analysis is frequently limited in quantity, we have elected to determine the two proteins, complement C_3 and transferrin, that showed the greatest difference in concentration between prostatic fluid from men with carcinoma and those with nonmalignant disease. Tables III–VI present a current summary with regard to complement C_3 and transferrin concentrations in relation to the pathologic state of the prostate [19]. The mean of all determinations of the complement C_3 concentrations in the prostatic fluid in patients with cancer exceeds the highest of the means of patients with histologically identified BPH, BPH with evidence

TABLE III. Mean of all observed prostatic fluid complement C_3 concentrations

Patient groups	No.	Mean	SE
Cancer (60)	97	16.878	± 1.1581
BPH (67)	157	3.859	± 0.2930
BPH + WBC (47)	126	4.996	± 0.3982
Normal (58)	58	1.822	± 0.2707

Mean of all our observations of complement C_3 concentration in prostatic fluid of patients studied as of 1/15/81. A group of 103 males with an unconfirmed clinical diagnosis of abacterial or bacterial prostatitis had a mean concentration of 4.547 ± 0.3868 with a total of 158 observations. The number in parentheses equals the number of individuals studied.

TABLE IV. Mean of individual mean prostatic fluid complement C_3 concentration

Patient groups	Mean	SE
Cancer (60)	17.863	± 1.5240
BPH (67)	3.633	± 0.3444
BPH + WBC (47)	5.390	± 0.6037
Normal (58)	1.822	± 0.2707

Mean of mean complement C_3 concentration in prostatic fluid from each patient studied as of 1/15/81. Mean of the means for patients designated as having prostatitis (103) was 4.473 ± 0.4877. The number in parentheses equals the number of individuals studied.

of inflammation, or a presumed normal prostate by more than three times (Table III). This significant difference persists if a mean of the mean values for each patient (Table IV) or a mean of the lowest value for each patient is utilized. Interestingly, the mean concentration for complement C_3 for patients with histologically confirmed BPH exceeds the mean of normal males, whether all observations (Table III, $P < 0.01$) and/or the mean of individual mean observations (Table IV, $P < 0.01$) are utilized.

The individual complement C_3 values are less than 10 mg% in over 95% of the combined BPH with and without evidence of inflammation and normal groups whether the mean of the observations or the lowest observed value for each individual are considered. All the designated normal individuals have complement C_3 levels below 10 mg%. The mean of the observed complement C_3 levels for individual patients is 10 mg% or over in 80% of the cancer patients, 4% of the patients with BPH without evidence of inflammation, and 13% of the patients with BPH with evidence of inflammation. The lowest observed complement C_3 level for individual patients is 10 mg% or over in 78% of the cancer patients, 3% of the patients with BPH without evidence of inflammation, and 11% of the patients with BPH with evidence of inflammation. Our preliminary observations [20] indicate that prostatic fluid from patients with Stage A carcinoma is very unlikely to have a complement C_3 level of 10 mg% or over. The validity of the observation must be accepted with reservation because of the small number of Stage A patients studied and the fact that the majority of them were first observed postoperatively. If the four patients with A_1 tumors are eliminated from consideration, the individual mean complement C_3 level is 10 mg% or over in 86%, and the minimum observed level in 84%, of the patients with carcinoma of the prostate.

With regard to the concentrations of transferrin in prostatic fluid, the mean of all determinations in patients with cancer exceeds the highest mean of all other groups by over two and a half times (Table V). This significant difference persists if a mean of the individual mean value (Table VI) or a mean of the lowest value for each of the patients is utilized. The mean of all observations and the mean of the individual means of transferrin concentrations in the prostatic

TABLE V. Mean of all observed prostatic fluid transferrin concentrations

Patient groups	No.	Mean SE
Cancer (58)	96	42.432 ± 2.5355
BPH (66)	158	12.284 ± 0.8586
BPH + WBC (48)	136	16.806 ± 1.7279
Normal (56)	56	5.348 ± 0.7147

Mean of all our observations of transferrin concentration in prostatic fluid of patients studied as of 1/15/81. A group of 101 patients with an unconfirmed clinical diagnosis of abacterial or bacterial prostatitis had a mean concentration of 14.554 ± 1.3895 with a total of 156 observations. The number in parentheses equals the number of individuals studied.

TABLE VI. Mean of individual mean prostatic fluid transferrin concentration

Patient groups	Mean SE
Cancer (58)	42.731 ± 3.2484
BPH (66)	11.451 ± 0.9740
BPH + WBC (48)	16.515 ± 2.2862
Normal (56)	6.464 ± 0.7147

Mean of mean transferrin concentration in prostatic fluid from each patient studied as of 1/15/81. Mean of the means for patients designated as having prostatitis (101) was 14.354 ± 1.7948. The number in parentheses equals the number of individual patients studied.

fluid of patients with BPH exceeds that of the concentrations of transferrin in fluid from normal individuals ($P < 0.01$). The means of the lowest transferrin concentrations for each individual with BPH (8.7 ± 0.714) exceeds that of the normal group (6.46 ± 0.8814) ($P < 0.01$). Over 95% of the patients with BPH with or without inflammation and the designated normal male group have a mean level of transferrin in the prostatic fluid of less than 30mg % and a minimum observed level of less than 25mg %. Only one designated normal patient had a mean or minimum level of transferrin exceeding 25 or 30mg %. The mean transferrin level was 30mg % or higher in 69% of patients with cancer, 3% of patients with BPH without evidence of inflammation, and 13% of patients with BPH with evidence of inflammation. The lowest observed transferrin level was 30mg % or higher in 66% of patients with cancer, 2% of patients with BPH without evidence of inflammation, and 4% of patients with BPH with evidence of inflammation. The mean and minimum transferrin levels were between 25 and 30mg % in 7 and 3% of the patients with cancer, respectively. Preliminary observations [20] indicate that prostatic fluid from patients with Stage A carcinoma is very unlikely to have a transferrin level of 30mg % or over. The validity of this observation must again be accepted with reservation because of the small number of Stage A patients studied and the fact that the majority of them were first observed postoperatively. If the four patients with A_1 tumors are eliminated from consideration, the individual mean transferrin level is 30mg % or over in 74% and 25mg % or over in 81% of the cancer patients; the lowest observed transferrin level is 30mg % or over in 70% and 25mg % or over in 74% of the cancer patients.

Additional Biochemical Observations

Anderson and Fair [31] noted that the mean cholesterol concentration was similar in prostatic fluid from normal males and those with BPH identified clinically. Prostatic fluid from patients with bacterial prostatitis had significantly lower mean concentrations of cholesterol, whereas prostatic fluid from patients with carcinoma tended to have higher concentrations. The mean citric acid and zinc concentrations were reduced in prostatic fluid from patients with bacterial prostatitis compared to prostatic fluid from normal males (7.4 ± 1.0 vs 18.7 ± 0.52 mg/ml for citric acid; 145 ± 16 vs 488 ± 18 ug/ml for zinc). The zinc concentration in prostatic fluid from patients with carcinoma of the prostate showed a reduction compared to the concentration in fluid from normal men as well as those with BPH.

Polyamine concentrations were evaluated as determined by Anderson and Fair [31] utilizing the paper electrophoresis technique. Spermidine concentration was significantly lower in the prostatic fluid of men with bacterial prostatitis and was slightly but insignificantly increased in the fluid from men with carcinoma. Our observations were carried out in collaboration with Dr. Laurence Marton utilizing a high-pressure liquid chromatographic technique to determine polyamine concentration. Prostatic fluid from a limited number of patients with carcinoma of the prostate did not show a detectable alteration in polyamine concentrations. Surprisingly, a group of 40 infertile males were found to have a number of individuals with elevated putrescine levels (>100 pm/μl) in the prostatic fluid. On further analysis of the data, it became apparent that the infertile patients with elevated prostatic fluid levels of putrescine had a significantly lower sperm count than that of the infertile males with normal putrescine levels in the prostatic fluid [32].

Physical Properties

Fair et al [33] reported that the pH of 136 prostatic fluid specimens from 93 normal males was 7.28±0.04. The mean pH of 41 samples of prostatic fluid from 14 patients with chronic bacterial prostatitis was 8.32±0.07. Almost 80% of the samples of prostatic fluid from patients with chronic bacterial prostatitis had a pH of 8 or over; and 10% (14 of 136) of specimens from normal men had a pH of 8.09 or over. An inverse relationship was noted between zinc concentration and pH in the expressed prostatic fluid of normal and prostatitis patients. Anderson and Fair [31] noted a significant decrease in specific gravity in the prostatic fluid from 13 patients with bacterial prostatitis and a significant increase in the specific gravity of prostatic fluid in 8 patients with carcinoma. No correlation between osmolarity and specific gravity of the prostatic fluid was noted.

DISCUSSION

Attempts to expand observations of expressed prostatic fluid to assist in identifying or understanding diseases of the prostate have been limited and are often regarded with suspicion. The fluid obtained by digital massage of the prostate has been suspicious because of the questionable effect on the observed results of trauma, possible selective sampling, or contamination by secretions of other accessory sex glands or urine. A critical study comparing analysis of fluid from split ejaculates and expressed fluid from the prostate is not available. Data available on the composition of fluid obtained by the split ejaculate technique are limited, but they do not suggest that digital massage produces a major alteration in prostatic fluid composition [12, 29, 34]. The concentrations of fructose, prostaglandin, and urea in expressed prostatic fluid have been determined by other investigators in an effort to identify the incidence and degree of contamination by secretions of other organs and urine. This has been found to be minimal and infrequent [10, 35]. To maximize the amount of fluid available for investigative biochemical analysis, we have elected in our studies to rely on microscopic evaluation to identify contamination by spermatozoa, seminal vesicle secretions, or blood. Comparative analysis of results observed in contaminated and noncontaminated specimens has been employed to attempt to assess the influence of the various degrees of contamination on the results observed. Observations of significant alterations in the composition of prostatic fluid obtained from patients with different pathologic conditions in the prostate by digital massage should probably be confirmed by analysis of fluid obtained directly from prostatic tissue or by selective tissue analysis before being accepted unequivocally as reflecting the metabolic status of the prostatic cells. However, the potential clinical value of recognized alterations in the composition of expressed prostatic fluid that allows identification of prostatic pathology would persist even in the unlikely event that the results of the tissue or specimen analysis differ from those in fluid analysis.

Evaluation of observations that are currently available indicates that abnormalities noted in the fluid from a prostate that is the site of pathologic change may definitely identify the pathology present or indicate an increased risk of its presence; in some instances, evaluation of prostatic fluid will identify a highly probable etiologic factor. Recognition of unequivocally malignant individual or groups of cells on microscopic examination of cytologic stains of prostatic fluid or post-prostatic massage urine seems sufficient to establish the diagnosis of carcinoma of the prostate, even though many may be reluctant to advise clinical management on the basis of this finding alone [6]. The finding on microscopic examination of the prostatic fluid of white blood cells in a concentration significantly exceeding the range noted in the prostatic fluid of men thought to have a normal prostate seems clearly to indicate some type of inflammatory response or prostatitis [1, 36]. In some instances microscopic evaluation of the expressed prostatic fluid may disclose a highly probable etiologic factor such as the presence of active motile Trichomonas vaginalis. In others, culture of the prostatic fluid and the post-prostatic massage urine may demonstrate the presence of pathologic bacteria in sufficient numbers to indicate a high probability that they are the cause of the prostatitis present. In a large number of individuals, the microscopic prostatic fluid findings indicate the presence of prostatic inflammation and do not provide evidence for etiologic factors that we have been able to recognize. Nevertheless, the evidence provided by microscopic analysis for an inflammatory condition of unknown etiology seems compelling, and the need to pursue its possible cause by subjecting the prostate and the prostatic fluid of this group of individuals to a continuing multifaceted analysis seems apparent to us.

The remainder of the observations reported in this review have the potential to assist in recognition of prostatic pathology by identifying the high risk of its presence and to direct clinical activity by adding information that increases our understanding of pathologic states. For example, as Fair reports and discusses in the accompanying article, analysis of zinc in the prostatic fluid has demonstrated that a markedly reduced concentration of this element is uniformly present in patients with bacterial prostatitis. The decreased zinc concentration may represent a significant etiologic factor in this disease; its recognition could have diagnostic and direct or indirect therapeutic implications. The increase in pH of the prostatic fluid that seems characteristic of bacterial prostatitis may aid in recognizing the cause of prostatic inflammation [2] and also may have therapeutic implications [33].

Patients with prostatitis without regard to etiology have a mean LDH-5/LDH-1 ratio in the prostatic fluid that is significantly greater than the ratio in prostatic fluid from normal men or men with histologically confirmed BPH with fewer than 10 WBC/hpf. This observation has served to provide further evidence that an increased number of white blood cells in the prostatic fluid is associated with significant intragland changes including metabolic ones and to reinforce the desirability of expanding the variety and number of biochemical observations in this group of patients. Improvement in clinical recognition and management of patients with so-called nonbacterial prostatitis will hopefully follow.

Review of the current data indicates that biochemical assessment of the composition of prostatic fluid seems to assist in identifying individuals with a high risk of carcinoma of the prostate. The mean LDH-5/LDH-1 ratio and the concentration of complement C_3, transferrin, and probably complement C_4 are increased significantly in the prostatic fluid of patients with carcinoma of the prostate as compared to normal men. The concentration of acid phosphatase per gram of protein equivalent is decreased markedly. The relatively increased LDH-5 concentration might be viewed as a quasi-qualitative change. It is also present in the prostatic fluid from men with BPH and prostatic inflammation; however, the degree of relative increase in LDH-5 is significantly greater in prostatic fluid from patients with carcinoma or prostatic inflammation than with BPH. The LDH-5/LDH-1 ratio in the prostatic fluid of the majority of men with carcinoma of the prostate is elevated if the levels observed in the fluid from 95% of normal men is accepted as normal. This elevated ratio is present with about equal frequency in the prostatic fluid from patients with all stages of malignancy. Men with 10 or more WBC/hpf in the prostatic fluid on microscopic examination have a high incidence of elevated LDH-5/LDH-1 ratios using this criteria.

The mean complement C_3 and C_4 and transferrin is significantly increased, and the mean acid phosphatase concentration is significantly decreased in prostatic fluid from patients with carcinoma of the prostate as compared to all other group studies. The great majority of men with Stage B_1 or greater carcinoma of the prostate has an elevated prostatic fluid level of complement C_3 or transferrin, if the level observed in fluid of 95% of the men without carcinoma is accepted as normal. However, even if the patients with Stage A_1 carcinoma of the prostate are excluded because of their small numbers and frequent postsurgical status, not every patient with this neoplasm has an elevated level of these proteins in the expressed prostatic fluid; nor does every prostatic fluid from a patient with carcinoma of the prostate demonstrate a decreased acid phosphatase concentration. Recognition that a small percentage of patients without evidence of carcinoma will demonstrate changes in concentration of these substances that are similar to those noted in patients with documented carcinoma of the prostate is of equal importance. Despite these observations, the evidence suggests that the determination of LDH-5/LDH-1 ratio and complement C_3 and C_4, transferrin, and acid phosphatase concentration in expressed prostatic fluid will assist in identifying individuals with increased risk of carcinoma of the prostate. It is our opinion that the value of these determinations is likely to be increased by combining them and carrying them out sequentially. The identification of these biochemical differences between prostatic fluid from patients with carcinoma of the prostate and normal individuals or those with benign prostatic pathology seems to justify further enthusiastic exploration of a relationship between fluid composition and prostatic pathology.

Recognition of changes in prostatic fluid composition associated with disease states may also lead to knowledgeable speculation regarding their pathophysiology. The observation that the LDH-5/LDH-1 ratio was increased in histologically benign tissue of the prostate gland containing carcinoma about 80% of the time was one of the major factors suggesting the possibility that carcinoma of the prostate might be associated with a field change. The fact that an increased LDH-5/LDH-1 ratio is present in the prostatic fluid of most patients with carcinoma and that, in the limited observations available, the increased ratio seems to be present with about equal frequency in patients with Stage A as with other stages of the disease, is regarded as supportive evidence of the possibility of a field change. The mechanism of increased complement C_3 and transferrin concentration is not clear but our speculation at this time is that these proteins are concentrated from systemic sources. Knowledge that these increased concentrations exist should stimulate attempts to identify the mechanisms involved and lead to an increasing understanding of the pathophysiology of prostatic malignancy.

Evaluation of prostatic fluid composition may lead to observations that are suggestively reflective of systemic changes possibly relating to pathologic phenomena. Biochemical alterations have been sought and identified that seem to relate to known endocrine alterations and have been cited to attempt to identify mechanisms for paradoxical biological changes [14]. The observation that elevated putrescine levels in the prostatic fluid of infertile males were associated with significantly lower sperm counts as compared to the sperm count in infertile males with putrescine levels in the normal range may identify an insignificant association or may indicate a relationship between testicular function and prostatic metabolism that has not been recognized previously [32]. The fact that infertile patients have been found to have an increased mean prostatic fluid leukocyte count compared to patients with no urologic disease seems to support an alteration in the prostate associated with infertility [1]. Consideration of these observations should stimulate further exploration of possible mechanisms underlying this interrelationship.

Finally, the observation that prostatic fluid from men with BPH without evidence of inflammation has a mean LDH-5/LDH-1 ratio and complement C_3 and transferrin concentration that differs from the prostatic fluid of normal men continues to intrigue and puzzle us. The biochemical observations noted parallel those seen in malignancy but differ significantly in magnitude. They may be the result of inclusion of patients with malignant or premalignant changes in the prostate in the BPH group. Equally feasible is the possibility that these changes are the result of a metabolic alteration that is a manifestation of the systemic or local effects of aging. At any rate, those interesting observations warrant our recognition and further study and thought.

The data presented seem to support the current and potential future value of a multifaceted effort to study prostatic fluid to learn more about the prostate and its diseases. The fact that the prostatic fluid composition may be altered by the digital pressure necessary to obtain it, by the proteolytic enzymes it contains, or by contamination by urine or secretions of other accessory sex glands warrants recognition. However, these factors seem to be of limited consequence or at least controllable. The opportunity to obtain a highly selective sample of secretion that is likley to reflect the metabolic activity of an endocrine-responsive organ that undergoes significant pathologic change is a unique one that should be exploited.

ACKNOWLEDGMENTS

This study is supported by NIH grant CA 16736 and by the Edwin and Lucy Kretschmer Fund of Northwestern University Medical School.

REFERENCES

1. Schaeffer A, Wendel EF, Dunn JK, Grayhack JT: Prevalence and significance of prostatic inflammation. J Urol 125:215–219, 1981.
2. Blacklock NJ: Prostatitis. The Practitioner 223:318–322, 1979.
3. Anderson RU, Weller C: Prostatic secretion leukocyte studies in non-bacterial prostatitis (prostatosis). J Urol 121:292–294, 1979.
4. Mardh PA, Colleen S: Search for urogenital tract infection in patients with symptoms of prostatitis. Scand J Urol Nephrol 9:8–16, 1975.
5. Summers JL, Ford ML: The Papanicolaou smear as a diagnostic tool in male trichomoniasis. J Urol 107:840, 1972.
6. Garret M, Jassie M: Cytologic examination of post-prostatic massage specimens as an aid in diagnosis of carcinoma of the prostate. Acta Cytol 20:126–131, 1976.
7. Meares EM, Stamey TA: Bacteriologic localization patterns in bacterial prostatitis and urethritis. Invest Urol 5:492–518, 1968.
8. Aumüller G, Adler G: Experimental studies of apocrine secretion in the dorsal prostate epithelium of the rat. Cell Tissue Res 198:145–148, 1979.

9. Huggins C: The physiology of the prostate gland. Physiol Rev 25:281–295, 1945.
10. Huggins C: The prostatic secretions. Harvey Lecture 42:148–193, 1946–47.
11. Huggins C, Scott WW, Heinen JH: Chemical composition of human semen and of the secretions of the prostate and seminal vesicle. Amer J Physiol 136:467–473, 1942.
12. Mann T: The Biochemistry of Semen and of the Male Reproductive Tract. London: Methuen & Co., New York: John Wiley & Sons, 1964.
13. Kirk E: The acid phosphatase concentration of the prostatic fluid in young, middle-aged, and old individuals. J Gerontol 3:98–104, 1948.
14. Grayhack JT, Kropp K: Changes with aging in prostatic fluid: Citric acid, acid phosphatase and lactic dehydrogenase concentration in man. J Urol 93:258–262, 1965.
15. Denis LJ, Prout GP, Jr, Van Camp K, Van Sande M: Electrophoretic characterization of prostate: Protein and lactic dehydrogenase in benign hyperplasia and carcinoma. J Urol 88:77–85, 1962.
16. Elhilali MM, Oliver JA, Sherwin AL, MacKinnon KJ: Lactate dehydrogenase isoenzymes in hyperplasia and carcinoma of the prostate: A clinical study. J Urol 98:686–692, 1967.
17. Oliver JA, Elhilali MM, Belitsky P, MacKinnon KJ: LDH isoenzymes in benign and malignant prostate tissue: The LDH-5/1 ratio as an index of malignancy. Cancer 25:863–866, 1970.
18. Grayhack JT, Lee C, Oliver L, Schaeffer AJ, Wendel EF: Biochemical profiles of prostatic fluid from normal and diseased prostate glands. The Prostate 1:227–237, 1980.
19. Grayhack JT, Lee C, Oliver L, Schaeffer AJ, Wendel EF: Manuscript in preparation.
20. Uke E, Falkowski W, Lee C, Grayhack JT: Manuscript in preparation.
21. Grayhack JT, Wendel EF: Hormone dependence of carcinoma of the prostate. In David Brandes (ed): "Male Accessory Sex Organs, Structure and Function in Mammals." New York, San Francisco, London: Academic Press 1974, 425–432.
22. Kent JR, Hill M, Bischoff A: Acid phosphatase content of prostate exprimate from patients with advanced prostatic carcinoma: A potential prognostic therapeutic index. Cancer 25:858–862, 1970.
23. Grayhack JT, Wendel EF, Lee C, Oliver L: Analysis of prostatic fluid in prostatic disease. Cancer Treat Rep 61:205–210, 1977.
24. Nylander G: The electrophoretic pattern of prostatic proteins in normal and pathologic secretion. Acta Chir Scand 109:473–482, 1955.
25. Soanes WA, Shulman S, Mamrod L, Barnes GW, Gonder MJ: Electrophoretic analysis of prostatic fluid. Invest Urol 1:269–278, 1963–64.
26. Resnick M, Stubbs AJ: Age specific electrophoretic patterns in prostatic fluid. J Surg Res 24:415–420, 1978.
27. Chodirker WB, Tomasi TB, Jr: Gamma globulins: Quantitative relationships in human semen and non-vascular fluids. Science 142:1080–1081, 1963.
28. Gray SP, Billings J, Blacklock NJ: Distribution of immunoglobulins G, A, and M in prostatic fluid of patients with prostatitis. Clin Chem Acta 57:163–169, 1974.
29. Shah N: Diagnostic significance of levels of immunoglobulin A in seminal fluid of patients with prostatic disease. Urology 8:270–272, 1976.
30. Grayhack JT, Wendel EF, Oliver L, Lee C: Analysis of specific proteins in prostatic fluid for detecting prostatic malignancy. J Urol 121:295–299, 1979.
31. Anderson RU, Fair WR: Physical and chemical determinations of prostatic secretions on benign hyperplasia, prostatitis, and adenocarcinoma. Invest Urol 14:137–140, 1976.
32. Kaplan L, Wendel EF, Oliver L, Marton L: High putrescine levels in prostatic fluid of men with history of infertility. To be submitted for publication.
33. Fair W, Crane DD, Schiller N, Heston WD: A reappraisal of treatment in chronic bacterial prostatitis. J Urol 121:437–441, 1979.
34. Homonnai ZT, Matzkin H, Farnaman H, Paz G, Kraicer PF: The cation composition of seminal plasma and prostatic fluid and its correlation to semen quality. Fertil Steril 29:539–542, 1978.

35. Fair W, Cordonnier J: The pH of prostatic fluid: A reappraisal and therapuetic implications. J Urol 120:695–698, 1978.
36. Drach GW: Prostatitis and prostatodynia: Their relationship to benign prostatic hypertrophy. Urol Clin N Amer 7:79–88, 1980.

The Prostatic Cell: Structure and Function
Part A, pages 247–264

Antibacterial Substances in Prostatic Fluid

William R. Fair and Richard F. Parrish

INTRODUCTION

Urinary tract infections occur 6–10 times more frequently in females than in males [1]. In adult males most urinary tract infections are secondary to a bacterial infection of the prostate which later ascends to infect the bladder urine [2]. The reason for the apparent difference in the sex ratio of urinary tract infections is unknown but may be related to a unique "defense mechanism" in the prostate secretion of normal males which serves to prevent bacterial infection. Until relatively recently, the nature of the antibacterial activity was unknown, although lysozyme [3] and the polyamine spermine [4–6] were suggested as the responsible agents. Previous work from our laboratories observed the finding of a pronounced antibacterial activity in the prostatic secretion of the dog [7–9], rat [10], and human [11, 12]. Although unknown to us at the time, our work with canine prostatic secretion was a confirmation of the pioneer observation in 1938 of Youmans et al [13] when they noted that the pilocarpine-stimulated prostatic fluid of the normal dog demonstrated marked antibacterial activity against E. coli, S. aureus, and streptocci; a lesser effect was noted against the gonococcus. Since our earlier observation, we have proved that the antibacterial activity of human and canine prostatic fluid was found in a low molecular weight, heat stable fraction that was not inactivated by heating to destroy complement and is not related to lysozyme or spermine. This activity is markedly diminished or absent in individuals with documented chronic bacterial prostatitis [12].

The purpose of this chapter is to review those observations and others which clearly establish that the prostatic antibacterial factor (PAF) in canine, rat, and human secretion is related to the zinc content of the prostatic fluid in each species. We also present preliminary evidence that the antibacterial activity in human expressed prostatic secretion (EPS) is due to free zinc rather than a zinc-peptide complex or zinc salt.

RESULTS

Demonstration of Antibacterial Activity

Canine studies. During experiments designed to study the diffusion of antibacterial agents from plasma to prostatic fluid in the dog, the pilocarpine-stimulated prostatic fluid was found to possess a remarkable bactericidal activity against a wide variety of gram-positive and gram-negative organisms including E. coli, Klebsiella, P. Mirabilis, Pseudomonas, and S. Faecalis. In initial experiments, 71 of 74 urinary tract pathogens inoculated into dog prostatic fluid at a bacterial density of 10^4 organisms per ml were totally eliminated within 24 hours of incubation. Further experiments revealed that the antibacterial activity of whole canine prostatic fluid and the low molecular weight, heat stable, active fraction isolated from canine prostatic fluid by gel filtration techniques could only be demonstrated in 0.15M NaCl, as it was found that the bactericidal action was inhibited by trypticase soy broth, casein, and peptone [7]. Later we developed an antibacterial assay using a defined medium substituting 1.5% agarose for agar which made it possible to assay prostatic fluid fractions for antibacterial activity in the standard agar diffusion type system [9] and allowed the further separation and purification of the fraction containing the antibacterial activity.

Lysozyme assays. Because of the reports that lysozyme was responsible for at least part of the antibacterial activity of human semen [3], the standard photometric determination of lysozyme activity was measured by plotting the increase in transmittance of a solution that contained a known weight of Micrococcus lysodeikticus cells lyophilized in phosphate buffered saline. The decrease in optical density was determined at 420 μm in a spectrophotometer using the interval between 30 seconds and 3 minutes to express lysozymal activity. Under these conditions there was no change in optical density when the suspension of Micrococcus lysodeikticus was treated with prostatic fluid, whereas marked clearing of the suspension was noted in the tube containing a lysozyme standard at a concentration of 10 μg/ml.

Based on these observations along with additional later experiments that confirmed the heat stability of the antibacterial activity and established its behavior in column chromatographic systems, it was obvious that the antibacterial activity of canine and human prostatic fluid was not due to lysozymal activity.

Role of spermine. Spermine $H_2N-(CH_2)_3-NH-(CH_2)_4-NH-(CH_2)_3-NH_2$, a polyamine widely distributed throughout animal tissues, was reported to have antibacterial activity against a variety of microorganisms [15, 16]. This compound, originally isolated from semen, occurs in very high concentrations in the prostate of many mammalian species [17] and is thought to be responsible for the antibacterial action of human semen [4, 5] against gram-positive organisms. In an effort to determine the role of spermine as a natural defense mechanism against urinary tract infections, we studied the effect of spermine against a variety of microorganisms responsible for the majority of such infections in the human. Antibacterial activity was assayed at two pH levels against a variety of gram-positive and gram-negative organisms isolated from the urine of patients with a urinary tract infection. Spermine at concentrations as high as 2,500 μg/0.1 ml had no effect on the gram-negative test organisms when assayed at pH 6.4. Spermine was more active at pH 7.4 but even at the highest concentrations only 16% of 45 test organisms showed any inhibition in growth due to spermine [18]. Furthermore the prostatic fluid demonstrated marked antibacterial activity against organisms that were totally resistant to spermine. Later, spermine assays on the PAF clearly established that spermine was not responsible for the antibacterial activity observed in canine and human prostatic fluid and human seminal plasma.

Isolation and purification of the prostatic antibacterial factor (PAF). The prostatic antibacterial factor (PAF) was isolated from prostatic fluid or semen by cation-exchange chromatography using a Dowex 50WX2 (H+ form) column [11]. The PAF eluted from the Dowex column was resistant to heating to 100°C for 15 minutes at pH 7.0. However, when the proteins in the whole prostatic fluid were coagulated by heating, no antibacterial activity was demonstrated in the supernatant fluid of heated whole prostatic fluid. Antibacterial activity could be recovered in the PAF fraction when the flocculant precipitate obtained by heating intact prostatic fluid or seminal plasma was treated with perchloric acid and centrifuged, after which the supernatant was placed on the Dowex column and eluted with HCl. This indicated that the loss of activity was the result of binding of the PAF, in neutral solution, to the heat-precipitated protein.

The PAF appeared to be freely soluble in water. Attempts to extract the antibacterial activity into a variety of organic solvents, eg, $CHCl_3$, ether, toluene, 1-butanol, 2-propanol, tertiary butyl alcohol, cyclohexane, ethyl acetate, and methylisobutylketone, were uniformly unsuccessful over a wide pH range.

Chemical identification of the PAF. The PAF fraction, purified at least 5,000-fold on a weight basis [11], was readily crystallized by increasing the pH to above 9 by adding 1 N NaOH. After separation, no antibacterial activity was observed in the supernatant fraction. The resulting crystals were submitted for ion probe and mass spectrographic analysis [12]. Both analytical methods indicated that the crystals were predominantly zinc chloride. The PAF fraction was not composed entirely of zinc salts, as was shown by the results of amino acid analysis and gas chromatography on the acid-hydrolyzed fraction. Under these conditions the following amino acids were also identified: alanine, glutamine, glycine, isoleucine, lysine, phenylalanine, proline, serine, threonine, tyrosine, and valine.

Relationship of antibacterial activity to zinc concentration. The experiments done following identification of zinc salts in the PAF proved that the fraction of canine and human prostatic fluid possessing antibacterial activity as well as a zinc chloride standard solution were eluted from ion exchange and gel filtration chromatography columns in an identical volume of eluate. Those substances previously demonstrated as inhibitors of PAF activity, ie, agar, casein, tartrate, or other anionic agents [7], also inhibited the normal bactericidal action of zinc salts in solution. The zones of inhibition measured on the PAF assay of both canine and human prostatic fluid were directly proportional to the zinc concentration of these fluids. The addition of a zinc chloride solution in varying concentrations to the prostatic fluid gave an increase in the bactericidal action which was proportional to the amount of zinc added. Additional indirect evidence presented in favor of the antibacterial action of prostatic fluid being directly related to its zinc content was the abolishment of the antibacterial effect when equimolar amounts of EDTA (ethylenediaminetetraacetic acid), a cation chelating agent, were added to the prostatic fluid (Fig. 1).

Antibacterial Activity of Human Semen and EPS

The PAF fraction obtained via ion-exchange chromatography [11] was used to quantitate the antibacterial activity of human semen or EPS in normal males and patients with documented bacterial prostatitis. Early in the study, observations were made on secretions obtained following prostatic massage. In 10 of 13 samples (77%) obtained from five patients documented as having chronic bacterial prostatitis, no PAF was demonstrable; when bactericidal activity was present, the diameter of the zone of inhibition averaged only 12.4 mm. Six samples of EPS from normal males all had evidence of antibacterial activity, with zones of inhibition averaging of 21.2 mm in diameter. Because of the small volume of fluid obtained on prostatic massage, the quantitative difference in PAF activities between patients and controls was more easily and more accurately assessed by using seminal plasma. In Figure 2, the diameter of the zone of inhibition shown by the PAF fractions from 63 seminal plasma specimens obtained from 49 controls is compared with the

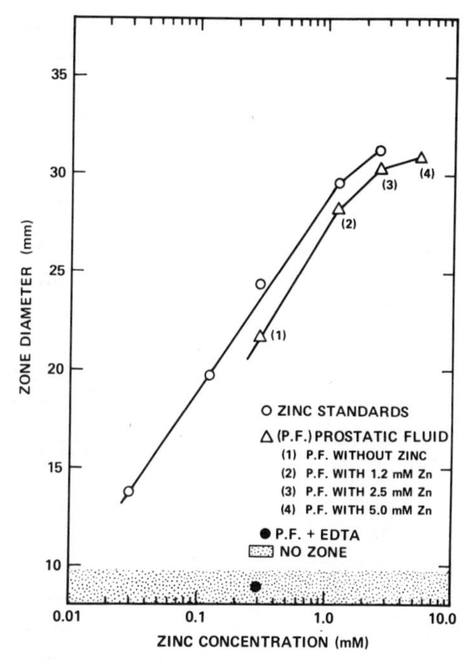

Fig. 1. Diameter of the zone of inhibition of various concentrations of zinc and prostatic fluid (P.F.) with increasing concentration of added zinc. Shaded area represents diameter (9 mm) of cylinder containing test solution. Figures 1–5 are taken from Urology 7:169–177, 1976, with permission.

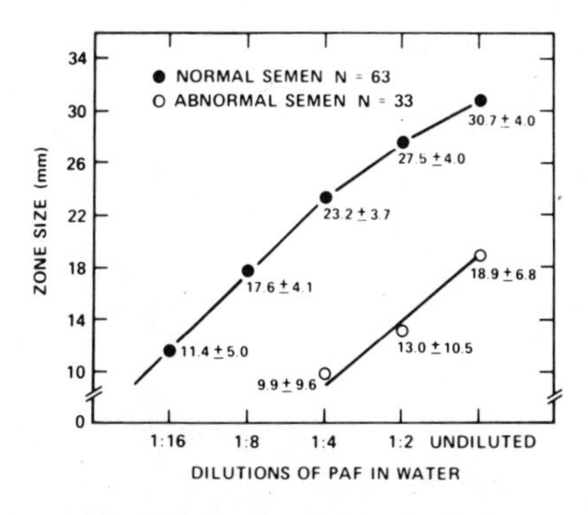

Fig. 2. Diameter of zones of inhibition obtained with various dilutions of PAF in water. Closed circles indicate semen samples from men with no history of prostatic infections and negative prostatic fluid cultures. Open circles are values measured in semen of men with documented bacterial prostatitis.

PAF activity of 33 seminal plasmas obtained from 15 men with chronic bacterial prostatitis. The diameter of the zone of inhibition obtained with the undiluted PAF fraction isolated from the seminal plasma specimens of patients with chronic bacterial prostatitis often had no demonstrable antibacterial activity. Even in samples where antibacterial activity was seen, the diameter of the zone of inhibition was much less (mean = 18.9 ± 6.8 mm) than that found in the control specimens. A comparison on the dilution curve (Fig. 2) enabled us to quantitate PAF activity in the seminal plasma of patients. Hence, a 1:4 dilution of a "normal seminal" plasma gave a larger zone size than the undiluted sample from the patient group, indicating that the mean PAF level in the patients' semen was less than 25% of that expected to be present in normal subjects. However, serial semen samples from the same normal individual assayed over a period of several months varied by as much as 5 mm from sample to sample, indicating a moderate degree of fluctuation

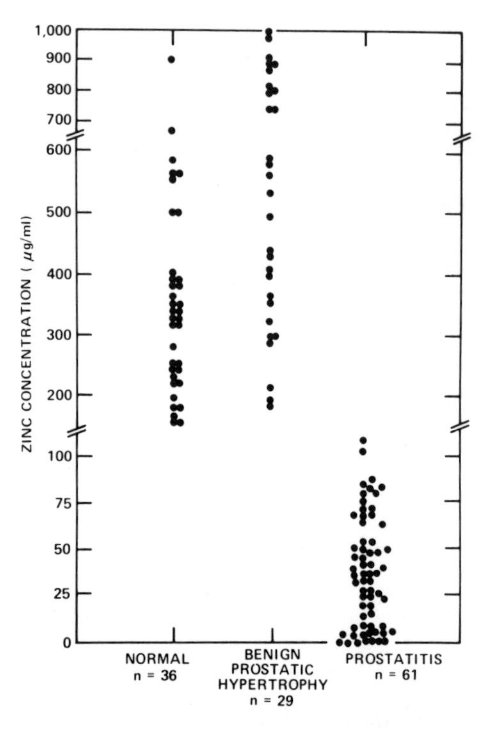

Fig. 3. Zinc levels in expressed prostatic secretion obtained from men without prostatic disease (normal), those with benign prostatic hypertrophy but free from prostate infections, and men with documented bacterial prostatitis.

in the amount of PAF normally present. Successive assays on the same sample over a 2-month period did not vary by more than 4%.

Role of Zinc as an Antibacterial Agent in Prostatic Fluid

Zinc levels in human prostatic fluid. Expressed prostatic secretions, collected from control males and patients with chronic bacterial prostatitis, were analyzed for zinc. The zinc concentration of the prostatic fluid showed a wide variation among individuals. The range of prostatic fluid zinc level in 65 EPS specimens obtained from 49 men free from bacterial prostatic infection (normals plus BPH group) was 150–1,000 μg per ml (Fig. 3). In sharp contrast, the zinc concentration in 61 specimens of EPS obtained from 15 patients with documented chronic bacterial prostatitis averaged only 50 μg per ml. Several of the specimens had no detectable zinc present by this sensitive atomic absorption spectrophotometric method and in no instance was a zinc level higher than 139 μg per ml obtained. In the absence of such data in the literature, we chose to establish a value of 150 μg per ml as the "lower limit of normal" for zinc in expressed prostatic secretions.

The zinc level in the prostatic fluid of a given individual appears to be relatively constant, particularly in the patient with prostatitis. Figure 4 illustrates typical serial prostatic fluid zinc levels found in two men (one patient and one normal) from whom we obtained multiple EPS collections, each of which was preceded by at least three days of sexual abstinence. Considering the value of 150 μg per ml suggested above as the lower limit of normal for zinc concentration in the EPS of normal men, it is apparent that the zinc level of the EPS in the normal man remained well above this value in multiple EPS specimens obtained during a 12-month period. Similarly, the patient

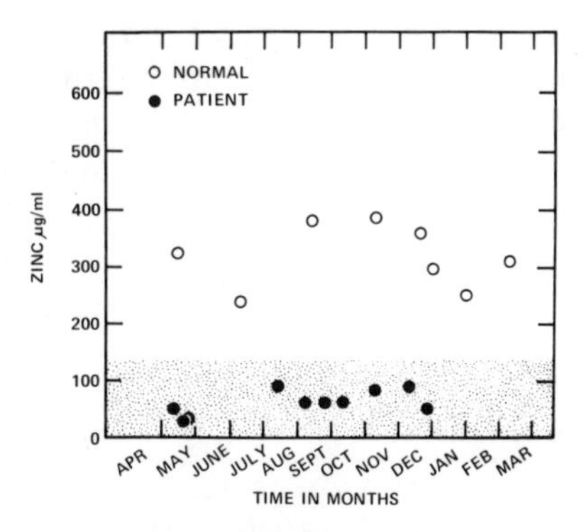

Fig. 4. Serial zinc levels in expressed prostatic fluid of normal male and patient with bacterial prostatitis. Stippled area indicates range of EPS zinc levels found in patients with bacterial prostatitis.

with a documented chronic bacterial prostatitis continued to have a low EPS zinc level over the course of the follow-up. In the example shown in Figure 4, the patient was *asymptomatic* and had *sterile urine* while on prolonged suppressive therapy with 100 mg minocycline HCl twice daily, although direct cultures of the EPS confirmed the presence of small numbers of *Pseudomonas* and the persistence of chronic bacterial prostatitis which was unaffected by the antibacterial therapy.

Serum zinc levels in normals and prostatic patients. Table I lists the serum zinc levels found in 61 samples from control men and 42 samples from patients with bacterial prostatitis. As with the EPS levels, there was no appreciable difference between the normal males and BPH patients with respect to serum zinc levels and both are included in the "control" group.

TABLE I. Serum zinc levels

Group	Number of samples	Age (yr)	Concentration μg/ml ± SD	Range
Control	61	41–81 (62)	0.89 ± 0.17	0.60–1.28
Prostatitis patients	42	27–70 (52)	0.80 ± 0.14	0.58–1.16

Figures in parentheses represent mean age.

Effects of exogenous zinc salts on serum and prostatic fluid levels (Table II). We studied the effect of exogenously administered zinc salts on serum and prostatic fluid zinc levels in seven patients with bacterial prostatitis. The patients received between 50 and 100 mg of elemental zinc orally per day for periods of three to six months. Serum zinc levels increased from a mean value of 0.80 μg per ml to 1.08 μg per ml, but prostatic fluid zinc levels did not undergo any appreciable change from the pretreatment levels while the patients were on this supplementation. More importantly, the additional oral zinc had no affect on the course of the infection and the prostatic fluid cultures were still diagnostic of chronic bacterial prostatitis.

TABLE II. Oral zinc supplementation (50–100 mg daily × 3 months)

Specimen (n = 7)	Pretreatment μg/ml	Post-treatment μg/ml
Serum	0.80 ± 0.14	0.96 ± 0.17
EPS	56 ± 8.7	49 ± 11.4

Prostatic fluid zinc levels following elimination or subsidence of prostatic infection. During the course of these studies two patients initially presenting with bacteriuria and subsequently diagnosed as having chronic bacterial prostatitis were observed to undergo complete clearing of the prostatic infection following antimicrobial therapy, and remain uninfected for periods varying from 6 to 12 months. One of these patients (Fig. 5) is discussed in detail below.

C.R., SMR # 39-33-57, was a 48-year-old white male who was first seen by one of us (WRF) in July of 1972 with a history of recurrent urinary tract infections. Segmented urine and prostatic fluid cultures done elsewhere confirmed the diagnosis of chronic bacterial prostatitis due to an E. coli infection. From January 1971 to July 1972 he had multiple episodes of urinary tract infections characterized by frequency, dysuria, nocturia, perineal pain, and occasional fever and chills. He had no nausea, vomiting, or flank pain. An intravenous urogram was normal, the prostate was not grossly enlarged, and no prostatic calculi were seen. The bladder appeared to empty normally with no significant residual. Physical examination was normal, the

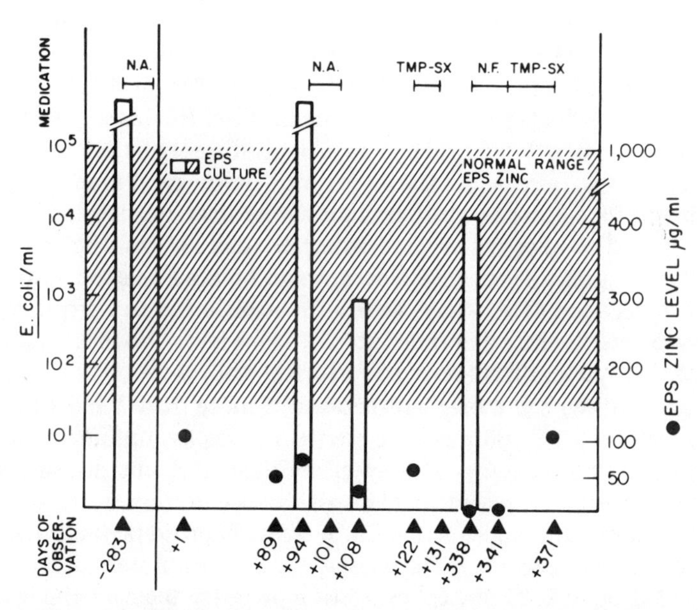

Fig. 5. Results of serial prostatic fluid zinc levels and cultures in patient in Case Report. Each culture is indicated by black triangle. Where no vertical striped bar is shown on graph, EPS culture was sterile. Black circles indicate EPS zinc levels. Days of observations are expressed as minus or plus the day of the first EPS zinc determination. N.A., nalidixic acid; TMP-SX, trimethoprin-sulfamethoxazole; N.F., nitrofurantoin.

prostate was minimally enlarged and firm but without nodules or tenderness. Initial urine and prostatic fluid cultures (day 283) contained greater than 10^5 E. coli per ml. The patient was treated with nalidixic acid, 500 mg four times daily for 10 days; his symptoms subsided and urine cultures became sterile. He had no further difficulty for more than one year; during this time he received no antibiotics. In this one-year interval, EPS zinc concentration was measured on two occasions and found to be 100 μg per ml (day 1) and 49 μg per ml (day 89). Both values are well below normal levels. Urine and EPS cultures were sterile both times. Five days later (day 94) or 377 days since his last urinary tract infection, he developed lower tract symptoms. Urine and EPS cultures grew 10^5 E. coli per ml. He was again treated with nalidoxic acid and his symptoms disappeared. Urine and EPS cultures were sterile one week later while the patient was still taking antibiotics. He returned for a follow-up visit four days after stopping the medication (day 108); a midstream urine culture contained only 90 E. coli per ml but the EPS grew out 1,000 E. coli per ml confirming the prostatic source of his infection. Twelve days later the patient again became symptomatic. He was seen by another physician who prescribed trimethoprim-sulfamethoxazole (TMP-SX), two tablets three times daily, but did not obtain a urine or prostatic fluid culture. His symptoms promptly cleared and when seen in our clinic (day 122) his cultures were sterile. An EPS zinc at this time was again markedly depressed at 60 μg per ml. The patient returned nine days later (day 131); at this time he was asymptomatic and had discontinued the medication. He was seen three more times during the next 6.5 months. The urine cultures remained sterile, and his EPS zinc levels were below 100 μg per ml. Almost eight months after his last positive EPS culture he again became symptomatic; urine and EPS cultures confirmed another urinary tract infection (day 338), and he was treated with nitrofurantion to clear the bacteriuria and placed on suppressive antibacterial medication (TMP-SX). Two subsequent urine and prostatic fluid cultures were sterile since that time. The EPS zinc levels, however, remained depressed. The patient has been lost to further follow-up.

The patient discussed above had periods of more than 7 and 12 months during which the EPS cultures were sterile, he was asymptomatic, and received no antibiotic therapy. However, multiple EPS zinc determinations during these periods revealed that the zinc concentration in the EPS was markedly depressed. It appears that the decrease in prostatic fluid zinc levels is not due simply to bacteria in the prostatic secretions. Rather, it seems as if the marked drop in EPS zinc concentration preceded the bacterial invasion and did not return to normal levels even when the prostatic fluid was sterile and the patient had discontinued antibiotic therapy. Unfortunately, serotyping of the organism was not done so that it is not possible to state whether a new organism was responsible for each of the infections, but the sterile urine and prostatic fluid cultures and the lack of symptoms for more than one year in the absence of antibiotic ingestion would suggest that relapse from a chronic prostatic infection was unlikely.

In vitro antibacterial activity of zinc salts. The antibacterial activity of various concentrations of a zinc sulfate solution was tested against a variety of bacteria isolated from the urine of patients with urinary tract infections. The organisms were deemed "sensitive" to a particular level of zinc, expressed as μg per ml only if *all* the strains tested at that level had a 50% or greater decrease in the number of bacteria within six hours after the addition of zinc salt to a culture of the organism in MOPS medium [12].

As shown in Table III, the sensitivity of the organisms varied widely but, with the exception of Proteus mirabilis and Streptococcus fecalis, all of the organisms were sensitive to levels of zinc that are easily attained in the prostatic fluid of most human males, even those with chronic bacterial prostatitis.

The 66 strains tested varied in sensitivity to zinc from 1.5 μg per ml for Klebsiella to >650 μg per ml for Streptococcus fecalis. Despite the relative resistance of the Strep. fecalis, Staph. albus, the other gram-positive organism tested, was very sensitive at the level of 20.4 μg per ml. No attempt was made to study the effect of protein binding or the possibility of an "in vivo" zinc inhibitor in this study.

To determine if a differential response to zinc could be of any significance in the observation that relatively few strains of E. coli are responsible for the majority of human urinary tract infections, we also quantified the response of the strains commonly found as urinary tract pathogens, ie, "common E. coli" were slightly more sensitive to the effect of the zinc salt, but the differences between the two groups were not significant.

TABLE III. In vitro antibacterial activity of zinc sulfate

Organism	Number of strains tested	Sensitivity μg/ml
E. coli "common"	19	20.4
E. coli "uncommon"	21	10.2
Pseudomonas sp.	5	40.8
Proteus mirabilis	6	81.6
Klebsiella sp.	5	5.1
Strep fecalis	5	>650.0
Staph albus	5	20.4

The Antibacterial Factor — Free or Complexed Zinc?

Interestingly, the zinc in canine prostatic secretions had previously been reported to be complexed to a peptide composed of eight amino acids [19]. In light of the loss of the antibacterial activity following incubation of prostatic secretions with EDTA it was necessary to determine if the putative zinc-peptide complex reported to be present in canine prostatic secretions demonstrated any antibacterial activity. Therefore a series of experiments was undertaken to purify the canine zinc-peptide complex.

Zinc in pilocarpine-stimulated canine prostatic secretions. Johnson et al [19] proposed that zinc in pilocarpine-stimulated canine prostatic secretions was complexed to a peptide composed of eight amino acids: arginine, aspartic acid, serine, glutamic acid, proline, glycine, alanine, and valine. This conclusion was based on the following experimental observations: 1) When radioactive zinc was administered to dogs and pilocarpine-stimulated prostatic secretions collected 24 hours later, no radioactivity was observed in the "protein staining" fractions after chromatography over Sephadex G-100. 2) No free amino acids were found in the fractions containing radioactive zinc, but after hydrolysis and re-analysis, the previously noted eight amino acids were detected. However, the following experimental deficiencies should be noted: 1) No control experiments in which free zinc was chromatographed on the same column were reported. 2) No evidence was provided to indicate any stoichiometry between zinc and the various amino acids that were measured. Based on this experimental data, the conclusion that the zinc present in pilocarpine-stimulated canine prostatic secretions is bound to an eight-amino-acid peptide must be considered tentative. Lack of a comparison chromatography for free zinc is a glaring deficiency since Sephadex G-100 has little, if any, resolving power for materials with molecular weights less than 4,000. Our results indicated that zinc nitrate and the zinc in pilocarpine-stimulated prostatic secretions were eluted in identical fractions from a Sephadex G-100 column. In addition, there was a significant overlap between zinc nitrate and the eight-amino-acid peptide bacitracin. These results indicate that Sephadex G-100 does not possess sufficient resolving power to discriminate between free zinc and zinc complexed to an eight-amino-acid peptide. It should be pointed out that Johnson et al [19] did not specifically claim that the zinc in pilocarpine-stimulated canine prostatic secretions was bound to an eight-amino-acid peptide. Rather, they claimed that the zinc was bound to a peptide composed of eight amino acids. If this peptide contained more than one residue of each amino acid, this should have been reflected in the stoichiometry between the amino acids and this would have resulted in a peptide larger than eight-amino-acid residues. This peptide-zinc complex might have been resolved from free zinc by the Sephadex G-100 chromatography. However, the similarities between the elution profiles for free zinc and the zinc in pilocarpine-stimulated canine prostatic secretions suggested that the prostatic fluid zinc was free zinc and not zinc complexed to a peptide composed of eight amino acids. What was required, therefore, was chromatography over a resin with a much smaller fractionation range. Bio Gel P-4 was selected because its exclusion molecular weight was 4,000 daltons. Figure 6 shows that the eight-amino-acid peptide bacitracin was easily resolved from free zinc by the Bio Gel P-4 column. Moreover, when pilocarpine-stimulated canine prostatic secretions were chromatographed over the same column (Fig. 7), the elution profile for zinc was identical to that of free zinc. Since a column chromatography system was utilized that readily separated free zinc from a peptide composed of eight amino acid residues, and since the zinc in pilocarpine-stimulated canine prostatic secretions did not elute in the position of the peptide, but rather eluted in the position of free zinc, it can be concluded that zinc in pilocarpine-stimulated canine prostatic secretions was not complexed to a peptide composed of eight amino acids, but rather was free zinc. Also, since the antibacterial activity of acid-treated prostatic secretions was directly related to the concentration of zinc, these results indicate that the antibacterial agent in pilocarpine-stimulated canine prostatic secretions is free zinc.

Zinc in human expressed prostatic secretions. Since it appeared that the antibacterial activity of canine prostatic secretions was dependent on

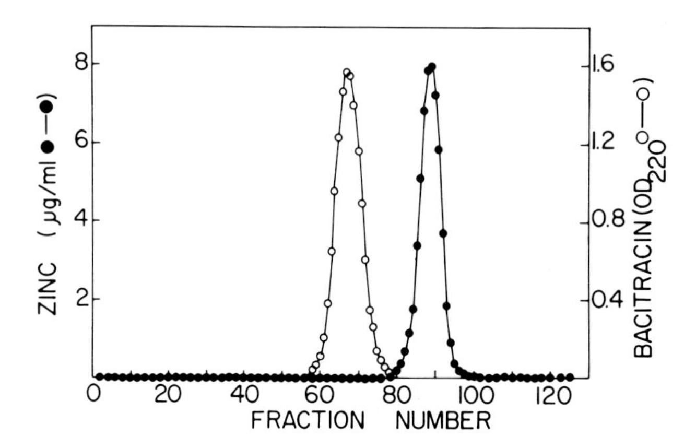

Fig. 6. Elution profile for zinc and bacitracin following chromatography over Bio Gel P-4. One ml of zinc nitrate (33 μg/ml) or bacitracin (2 mg/ml) was applied to Bio Gel P-4 column (1.5 × 80 cm) equilibrated with 0.1 M phosphate pH 6.8. Fractions (1.1 ml) were collected and analyzed for zinc (•) by atomic absorption spectropscopy or bacitracin (o) by absorbance at 220 nm.

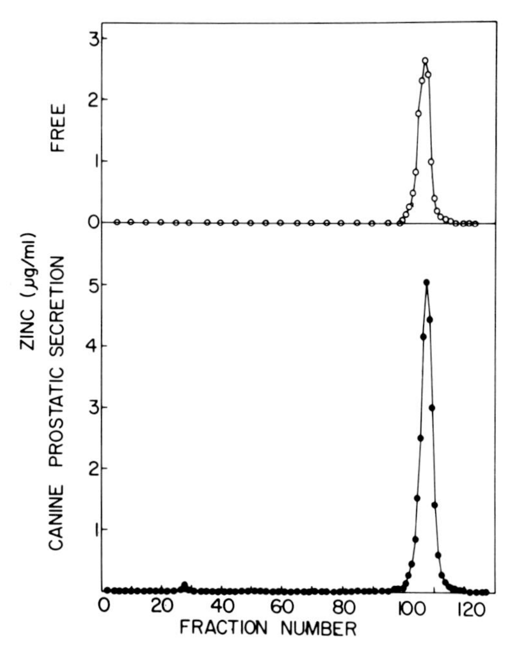

Fig. 7. Elution profile for free zinc and zinc in pilocarpine-stimulated canine prostatic secretions after gel chromatography over Bio Gel P-4. One ml of pilocarpine-stimulated canine prostatic secretion (•) or zinc nitrate (16 μg/ml) (o) were applied to a Bio Gel P-4 column under conditions similar to those described in Figure 6. One-ml fractions were collected and assayed for zinc by atomic absorption spectroscopy.

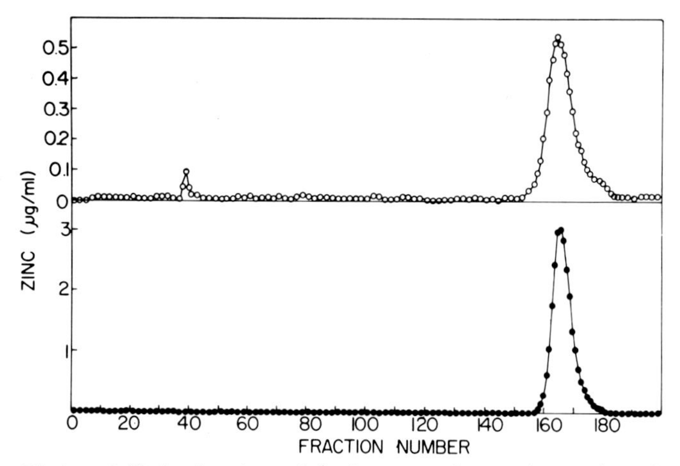

Fig. 8. Elution profile for free zinc and zinc in expressed prostatic secretions obtained from a patient with documented bacterial prostatitis. One ml of zinc nitrate (28 μg/ml) (•) or a 1.0-ml aliquot of diluted prostatic secretion (o) (0.1 ml of secretion added to 1.0 ml of buffer) was applied to a Bio Gel P-4 column (1.5 × 80 cm) equlibrated with 0.01 M MOPS, 0.1 M sodium chloride, pH 6.5, and 1.05-ml fractions collected. Fractions were analyzed for zinc by atomic absorption spectroscopy.

free zinc, it was necessary to examine human expressed prostatic secretions in a similar manner. In Figure 8 the elution profile for the zinc in human expressed prostatic secretions from a male with bacterial prostatitis is compared to the elution profile for free zinc. A Bio Gel P-4 column was utilized in these studies. It is clear that the zinc in the prostatic secretions elutes from the column in the same position that free zinc elutes. When a similar experiment was performed with EPS obtained from a male with a documented bacterial prostatic infection and the EPS from a normal male, it was again observed that the prostatic fluid zinc eluted from the column in the same position as free zinc. These results indicate that the zinc in human expressed prostatic secretions is chromatographically identical to free zinc and is not bound to a peptide or protein component. These results also indicate that the antibacterial activity of human expressed prostatic secretions is due to free zinc.

DISCUSSION

Our initial observations on the antibacterial activity of canine prostatic fluid have previously been reported. Unknown to us at that time similar observations were made almost 30 years previously by Youmans, Liebling, and Lyman [13]. In both these reports the experiments were done on canine prostatic fluid, and it appeared that the antibacterial activity described was due to a similar substance. Since that time additional experiments in our laboratory confirmed antibacterial action in the fluid of the dorsolateral lobe of the rat prostate [10] and in the seminal plasma or prostatic fluid of human males as reported here. Furthermore, the EPS or seminal plasma obtained from the normal human male quantitatively had a much greater antibacterial activity than that found in men with proven bacterial prostatitis and raised the possibility that the PAF might serve as a defense mechanism against prostatic and urinary infections in the male.

Purification and crystallization of this material led to identification of the antibacterial activity of prostatic fluid as being related to its concentration of zinc. The high zinc content of prostatic tissue was first observed by Bertrand and Vladesco in 1921 [20]. Other investigators reported later that the prostate contained more zinc than any other organ in the body [21]. Only about 20% of the zinc in the prostate can be accounted for by carbonic anhydrase and other enzyme systems [22]. In 1962 McKenzie, Hall, and Whitmore [23] measured the zinc level in expressed human prostatic fluid and reported that the fluid contained more zinc on a dry weight basis than any human tissue or any other human secretion. The reason for the high level of zinc in the prostate and its secretion is not known.

Tissue levels of zinc have been reported as being altered secondary to various prostatic disease states [24]. Mawson and Fischer [21] noted that the amount of zinc present in the prostate was directly proportional to the amount of glandular (alveolar) tissue present. They reported a decrease in the tissue zinc in one specimen with a histologic diagnosis of chronic prostatitis. Hoare, Delory, and Penner in 1956 also documented decreased tissue levels of zinc in some patients diagnosed as chronic bacterial prostatitis on the basis of histology [25].

Several authors have commented on the decreased levels of zinc in the seminal plasma of patients with prostatitis [26, 27]. However, the zinc level of the expressed prostatic secretion was not measured in these studies. More importantly, the diagnosis of chronic prostatitis was made by the microscopic finding of more than 10 white blood cells per high-powered field, and bacteriologic studies were not done. Microscopic examination of EPS is highly inaccurate in diagnosing chronic bacterial prostatitis [28], a diagnosis that can be made only by actually culturing the organisms from the prostatic secretion [29]. Many patients with symptoms of prostatitis do not have a bacterial infection; the term "prostatosis" has been suggested for this uninfected symptomatic condition. As a result of their own investigations and a review of the literature, Brostrom and Andersson [26] concluded "that the values noted in the group with chronic prostatitis overlap those without demonstrable inflammation. Although a low value suggests prostatic inflammation, such a condition is not excluded by a high one. This limits the diagnostic value of these determinations." In our study no overlap was noted. We believe that this is due to the fact that only those patients with unequivocally documented prostatic infections were included in the patient group.

Of particular significance are a few patients that we have been able to follow between episodes of infection. The patient in the case reported here was asymptomatic and free of prostatic infection as determined by sterile EPS cultures for more than one year, yet persisted with low EPS zinc levels and later another prostatic infection developed. This pattern of repeated episodes of infection or relapse is characteristic of chronic bacterial prostatitis and may be due to a decrease in normal defense mechanisms. The prostatic fluid and seminal plasma of patients with chronic bacterial prostatitis showed a marked decrease in antibacterial activity normally present in these secretions. The antibacterial activity of the EPS specimens appeared to be directly related to the zinc content of the fluids. Hence, a decreased zinc content in prostatic fluid may be a necessary prelude to bacterial growth and multiplication in prostatic fluid. It is thus possible that the zinc content of prostatic secretion serves a role as a defense mechanism in the normal male, rather than a decreased zinc level being simply a secondary effect of bacterial growth. This may also help to explain the much lower incidence of urinary tract infections in the male as compared with the female.

The in vitro study included here confirms the marked sensitivity of the usual urinary tract pathogens to a zinc salt at concentrations far below those normally present in the prostatic fluid. In these experiments, 55 of the 66 organisms tested were sensitive to levels of zinc that were much below normal levels and similar to those found only in patients with chronic bacterial prostatitis. However, no attempt was made to study the effect of anionic binding agents or the effect of other in vivo zinc inhibitors in this study. The antibacterial activity of zinc is well documented.

SUMMARY

We have identified the "prostatic antibacterial factor," responsible for the antibacterial activity of normal prostatic fluid as free zinc. It appears as if the bactericidal activity of the EPS is related to the amount of zinc present in the fluid and may play a role in the natural resistance of the male urinary tract to infection. In addition, the determination of the zinc content of the expressed prostatic secretion may be a useful test in diagnosing patients with chronic bacterial prostatitis or those who are likely to be susceptible to prostatitis. The factors responsible for the marked decrease of zinc in the prostatic fluid of patients with bacterial prostatitis and methods of altering the zinc level in the fluid as a possible means of eradicating chronic bacterial prostatitis or increasing the resistance of the patient to the disease are important questions requiring further study.

REFERENCES

1. Freedman LR, Phair JP, Seki M, Hamilton HB, Nefzger MD: The epidemiology of urinary tract infection in Hiroshima. Yale J Biol Med 37:262–282, 1965.
2. Stamey TA: "Urinary Infections," Baltimore:Williams and Wilkins, 1972, pp 161–212.
3. Taylor PW, Morgan HR: Antibacterial substances in human semen and prostatic fluid. Surg Gynecol Obstet 94:662–668, 1952.
4. Gurevitch J, Rozansky R, Weber D, Brzezinsky A, Eckerling B: The role of spermine in the inhibition of Staphylococcus aureus by human semen. J Clin Pathol 4:360–365, 1951.
5. Razin S, Rozansky R: The responsibility of spermine for the antibacterial action of human semen. J Lab Clin Med 49:877–881, 1957.
6. Razin S, Rozansky R: Mechanism of the antibacterial action of spermine. Arch Biochem Biophys 81:36–54, 1959.
7. Fair WR, Stamey TA: Bactericidal properties of prostatic fluid in bacterial infections of male genital system (Workshop), Warrenton, Virginia:National Research Council, National Academy of Science, October, 1967, pp 199–211.
8. Stamey TA, Fair WR, Timothy MM, Chung HK: Antibacterial nature of prostatic fluid. Nature 218: 444–447, 1968.
9. Fair WR, Wehner N: The antibacterial action of canine prostatic fluid and human seminal plasma in an agar diffusion assay system. Invest Urol 10:262–265, 1973.
10. Levy, BJ, Fair WR: The location of antibacterial activity in the rat prostatic secretions. Invest Urol 11: 173–177, 1973.

11. Fair WR, Couch J, Wehner N: The purification and assay of the prostatic antibacterial factor (PAF). Biochem Med 8:329–339, 1973.
12. Fair WR, Couch J, Wehner N: Prostatic antibacterial factor, identity and significance. Urology 7:169–177, 1976.
13. Youmans GP, Liebling J, Lyman RY: The bactericidal action of prostatic fluid in dogs. J Infect Dis 63: 117–121, 1938.
14. Anderson RU, Fair WR: Physical and chemical determinations of prostatic secretion in benign hyperplasia, prostatitis, and adenocarcinoma. Invest Urol 14: 137–140, 1976.
15. Grossowicz N, Razin S, Rozansky R: Factors influencing the antibacterial action of spermine and spermidine on Staphylococcus aureus. J Gen Microbiol 13: 436–441, 1955.
16. Rozansky R, Bachrach U, Grossowicz N: Studies on the antibacterial action of spermine. J Gen Microbiol 10:11–16, 1954.
17. Mann T: "The Biochemistry of Semen and the Male Reproductive Tract." London: Methuen, 1964, pp 193–200.
18. Fair WR, Wehner N: Antibacterial action of spermine: Effect on urinary tract pathogens. Appl Microbiol 21: 6–8, 1971.
19. Johnson L, Wikström S, Nylander G: The vehicle for zinc in the prostatic secretion of dogs. Scand J Urol Nephrol 3:9–11, 1969.
20. Bertrand G, Vladesco R: Intervention probably du zinc dans les phénomenes de fécondation chez les animaux vertébrés, Compt rend Acad de sc 173:176–179, 1921.
21. Mawson CA, Fischer MI: The occurrence of zinc in the human prostate gland. Canad J Med Sci 30:336–339, 1952.
22. Mawson CA, Fischer MI: Carbonic anhydrase and zinc in the prostate glands of the rat and rabbit. Arch Biochem Biophys 36:485–486, 1952.
23. Mackenzie AR, Hall T, Whitmore WF Jr: Zinc content of expressed human prostatic fluid. Nature 193:72–73, 1962.
24. Schrodt GR, Hall T, Whitmore WF Jr: The concentration of zinc in diseased human prostate glands. Cancer 17:1555–1566, 1964.
25. Hoare R, Delory GE, Penner DW: Zinc and acid phosphatase in the human prostate. Cancer 9:721–726, 1956.
26. Boström K, Andersson L: Creatinine phosphokinase relative to acid phosphatase, lactate dehydrogenase, zinc and fructose in human semen with special reference to chronic prostatitis. Scand J Urol Nephrol 5:123–132, 1971.
27. Eliasson R: Biochemical analyses of human semen in the study of the physiology and pathophysiology of the male accessory genital glands. Fertil Steril 19:344–350, 1968.
28. O'Shaugnessy EJ, Parrino PS, White, JD: Chronic prostatitis—fact or fiction? JAMA 160:540–542, 1956.
29. Meares EM, Stamey TA: Bacteriologic localization patterns in bacterial prostatitis and urethritis. Invest Urol 5:492–518, 1968.

The Prostatic Cell: Structure and Function
Part A, pages 265–277

Contribution of Prostatic Fluid Components to the Ejaculate

Lourens J.D. Zaneveld and Peter F. Tauber

INTRODUCTION

Secretion of compounds by the prostate gland depends on the synthetic activity of its epithelial cells and transudation from serum. Prostatic disease affects these processes and will alter the secretory activity of the prostate. This is exemplified by the changes in the serum levels of acid phosphatase, aldolase, lactate dehydrogenase and its isozymes, plasminogen activator, acid β-glycerophosphatase, and others in cases of prostatic carcinoma. Changes in serum enzymes are often not detected until the later stages of prostatic disease. Study of the biochemical composition of the fluid produced by the prostate gland should allow much earlier detection of prostatic pathology. Human prostatic fluid can fairly readily be obtained by prostatic massage. However, this procedure is not always comfortable and is not readily performed on a large number of men, ie, for screening purposes. It would be beneficial if prostatic fluid components could be studied in more easily obtained samples.

Prostatic fluid is excreted while ejaculation takes place. During this process, it is mixed with spermatozoa, and the secretions of the epididymides, ampullae of the vas deferens, seminal vesicles, and Cowper's (bulbourethral) glands. Semen samples are readily obtained in good quantities by masturbation and would be very useful for the detection of the biochemical components secreted by the prostate gland and, thus, the activity of the gland. Indeed, a number of seminal components typical of prostate gland origin, eg, lysozyme, acid phosphatase, zinc, cholesterol, and citric acid have been shown to be altered as a result of prostatic disease.

A problem in the use of the ejaculate for the detection of biochemical changes caused by prostatic disease is the presence of many other accessory sex gland components besides those produced by the prostate gland. Additionally, the volume and other aspects of the ejaculate vary from ejaculation to ejaculation.

Therefore, the concentration of a specific prostatic component may vary significantly between ejaculates, often making the analysis of a single component unreliable for the early detection of disease.

Two methods may be useful to avoid this problem. First of all, the ratio of one component to another may be a more accurate indicator of a pathological change. Such components may either both derive from the prostate gland or one may originate from the prostate gland and the other from another accessory sex gland, eg, the seminal vesicles, which is presumably not altered by prostatic disease. The second method involves the collection of ejaculated fluid that consists primarily of prostatic fluid. This can be done by the split ejaculation technique [1]. During the ejaculatory process, spermatozoa and the secretions of the epididymis, ampullae, prostate gland, and Cowper's glands are excreted first, followed by the seminal vesicle secretions. The spermatozoa and epididymal, ampullary, and Cowper's gland secretions comprise only approximately 5% of the volume of the ejaculate, and almost the entire first portion of an ejaculate is composed of prostatic fluid. Analysis of the biochemical composition of this portion should give a good indication of the activity of the prostate gland.

The clinical application of these methods either by themselves or in combination with each other, remains to be established. At present, it is mostly a hypothesis although it already appears that the ratio of the isozymes LDH V to LDH I is a better indicator of prostatic pathology than either one of these isozymes alone. Much more work is required to determine the contribution of prostatic fluid components to the overall composition of seminal plasma, as well as to the first portion of ejaculated semen. Some results have already been published in this regard and the following represents an overview of the biochemical composition of human prostatic fluid as it compares to that of seminal plasma. A study undertaken to determine the distribution of protein components in split ejaculates is also reported.

BIOCHEMICAL COMPOSITION OF HUMAN PROSTATIC FLUID

The prostatic contribution to an average ejaculate (3.5 ml) is usually 0.5 to 1.0 ml, ie, from 15–30% of the total volume (Table I). Approximately 5% of the ejaculate is contributed by the spermatozoa and the secretions of the epididymis, ampulla, and the Cowper's gland. The rest is produced by the seminal vesicles. By prostatic massage, between 0.1 and 1.0 ml can routinely be collected.

Most of the data on human prostatic secretions are based on fluid obtained by prostatic massage. This type of fluid can be considered as "resting" fluid and differs somewhat in composition from "stimulated" fluid that is obtained during emission and ejaculation. During excitation, secretion of certain compounds from the tissue occurs at an enhanced rate. For example, in man, the concentration of acid phosphatase in "resting" fluid is 117 to 1192 U/ml [2], whereas that of "stimulated" fluid is 1890 to 3950 U/ml [3].

TABLE I. Some physicochemical properties of human prostatic fluid and seminal plasma [19]

Property	Unit	Prostatic fluid	Seminal plasma
Volume	ml	0.5–1.0	3.5
pH		6.5	7.0–7.5
Specific gravity		1.022	1.035
Water content	gm/100 ml	93	22
Total protein	gm/100 ml	25.5	45.0

TABLE II. Electrolytes of human prostatic fluid and seminal plasma [19]

Electrolyte (mM)	Prostatic fluid	Seminal plasma
Sodium	153	122
Potassium	48	23
Calcium	30	7
Chloride	38	44
Magnesium	20	6
Bicarbonate	20	6

The fluid obtained by prostatic massage is a homogeneous, serous, milky fluid that is normally slightly acidic in contrast to seminal plasma that is normally basic (Table I). Prostatic fluid has a tendency to become basic (pH 7.7) in case of prostatitis. The specific gravity and water content of prostatic fluid and seminal plasma are essentially identical.

Human prostatic fluid contains considerably higher amounts of sodium, potassium, and calcium than blood but has lower amounts of chloride, bicarbonate, and phosphate. Compared to seminal plasma, prostatic fluid contains much higher concentrations of calcium, magnesium, and bicarbonate indicating that in the ejaculate these compounds primarily originate from the prostate gland (Table II). Prostatic fluid also has higher concentrations of sodium and potassium than seminal plasma but contains approximately equal concentrations of chloride ions.

Prostatic fluid is rich in citric acid, and all the citric acid of human semen appears to originate from the prostate (Table III). The high amounts of citric acid causes the prostatic fluid to prevent the coagulation of blood when these two body fluids are mixed. Ascorbic acid is also present in prostatic fluid but in much lower concentrations than in seminal plasma.

Human prostatic secretions are eosinophilic and stain with PAS for neutral mucopolysaccharides but not with alcian blue for acid mucopolysaccharides.

TABLE III. Some low molecular weight constituents of human prostatic fluid and seminal plasma [19]

Constituent (mg/100 ml)	Prostatic fluid	Seminal plasma
Glucose	8	7
Myoinositol	148	57
Citric acid	1580	376
Ascorbic acid	0.5	2.6
Sialic acid	61	124
Spermine	243	20–250
Zinc	5	2

TABLE IV. Some lipid constituents of human prostatic fluid and seminal plasma [19]

Lipid (mg/100 ml)	Prostatic fluid	Seminal plasma
Total lipid	286	186
Cephalin	107	3
Cholesterol	80	47
Lecithin	0	3

Even so, significant concentrations of sialic acid are present in prostatic fluid although much less than those found in seminal plasma (Table III). As compared to seminal plasma, prostatic fluid contains only a very small amount of reducing sugars (16.4 mg/100 ml). Since fructose is the primary reducing sugar of semen with a concentration of 300 mg/100 ml, it is apparently virtually absent from prostatic fluid. The glucose concentrations of prostatic fluid and seminal plasma are approximately equally as low. The human prostate is the major contributor of myoinositol in seminal plasma. This is in contrast to other species where this sugar originates mostly from the seminal vesicles. The level of myoinositol in prostatic fluid is approximately 200 times higher than that in human blood.

Human seminal plasma contains much spermine but only small amounts of spermidine and putrescine. Most of the seminal spermine and spermidine are produced by the prostate gland (Table III). A characteristic component of prostatic fluid is zinc which is present in relatively high concentrations. The zinc content of seminal plasma is largely of prostatic origin.

Human prostatic fluid is rich in fats. It frequently contains yellow, refractile fat particles that occasionally give prostatic fluid a yellowish color. The total lipid content of prostatic fluid is much higher than that of seminal plasma, indicating that a significant portion of the ejaculated lipids originate from the prostate gland (Table IV). The total phosphatide concentration of the fluid measures 180 mg/100 ml [4]. Of this, 107 mg/100 ml is comprised of ether-soluble

TABLE V. Phosphorus and nitrogen of human prostatic fluid and seminal plasma [19]

Constituent	Unit	Prostatic fluid	Seminal plasma
Inorganic phosphorus	mg/100 ml	3	11
Total lipid phosphorus	mg/100 ml	2	6
Acid-soluble phosphorus	mM	1	27–140
Total nitrogen	mg/100 ml	416	913
Non-protein nitrogen	mg/100 ml	54	90

phosphatides. Cephalin is the major ether soluble lipid. No lecithin is present in the fluid. The phospholipids amount to 60% of the lipids and together with cholesterol account for much of the fat present. Most, if not all, of the cholesterol and cephalin in seminal plasma originates from the prostate. Little, if any neutral fat is present in prostatic fluid [4]. The total lipid carbon in the fluid measures 1220 mg/100 ml [5]. No lipid nitrogen has been detected. The total lipid phosphorus concentration of prostatic fluid is approximately three times less than that of seminal plasma.

Prostaglandin activity has been found in prostatic tissue of man, but the entire prostaglandin content of the seminal plasma appears to originate from the seminal vesicles.

The phosphorus concentrations of prostatic fluid are much less than those of seminal plasma (Table V). The concentrations of total nitrogen and nonprotein nitrogen are approximately half those of seminal plasma.

Prostatic fluid has a much lower level of proteins than seminal plasma (Table I). Most of the proteins in prostatic fluid are not coagulated by heat, pass readily through semipermeable membranes, and are thus of low molecular weight. Three to seven electrophoretically different protein components have been found that migrate similar to serum proteins. All the components stain for glycoprotein and some for lipoprotein.

Prostatic fluid is particularly rich in enzymes. A characteristic enzyme is acid phosphatase and, similar to almost all other species, the prostate is the site of origin of this enzyme in human seminal plasma. Most of the acid phosphatase found in urine originates from the prostate gland so that early urine fractions contain much higher acid phosphatase levels than fractions that are voided later. A striking increase in urine acid phosphatase is found if urine is collected immediately after ejaculation. After prostatectomy, the urine acid phosphatase levels drop to very low levels, approximately equal to those in women.

Another typical prostatic enzyme is lactate dehydrogenase (LDH), and the prostate gland is the major contributor of LDH to semen [6]. At least two isozymes (V and I) are present whose ratio is less than 3 in normal individuals [7]. Human prostatic secretion also possesses β-glucuronidase in high concentrations, much higher than those found in other species. It also possesses a diastase, esterase, aminopeptidase, and succinic dehydrogenase as well as other enzymes and inhibitors, a number of which are described in the following section.

COMPOSITION OF HUMAN SPLIT EJACULATES

During ejaculation, the secretions of the male reproductive tract are released in a sequential manner, the prostatic fluid components appearing mostly in the early fraction. The biochemical composition of this fraction is of potential interest from a diagnostic standpoint to determine the presence of prostatic disease (see above). Although a single component would be too variable to be useful as an indicator, the ratio of one component to another should be quite consistent and could be potentially applicable clinically. Therefore, a study was undertaken to determine the biochemical composition of the first portion of the human ejaculate [8,9].

Split ejaculates (41) were obtained from 10 healthy donors aged 22–34 years after 2–3 days of sexual abstinence. Owing to the volume requirements for these studies, the donors were asked to split their ejaculates into three portions. The donors each received three jars and were advised to place the discharged material of the first one or two orgasmic contractions into the first jar (fraction 1). The subsequent two contractions were to be deposited into the second jar (fraction 2), and the material released during the final contractions into the third container (fraction 3). Following liquefaction, the volumes of the samples were measured with a calibrated pipette and sperm counts were determined with a hemocytometer. The specimens were centrifuged to separate the seminal plasma from the spermatozoa. The supernatant plasma was stored at −20°C in aliquots of 0.1–0.2 ml.

The volume of the first fraction of the ejaculate averaged approximately twofold less than that of the third fraction and fourfold less than that of the entire ejaculate (Table VI). The sperm concentration was about sixfold higher in the first fraction than in the third fraction and twofold higher than that of the ejaculate. The opposite was found for fructose, a sugar that is secreted by the seminal vesicles and is essentially absent from prostatic secretions. Three- to fourfold higher concentrations of fructose were found in the final portion of the ejaculate. Thus, the technique employed to obtain the split ejaculates resulted in a reasonable separation of the accessory sex gland secretions.

Previous experiments have shown the presence of high concentrations of citric acid, zinc, and acid phosphatase in the first portion of the split ejaculate. Instead of investigating these typical prostatic fluid components again, the protein composition was investigated. The protein components appear to be of particular importance from a clinical standpoint because prostatic disease may cause the more active secretion of such proteins either through increased transudation from serum or via enhanced cellular synthesis. This was, for instance, reported to be

TABLE VI. Composition of human split ejaculates[a] [8]

		Fractions							
		1		2		3		Whole semen	
Constituent	Unit	conc.	amount	conc.	amount	conc.	amount	conc.	amount
Volume	ml	—	0.64	—	0.90	—	1.35	—	2.89
Spermatozoa	$\times 10^6$	203.4	123.5	134.9	98.6	36.6	54.9	111.1	277.0
Fructose	mg	1.32	0.97	2.56	2.85	4.14	5.29	3.02	9.11

[a]Based on 41 split ejaculates obtained from 10 different donors.

TABLE VII. Nonenzyme protein components of human split ejaculates [8]

	Fractions							
	1		2		3		Whole semen	
Constituent*	conc.	amount	conc.	amount	conc.	amount	conc.	amount
IgG	0.14	0.08	0.09	0.08	0.07	0.09	0.09	0.25
IgA	0.05	0.03	0.03	0.03	0.03	0.04	0.03	0.10
Albumin	0.94	0.64	0.73	0.61	0.47	0.48	0.63	1.73
Transferrin	0.10	0.07	0.08	0.09	0.05	0.06	0.07	0.22
Lactoferrin	0.81	0.55	1.11	1.13	1.33	1.39	1.18	3.07

*mg/ml. IgM, secretory piece of IgA, β_1C/β_1A-Globulin, ceruloplasmin or fibrinogen were only rarely or not detected.

the case for lipoproteins, α_2-macroglobulin, and fibrinogen [10–12]. Measurements of the non-enzyme proteins was done by radial immunodiffusion [8,9]. The enzymes, with the exception of the neutral proteinase (seminin), were measured by microradial diffusion [9]. Seminin activity was determined by the amount of gelatin digestion.

Various components of the immune system were detected in the split ejaculates, although others, ie, IgM, secretory piece of IgA, and α_1C/β_1A-globulin (C'_3 component of complement) could only rarely be found (Table VII). Both IgG and IgA showed twofold higher concentrations in the first fraction of the ejaculate than in the third fraction and in the whole ejaculate. Thus, the prostate gland may be the primary contributor of these globulins to the ejaculate. It is known that IgA is the predominant immunoglobulin in the majority of external fluids such as saliva, urine, tears, and secretions from the tracheobronchial and intestinal tract. IgA may enter these secretions in various forms. One is the basic IgA unit (7S molecule with a molecular weight of ~ 170,000) representing free IgA which is immunochemically identical to serum IgA. Although higher polymers (16–20S) also occur, the principal IgA form found in seromucous secretions occurs as an 11S molecule with a molecular weight of ~ 400,000 (secretory IgA) that has two 7S units conjugated through an interconnecting protein with a molecular weight of ~ 50,000. This protein is called the "secretory piece." Since free secretory piece could not be detected in the semen samples, IgA is probably derived as a serum transudate.

No ceruloplasmin could be found in the split ejaculate but lactoferrin and transferrin, both iron-binding proteins, were detected (Table VIII). These proteins showed opposite distribution patterns, however. The transferrin concentrations were twofold higher in the early portion of the ejaculate, whereas the lactoferrin levels were highest in the final fraction. Prostatic fluid appears to be the major contributor of transferrin. Lactoferrin is absent from serum and is most likely synthesized by the seminal vesicles. The concentration of transferrin in semen is approximately one third of that in serum, and this protein probably derives from blood although the local synthesis by the prostate gland cannot be excluded.

The presence of a number of enzymes and enzyme inhibitors was also investigated (Table VIII). Lysozyme concentrations were somewhat higher in the first portion of the ejaculate than in the last portion but the difference was not statistically significant. Therefore, the accessory sex glands contribute approximately equal amounts of the enzyme to the ejaculate. This corroborates other studies where tissue sections were collected and the lysozyme levels determined [9]. The epididymis, ampulla, vas deferens, prostate gland, and seminal vesicles each contained approximately equal amounts of this enzyme. By contrast, the α-amylase levels were significantly higher in the early portion of the ejaculate, confirming previous results [13]. Prostatic fluid appears to be an important contributor of this enzyme to semen.

The distribution patterns of the neutral proteinase, seminin, and the plasminogen activator were similar and clearly showed highest levels in the early portion of the ejaculate (Table VIII). The high concentrations of seminin in the first portion of the ejaculate may indicate that it is almost entirely of prostatic origin. Recent studies have shown that seminin is the primary agent responsible for the liquefaction of the seminal coagulum [14,15]. The major source of plasminogen activator in semen also seems to be the prostate gland, but other accessory glands may contribute as well [16]. The function of this activator is not known. No plasminogen could be detected in the ejaculates nor did the addition of plasminogen activator, purified to homogeneity, cause liquefaction of the seminal coagulum [17]. No prothrombin or Factor XIII were detected in the ejaculates.

The total inhibitory activity of the fractions towards trypsin showed a distribution favoring the seminal vesicle as origin (Table IX). This is not surprising since the seminal vesicles appear to be the primary source of two low molecular weight inhibitors (5000–13,000 daltons) in semen [18]. Several of the high molecular weight, serum proteinase inhibitors were also detected in the ejacu-

TABLE VIII. Enzyme components of human split ejaculates [9]

	Fractions							
	1		2		3		Whole semen	
Enzyme*	conc.	amount	conc.	amount	conc.	amount	conc.	amount
Lysozyme (μg chicken egg white equiv.)	80	50	60	60	60	70	70	180
α-Amylase (μg bovine pancreatic amylase equiv.)	0.52	0.39	0.35	0.33	0.36	0.37	0.41	1.09
Neutral proteinase (seminin) (μg bovine pancreatic trypsin equiv.)	2.44	1.88	0.76	0.70	0.47	0.50	1.14	3.08
Plasminogen activator (ploug U. urokinase equiv.)	23.05	14.91	14.34	13.49	9.27	12.21	14.00	40.61

*No plasminogen, prothrombin, or Factor XIII were detected.

TABLE IX. Inhibitors of human split ejaculates [9]

		Fractions							
		1		2		3		Whole semen	
Inhibitor*	Unit	conc.	amount	conc.	amount	conc.	amount	conc.	amount
Total trypsin inhibitor	mIU	3,777	2,688	4,635	4,297	4,992	4,601	4,513	11,586
α_1-Antitrypsin	μG	80	57	90	85	90	88	85	230
α_{1X}-Antichymotrypsin	μG	40	30	40	40	40	50	40	120

*No antithrombin III, α_2-macroglobulin, inter-α-trypsin inhibitor, or C_{1s}-inactivator were detected.

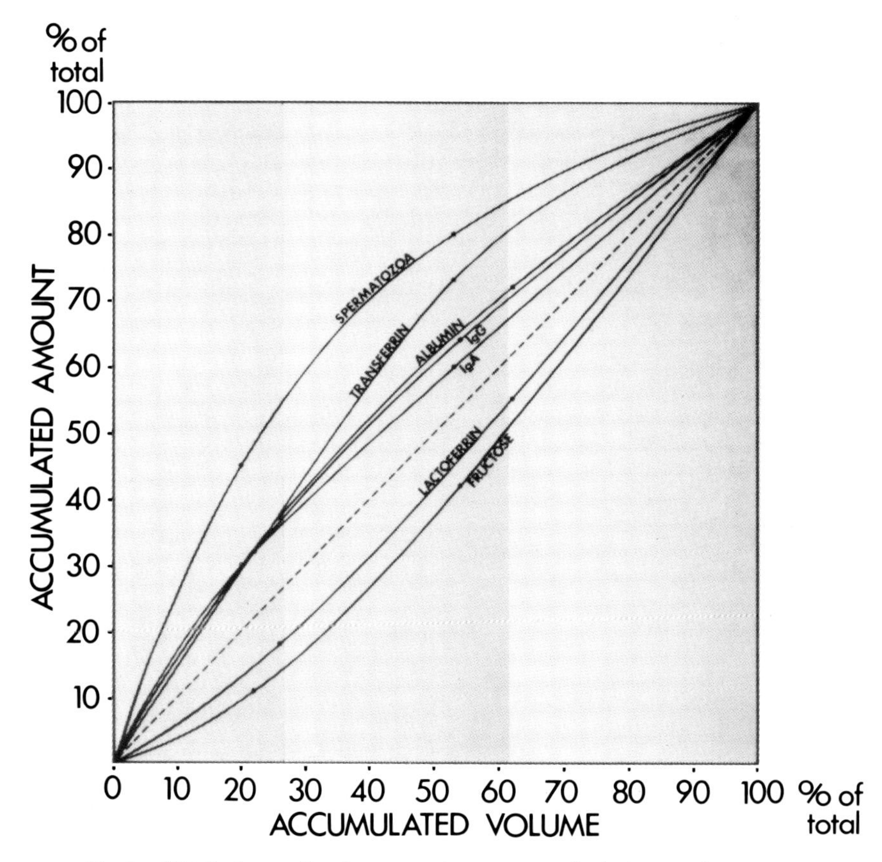

Fig. 1. Distribution profile of nonenzymic components in the human ejaculate [8].

lates, but other serum inhibitors (antithrombin III, α_2-macroglobulin, inter-α-trypsin inhibitor, and C_1s-inactivator) could not or could only occasionally, be found. The levels of both α-$_1$-antitrypsin and α_{1x}-antichymotrypsin tended to increase towards the third fraction of the ejaculate but the differences were not statistically significant. The accessory glands appear to contribute equally to these inhibitors.

A visual comparison of the data may be obtained by plotting the accumulated amounts of the components (as a percentage of the total) against the accumulated volumes (as a percentage of the total) corresponding to these amounts (Figs. 1, 2). The resulting curve then reflects the concentration changes that occur during the ejaculation process. The higher the rate of increase at the beginning of such

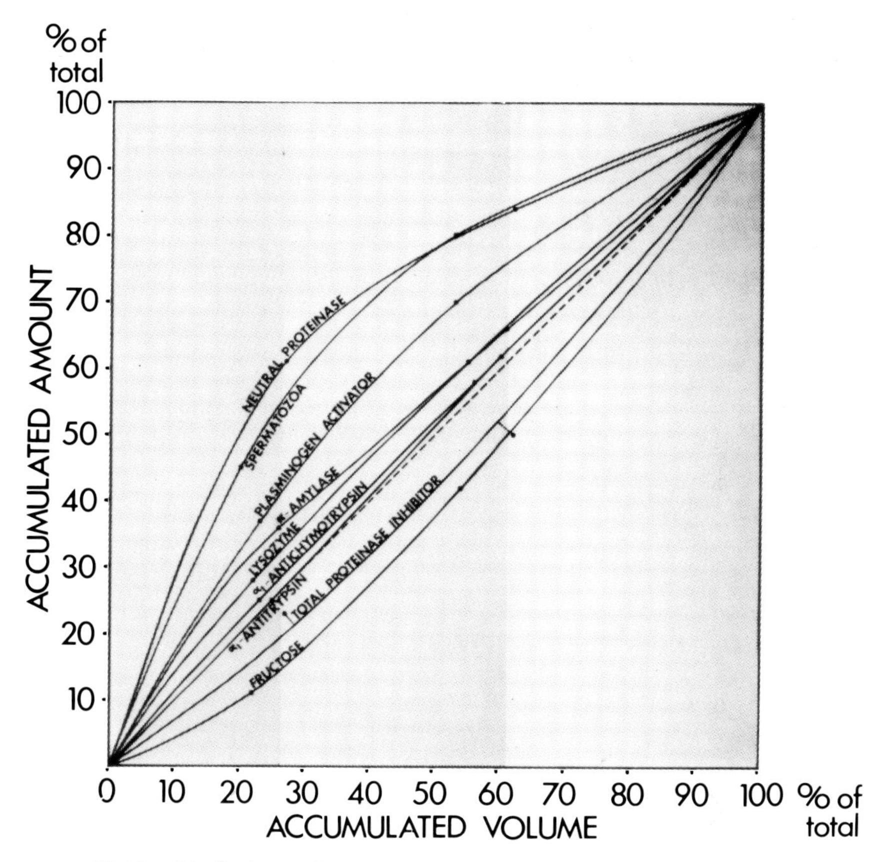

Fig. 2. Distribution profile of enzymic components in the human ejaculate [9].

a curve, the higher the input of that component in the semen at the early stages of ejaculation, ie, from the prostate, Cowper's gland, epididymis, or ampulla. A lower rate of increase at the beginning followed by a higher rate of increase toward the end characterizes a higher input at later stages of ejaculation, ie, from the seminal vesicles. A straight line drawn between 0 and 100% separates these two types of curves. Typical examples are the curves for the number of spermatozoa and for the amount of fructose. Spermatozoa are ejaculated very early and their curve shows a rapid initial increase, levelling off toward the end of the ejaculation. By contrast, fructose which is known to originate almost entirely from the seminal vesicles, increases slowly in the beginning but more rapidly towards the end. Transferrin, albumin, IgG, IgA, neutral proteinase (seminin), plasminogen activator, and α-amylase clearly show a "sperm-like" distribution, whereas lactoferrin and total trypsin inhibitory activity show "fructose-like" distributions. Lysozyme, α_1-antitrypsin and α_{1x}-antichymotrypsin did not show significant deviations from the central line. Since the spermatozoa and the secretions from the Cowper's gland, the ampulla, and the epididymis only contribute a very small portion of the ejaculate (see above), it can be assumed that most of the components showing a "sperm-like" distribution have their primary origin in the prostate gland. Experiments with vasectomized men (eliminating the spermatozoa and epididymal secretions) produced identical results as those reported above, confirming this assumption.

REFERENCES

1. Zaneveld LJD, Polakoski KL: Collection and physical examination of the ejaculate. In Hafez ESE (ed): "Techniques of Human Andrology." New York: N. Holland Publishers, 1977, pp 147–172.
2. Gutman AB, Gutman EB: Quantitative relations of a prostatic component (acid phosphatase) of human seminal fluid. Endocrinology 28: 115–118, 1941.
3. Huggins C: The prostatic secretion. Harvey Lect 42: 148–193, 1946.
4. Scott WW: The lipids of prostatic fluid, seminal plasma and enlarged prostate gland of man. J Urol 53: 712–718, 1945.
5. Moore RA, Miller MA, McLellan A: The chemical composition of prostatic secretion in relation to benign hypertrophy of the prostate. J Urol 46: 132–137, 1941.
6. MacLeod J, Wroblewski F: Lactic dehydrogenase activity in human semen. Proc Soc Exp Biol Med 99: 265–267, 1958.
7. Hein RC, Grayhack JT, Goldberg E: Prostatic fluid lactic dehydrogenase isoenzyme patterns of prostatic cancer and hyperplasia. J Urol 113: 511–516, 1975.
8. Tauber PF, Zaneveld LJD, Propping D, Schumacher GFB: Components of human split ejaculates I. Spermatozoa, fructose, immunoglobulins, albumin, lactoferrin, transferrin and other plasma proteins. J Reprod Fertil 43: 249–267, 1975.
9. Tauber PF, Zaneveld LJD, Propping D, Schumacher GFB: Components of human split ejaculates. II. Enzymes and proteinase inhibitors. J Reprod Fertil 46: 165–171, 1976.
10. Nylander G: The electrophoretic pattern of prostatic lipid secretion in normal and pathological conditions. Scand J Clin Lab Invest 7:250–253, 1955.
11. Leithoff H, Leithoff I: Der Nachnweis von Blutweisskorpern in Menschlichen Spermaplasma. Med schl Welt Stuttg 21:1137–1141, 1961.
12. Ablin RJ, Soanes WA, Gonder MJ: In vivo bound immunoglobulins in the human prostate—their identification and possible significance. Z Immun -Forsch. 144:233–241, 1972.
13. Moon KM, Bunge RG: Observations on the biochemistry of human semen. Fertil Steril 19: 977–981, 1968.
14. Syner FN, Moghissi KS, Yanez J: Isolation of a factor from normal human semen that accelerates dissolution of abnormally liquefying semen. Fertil Steril 26:1064–1069, 1975.
15. Tauber PF, Propping D, Schumacher GFB, Zaneveld LJD: Biochemical aspects of the coagulation and liquefaction of human semen. J Andrology 1: 281–288, 1980.
16. Kester RC: The distribution of the plasminogen activator in the male genital tract. J Clin Pathol 24:726–731, 1971.
17. Propping D, Zaneveld LJD, Tauber PF, Schumacher GFB: Purification of plasminogen activators from human seminal plasma. Biochem J 171: 435–444, 1978.

18. Fritz H, Schiessler H, Schill WB, Tschesche H, Heimburger N, Wallner: Low molecular weight proteinase (acrosin) inhibitors from human and boar seminal plasma and spermatozoa and human cervical mucus—isolation, properties and biological aspects. In Reich E, Ritkin DB, Shaw E (eds): "Proteases and Biological Control." Cold Spring Harbor: Cold Spring Harbor Laboratory, 1975, pp 737–766.
19. Beyler S, Zaneveld LJD: The male accessory sex glands. In Zaneveld LJD, Chatterton R (eds): "Biochemistry of Mammalian Reproduction." New York: J. Wiley (in press).

The Prostatic Cell: Structure and Function
Part A, pages 279–324

Prostatic Cholesterol Metabolism: Regulation and Alteration

Carl P. Schaffner

Although cholesterol metabolism has been studied extensively in the liver, intestinal tract, and other tissues of the human and experimental animal, little attention has been directed to that of the prostate gland both in its normal and pathological states. There are many instances of cholesterol involvement in neoplasia. The dramatic changes in feedback regulation of cholesterol synthesis in hepatomas [1], in other malignant tissues [2], and in leukemias [3,4] are typical examples. The observation made in 1942 by Swyer [5] that the cholesterol content of the prostatic adenoma doubled as compared to normal tissue received only moderate attention. Later reports on the effects of hypocholesterolemic agents on the benign enlargements of the prostate glands of dogs [6], hamsters [7], and humans [8–12], as well as on prostatic carcinoma [13], motivated the series of studies reported here dealing with different aspects of prostatic cholesterol metabolism in experimental animals and humans. It was the hope that some possible relationship between cholesterol metabolism and the etiology of benign prostatic hyperplasia and prostatic carcinoma might be uncovered.

CHOLESTEROL IN THE PROSTATE GLAND

There are relatively few reports dealing with cholesterol in the prostate gland. Lipids, and in particular cholesterol, have long been observed as components of the human prostate gland and of prostatic secretion. In 1873 Thompson [14] reported that in histological studies lipids were found in the epithelial cells of the prostate glands. He first recognized the presence of doubly refractive materials within various cells. Other investigators [15,16] confirmed the presence of lipids in the prostate gland. Fat droplets were identified not only in the epithelial cells lining the prostatic acini but also in the lumen of the acinus. None of these studies, however, were quantitative in nature.

Prostatic fluid has also been examined for the presence of lipids. Thompson [14] had observed as well that human prostatic fluid contained yellow refractile bodies which stained as fat. Fürbringer [17] in 1881 also recognized the presence of similar substances in these prostatic secretions. He further attributed the opalescence of prostatic fluid to fat droplets which he called "lecithin bodies"—a term still employed today. Studies by Goldblatt [18] and Eliasson [19] that followed much later dealt as well with cholesterol in semen and seminal plasma. Speculations were made with regard to the source of the lipids found in prostatic fluid and seminal plasma. The origin of cholesterol in human semen was believed to be mainly the prostate gland.

In animal studies Miyao [20] using Huggins' dogs and rats determined quantitatively cholesterol and phospholipid in prostatic secretions. The cholesterol of the prostatic secretion was largely free and not esterified as it is in the serum. He also believed that the cholesterol in the prostate gland was derived from the blood since radiocarbon-labeled cholesterol given parenterally was found in the prostatic secretion of the dog. Artificially induced hypercholesterolemia in the rat also was observed to produce elevated cholesterol levels in the prostatic secretion. The ability of prostate tissues to synthesize cholesterol directly was not determined at that time.

With the consideration that cholesterol in seminal plasma is derived from the prostate, Moon and Bunge [21] in 1970 made further investigations into the possible relationship between the concentration of cholesterol in seminal plasma and various qualities of human semen. In their studies they found no unusual correlation between the cholesterol content and the sperm count in semen and assumed that cholesterol played no significant role in sperm metabolism. Measurements of seminal cholesterol before and after castration and with androgenic or estrogenic therapy in a few patients supported their further conclusion that there was no hormonal influence on the production of cholesterol and its level in seminal plasma. In acute or chronic prostatitis, however, they found the concentration of cholesterol in the prostatic secretion to be significantly higher than in the normal controls.

In pathological states of the human prostate gland Swyer [5] in 1942 was among the first to report the increase of cholesterol content in the adenoma of the enlarged gland. Quantitatively there appeared to be a doubling of cholesterol concentration in adenomous tissue as compared to normal tissue. Later studies by Scott [22] dealt in general with the lipids of the prostatic fluid and seminal plasma as well as in the tissues of the enlarged human prostate gland. He determined that most of the cholesterol in the prostate was also nonesterified since cholesterol esters represented only about 10% of the total cholesterol content. The phospholipid/cholesterol ratio in the enlarged gland was found to be low.

Since earlier studies by Acevedo [23] with women suffering from carcinoma of the steroid-producing glands and their target organs had revealed urinary nonesterified cholesterol (NEC) hyperexcretion, similar investigations [24] with males suffering from various testicular and prostatic neoplasms were undertaken. Since cholesterol in prostatic fluid and seminal plasma was believed to be derived from the prostate gland, it was reasonable to expect that urinary NEC as a protein-bound complex [25] had a similar origin. These studies [24] revealed significant urinary NEC hyperexcretion in patients with testicular and prostatic neoplasm as compared to normal young males. Approximately 25% of normal controls over 45 years of age and those diagnosed as suffering from benign prostatic hyperplasia also revealed urinary NEC hyperexcretion. This was explained as possibly due to the undetected presence of "latent" prostatic adenocarcinoma. The lack of correlation observed between urinary excretion of NEC and the serum cholesterol levels observed in male patients with cardiovascular diseases provided support to the further conclusion that urinary cholesterol was of endogenous origin which had little relationship with the exogenous pool. Later studies [26] dealing with physical and chemical determinations of prostatic secretion also suggested that the cholesterol content in prostatic fluids of patients suffering from prostatic carcinoma were elevated, although statistically not significant. As opposed to results of earlier investigations [21] these studies further revealed that the cholesterol content of secretions of patients with bacterial prostatitis was most significantly decreased. Variations in analytical procedures employed for the determination of cholesterol might easily explain the differences in results of the respective studies.

Since there were substantial indications from previous studies that the cholesterol content of the prostate gland was altered with the appearance of carcinoma, it was reasonable to examine the tissues histochemically for cholesterol content. The presence of lipids, including cholesterol, in carcinoma of the prostate gland has been investigated histochemically by Braunstein [27]. Twenty-four cases of adenocarcinoma of the prostate gland, including five with metastases, were studied for lipid using a variety of techniques including those for cholesterol. Stains for the presence of lipid gave a positive reaction in all cases. When normal and neoplastic glands were compared, the normal prostatic acini and lumens contained droplets of lipid but in lesser quantity than in the neoplastic acini. It was suggested that the positive staining in neoplastic acini represents "stuffing" of tumor cells unable to gain access to a secretory duct for their secretions.

Swyer [5] during the course of an investigation into the histology of enlarging human prostates also found that in most cases where the Schultz reaction [28] was employed, the reaction was more positive in the hyperplastic regions than elsewhere, the characteristic green color being more intense in the glandular cells themselves than seen in normal prostates. It was on this basis that he compared quantitatively the cholesterol content of the prostatic adenoma with that of normal tissue.

In more recent studies by Mallouh and his co-workers [29], cholesterol in the human prostate gland was studied by both histochemical and gas chromatographic techniques. Free cholesterol was clearly identified in the secretions and the contents of the lumen and the glandular epithelial acini. Quantitatively, there was at least an 80% increase of cholesterol in the hyperplastic and cancerous tissue as compared to normal glands. The cholesterol content of prostatic carcinoma tissue appeared to be even higher than that of tissues histologically defined as benign prostatic hyperplasia (BPH), although statistically the observed difference was not significant. From the histochemical studies also employing the Schultz reaction, the observed increase in content in BPH tissues appeared to be due to the accumulation of cholesterol specifically in the lumen of the acinus of the glandular epithelium. In instances where serial sections were examined by conventional histopathological techniques, those acini containing large amounts of cholesterol were often found to be degenerated. In a typical illustration (Fig. 1) the cholesterol as shown by the dark color reaction appears to be crystalline in nature and practically occupies the entire space of the acinus lumen. Histologically, the epithelium was considered to be atrophied when examined by standard hematoxylin-eosin stains.

Additional studies by Goldstein [30] examined the total cholesterol content of human prostatic tissues from autopsy by employing gas-liquid chromatography to separate and quantitate the cholesterol. The summary of results (Fig. 2) obtained with (in parentheses) a number of tissues histopathologically characterized as normal (8), fibromuscular (8), benign prostatic hyperplasia (16), and prostatic carcinoma (8) are presented graphically. It is evident that the total cholesterol content in BPH and CA is significantly higher than seen in normal glands or in the fibromuscular (leiomyoma) tissue of the prostate. All of these studies speculated on the possible relationship of the production and accumulation of cholesterol in the prostate gland to testicular function. While it is well recognized that the production of prostatic secretion within the lumen of the acini is testosterone dependent, the nature of possible hormonal regulation of sterogenesis in the prostate gland, if any, was not known up to this time. The results of preliminary studies here indicated that the cholesterol content of the prostate might indeed be testosterone-dependent.

Later studies by Singhal [31] were concerned with the role of testicular function in rat prostatic cholesterogenesis. Initially, the studies investigated the sterol composition of the rat ventral prostate as compared to the liver. Preliminary examination of the free and esterified cholesterol content of the liver and the rat ventral prostate as shown in Table I readily reveals that the cholesterol of the prostate is largely unesterified whereas that of the liver is largely esterified. A comparison of the different sterols to be found in the rat ventral prostate and liver was also made and is given in Table II. Cholesterol is found to be the major sterol present in both tissues although the relative concentration in the prostate

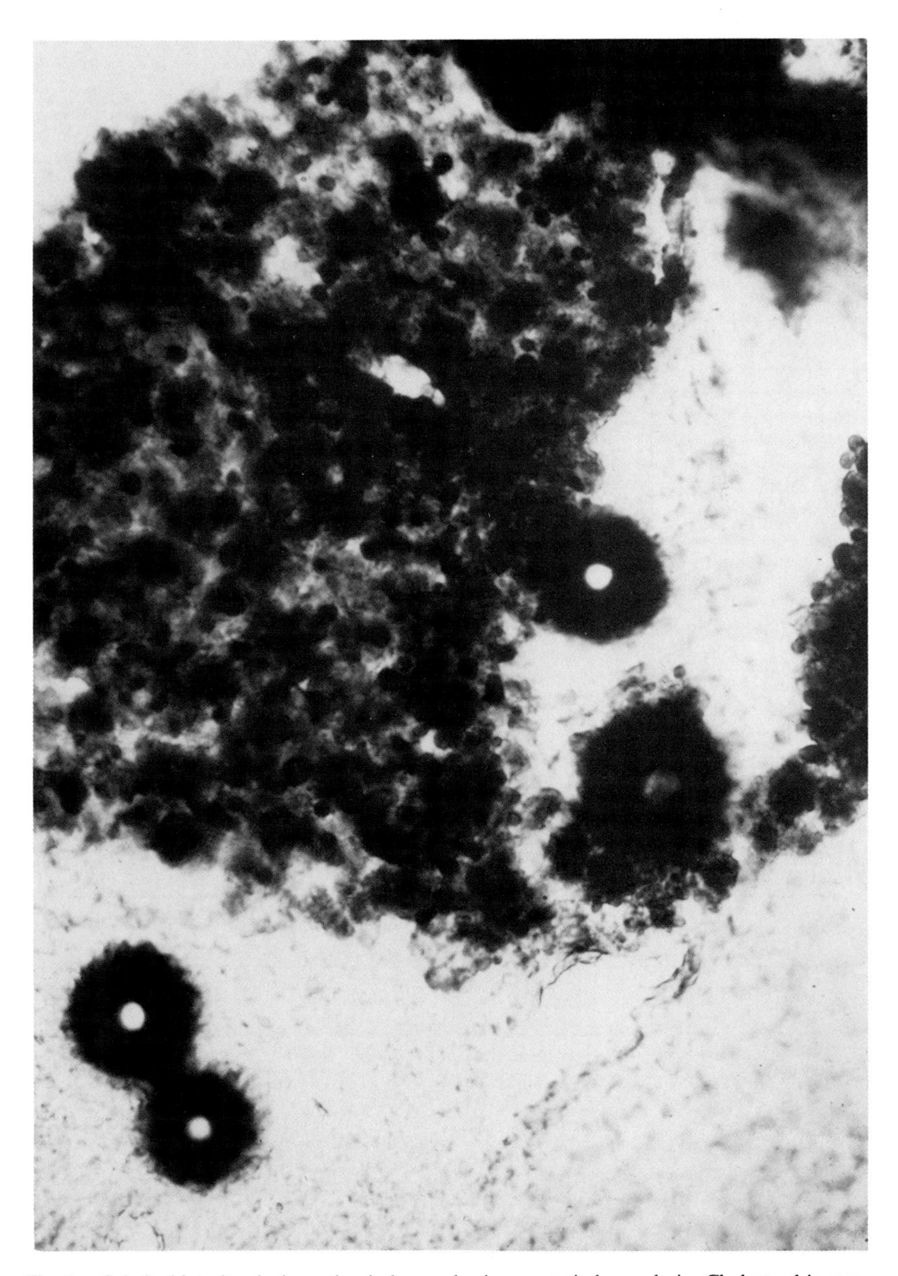

Fig. 1. Schultz histochemical reaction in human benign prostatic hyperplasia. Cholesterol is seen as the dark-colored solid deposits in the lumen. From Mallouh, Goldstein, Keshin, Pellman, and Schaffner [29].

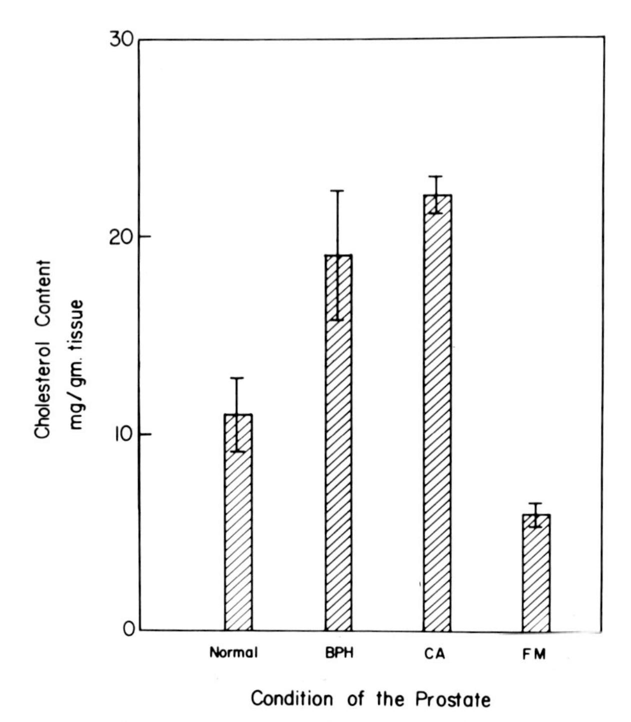

Fig. 2. Total cholesterol content versus condition of the human prostate gland. Adapted from Goldstein [30].

TABLE I. Comparison of relative contents of "free" cholesterol and cholesterol esters in rat ventral prostate and liver

	"Free" cholesterol[a] (%)	Cholesterol esters[a] (%)
Prostate	86.27 ± 4.32	13.73 ± 2.21
Liver	41.79 ± 8.09	58.21 ± 7.54

[a]Total lipids were extracted by chloroform:methanol (2:1,v/v), and free cholesterol and cholesterol esters were separated by digitonide precipitation.
From Singhal [31].

is higher than in the liver. Significantly higher quantities of lanosterol, desmosterol, zymosterol, and miscellaneous sterols are to be found in the liver than in the rat ventral prostate.

It thus appears that cholesterol in the nonesterified form is the principal sterol to be found in the tissues and secretions of the prostate gland of humans and animals. It is also apparent that the cholesterol content of the glandular component

TABLE II. Comparison of composition of sterols in rat ventral prostate and liver

	Cholesterol (%)	Lanosterol (%)	Desmosterol (%)	Zymosterol (%)	Miscellaneous (%)
Prostate					
i[a]	92.78 ± 4.25	2.75 ± 0.91	2.35 ± 0.49	—	2.12 ± 0.45
ii[b]	93.12 ± 5.71	4.22 ± 0.62	—	—	2.50 ± 0.207
Liver					
i[a]	70.09 ± 4.92	8.26 ± 1.99	7.06 ± 1.72	3.772 ± 0.995	10.80 ± 1.72
ii[b]	67.52 ± 6.74	7.07 ± 2.14	6.91 ± 0.97	4.440 ± 1.75	15.40 ± 4.21

[a]Determined by gas chromatography on 3% OV-17 column at 250°C using a flame ionization detector.
[b]Determined by TLC using silica gel G and solvent system [benzene-ethyl acetate (9:1, v/v)].
From Singhal [31].

of the prostate increases with the development of benign prostatic hyperplasia and prostatic carcinoma in humans. The exact role, if any, of cholesterol in these human diseases is at the moment unclear and is worthy of further study. The synthesis of cholesterol in the glandular epithelium and its hormonal regulation became subjects of investigation.

ANDROGEN REGULATION OF PROSTATIC STEROGENESIS

It has been well established [32–34] that testosterone and its major metabolite, dihydrotestosterone, maintain the morphology and secretory activity of the prostate gland in both in vitro and in vivo systems. It is very well known that testosterone also significantly affects the rates of DNA, RNA, and protein synthesis in the rat ventral prostate [35–38]. With castration there is a rapid regression of the rat ventral prostate including the cessation of secretory function. Cholesterol is one of the major constituents of the prostatic secretion.

In order to compare the relative in vitro synthesis of cholesterol in the liver and rat ventral prostate, Singhal [31] employed radiolabeled acetate and minced tissues of normal Wistar male rats. Table III presents a comparison of the rate of cholesterol synthesis in both tissues taken from rats 12–20 weeks of age. At all ages the ventral prostate was found to synthesize cholesterol at a much higher rate than the liver. It was also apparent that between 12 and 13 weeks of age the rate of cholesterol synthesis in the ventral prostate increased most sharply. It was also interesting to note that this increase in cholesterol synthesis occurred simultaneously with an infolding of the epithelial wall of the acinus as observed histopathologically.

Since castration and the subsequent lowering of body testosterone so adversely affects the prostate gland and its function in man and animals, studies [39] were initiated to evaluate the effects of 7-day castration and subsequent testosterone administration on prostate weights and on the content and rate of synthesis of

TABLE III. Comparison of rate of in vitro cholesterol synthesis in rat ventral prostate and liver

Age of rats (weeks)	Rate of cholesterol synthesis[a] (cpm/gm tissue) × 10^5	
	Prostate	Liver
12	2.594 ± 0.214	0.775 ± 0.194
13	6.471 ± 1.782	1.382 ± 0.350
14	5.310 ± 0.984	1.058 ± 0.515
20	6.726 ± 0.133	0.960 ± 0.101

[a]Adult Wistar rats were killed by exsanguination. Ventral prostate and liver slices were excised and the minced tissues (approximately 25–35 mg) were incubated with 2 ml of HBSS supplemented with 1 μCi/ml of 2-^{14}C-acetate (specific activity, 50.3 mCi/mmole) for 2 hours at 37°C. At the end, the tubes were saponified and cholesterol was separated by digitonin precipitation. Digitonin precipitates were dissolved in methanol and counted for ^{14}C activity.
From Singhal [31].

TABLE IV. Effect of castration on the synthesis of prostate cholesterol, protein, and DNA

Type	Body weight (gm)	Wet prostate weight (mg)[a]	Prostate cholesterol Total content (μg)[a]	Prostate cholesterol Rate of synthesis (cpm)[b]	Prostate protein Total content (mg)[a]	Prostate protein Rate of synthesis (cpm)[b]	Prostate DNA Total content (μg)[a]	Prostate DNA Rate of synthesis (cpm)[b]
Normal	275.5 ± 11.5	116.02 ± 21.06	237.5 ± 48.1	46.62 ± 11.98	5.83 ± 0.983	108.91 ± 70.49	293.17 ± 57.97	128.83 ± 23.59
Castrated[c]	256.0 ± 16.1	17.75 ± 1.26	32.04 ± 9.46	3.816 ± 0.642	0.728 ± 0.106	102.62 ± 33.07	78.38 ± 12.43	6.53 ± 1.30

[a]All the total contents are expressed in terms of per 100 gm body wt.
[b]The rate of synthesis is expressed as cpm/μg of prostate DNA isolated.
[c]Rats were castrated for 7 days.
From Singhal, Bonner, and Schaffner [39].

cholesterol, protein, and DNA in the rat ventral prostate. The results shown in Table IV clearly reveal that 7 days after castration there is no significant difference in body weight but a very great reduction of wet prostate weights. The content of prostate cholesterol, protein, and DNA all are significantly reduced to 13%, 12%, and 27% of their respective normal values. Whereas there is a significant reduction in the rate of synthesis of cholesterol and DNA, that of protein is not significantly reduced. Contrary to the decreases in the rates of synthesis of DNA and cholesterol, the rate of protein synthesis per μg prostatic DNA remains constant in the animal 7 days after castration even though the total amount of protein present in the prostate gland is significantly lower than in normal animals. This may be due to the synthesis of autolytic enzymes that would hydrolyze proteins and other constituents in the normal gland.

To illustrate the effects of castration after 7, 10, and 14 days on prostate weight and on the content of cholesterol, protein, and DNA, the results of another study are graphically presented (Fig. 3). The results indicate that most of the

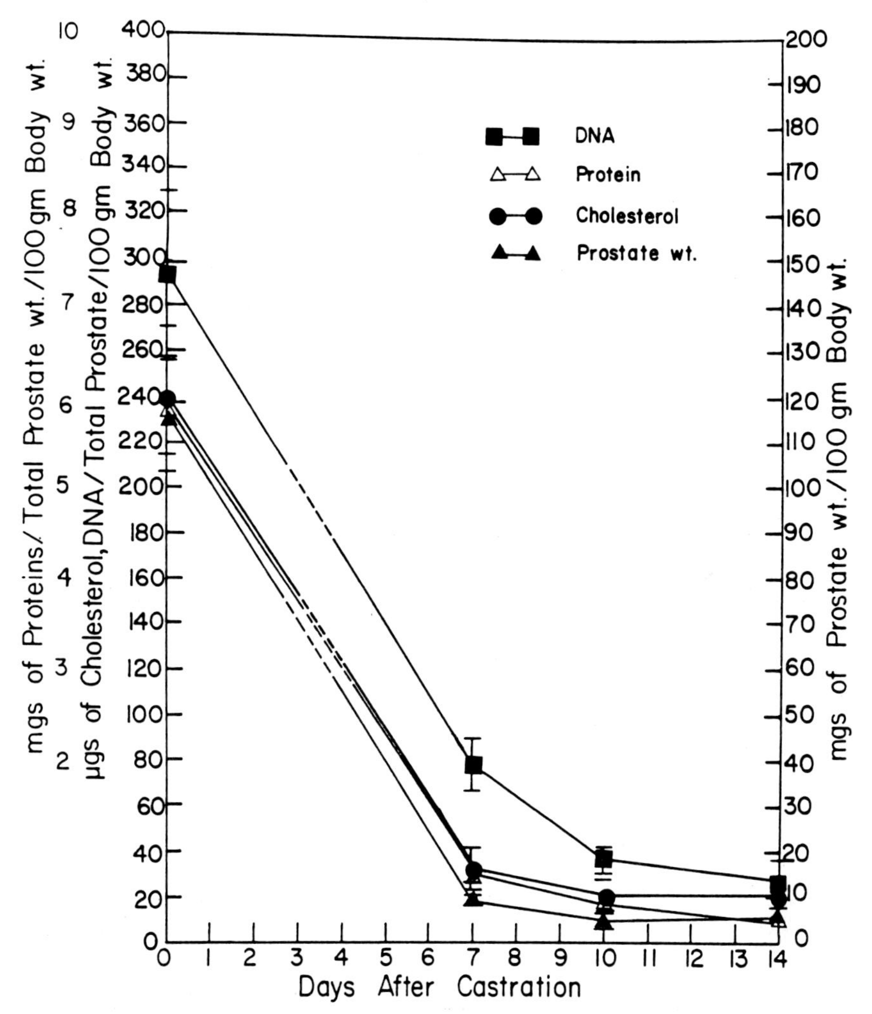

Fig. 3. Prostate weight and content of cholesterol, protein, and DNA in rat ventral prostate 7, 10, and 14 days after castration. The mean values are obtained from groups of six rates. From Singhal [31].

regression of the prostate gland occurred within 7 days of castration. Although there were significant reductions in prostate weight and in the contents of cholesterol, protein, and DNA between 7 and 14 days after castration, these reductions were slight when compared to the first 7 days after castration. After 14 days the content of cholesterol was reduced to 10% of the normal value. The results clearly indicate that testicular function is also essential for the maintenance of glandular cholesterol synthesis in the rat ventral prostate.

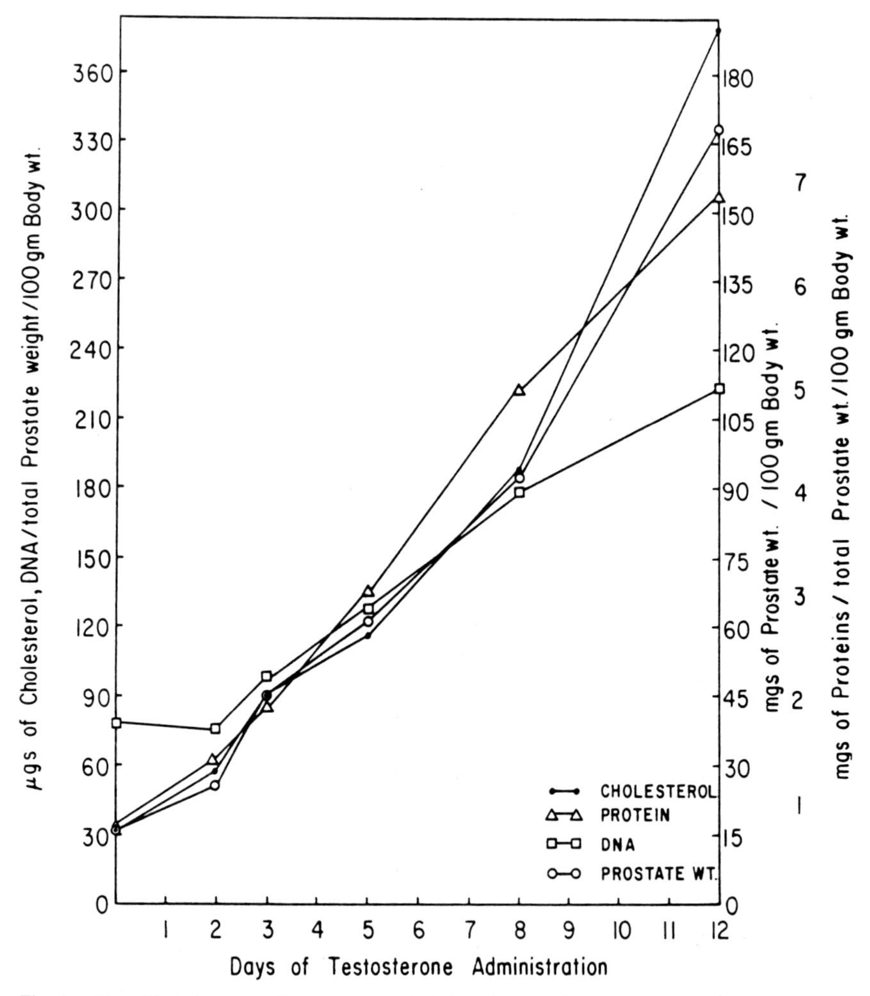

Fig. 4. The effect of parenteral testosterone administration to 7-day castrated rats on prostate weight and the contents of cholesterol, protein, and DNA in the ventral prostate. The mean values are obtained from groups of six rats. From Singhal, Bonner, and Schaffner. [39].

To examine whether or not testosterone would also restore the levels of cholesterol in the ventral prostate of the rat 7 days after castration, 2 mg of testosterone propionate in sesame oil was administered daily by subcutaneous route for varying periods of time up to 12 days. The results presented (Fig. 4) clearly reveal that the administration of testosterone to castrated rats increased the amount of cholesterol in the prostate gland. As expected, the prostate weights and content of protein and DNA also increased. All four parameters tested increased almost equally between 2 and 5 days of testosterone administration. The amount of protein increased sharply after 5 days of treatment which was followed after 8 days by sharp increases in prostate weight and the content of cholesterol.

Rates of cholesterol, protein, and DNA synthesis were also determined at varying intervals of time up to 14 days with the daily subcutaneous administration of testosterone propionate to rats 7 days after castration. The rates (Fig. 5) of synthesis of protein and cholesterol peak 2 days after testosterone administration, whereas DNA synthesis peaks after 4 days of treatment. The two peaks in protein and cholesterol synthesis after 2 days and again after 5 days might indicate the synthesis of structural components followed by synthesis of secretory components. After 5 days the synthesis of cholesterol, protein, and DNA decreases and remains at a steady state for the remainder of the 14 days of testosterone administration.

In more recent studies [40] the synthesis of cholesterol in the different lobes of the rat prostate were compared to that of the liver employing both acetate and mevalonic acids as precursors of cholesterogenesis. With acetate the ventral prostate in the daytime synthesized more cholesterol than the liver. The reverse was true when mevalonic acid was employed as a precursor. In contrast, the dorsolateral prostate synthesized only a little cholesterol with either precursor. Therefore, it was concluded that the ventral lobe is the major site of cholesterogenesis in the rat prostate. Although a diurnal change in cholesterol synthesis from acetate as seen in the liver was also observed in the rat ventral prostate, the observed circadian rhythm amplitude in the ventral prostate was indeed smaller than that in the liver. In contrast with the hepatic diurnal rhythm, cholesterogenesis in the ventral prostate was found to be predominant in the daytime.

Castration also significantly reduced the synthesis of cholesterol from acetate in the rat ventral prostate, whereas the amount of cholesterol synthesized from mevalonate decreased slightly, but not significantly. In the dorsolateral lobe of the prostate, there was no change in the synthesis of cholesterol from acetate or from mevalonate. Testosterone administration likewise restored cholesterogenesis in the rat ventral prostate but exerted no influence on dorsolateral synthesis. In contrast with the ventral prostate, it was found that hepatic cholesterogenesis was increased by castration and suppressed by testosterone. Hence, it was also postulated that testosterone is essential for some enzymatic regulatory activity

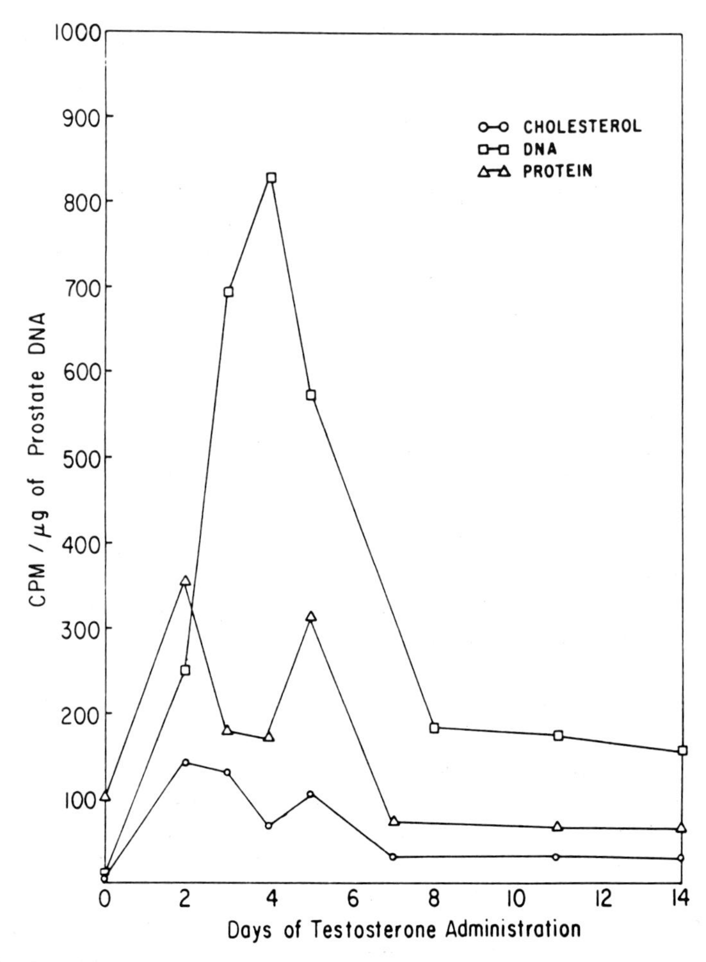

Fig. 5. The effect of parenteral testosterone adminstration to 7-day castrated rats on the rates of cholesterol, protein, and DNA synthesis in the ventral prostate. The mean values are obtained from groups of six rats. From Singhal, Bonner, and Schaffner [39].

prior to mevalonate and after acetate in the cholesterol synthesis pathway in the rat ventral prostate. As in the liver, β-hydroxy-β-methylglutaryl coenzyme A (HMG-Co A) reductase was believed to play a major role as the rate-limiting enzyme for cholesterogenesis in the prostate gland.

In comparing cholesterol synthesis in the liver and prostate glands of rats 72 weeks old with those 8 weeks old, it was apparent from these studies [40] that the aged rats synthesized less cholesterol than the young rats with acetate as a precursor. There was no significant difference in cholesterol synthesis in either age group, however, when mevalonate was used as a precursor. This decline in liver and prostate cholesterogenesis in aged rats was attributed to the decreased activity of HMG-Co A reductase.

The results of these studies [39,40] clearly reveal that cholesterol synthesis in the rat ventral prostate gland is androgen dependent. Specifically, testosterone appears to regulate cholesterogenesis, possibly through some control on the level of activity of the rate-limiting enzyme, HMG-Co A reductase. It appears more than likely that cholesterol synthesis in the prostate glands of other species, including man, are likewise controlled by testicular function.

CYCLIC ADENOSINE PHOSPHATE AND CHOLESTEROGENESIS

In vitro studies [41] have revealed that testosterone significantly increased cyclic adenosine monophosphate (cAMP) formation in the prostate tissues of the mouse. Likewise, cAMP has been reported [42] to produce testosterone-like induction of hexokinase, phosphofructokinase, pyruvate kinase, and glucose 6-phosphate dehydrogenase in the seminal vesicles of castrated rats. This effect is further enhanced by the simultaneous administration of theophylline, an inhibitor of the phosphodiestrase that is known to inactivate cAMP. Likewise in vivo studies [43] showed a significant increase in the prostate weight and comparable increases in the level of glycolytic enzymes when testosterone or cAMP and theophylline were administrated parenterally to castrated rats. In other studies [44,45] the rate of cholesterol synthesis was shown to decrease when cAMP was added to liver slices or to homogenates. In contrast, in vitro studies [46] with rat hepatoma tissues incubated with cAMP or dibutyrl cAMP and radiolabeled acetate demonstrated unsupressible cholesterol and fatty acid synthesis as compared to normal controls.

More recent investigations [47] have studied the in vitro effect of testosterone and cAMP on cholesterol synthesis in the rat ventral prostate. At the same time in vitro effects of the metabolic inhibitors, actinomycin D and cycloheximide, on the testosterone-dependent cholesterol synthesis in the ventral prostate of castrated rats were also determined. As shown in Table V, actinomycin D (4 μM/ml) and cycloheximide (0.5 mM/ml) significantly inhibited the testosterone-dependent increase in cholesterol, protein, and RNA synthesis in the ventral prostate of the castrated rats within 4 hours of incubation with testosterone. The known inhibitor of RNA synthesis, actinomycin D, in the presence of testosterone reduced the rates of RNA synthesis by 42% and 70% of that exhibited by the controls without (group I) and with (group II) testosterone, respectively. Likewise, the known inhibitor of protein synthesis, cycloheximide, in the presence of testosterone reduced the rates of protein synthesis by 59% and 77% of that exhibited by the controls without (group I) and with (group II) testosterone, respectively. Simultaneously, actinomycin D and cycloheximide, in the presence

TABLE V. In vitro effect of actinomycin D and cycloheximide on the testosterone stimulation of cholesterol, protein, RNA, and DNA synthesis in ventral prostate of castrated rats

Group		Rate of synthesis (cpm/gm tissue) × 10^4			
		Prostate cholesterol	Prostate protein	Prostate RNA	Prostate DNA
I	Control	5.78 ± 1.27	51.3 ± 7.0	35.1 ± 4.5	3.63 ± 0.57
II	+ Testosterone	10.7 ± 1.3	89.9 ± 9.4	67.3 ± 9.4	4.23 ± 0.92
III	+ Testosterone + Actinomycin D	5.55 ± 1.61	49.0 ± 6.2	20.2 ± 3.2	3.71 ± 1.32
IV	+ Testosterone + Cycloheximide	4.67 ± 0.86	21.1 ± 4.9	40.7 ± 7.2	2.89 ± 0.39

All the values are obtained from groups of six rats and expressed as mean ± SE. The radioactive precursors, [1,2-^{14}C] acetate, L-[4,5-^{3}H] leucine, [5-^{3}H] uridine, and [5-methyl-^{3}H] thymidine, were employed for the cholesterol, protein, RNA, and DNA incorporation studies, respectively. The rats were castrated for 7 days.
From Singhal and Schaffner [47].

of testosterone, reduced the cholesterol synthesis by 49% and 56%, respectively, of that exhibited by controls with testosterone (group II). Neither actinomycin D nor cycloheximide in these studies produced a significant change in DNA synthesis.

The results of in vitro studies [47] dealing with the effects of cAMP on the rates of cholesterol, protein, and RNA synthesis in the ventral prostate of castrated rats are presented in Table VI. The effects of the metabolic inhibitors actinomycin D, cycloheximide, and theophylline on these cAMP-dependent syntheses in the ventral prostate of castrated rats were also determined. For better tissue absorption the N^6, $O^{2'}$-dibutyryl derivative of cAMP was employed in these studies. The synthesis of RNA, protein, and cholesterol as compared to controls were reduced by 28%, 33%, and 41%, respectively, when actinomycin D (4 μM/ml) was added to ventral prostate tissues of castrated rats. The addition of cycloheximide (0.5 mMml) reduced the synthesis of protein and cholesterol by 86% and 59%, respectively. Although there was a slight reduction in the synthesis of RNA, this change could not be considered as significant. As compared to controls the cAMP derivative (0.5 mM/ml) increased RNA and protein synthesis by 31% and 29%, respectively, whereas it decreased cholesterol synthesis by 73%. The addition of theophylline (0.5 mM/ml) to the cAMP group further increased RNA and protein synthesis to 36% and 43% of control values, respectively, whereas cholesterol synthesis further declined by 78% of that of the controls. Theophylline itself exhibited no significant effect on cholesterol, protein, or RNA synthesis. When actinomycin D (4 μM/ml) was added to the cAMP group, both protein and RNA synthesis were decreased by 43% and 39% of the cAMP control (group V), respectively, whereas cholesterol synthesis was increased by 40% of the cAMP control. When cycloheximide (0.5 mM/ml) was added to the cAMP group both protein and RNA synthesis declined by 88% and 16% of the cAMP control values, respectively. Cholesterol synthesis increased by 128% of cAMP control levels.

In these studies it is clear that cAMP increased protein and RNA synthesis in the ventral prostate of the castrated rat. The simultaneous addition of theophylline further increased this stimulating effect, whereas the other metabolic inhibitors, actinomycin D and cycloheximide, inhibited the cAMP-stimulated increases in the rates of protein and RNA synthesis. In sharp contrast, however, the synthesis of prostatic cholesterol was significantly inhibited by the addition of cAMP. This inhibitory effect was further enhanced by the simultaneous addition of theophylline. Actinomycin D and particularly cycloheximide somewhat reversed the inhibitory effect of cAMP on cholesterol synthesis, perhaps suggesting that the effect of cAMP on prostatic cholesterol synthesis, in part, depends on the de novo synthesis of one or more proteins that is involved in the biosynthetic pathway of cholesterol synthesis. This decrease of in vitro cholesterol synthesis in the prostate by the action of cAMP agrees with the results of similar studies [44,45] involving tissue preparations of the liver.

It has been suggested [42] that cAMP may play the role of a second messenger in the action of testosterone on the secondary sex organs of the rat. Other earlier in vivo studies [43] involving the stimulating effects of cAMP on the prostate

TABLE VI. Effect of N^6, $O^{2'}$-dibutyryl cAMP, actinomycin D, cycloheximide, and theophylline on the rate of synthesis of prostate cholesterol, protein, and RNA in castrated rats

		Rate of synthesis (cpm/gm tissue) × 10^4		
	Group	Prostate cholesterol	Prostate protein	Prostate RNA
I	Control	16.3 ± 2.1	32.7 ± 4.2	20.6 ± 1.6
II	+ Actinomycin D	9.61 ± 0.48	22.0 ± 3.5	14.8 ± 0.9
III	+ Cycloheximide	6.66 ± 0.35	4.46 ± 0.57	17.8 ± 1.6
IV	+ Theophylline	18.8 ± 1.2	35.2 ± 3.4	21.4 ± 2.3
V	+ cAMP	4.48 ± 0.38	42.2 ± 1.6	26.9 ± 2.2
VI	+ cAMP + actinomycin D	6.28 ± 0.43	24.1 ± 3.0	16.5 ± 1.1
VII	+ cAMP + cycloheximide	10.2 ± 1.8	4.95 ± 0.69	22.6 ± 1.6
VIII	+ cAMP + theophylline	3.62 ± 0.31	46.9 ± 2.0	28.1 ± 2.0

All the values are obtained from groups of six rats and expressed as mean ± SE. The radioactive precursors, [2-^{14}C] acetate, L-[4,5-^{3}H] leucine, and [5-^{3}H] uridine, were employed for the cholesterol, protein, and RNA incorporation studies, respectively. The rats were castrated for 7 days.
From Singhal and Schaffner [47].

gland of castrated animals resulted in increases in prostate weight and levels of glycolytic enzymes, mimicking the effect of testosterone. This is further seen in the more recent results [47] concerning the stimulating effect of cAMP like that of testosterone on the in vitro synthesis of protein and RNA in the ventral prostate of castrated rats. Nevertheless, although cAMP stimulated protein and RNA synthesis somewhat in the castrated rat ventral prostate, the effect was not as marked as that produced by testosterone itself. At the same time the inhibitory effect of cAMP on prostatic cholesterol synthesis is in sharp contrast to the effect of testosterone. Other studies [48] dealing with the effects of cAMP on the function and morphology of the rat prostate gland revealed that testosterone given subcutaneously to castrated rats stimulated prostate gland RNA polymerase, ornithine decarboxylase, S-adenosylmethionine decarboxylase, and glucose-6-phosphate dehydrogenase. In contrast, cAMP given intraperitoneally primarily stimulated the dehydrogenase. Unlike testosterone, cAMP did not fully restore the morphology of the prostate gland after castration nor did cAMP unlike 5α-dihydrotestosterone bind to nuclear chromatin or to cytoplasmic androgen receptors. These results would suggest that cAMP is not a major intermediary in the response of the prostate gland to testosterone. Nevertheless, the effect of cAMP on prostatic cholesterol synthesis is of fundamental importance.

HYPOCHOLESTEROLEMIC AGENTS AND THE PROSTATE GLAND

The observation [6] originally made in experimental animals that the polyene macrolide antibiotic, candicidin, and other related compounds produced marked reductions in prostate gland volumes was the basis for many animal and clinical studies to follow. At the same time this observed effect of the polyene macrolides on the prostate gland motivated the different studies into various aspects of the cholesterol metabolism of the prostate gland and its unique testosterone dependence.

In a series of oral toxicity studies [6] in rats and dogs with the heptaene macrolide, candicidin, an interesting physiological effect involving the prostate gland was observed. A marked reduction of the prostate gland was noted in young rats after 30 days or more of treatment with oral candicidin at 20 mg/kg. These initial observations were followed by further studies made in old mongrel dogs afflicted with benign prostatic hyperplasia where the oral administration of different polyene macrolides at doses of 5–20 mg/kg reportedly produced in 30 days or more varying reductions in the size and changes in the texture of the prostate gland, as associated in some cases with marked histological transformations. The heptaene macrolides, candicidin and amphotericin B less so, appeared to be significantly more active than the other polyene macrolide antibiotics tested. The tetraene antibiotic, nystatin, exhibiting far less antifungal activity than candicidin, also exhibited little or no activity towards canine prostatic hyperplasia. There thus appeared to be some correlation between the degree of antifungal activity of the polyene macrolide and its effect on the enlarged prostate gland.

Since there was no evidence of histopathologic drug toxicity due to the continued oral polyene macrolide treatment nor apparent absorption from the gastrointestinal tract, it was difficult to understand the exact mechanism of action on the prostate gland. The fact that the polyene macrolides as a group are quite active against the fungi appears to be dependent on the ability of the susceptible cells to bind these antibiotics. The exact nature of the binding site has been identified [49] as a sterol-containing structure in the cell membrane. The sensitivity of yeasts and fungi has thus been linked to ergosterol whereas that of erythrocytes to cholesterol. It has now been well established that the polyene macrolides as a group have a specific physical-chemical affinity for the sterols and sterol-containing biological membranes. The in vitro formation of specific polyene macrolide-sterol complexes has been clearly demonstrated and reviewed [49]. Based on a hypothetical polyene macrolide-cholesterol interaction in the gastrointestinal tract of animals, studies [50] were initially carried out to determine the potential hypocholesterolemic action of these drugs. These studies in dogs clearly revealed a hypocholesterolemic effect with the polyene macrolides when administered orally. Again there appeared to be some distinct correlation between the degree of antifungal activity and the hypocholesterolemic activity of the various polyene macrolides tested.

Other investigators [51] soon reported on the inhibitory effects of relatively low doses of oral amphotericin B on canine prostatic secretions, serum testosterone levels, testicular function, and prostatic histology. These effects were observed to persist for several months after withdrawal of the treatment. The tests showed pronounced degeneration of seminiferous epithelial component with a cessation of spermatogenesis. The testicular changes appeared to be reversible after several months without treatment. However, extensive efforts to duplicate these initial findings of canine "castration" with oral amphotericin B met only continued failure. The effects originally observed here may have been solely due to the "caging phenomenon" which is a state of temporary infertility due to restraining old mongrel dogs in cages. An alternate, but less likely, possibility may have been the presence of some anti-androgenic impurity in the amphotericin B preparation employed in the initial study.

Primarily on the basis of observed differences in food intake and weight gain, another group concluded [52] that the nutritional state and well-being of the rat and dog were directly involved in the prostate response to certain polyene macrolides by the oral route. In other studies [53] the oral administration of the polyene macrolides, filipin, nystatin, and amphotericin B produced no loss of appetite, no gastrointestinal disturbances, nor testicular alterations. Examination of the prostate tissues in the amphotericin B-treated dogs revealed a smaller transformation of testosterone to dihydrotestosterone and a smaller concentration of testosterone in the tissue. The results of these studies have likewise not been confirmed.

With the clinical availability of the tetraene macrolide, nystatin, several experimental trials [54–57] were soon initiated in patients suffering from benign prostatic hyperplasia. Nystatin was administered in these studies for a maximum period of up to 2 months at dosage levels comparable to those employed in the previous canine studies [6,50]. Since nystatin had exhibited in these studies dealing with canine prostatic hyperplasia and hypercholesterolemia little or no activity, failure of these clinical investigators to demonstrate significant efficacy in human BPH trials was not too surprising.

In another study [58] amphotericin B was administered to 10 patients of prostatic hypertrophy with a daily dose of 800–1200 mg for a period of 2–10 weeks. All of the cases were originally on conservative therapy. Although uncontrolled, the results of the study indicated partial success with marked reduction of the adenoma observed in one case, moderate reduction in five patients, and three cases with little change. Improvement of dysuria and frequency was noted in seven cases. Disappearance of residual urine was observed in four patients, whereas some reduction of symptoms was observed in three other patients, and the remaining patients exhibited no change.

With established safety of the heptaene macrolide, candicidin, administered by the oral route and its observed superior effect on canine prostatic glandular hyperplasia, long-term studies in humans were then initiated. The first clinical trial with oral candicidin for the treatment of human benign prostatic hyperplasia (BPH) was carried out by Keshin [9]. The study involved a group of 92 patients, all surgical candidates suffering with advanced prostatism. Prolonged oral candicidin treatment of six months or longer at doses of 2–5 mg/kg was reported to be effective. There was a relatively rapid subjective improvement in over 70% of the group. Marked reductions of the glandular enlargement associated with increased glandular fibrosis with resultant lessening of the clinical symptoms of urinary retention, hesitancy, and nocturia were all reported only after prolonged treatment with relatively low levels of oral candicidin. No adverse toxic reactions were seen in this clinical trial.

The initial studies were soon followed by two controlled studies [11,12] with oral candicidin and placebo. Since spontaneous remission was often claimed to be responsible for the improvement of clinical symptoms of prostatism, these controlled studies were important. With active candicidin treatment as compared to placebo, overall clinical improvement of benign prostatic hyperplasia symptoms occurred in over 80% of the patients. Aside from improvement of the subjective symptoms there appeared to be significant improvement of objective symptoms such as urinary retention volumes and flow rates. It appeared obvious that spontaneous remission was not responsible for the apparent efficacy of oral candicidin therapy.

In 1970, clinical studies [10] were initiated in the Soviet Union with a polyene macrolide, levorin, known to be identical to candicidin [59]. Here the efficacy of the drug against human prostatic adenoma in the first and second stages of the disease was determined. Treatment with oral levorin leading to considerable improvement of the subjective and objective symptoms was reported. As a result of the Soviet clinical studies the Pharmacological Committee of the U.S.S.R., Ministry of Health, gave permission in 1975 for broad clinical application of levorin.

In a later randomized double-blind study by Abrams [60] 52 patients with benign prostatic hypertrophy were treated for 6 months with oral candicidin at 300 mg daily. Subjective improvement was reported in treated and control groups, and the general conclusion of the study did not clearly support the view that candicidin is a useful drug for the treatment of benign prostatic hypertrophy. Nevertheless, the investigator reported that "an increase in the mean flow rate of the treated group was noted and was the only finding to suggest that candicidin might be an active drug." It is certainly apparent that further long-term and controlled studies into the efficacy of candicidin are needed before conclusions on its efficacy for human benign prostatic hyperplasia (BPH) are drawn.

A BPH clinical trial in Italy with an undefined polyene macrolide has also been reported [8]. This study involved patients with advanced prostatism suffering with adenoma and hyperplasia of the prostate gland. Considering all methods of treatment recommended to date it was concluded that polyene macrolide therapy was the method of choice. It was also reported that polyene macrolide therapy affected the course of prostatic carcinoma in humans—an important but unsubstantiated observation.

Considering that an increase of cholesterol content and the appearance of unesterified cholesterol deposits in the lumen of the glandular acinus is associated with BPH, a reasonable hypothesis of polyene macrolide drug action could be constructed based on the hypocholesterolemic action of these drugs by the oral route of administration. In the BPH clinical trial with candicidin by Sporer [12] a summary of the histopathological findings with prostatic tissues available from patients treated with candicidin who demonstrated partial success with the drug and from those patients who served as untreated controls was prepared. The prostatic tissue from candicidin-treated patients was reported to reveal more fibrosis in nodular areas; showed lower, less active, epithelial-lined cysts in nodular areas. These qualitative evaluations might be consistent with the interpretation that candicidin exerted an atrophic influence upon prostatic epithelium with an increase in nonepithelial elements of the hyperplastic prostate. The reported efficacy of candicidin might reside in its reduction of epithelial elements in the hyperplastic elements of the prostate where the massive cholesterol accumulation has been consistently detected by histochemistry. It was increasingly apparent that further studies into the possible relationship of cholesterol and the etiology of human BPH were needed.

At the time it was also apparent that no uniform experimental animal disease model of prostatic hypertrophy comparable to human BPH was available for study in the evaluation of potential chemotherapeutic drugs and of the possible etiology of the disease. In the past, studies in the dog have been at best limited because of the nonuniformity of the naturally occurring disease and the general scarcity of the afflicted animals. Investigators in 1970 described [61] an age-dependent, spontaneous, cystic prostatic hypertrophy in two inbred lines of male Syrian hamster (Mesocricetus auratus). Histopathological examination revealed that the marked prostate weight changes at ages of 160 days or more were the result of a cystic dilation of the prostatic acini which appeared to be filled with an eosinophilic amorphous material. They observed minimal stromal hyperplasia and minimal changes in the epithelial cells. In some respects the histopathology resembled canine cystic prostatic hypertrophy.

In a later study [7] one of the two inbred male hamster lines, BIO 87.20, was employed to evaluate the possible effect of the heptaene macrolide, candicidin, and of the bile acid-sequestering anion exchange resin, colestipol, on this more uniform animal disease model. The availability of this interesting inbred line of Syrian hamster represented a unique opportunity to test the effect of two structurally unrelated hypocholesterolemic drugs in this animal disease model.

The results presented in Table VII clearly revealed that by the oral route both candicidin and colestipol prevented the enlargement of the ventral prostate gland seen in the untreated controls. It is immediately evident that the ventral prostate weights of animals treated with candicidin at the higher dosage level (75 mg/kg/day) were significantly lower than those of all other experimental and control animals, falling in the weight range of those reported for normal hamsters. It was particularly interesting to note that the hamsters treated with the anion exchange, bile acid-binding resin, colestipol, at the high dosage level (400 mg/kg/day), revealed ventral prostate weights comparable to those of animals treated with candicidin at the low dosage level (40 mg/kg/day). Treatment with colestipol at the low dosage level (200 mg/kg/day) apparently produced ventral prostate weights not significantly different from those of untreated control animals. Considering the ratios of ventral prostate weight-to-body weight, it is very evident that candicidin at both high and low dosage levels and colestipol at the high dosage level produced significant differences compared with the control and low dosage colestipol-treated groups.

Microscopic examination of the excised ventral prostate glands of control and high dosage candicidin-treated animals revealed an interesting difference. As

TABLE VII. Summary of body weight, ventral prostate weight, and the weight ratios in all groups of BIO 87.20 Syrian hamsters

	Animal group	No. of animals	Body weight (gm)	Ventral prostate weight[a] (mg)	Weight ratio[b] × 10^{-3}
I	Candicidin (75 mg/kg/day)	8	101.88 ± 5.88	60.63 ± 4.45	0.60[c] ± 0.04
II	Candicidin (40 mg/kg/day)	8	116.98 ± 4.48	95.63 ± 9.23	0.82* ± 0.08
III	Colestipol (400 mg/kg/day)	9	118.89 ± 3.98	99.00 ± 8.42	0.83* ± 0.05
IV	Colestipol (200 mg/kg/day)	8	117.88 ± 3.47	126.50 ± 9.17	1.10 ± 0.12
V	Control (no treatment)	7	124.43 ± 5.04	138.43 ± 11.89	1.11 ± 0.08

Values are means ± SE.
[a]Wet weight.
[b]Weight ratio = ventral prostate weight/body weight.
[c]Statistical evaluation of t and probability; $P < 0.001$.
*$P < 0.01$.
From Wang and Schaffner [7].

shown in the histopathological section of the ventral prostate gland of a control animal (Fig. 6), there is a marked cystic dilation and distention of the acini, which appear to be filled with a large quantity of eosinophilic fluid. In the histologic section of the ventral prostate of a high dosage candicidin-treated animal (Fig. 7), the prostatic acini appear to be less distended as compared with those of the control animals, and the quantity of eosinophilic fluid seems to be reduced.

It was also interesting to note that the effect of both drugs was associated with a marked lowering of the cholesterol content of the prostate gland. From histopathological studies both drugs apparently had no effect on the testes of these animals since spermatogenesis and normal morphology were evident. Hence, the effect of these drugs was not associated with any inhibitory or antiandrogenic effect on the testes but more likely due to an effect on the cholesterol content of the gland.

Based primarily on differences in food intake and weight gain, an earlier claim [52] that the nutritional state and well-being of the rat and dog are directly involved in the prostate response to certain polyene macrolides by the oral route did not seem to be applicable here. Although there was some loss of body weight in the high dosage candicidin-treated group of hamsters, no significant differences

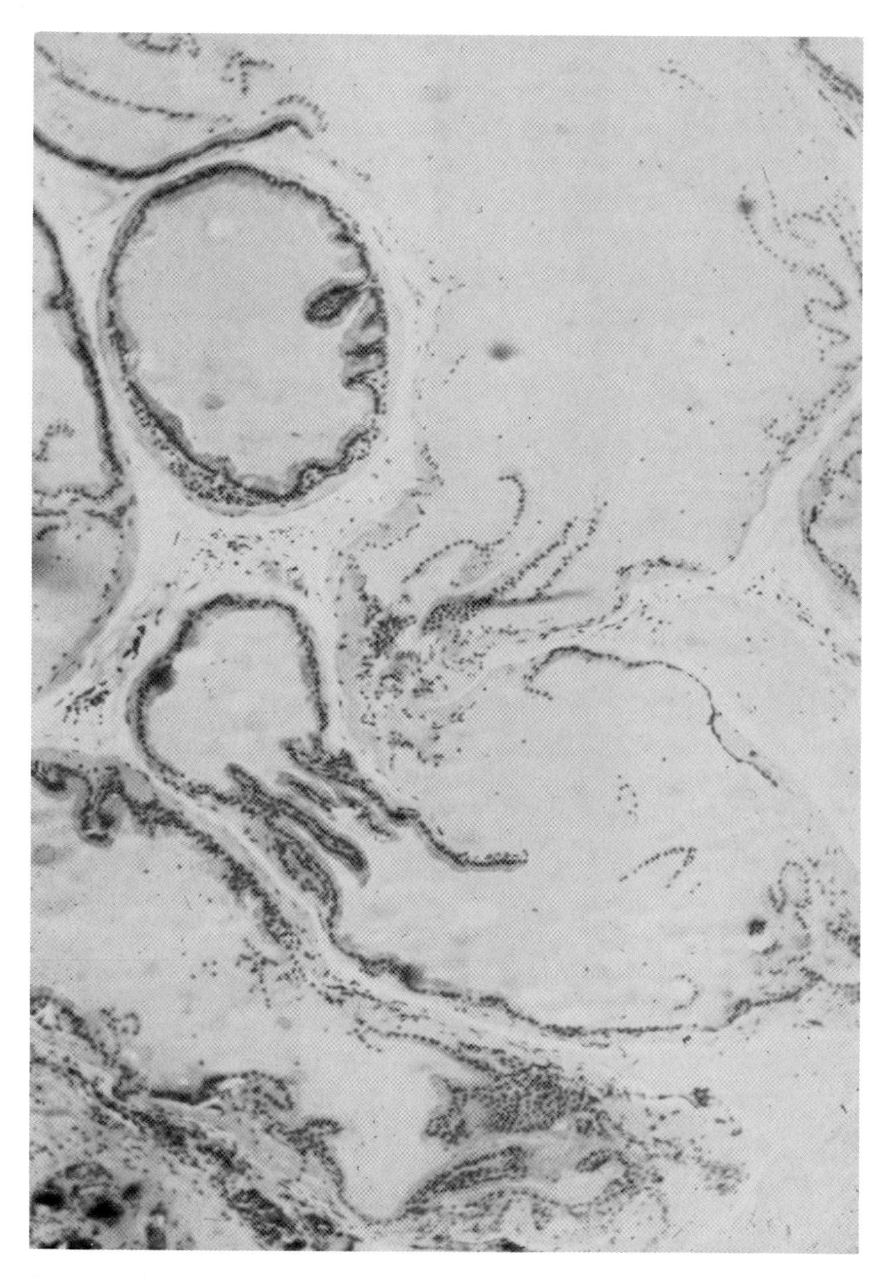

Fig. 6. Histologic section of the ventral prostate of a control BIO 87.20 Syrian hamster. Hematoxylin and eosin; × 100. From Wang and Schaffner [7].

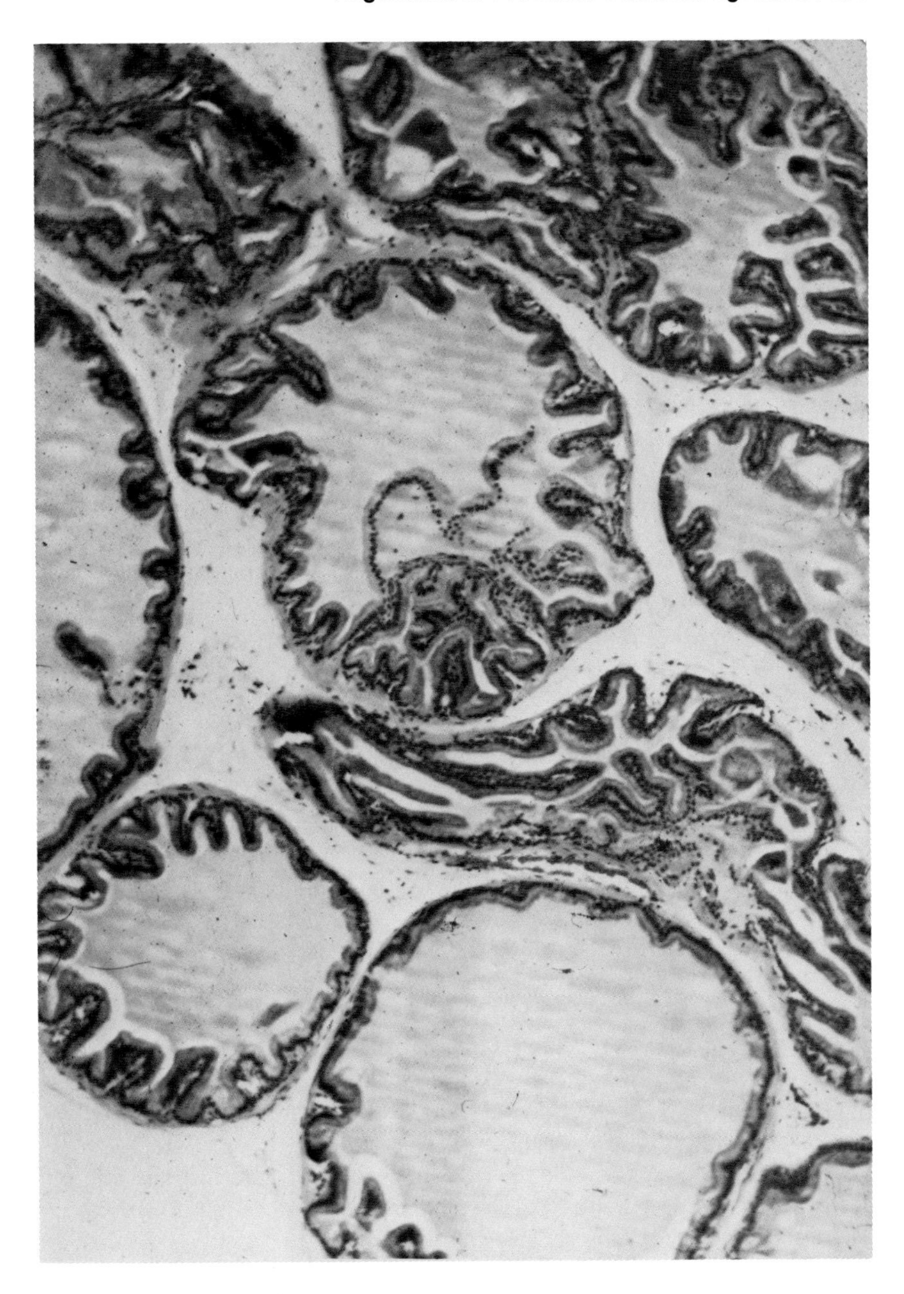

Fig. 7. Histologic section of the ventral prostate gland of a candicidin-treated BIO 87.20 Syrian hamster. Hematoxylin and eosin; × 100. From Wang and Schaffner [7].

in body weight as compared to the control group were seen in the low-dosage candicidin and high-dosage colestipol-treated groups, where significant differences in prostate weights were observed. In all animals the food consumption also seemed to be comparable. The response of the ventral prostate gland of the BIO 87-20 hamster to oral candicidin and colestipol treatment therefore does not appear to be related directly to decreased food intake or to losses in body weight, but may be directly or indirectly related to the observed [49] inhibition of the absorption-resorption of the exogenous cholesterol pool in the gastrointestinal tract. Both candicidin and colestipol are not absorbed from the gastrointestinal tract. Hence, this observation in a new experimental animal disease model apparently suggests that cholesterol might play some role in the etiology of this prostatic enlargement.

More recent investigations [62] compared the effect of diets containing cholesterol and the hypocholesterolemic drugs, candicidin and clofibrate, on cholesterol metabolism of normal and BIO 87.20 male Syrian hamsters. Since the reduction of the enlarged ventral prostate glands of the BIO 87.20 Syrian hamsters with hypocholesterolemic drugs reported earlier [7] might be related to decreased body cholesterol levels or possibly to changes in cholesterogenesis in the gland, studies were designed to compare the effects of dietary cholesterol, candicidin, and clofibrate on the content of cholesterol in the serum and liver of normal and BIO 87-20 male Syrian hamsters. The rates of cholesterol synthesis in the liver and ventral prostate glands were also determined.

The ventral prostate gland of the normal and BIO 87.20 male Syrian hamster was found to synthesize cholesterol at a rate greater than that of the liver. Whereas a cholesterol diet reduced the rate of cholesterogenesis in the liver of the normal Syrian hamster, it produced no such response in the liver of the BIO 87.20 strain nor in the ventral prostate gland of either strain. It was thus seen that while hepatic cholesterol synthesis in the normal Syrian hamster is under negative feedback control with dietary cholesterol, hepatic cholesterol synthesis in the BIO 87.20 hamster as well as prostatic cholesterol synthesis in either strain are under no such control. This apparent regulatory defect in the BIO 87.20 hamster, which results in a most dramatic accumulation of cholesterol in the liver and in hypercholesterolemia in animals on a cholesterol diet, might indeed be related to the observed increase in ventral prostate cholesterol with the development of cystic prostatic hypertrophy.

In these studies [62] the effect of two different hypocholesterolemic drugs on cholesterol metabolism in the liver and ventral prostate of the two hamster strains was also determined. Clofibrate and candicidin clearly revealed opposing effects on the rates of cholesterol synthesis in the liver and prostate gland of both hamster strains. Treatment with clofibrate, which illicits its hypocholesterolemic effect by inhibiting cholesterol synthesis, displayed this inhibition in the liver and prostate of both hamster lines. Candicidin is believed to lower serum and body cholesterol levels by preventing the absorption-resorption of cholesterol from the intestinal tract, thus interfering with enterohepatic circulation of cholesterol and the absorption of dietary cholesterol. In both the normal and BIO 87.20 Syrian hamsters dietary candicidin clearly stimulated cholesterol synthesis in the liver to a significant extent and much less so in the prostate gland. In the normal Syrian hamster where hepatic cholesterol synthesis is under negative feedback control by exogenous cholesterol, the stimulation of cholesterol synthesis by candicidin treatment is understandable. In the BIO 87.20 hamster where hepatic cholesterol synthesis is not under the usual negative feedback regulation by exogeneous cholesterol, candicidin treatment in sharp contrast to the effects of dietary cholesterol produced a marked increase in the hepatic synthesis of cholesterol. This suggests the presence of some sort of positive feedback regulation of cholesterogenesis in the liver of both hamster lines. The major conclusion of these studies is that the ventral prostate gland of either hamster line and the liver of the BIO 87.20 line are not under negative feedback regulation of cholesterogenesis but rather under some degree of positive feedback control. It is apparent that the male BIO 87.20 Syrian hamster is a potentially valuable in vivo animal model for the study of cholesterol metabolism and prostatic disease.

It is also interesting to note that other investigators [63] reported that the prostate glands and seminal vesicles of BIO 87.20 male hamsters in constrast to normal strains undergo a profound atrophy with advancing age and do not develop cystic prostatic hypertrophy. The immature size of the observed prostates and seminal vesicles was related to the marked testicular atrophy also observed in these animals. Both prostatic and seminal vesicular conditions appeared to be reversible with testosterone administration as was the atrophic conditions due to castration. It was subsequently explained [64] that the lack of female companionship results in these atrophic changes in the testis, prostate gland, and seminal vesicle of the BIO 87.20 hamster. Intact testicular function is obviously required for the maintenance of normal prostate function and the development of cystic prostatic hypertrophy in this aging male hamster strain.

The apparent lack of negative feedback regulation of cholesterol synthesis in the hamster ventral prostate is not an unusual finding. Rates of cholesterol synthesis measured [65] in 17 tissues of the rat revealed that the liver is primarily affected by dietary cholesterol. The liver and the gastrointestinal tract together account for 90% of the cholesterol synthesis in the rat. Synthesis in the prostate gland, however, was not measured at that time. Later in vitro studies [31] employing ventral prostate and liver tissues of the rat and delipidized serum of castrated rats clearly revealed the absence of negative feedback control of cholesterol synthesis in the ventral prostate of the rat. Whereas the synthesis of cholesterol from radiolabeled acetate in the liver increased (Fig. 8) by the addition of the cholesterol-free, delipidized serum, the synthesis in the ventral prostate was unaffected by this absence of cholesterol-containing lipoproteins. With the

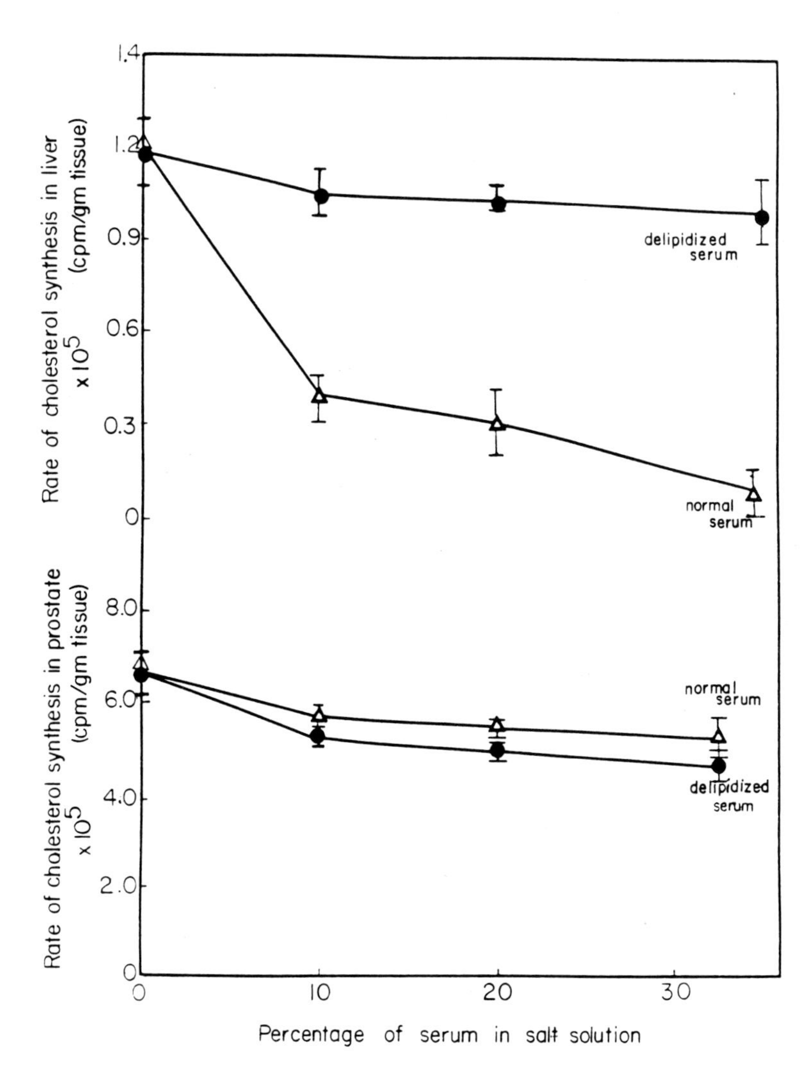

Fig. 8. Feedback regulation of cholesterogenesis by lipoproteins. Serum from castrated rats was delipidized using 1-butanol and diisopropyl ether (40:60, v/v). Ventral prostate and liver tissues were incubated at 37°C for 2 hours with HBSS containing 10, 20, or 30% normal or delipidized serum containing 1 Ci/ml of 2-^{14}C-acetate (specific activity, 50.3 mCi/mmole). From Singhal [31].

use of serum of castrated animals any stimulation of prostatic cholesterol synthesis due to the presence of testosterone was avoided.

In another study [66] the measured levels of β-hydroxy-β-methylglutaryl-coenzyme A-reductase (HMG-CoA-reductase), the rate-limiting enzyme involved in the formation of mevalonic acid, were clearly elevated (30%) in the liver of rats treated with oral candicidin. Whereas prostatic HMG-CoA-reductase levels were three times higher than that of the liver, the enzyme activity in the prostate was unchanged by candicidin in the diet. The weight of the ventral prostate was also reduced (33%) as a result of the candicidin treatment. Unlike that of the dorsolateral lobe of the rat prostate gland, the HMG-CoA-reductase levels of the ventral lobe are under testosterone regulation since with castration the conversion of acetate to cholesterol is primarily inhibited [40]. The conversion of mevalonate, however, is not affected by testosterone. It appears that the levels of HMG-CoA-reductase are not influenced by hypocholesterolemic drugs which primarily interfere with cholesterol absorption-resorption in the gastrointestinal tract. The ventral prostate of the rat thus lacks both negative and positive regulation of cholesterol synthesis in spite of the fact that its rate of synthesis is much greater than that of the liver.

Synthetic drugs which are known to inhibit the synthesis of cholesterol have also been employed in rat prostate studies. Clofibrate [ethyl 2-(4-chlorophenoxy)-2-methyl propionate] was shown [62] to inhibit the synthesis of cholesterol and lower its content in the ventral prostate of hamsters. In other studies [67] the effect of clofibrate on cholesterol and DNA synthesis in the rat ventral prostate was determined. The results presented in Table VIII reveal that there were no significant differences in the body and prostate weights between control and 0.3% dietary clofibrate-treated rats after 2,3,4 and 10 weeks. The serum cholesterol levels in the clofibrate-treated rats decreased approximately by 36% of the average for all control groups. The concentration of cholesterol in the liver on the unit weight basis decreased to about 80% in all groups. The total cholesterol and DNA content in the prostate was reduced approximately on the average by 27% and 28%, respectively, in all groups.

The effect of clofibrate on the rates of synthesis of liver cholesterol, prostate cholesterol, and prostate DNA was also investigated, A summary of results is presented in Table IX and reveals that liver cholesterol synthesis was reduced to about 25–40% of its control value between 14 and 70 days of clofibrate treatment. The prostate cholesterol synthesis decreased to about 75% after 14 days of treatment whereas between 21 and 70 days the synthesis in the ventral prostate followed a similar pattern. The synthesis of DNA was reduced to approximately 80% after 14 days of clofibrate treatment, and between 21 and 70 days the rate of synthesis remained constant at 30–40% of control values.

The effect of clofibrate by oral route on the histopathology of the rat ventral prostate was also determined. The microscopic section (Fig. 9) of a prostate

TABLE VIII. Effect of oral clofibrate treatment on the body weight, prostate weight, total prostate cholesterol, and the levels of DNA, liver cholesterol, and serum cholesterol of normal rats

Treatment period (days)	Group	Body weight (gm)	Prostate weight (mg)[a]	Total prostate cholesterol (μg)[a]	Total prostate DNA (μg)[a]	Liver cholesterol conc. (mg/gm of tissue)	Serum cholesterol (μg/100 μl)
14	Control	332 ± 4	105.0 ± 10.1	317.0 ± 21.7	301.0 ± 15.7	5.43 ± .30	95.5 ± 5.2
	Clofibrate	328 ± 9	95.4 ± 7.7	223.0** ± 12.1	209.0*** ± 6.7	4.48* ± .18	61.5*** ± 2.6
21	Control	350 ± 5	108.0 ± 5.5	326.0 ± 11.7	333.0 ± 15.4	5.11 ± .17	105.0 ± 5.9
	Clofibrate	343 ± 13	114.0 ± 5.9	288.0** ± 2.7	265.0** ± 9.1	4.24* ± .09	68.3*** ± 4.7
28	Control	376 ± 6	110.0 ± 6.2	326.0 ± 10.7	359.0 ± 16.9	5.46 ± .08	105.0 ± 0.6
	Clofibrate	385 ± 9	84.2 ± 9.1	238.0*** ± 11.6	245.0*** ± 12.0	4.59* ± .21	58.3*** ± 1.8
70	Control	475 ± 15	122.0 ± 7.4	343.0 ± 10.1	352.0 ± 22.5	5.29 ± .11	122.0 ± 1.1
	Clofibrate	490 ± 15	113.0 ± 5.9	246.0*** ± 6.2	243.0** ± 11.4	4.32* ± .22	85.5*** ± 2.4

All the values are obtained from groups of 6–8 rats.

[a]Prostate weights, prostate cholesterol, and DNA contents are expressed as mean ± SE/100 gm body weight.

*$P < 0.05$.

**$P < 0.01$.

***$P < 0.001$.

From Singhal, Brill, and Schaffner [67].

TABLE IX. Effect of oral clofibrate treatment on the rate of synthesis of liver cholesterol, prostate cholesterol, and DNA in normal rats

Treatment period (days)	Group	Rate of synthesis (cpm/gm/tissue) × 10^5		
		Liver cholesterol	Prostate cholesterol	Prostate DNA
14	Control	0.78 ± 0.08	2.59 ± 0.09	2.31 ± 0.15
	Clofibrate	0.33 ± 0.07*	1.90 ± 0.11**	1.89 ± 0.18
21	Control	1.38 ± 0.16	6.47 ± 0.79	2.78 ± 0.21
	Clofibrate	0.36 ± 0.19*	2.15 ± 0.24**	1.19 ± 0.17**
28	Control	1.06 ± 0.23	5.31 ± 0.44	2.79 ± 0.20
	Clofibrate	0.25 ± 0.04*	2.51 ± 0.35**	0.82 ± 0.14**
70	Control	0.96 ± 0.04	6.73 ± 0.06	2.43 ± 0.16
	Clofibrate	0.36 ± 0.02**	2.79 ± 0.22**	0.99 ± 0.06**

All the values are obtained from groups of 6–8 rats and expressed as mean ± SE.
*$P < 0.01$.
**$P < 0.001$.
From Singhal, Brill, and Schaffner [67].

taken from a 20-week-old rat of the control group reveals the typical epithelial infolding of the acinus usually seen after 12 weeks of age in the normal male Wistar rat where a significant increase of cholesterol synthesis is also noted. A microscopic section (Fig. 10) of a ventral prostate taken from a 20-week-old rat of the clofibrate group reveals a remarkable absence of the epithelial infolding of the acinus. Clofibrate treatment obviously affects the morphology of the prostate gland as it reduces the rate of cholesterogenesis. Whether this effect of dietrary clofibrate is mediated through some direct influence on androgen metabolism remains to be determined.

Hypolipdemia produced by feeding a related drug, simfibrate [1,3-propyl-bis(2-p-chlorophenoxy)-2-methyl propionate], for 3 weeks was also shown [68] to reduce in parallel with the cholesterol content of the prostate the responses to testosterone adminstration of weight gain and nucleic acid content in the ventral prostates of castrated rats. When clofibrate-treated, castrated rats were injected with testosterone, the prostate weight, the contents and synthesis of cholesterol and DNA were also shown [67] to be reduced as compared to those seen in control castrated rats treated with testosterone. These results indicate that the inhibition of cholesterol synthesis interferes with the testosterone-dependent proliferation of the prostate gland in the castrated rats. The effect of such inhibitors of cholesterol synthesis on the human prostate gland and its diseases remains to be determined.

Aside from the hypocholesterolemic polyene macrolides a variety of other lipid-lowering drugs have also been reported to affect human prostatic diseases.

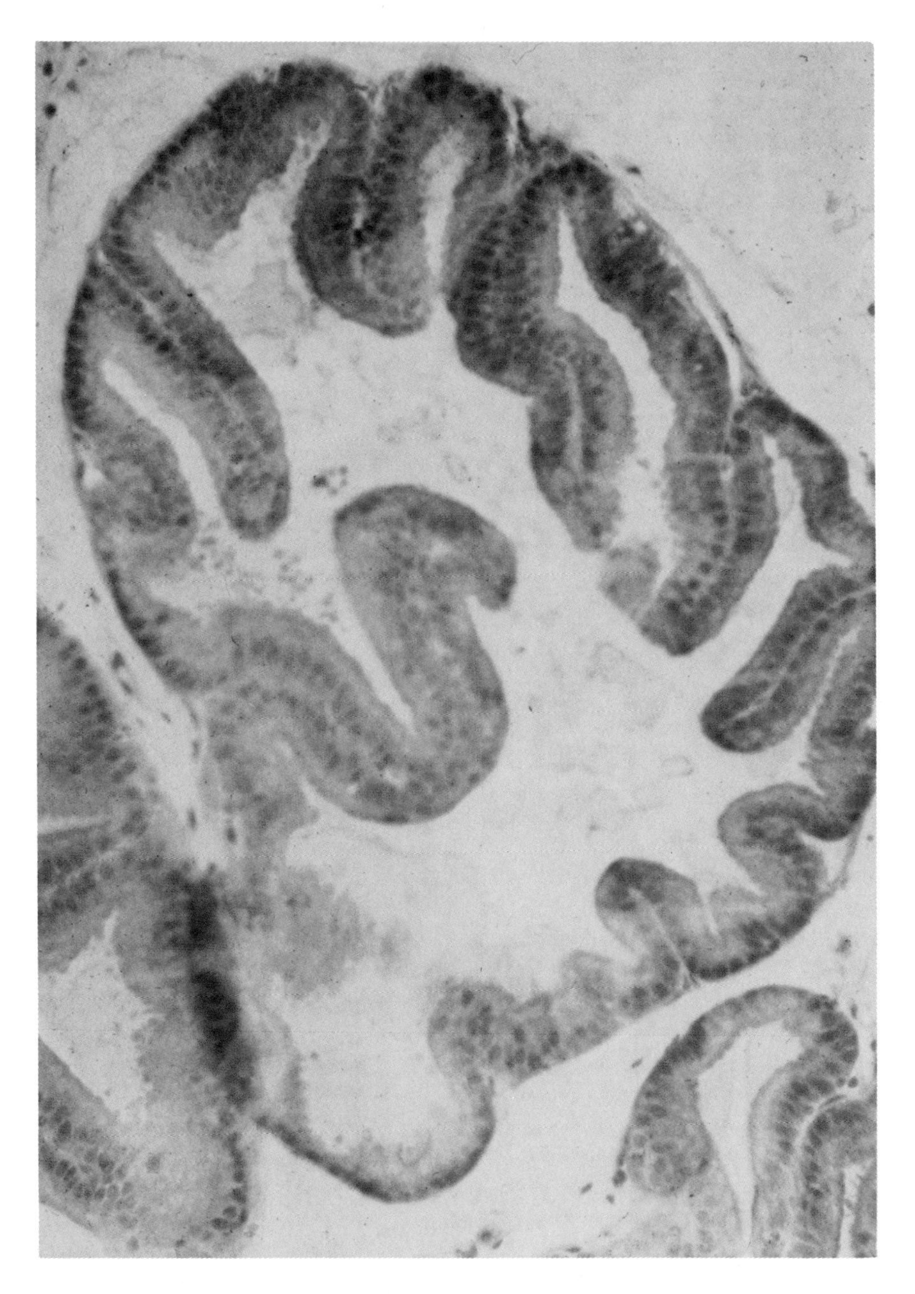

Fig. 9. Microscopic section of a ventral prostate gland from 20-week-old normal rat. Hematoxylin and eosin; × 160. From Singhal, Brill, and Schaffner [67].

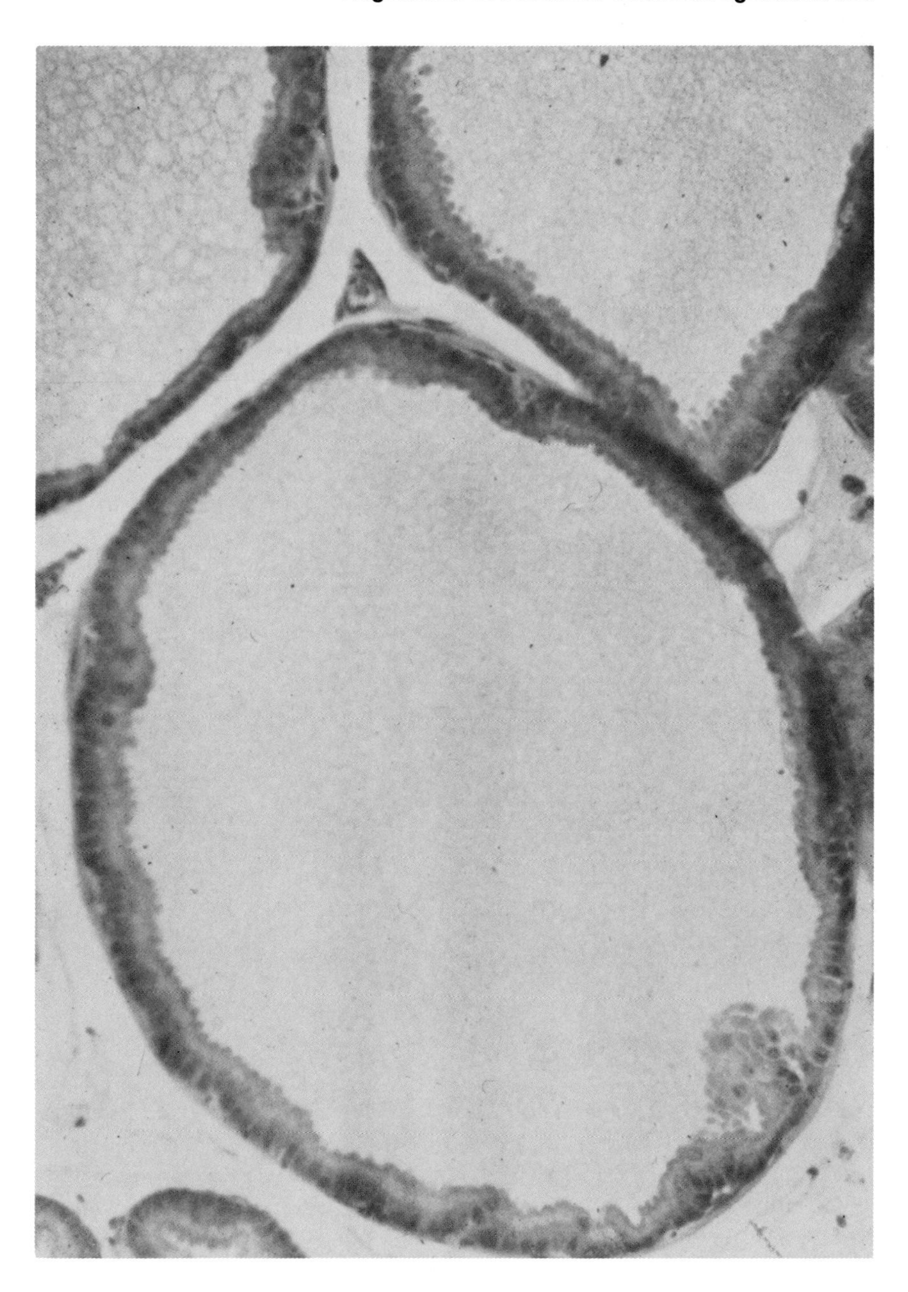

Fig. 10. Microscopic section of a prostate gland from 20-week-old rat after oral administration of clofibrate for 10 weeks. Hematoxylin and eosin; × 160. From Singhal, Brill, and Schaffner [67].

The cholesterol-lowering drug, beta sitosterol, has been in clinical use in Germany based on studies [69,70] dealing with its effect on human benign prostatic hypertrophy. The nonabsorbable sterol of plant origin also interferes with the absorption-resportion of cholesterol in the gastrointestinal tract but in a rather nonspecific manner.

The bile acid sequestering anion exchange resin, cholestyramine, which is chemically related to colestipol, has also been reported [13] for its clinical effect on prostatic carcinoma. Regressions of the course of the disease were noted in several patients who were originally treated for hyperlipidemia with cholestyramine. It is also interesting to note that other investigators [71] soon thereafter evaluated the possible anti-androgenic effect of oral cholestyramine in rats as a possible explanation for its reported antitumor effect in humans. Significant differences in ventral and dorsolateral prostate weights were noted in a group of rats treated with oral cholestyramine for one month. As a measure of anti-androgenic action the arginase activity of the prostate tissues was also determined. Some reduction in arginase activity was noted in the ventral prostate and to a greater degree in the dorsolateral prostate. Nevertheless it was concluded that oral cholestyramine had minimal anti-androgenic and antiprostatic effects. In comparison to the effect of more active anti-androgenic drugs the action of cholestyramine appeared uninteresting. The direct effect of cholestyramine on the lipid levels of the rat prostate tissues, however, at that time was not determined. It is thus conceivable that any antitumor effect of oral cholestyramine on prostatic carcinoma may be more directly related to its lipid-lowering effects than to any direct effect on andogen metabolism. Also, cholesterol and lipids in general have often been implicated in the neoplastic process. In one particular study [72] the investigators observed that a cholesterol-free, fat-free diet retarded the growth of solid Sarcoma 180 in mice and prolonged the survivial time of mice bearing either the solid or ascitic form. Similar tumor-retarding effects were noted with the Ehrlich carcinoma and adenocarcinoma 755 in mice and the Novikoff hepatoma in rats. In addition, a number of hypocholesterolemic agents that exert a blocking action at different points in the cholesterol biosynthetic pathway also retarded the growth of these transplantable tumors.

It is thus apparent that the hypocholesterolemic drugs in general are useful agents for the study of cholesterol metabolism of the prostate gland both in its normal and disease states. The variety of hypocholesterolemic drugs tested all appear to exert some specific effect on prostatic cholesterogenesis. The inhibitors of cholesterol synthesis whether they act directly on some step in the pathway of cholesterogenesis (clofibrate) or indirectly as through the inhibition of protein (cycloheximide) or RNA (actinomycin D) synthesis, all appear to decrease endogenous cholesterol synthesis in the prostate gland. Likewise, inhibitors of cholesterol absorption-resorption in the enterohepatic circulation also lower the cholesterol content of the prostate gland. The latter process apparently takes place more slowly since it is dependent on the overall lowering of the body cholesterol pool. The effects of hypocholesterolemic drugs on benign prostatic hyperplasia and prostatic carcinoma may be worthy of further clinical investigation.

CHOLESTEROL METABOLITES IN THE PROSTATE EPOXYCHOLESTEROLS

In the course of gas liquid chromatographic analyses of cholesterol in lipid extracts of human prostate tissue another sterol component more polar than cholesterol was generally detected (Fig. 11) in minor quantities, particularly in specimens taken from older males diagnosed as suffering with benign prostatic hyperplasia (BPH) or prostatic carcinoma (CA). This sterol was not seen in the lipid extracts of tissue taken from young normal males. After isolation by thin-layer chromatography (TLC) this minor sterol component was identified by mass spectrometric analysis to be cholesterol epoxide, a product formed by the addition of a single oxygen atom to the double bond of the cholesterol molecule.

In a specific study [73] designed to ascertain the presence of this cholesterol metabolite in the prostate gland with age, samples were taken either during surgery or at autopsy from the prostates of 49 individuals ranging in age from 17 to 85 years. After histopathological examination followed by lyophilization and lipid extraction, the crude lipid mixture was fractionated into various lipid classes by TLC procedures. The sterol-containing fraction after conversion to

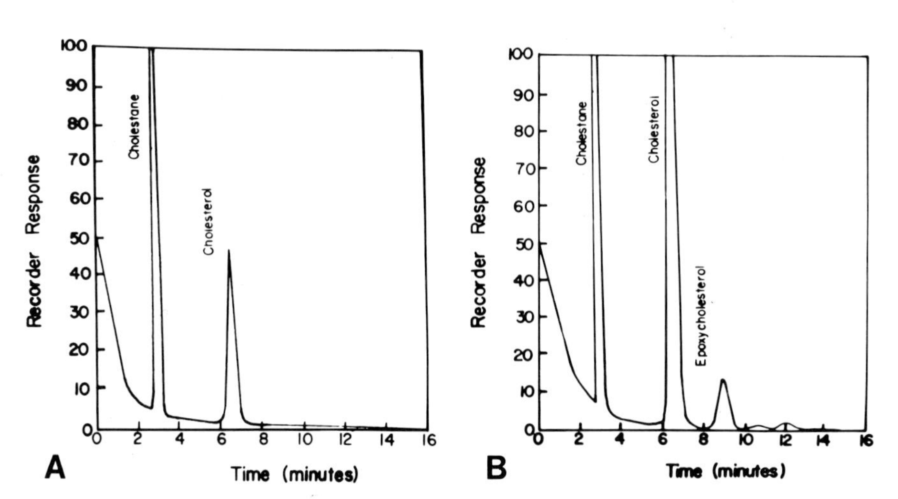

Fig. 11. Gas liquid chromatographic analysis of human prostate sterols. Cholesterol and epoxycholesterol were separated as TMS ethers. 5α-cholestane served as an internal standard. A. 19-Year-old subject. B. 83-year-old subject. From Schaffner, Brill, and Singhal [73].

TABLE X. Cholesterol and epoxycholesterol content of human prostate tissues

No. of specimens	Age range (years)	Histopathology	Cholesterol (mg/gm dry tissue)	Epoxycholesterol (μg/gm dry tissue)
12	19–42	normal	10.2 ± 2.0	0
3	44–53	normal	7.5 ± 2.3	31.1 ± 18.2
21	45–83	BPH	18.2 ± 4.0	150.4 ± 28.6
13	61–90	BPH-CA	21.1 ± 5.4	170.6 ± 40.8

Histopathological studies were carried out with paraffin sections stained with eosin and hematoxylin. Gas liquid chromatographic analyses of cholesterol and epoxycholesterol as TMS ethers were carried out on a 3.0% SE-30 column (4 ft × 3mm) operated at 245°C with nitrogen carrier gas. Injection and detector temperatures were maintained at 265°C. Flame ionization detectors were employed. The internal standard was 5α-cholestane.
From Schaffner, Brill, and Singhal [73].

trimethylsilyl (TMS) ethers was further separated by gas liquid chromatography and the components detected and measured by flame ionization. The results given in Table X summarizes the quantity of cholesterol and cholesterol epoxide directly measured in the prostatic tissues of the different human subjects. For the 12 individuals in the 19–42 year age group, characterized as having normal prostate glands, the observed cholesterol content is within normal limits. No epoxycholesterol was detected. In 3 individuals at 44, 50, and 53 years of age and exhibiting normal histopathology, the observed cholesterol content was also within normal limits. However, a small quantity of epoxycholesterol was detected as well. In the sampling of prostate tissues of 21 individuals characterized histopathologically as suffering with BPH, the cholesterol content is seen to be significantly elevated, and the measured amount of epoxycholesterol approaches 1% of the total sterol level. In the 13 prostate specimens taken from individuals shown histopathologically as suffering with BPH and CA the cholesterol content was also shown to be elevated. The level of epoxycholesterol detected also approached 1% of the total sterol content. Epoxycholesterol was uniformly detected in all specimens of prostate tissue diagnosed histopathologically as BPH or CA. It is further interesting to note that the cholesterol epoxide detected in the human prostate gland appears to be unesterified, suggesting that it is derived from the endogeneous free cholesterol of the gland and its secretion.

In the presence of molecular oxygen and light cholesterol readily autoxidizes to form intermediate, chemically labile hydroperoxides which decompose into a number of secondary products. Fioriti and Sims [74] were among the first to report the appearance of cholesterol 5α, 6α-epoxide in heat-treated cholesterol or in cholesterol stored in the presence of air for years. Smith and Kulig [75] likewise reported the formation of the isomeric cholesterol 5α, 6α-epoxide and cholesterol 5β, 6β-epoxide in the relative proportions of 1:8 and 1:11 when cholesterol was treated with sterol hydroperoxides. Similar proportions of the epoxycholesterols were observed [76] in dried egg products. Hence, it appears evident that in the autoxidation of cholesterol, a greater proportion of cholesterol 5β, 6β-epoxide is produced than of the corresponding alpha isomer.

In the gas liquid chromatographic procedure [73] employed for the detection of epoxycholesterol in lipid extracts of human prostate tissues, no direct resolution of the isomeric cholesterol oxides could be achieved. Nevertheless, a suitable TLC method [77] was employed to separate the isomers directly as TMS ethers. Here it was revealed that the usual proportions of alpha to beta isomers obtained on autoxidation were not present in the prostate tissues. The relative content of the alpha isomer was significantly increased. In more recent studies [78] the epoxycholesterol contents of human prostatic secretion taken prior to surgery and of the respective isomers in prostate tissue taken during surgery were determined. Here it was seen that as much as a tenfold increase of the alpha isomer over the beta isomer was to be found in the aged human prostate when a capillary gas liquid chromatographic technique was applied for the separation of the isomeric epoxycholesterols. The level of the alpha isomer was particularly elevated when the tissues were diagnosed histopathologically as BPH and CA. These findings suggest that the epoxycholesterols in the human prostate gland are formed by some biochemical mechanism other than by simple autoxidation of cholesterol with molecular oxygen.

Considering the results of the cholesterol and epoxycholesterol studies with the human prostate gland reported here, it is especially interesting to note that Petrakis [79] initially developed a biologic model that related epidemiologic evidence for an association of reproductive experience with risk of breast cancer to findings of the fact that exogenously derived substances are secreted into breast fluid. Later studies [80] applying the Ames Salmonella mutagenesis test [81] to nipple aspirates of breast fluid of 456 women detected a significant percentage (6.7%) of positive reactions. These results supported the hypothesis that mutagenic substances reach the breast epithelia, with etiological implications for the development of benign disease and cancer of the breast. More recent studies [82,83] subsequently determined the cholesterol and cholesterol-α-epoxide levels in nipple aspirates of breast fluid from nonpregnant women, employing both gas-liquid chromatographic and mass spectrometric procedures. Cholesterol levels in breast fluid were found to be elevated above plasma levels and showed progressive increases with advancing age, averaging 187 mg %, 1957 mg %, and 3554 mg % in women of age groups 20–29, 30–39, and 40–49 years, respectively. Both cholesterol 5β,6β-epoxide and cholesterol 5α,6α-epoxide were also detected in a significant number of women exhibiting elevated cholesterol levels in breast fluid. It was thus postulated that these findings may be a significant factor in the pathogenesis of benign and malignant diseases of the female breast.

The possible role of cholesterol and its secondary oxidation products in carcinogenesis has long been a controversial topic of discussion. Earlier investigation [84] revealed the production of sarcomas and other tumors when cholesterol and cholesterol epoxides were administered subcutaneously to rats and mice. A series of other studies [85–88] utilizing the skin of humans and hairless mice revealed the dose-dependent formation of cholesterol 5α,6α-epoxide after ultraviolet irradiation. It was postulated that the formation of skin tumors was related to the formation of this suspected carcinogen with ultraviolet exposure. The reported [89] angiotoxicity of oxygenated sterols and not cholesterol itself may play the primary role in arterial wall damage and the development of atherosclerotic lesions. These observations hold particular significance in light of the earlier findings [90] that cholesterol 5α,6α-epoxide is present in signficant quantities in human serum particularly when serum cholesterol levels are elevated as in the case of familial hypercholesterolemia.

Although cholesterol 5α,6α-epoxide has been shown to be nonmutagenic in the Ames test by other investigators [91,92], it is possible that other factors such as poor solubility and membrane penetrability in bacteria might be responsible for the lack of activity. Bacteria are known for their lack of structural sterols. In human fibroblasts Parsons and Goss [93] demonstrated that cholesterol-α-oxide induced a similar degree of increased chromosome damage and DNA repair synthesis as low doses of ultraviolet light but did not produce single-strand DNA breaks or DNA damage detectable by inhibition of thymidine incorporation. It was also interesting to note that chromosomal aberrations with this cholesterol oxide were detected up to 8 weeks after treatment. In other studies [94] it was likewise demonstrated that cholesterol 5α,6α-epoxide forms a strong physical complex with calf thymus DNA which, on incubation, leads to a significant amount of covalent attachment of steroid to DNA. Attempts at subjecting the cholesterol oxide here to the Ames test showed it to be sufficiently cytotoxic to preclude evaluation of its mutagenicity.

Kelsey and Pienta [95] reported that cholesterol-α-oxide and not cholesterol was able to transform hamster embryo cells in tissue culture. They found the oxide to be as potent an agent as the well-known carcinogen, 3-methylcholanthrene. They likewise found lithocholic acid to be significantly active in transforming the hamster cells. Lithocholic acid, known as a major fecal bile acid resulting from the bacterial metabolism of chenodeoxycholic acid, is also implicated in colon carcinogenesis. The results presented in this study were the first examples of in vitro cell transformation activity by cholesterol oxidation products possibly important in the etiology of cancer. Other studies [96] in germ-free rats indicated that lithocholic acid without further modification by gut microflora acts as a colon tumor promoter in the presence of the carcinogen, N-methyl-N′-nitro-N-nitrosoguanidine. It is possible that cholesterol epoxides may share a similar role in the human prostate gland.

The exact formation and metabolic fate of the epoxycholesterols in the human prostate gland and its secretions are still obscure and obviously need further study. The studies in the human male prostate [73,78] and in the female breast [82,83], however, both suggest some other mechanism for epoxycholesterol formation than simple autoxidation. In contrast to what is found in the human prostate, studies in rats [77] concerning the synthesis of these metabolities of cholesterol in liver subcellular fractions revealed the formation of the β-epoxide in 3–4-fold excess over the α-epoxide. These epoxides are formed by a microsomal NADPH-dependent lipid peroxidation system. The results also indicated that epoxidation in the rat liver seems to occur only in connection with the nonspecific tissue oxidation of sterols. Both cholesterol epoxides were also efficiently converted by a liver microsomal hydrolase to cholestan-3β,5α,6β-triol. From results of other studies [97,98] cholesterol 5α-6α-epoxide is likewise readily transformed in the gastrointestinal tract of the rat to cholestan-3β,5α,6β-triol which is largely excreted as such in the feces. In mice [99] cholesterol 5α,6α-epoxide is mainly excreted intact in the feces, perhaps relating to differences in the level of available hydrases. Increases in the amount of cholesterol oxide in the tissues of the rat lung were not observed [100] to correlate with cholesterol epoxide hydrase levels. It is thus very evident that the observed level of cholesterol epoxide hydrase activity is very tissue specific. Many tissues contain cholesterol oxides which appear to be controlled by hydrases. The unavailability of hydrases may account for the accumulation of cholesterol oxides.

In humans, aside from the female breast and male prostate gland, epoxycholesterol accumulation has been observed [101] in tissues of patients affected by Wolman's disease. Here it is postulated that cholesteryl ester hydrolase deficiency in patients with this disease might lead to the accumulation of oxygenated sterol esters in the tissues not seen in normal controls. Cholesterol 5α,6α-epoxide has long been implicted as an etiologic agent in human colon cancer. The epoxide is generally metabolized [102] by human intestinal microflora to cholestan-3β,5α,6β-triol. The presence of microbial epoxide hydrase activity in the human colon resembles that of the other animal species. Cholesterol-α-epoxide level is suggested as a biochemical marker in studies of normal and high-risk colon cancer populations in order to identify susceptible individuals. It is conceivable that a measure of this suspected carcinogen in the prostatic fluid or semen of humans may also serve as a possible risk factor for benign and malignant prostate diseases.

Considering the possible role of the cholesterol oxides in the etiology of cancer, it is well known that spontaneous transformations of cell lines in tissue or organ culture can take place. Fraley and Ecker [103] observed spontaneous in vitro neoplastic transformation in tissue culture of epithelial cells derived from a benign human prostatic adenoma containing glandular hyperplasia. Heidelberger reported [104] on the spontaneous transformation of cell lines derived from dispersed organ cultures of mouse ventral prostate. Other studies [105,106] involved the in vitro induction of a malignant transformation with mouse prostate organ cultures employing the carcinogenic hydrocarbons, methylcholanthrene and 9,10-dimethyl-1,2-benzanthracene. In general, aromatic and olefinic compounds can be metabolized by mammalian microsomal mono-oxygenases to electrophilically reactive epoxides, which are believed to be the mutagenically active species [107,108]. Simultaneous topical application of an inhibitor of epoxide hydratase with 3-methylcholanthrene was shown [109] to stimulate 3-methylcholanthrene-induced tumor formation, indicating that the epoxide derivative is the mutagenically active species.

The fact that cholesterol epoxides, and particularly cholesterol 5α,6α-epoxide, accumulate along with cholesterol in the aging human prostate gland may be related in some way to the development of benign prostatic hyperplasia and prostatic carcinoma. The marked cytotoxic properties of cholesterol 5α,6α-epoxide at levels lower than seen in the prostate gland and its secretion may indeed be responsible for the atrophy of glandular epithelium associated with benign hyperplastic disease. Since these metabolites appear in the prostatic fluid, they are in close contact with the epithelial cells of the prostatic acini. The lack of protective hydrases obviously might be related to the fact that these cholesterol oxides accumulate in the prostate. Apparently this accumulation correlates very well with the incidence of benign and malignant prostate diseases. In considering the many studies attempting to link the cholesterol oxides to carcinogenesis, it obviously is important to study further the formation, metabolic fate, and role of these metabolities of cholesterol in the human prostate gland.

CONCLUSIONS

The primary need to explain the mode of action of a hypocholesterolemic agent such as a polyene macrolide antibiotic on the benign enlargement of the canine and human prostate gland motivated the investigations into the nature, synthesis, catabolism, and general role of cholesterol in the prostate gland. Since the polyene macrolides generally are not absorbed from the gastrointestinal tract and primarily exert their hypocholesterolemic effect by inhibiting cholesterol absorption-resorption, the effect of the body cholesterol pool on cholesterol metabolism in the prostate gland was an obvious consideration. The earlier observations of Swyer [5] had indicated that the cholesterol levels in human prostatic adenoma were double that of normal prostate tissue. In studying further the nature of cholesterol in the normal human prostate and in its disease states of benign prostatic hyperplasia and carcinoma, it became more evident that cholesterol and its metabolites may play some role in the etiology of these important human diseases.

In order to understand the nature of cholesterol synthesis in the prostate, a number of studies were carried out in experimental animals. In rat ventral prostate a unique dependence of cholesterol synthesis on intact testicular function, or testosterone specifically, was discovered. Normal synthesis of cholesterol in the prostate also appeared to be several times greater than in the liver, the organ generally considered a major site for cholesterogenesis. In spite of this elevated rate of synthesis, the rat ventral prostate apparently exhibits no negative and little positive feedback control of cholesterol synthesis. Dietary cholesterol fails to decrease cholesterol synthesis in the rat ventral prostate as it does in the liver. Inhibitors of cholesterol and bile acid absorption-resorption in the gastrointestinal tract produce only minor increases, if any, in prostatic cholesterogenesis. Inhibitors of cholesterol synthesis clearly reduce prostate synthesis. It is particularly interesting to note that changes in cholesterol synthesis in rat ventral prostate due to these drugs coincide with alterations in prostatic epithelial histology. Changes in cholesterogenesis, mediated through the rate-limiting enzyme, β-hydroxy-β-methylglutaryl-coenzyme A-reductase, are apparently hormone dependent.

It is thus conceivable that the increase in cholesterol content seen in human prostatic diseases may be related to a variety of factors including increased body cholesterol pools, decreased elimination of secretory cholesterol, or increased cholesterogenesis mediated through changes in hormone levels. Hypocholesterolemic drugs thus affect the cholesterol levels of the prostate gland either by lowering the body cholesterol pool or by inhibiting cholesterogenesis. None appear to act as inhibitors of testicular function. Studies in the BIO 87.20 male Syrian hamster, exhibiting age-dependent cystic prostatic hypertrophy, clearly indicated that different hypocholesterolemic agents altered the disease process. Cholesterol levels in the ventral prostate were lowered, and no direct effect on the testes could be seen. It was further interesting to note that this particular hamster line also lacks negative feedback control of cholesterogenesis in the prostate as well as in the liver which is considered to be a major metabolic defect. The lack of adequate control of cholesterol metabolism may be directly related to this prostatic disease, giving some rationale to the effect of hypocholesterolemic drugs in this animal disease model.

Virtually little or nothing is known about the exact etiology and natural history of human benign prostatic hyperplasia and carcinoma. There has been considerable debate [110–113] as to whether the prostatic cancer arises de nova from normal prostatic cells or whether the benign hyperplastic epithelial cells serve as an intermediate stage of development. Some results from tissue culture studies [103] support the latter hypothesis. Nevertheless, it is quite evident that human benign prostate disease involves the periuretheral zone of the gland where glandular cholesterogenesis takes place whereas prostatic carcinoma primarily involves the peripheral zone.

Some viral involvement in the etiology of prostatic carcinoma is certainly well documented. Animal and human prostate cells have been transformed to neoplastic cells by viruses. In one study [114] hamster prostatic tissue was transformed in vitro with SV40, a DNA oncogenic virus. Differentiated tumors were produced when these transformed cells were introduced to living animals. The cytomegaloviruses have also been implicated in prostatic carcinoma. A human genital isolate of cytomegalovirus was shown [115] to have transformed human embryonic lung cells in vitro. These cells also produced tumors when injected into athymic nude mice. Cell lines derived from human prostatic carcinoma tissues also contained cytomegaloviral specific membrane antigens.

The appearance of the epoxycholesterols in the tissues and secretions of the human prostate gland with aging and particularly with the development of benign and malignant diseases might be of fundamental importance in the etiology of these diseases. The number of studies implicating these cholesterol metabolites with carcinogenesis is ever increasing. It is of particular significance that the epoxycholesterols have been recently also observed in the female breast secretions. Both the breast and the prostate are glandular secretory organs producing cholesterol among other functions which are hormonal regulated. Both organs are also very prone to the increasing incidence of benign and malignant disease with increasing age, when the increase in glandular cholesterol and appearance of epoxycholesterols takes place. In the benign hyperplastic process it is conceivable that since the cytotoxic epoxycholesterols appear in the prostatic secretion, they are also responsible for the atrophy of glandular epithelium with subsequent regeneration mediated through continuing testicular function.

The fact that cholesterol 5α, 6α-epoxide will transform hamster embryo cells in tissue culture is of great importance, suggesting that these particular cells lack hydrases which would efficiently degrade the epoxides. In attempts to transform mammalian cell lines with cholesterol 5α, 6α-epoxide, it would appear to be important whether or not hydrases were present. Consistant with a viral etiology of prostatic carcinoma it is conceivable that the epoxycholesterols might serve as promotors or co-carcinogenic agents in the process. It is well documented [116–119] that there is frequent existence of "latent" or "occult" prostatic carcinoma found during autopsies performed in individuals who have died from causes other than cancer. After the fifth decade of life the level of these "latent" carcinomas in the prostate gland becomes most significant. It is conceivable that the epoxycholesterols also play some role in this process.

Considering that the cholesterol epoxides are present at rather elevated levels in the prostatic secretion and subsequently in the semen of individuals suffering from benign and malignant prostate diseases, it is also interesting to speculate as to their possible effect on the sperm and in the female partner. It is known that birth defects increase in later-life conceptions and that the incidence of uterine and cervical carcinomas also increases in women whose male partners suffer with prostatic carcinoma. Through epidemioloical studies cholesterol in the diet has also been long implicated in the etiology of prostate, breast, and colon cancer. It is interesting to speculate further as to whether all three diseases may have a common etiological agent—namely, cholesterol 5α, 6α-epoxide.

REFERENCES

1. Siperstein MD, Fagan VM: Deletion of the cholesterol-negative feedback system in liver tumors. Cancer Res 24:1108–1115, 1964.
2. Siperstein MD: Regulation of cholesterol biosynthesis in normal and malignant tissues. Curr Top Cellular Reg 2:65–100, 1970.
3. Chen HW, Kandutsch AA, Heiniger HJ, Meier H: Elevated sterol synthesis in lymphocytic leukemia cells from two inbred strains of mice. Cancer Res 33:2774–2778, 1973.
4. Chen HW, Heiniger HJ: Stimulation of sterol synthesis in peripheral leukocytes with leukemic mice. Cancer Res 34:1304–1307, 1974.
5. Swyer GI: The cholesterol content of normal and enlarged prostates. Cancer Res 2:372–375, 1942.
6. Gordon HW, Schaffner CP: The effect of the polyene macrolides on the prostate gland and canine prostatic hyperplasia. Proc Natl Acad Sci USA 60:1201–1208, 1968.
7. Wang GM, Schaffner CP: Effect of candicidin and colestipol on the testes and prostate glands of BIO 87.20 hamsters. Invest Urol 14:66–71, 1976.
8. Casella G: Terapia medica dell'adenoma prostatico. La Chirurgia Generale 19:1–43, 1970.
9. Keshin JG: Effect of candicidin on the human hypertrophied prostate gland. Int Surg 58:116–122, 1973.
10. Kljucharev BV, Mikhailets GA, Berman NA, Ivanov NM, Margolin AM: Therapeutic action of levorin in adenoma of the prostate. Urologiia i Nefrologiia (Moscow) 38:40–43, 1973.
11. Orkin LA: Efficacy of candicidin in benign prostatic hypertrophy. Urology 4:80–84, 1974.
12. Sporer A, Cohen S, Kamat MH, Seeboda JJ: Candicidin: physiological effect on prostate. Urology 6:298–305, 1975.
13. Addleman W: Cancer, cholesterol and cholestyramine. N Engl J Med 287:1047, 1972.
14. Thompson H: In: "The Diseases of the Prostate." Philadelphia: HC Lea, 1873, p. 308.
15. Posner C, Scheffer W: Beiträge zur klinischen mikroskopie und mikrophotographie. Berl Klin Woch 46:254–257, 1909.
16. Plenge C: Über lipoide und pigmente der prostata des menschen. Virchow's Arch Pathol Anat 253:665–678, 1924.
17. Fürbringer P: Untersuchungen über die herkunft und klinische bedeutung der sogen. Spermakrystalle nebst bemerkungen über die componenten des menschlichen samens und die prostatorrhöe. Ztschr Klin Med 3:287–316, 1881.
18. Goldblatt MW: Constituents of human seminal plasma. Biochem J 29:1346–1357, 1935.
19. Eliasson R: Cholesterol in human semen. Biochem J 98:242–243, 1966.
20. Miyao N: Male accessory sexual organs and lipid. I. Cholesterol and phospholipid in the prostatic secretion and tissue. Acta Urol Jpn 11:1197–1202, 1965.
21. Moon KH, Bunge RG: Observations on the biochemistry of human semen. 4. Cholesterol. Fertil Steril 21:80–83, 1970.
22. Scott WW: The lipids of the prostatic fluid, seminal plasma, and enlarged prostate gland of man. J Urol 53:712–718, 1945.
23. Acevedo HF, Campbell EA, Hayeslip DW, Gilmore J, Merkow LP, Frich Jr JC, Grauer RC: Urinary Cholesterol IV. Its excretion in women with neoplasms of the genital system. Obstet Gynecol 37:425–436, 1971.
24. Acevedo HF, Campbell EA, Saier EI, Frich Jr JC, Merkow LP, Hayeslip DW, Bartok SP,

Grauer RC, Hamilton JL: Urinary cholesterol V. Its excretion in men with testicular and prostatic neoplasms. Cancer 32:196–205, 1973.
25. Acevedo HF, Campbell EA: Urinary cholesterol III. Its excretion as a protein bound complex. Steroids 16:569–577, 1970.
26. Anderson RU, Fair WR: Physical and chemical determinations of prostatic secretions in benign hyperplasia, prostatitis, and adenocarcinoma. Invest Urol 14:137–140, 1976.
27. Braunstein H: Staining lipid in carcinoma of the prostate gland. Am J Clin Pathol 41:44–48, 1964.
28. Schultz A: Eine methode des mikrochemische cholesterinnachweises am gewebschnitt. Centralbl f allg Path u Path Anat 35:314–317, 1924–25.
29. Mallouh C, Goldstein NL, Keshin JG, Pellman CM, Schaffner CP: Cholesterol in the prostate I: Qualitative and quantitative analysis—clinical implications. Abstr 71st Annual Meeting, American Urological Association, May 17–20, 1976.
30. Goldstein NI: Cholesterol synthesis in the prostate gland and its relationship to benign prostatic hyperplasia. Ph.D. Dissertation, Rutgers University, New Brunswick, New Jersey, 1975.
31. Singhal AK: Cholesterol metabolism and its regulation in rat ventral prostate. Ph.D. Dissertation, Rutgers University, New Brunswick, New Jersey, 1978.
32. Baulieu EE, Lasnitzki I, Robel P: Metabolism of testosterone and action of metabolites on prostate glands grown in organ culture. Nature 219:1155–1156, 1974.
33. Robel P, Lasnitzki I, Baulieu EE: Hormone metabolism and action: Testosterone and metabolites in prostate organ culture. Biochimie 53:81–96, 1971.
34. Baulieu EE, Le Goascogne C, Groyer A, Feyel-Cabanes T, Robel P: Morphological and biochemical parameters of androgen effects on rat ventral prostate in organ culture. Vitam Horm 33:1–38, 1975.
35. Coffey DS, Shimazaki J, Williams-Ashman HG: Polymerization of deoxyribonucleotides in relation to androgen-induced prostatic growth. Arch Biochem Biophys 124:184–198, 1968.
36. Liao S, Leininger KR, Sagher D, Barton RW: Rapid effect of testosterone on ribonucleic acid polymerase activity on rat ventral prostate. Endocrinology 77:763–765, 1965.
37. Liang T, Liao S: A very rapid effect of androgen on initiation of protein synthesis in prostate. Proc Natl Acad Sci USA 72:706–709, 1975.
38. Silverman DA, Liao S, Williams-Ashman HG: Influence of testosterone and polyuridylic acid on the incorporation of phenylalanine into peptide linkage by prostatic ribosomes. Nature 199:808–809, 1963.
39. Singhal AK, Bonner DP, Schaffner CP: Kinetics of testosterone induced-cholesterol synthesis in rat ventral prostate. Proc Soc Exp Biol Med 159:1–5, 1978.
40. Osafune M, Usami M, Miki T, Nakano E, Matsuda M, Kotake T, Sonoda T, Wada F: Physiologic regulation of cholesterol synthesis in rat prostate. Jpn J Urol 71:437–448, 1980.
41. Smith CG, Thomas JA, Mawhinney MG, Lloyd JW: Effect of testosterone (T) or dihydrotestosterone (DHT) on the in vitro synthesis of labelled cyclic adenosine nucleotide (c-AMP-H^3) by sex accessory organs of reproduction. Fed Proc 31:295, 1972.
42. Singhal RL, Vijayvargiya R, Ling GM: Cyclic adenosine monophosphate: Andromimetic action on seminal vesicular enzyme. Science 168:261–263, 1970.
43. Singhal RL, Thomas JA, Sutherland DJB: Cyclic 3′, 5′-adenosine monophosphate-adenyl cyclase system in prostate gland and other androgen-dependent tissues. In Goland M (ed): “Normal and Abnormal Growth of the Prostate.” Springfield: Charles C. Thomas, 1974, pp 445–493.
44. Beg ZH, Allman DW, Gibson DM: Modulation of 3-hydroxy-3-methyl-glutaryl coenzyme A reductase activity with cAMP and with protein fractions of rat liver-cytosol. Biochem Biophys Res Commun 54:1362–1369, 1973.
45. Raskin P, McGarry JD, Foster DW: Independence of cholesterol and fatty acid biosynthesis

from cyclic adenosine monophosphate concentration in the perfused rat liver. J Biol Chem 249:6029–6039, 1974.
46. Bricker LA, Levey GS: Autonomous cholesterol and fatty acid synthesis in hepatomas: Deletion of the adenosine 3′,5′-cyclic monophosphate control mechanism of normal liver. Biochem Biophys Res Commun 48:362–365, 1972.
47. Singhal AK, Schaffner CP: In vitro effect of testosterone and cAMP on cholesterol synthesis in rat ventral prostate. Proc Exp Biol Med 164:45–50, 1980.
48. Mangan FR, Pegg AE, Mainwaring WIP: Effects of cyclic 3′,5′-monophosphate on the function and morphology of the rat prostate gland. Biochem J 134:129–142, 1973.
49. Schaffner CP: The biochemical implication of polyene macrolide-sterol interaction, Proc IV IFS: Ferment Technol Today :393–399, 1972.
50. Schaffner CP, Gordon HW: The hypocholesterolemic activity of orally administered polyene macrolides. Proc Natl Acad Sci USA 61:36–41, 1968.
51. Texter JH, Coffey DS: The effects of amphotericin B on prostatic and testicular function in the dog. Invest Urol 7:90–106, 1969.
52. Robb CA, Carrol PT, Langston JB, Zellers RL: Evidence that nutritional state and well-being are involved in the prostate response to certain polyene macrolides. Invest Urol 9:47–54, 1971.
53. Grant JK, Giorgi EP: The study of the prostate *in vitro* by continuous flow incubation. In Williams DC, Briggs MH, Stanford M (eds): "Advances in the Study of the Prostate." London: William Heinemann Medical Books, Ltd, 1970, p. 121.
54. Aalkjaer V: Antimycotics in hypertrophy of the prostate. Urol Int 25:196–199, 1970.
55. Lunglmayr G, Spona J: Effect of polyene macrolide compounds on plasma cholesterol and luteinizing hormone in man. Int Urol Nephrol 5:223–227, 1973.
56. Theodorides P, Bourke JB, Griffin JP: Evaluation of a polyene macrolide: nystatin. Proc R Soc Med 65:130–131, 1972.
57. Bourke JB, Griffin JP, Theodorides P: A double blind trial of a polyene macrolide—nystatin—in the treatment of benign prostatic hyperplasia in man. Br J Urol 46:463–466, 1974.
58. Yamamoto C, Miyoshi T, Namikawa K, Onoe Y: Effect of polyene macrolide administration on prostatic hypertrophy. Bull Urol Soc 18:45–41, 1972.
59. Mechlinski W, Schaffner CP: Characterization of aromatic heptaene macrolide antibiotics by high performance liquid chromatography. J. Antibiot 33:591–599, 1980.
60. Abrams PH: A double-blind trial of the effects of candicidin on patients with benign prostatic hypertrophy. Br J Urol 49:67–71, 1977.
61. Homburger F, Nixon CW: Cystic prostatic hypertrophy in two inbred lines of Syrian hamsters. Proc Soc Exp Biol Med 134:284–286, 1970.
62. Schaffner CP, Brill DR, Singhal AK, Bonner DP, Goldstein NI, Wang GM: Absence of cholesterogenesis regulation in the liver and prostate of the BIO 87.20 hamster. Lipids 1981 (in press).
63. Butler M, Sawyer WK, Giannina T, Steinetz BC: Studies on the prostate glands of adult inbred LSH hamsters. Proc Soc Exp Biol Med 149:506–510, 1975.
64. Homburger F: Personnal communication.
65. Dietschy JM, Siperstein MD: Effect of cholesterol feeding and fasting on sterol synthesis in seventeen tissues of the rat. J Lipid Res 8:97–104, 1967.
66. Singhal AK, Mosbach EH, Schaffner CP: Effect of candicidin on cholesterol and bile acid metabolism in the rat. Lipids 16:423–426, 1981.
67. Singhal AK, Brill DR, Schaffner CP: Effect of clofibrate on cholesterol and DNA synthesis in rat ventral prostate. Proc Soc Exp Biol Med 160:405–409, 1979.
68. Yamanaka H, Shimazaki J, Koya A, Mayuzumi T, Imai K, Yoshikazu I, Shida K: Effect of hypolipidemia on testosterone-stimulated prostatic growth in castrated rats. Endocrinol Jpn 24:213–217, 1977.

69. Ebbinghaus KD: Die konservative therapie des prostata-adenoms. Münch med Wschr 116:2209–2212, 1974.
70. Ebbinghaus KD, Baur MP: Ergebnisse einer Doppelblindstudie über die Wirksamkeit eines Medikamentes zur konservativen Behandlung des Prostata-Adenoms. Z Allg Med 53:1054–1058, 1977.
71. Murphy GP, Williams PD, Yamanaka H, Chu M: The effects of cholestyramine on prostatic function. Res Commun Chem Pathol Pharmacol 6:1027–1032, 1973.
72. Littman ML, Taguchi T, Mosbach EH: Effect of cholesterol-free, fat-free diet and hypocholesteremic agents on growth of transplantable animal tumors. Cancer Chemother Rep 50:25–45, 1966.
73. Schaffner CP, Brill DR, Singhal AK: Presence of epoxycholesterols in the aging human prostate gland as a risk factor in cancer. Cancer Detect Prevent 3:134, 1980.
74. Fioriti JA, Sims RJ: Autoxidation products of cholesterol. J Am Oil Chem Soc 44:221–224, 1967.
75. Smith LL, Kulig MJ: Sterol metabolism XXXIV. On the derivation of carcinogenic sterols from cholesterol. Cancer Biochem Biophys 1: 79–84, 1975.
76. Tsai LS, Ijichi K, Hudson CA, Meehan JJ: A method for the quantitative estimation of cholesterol α-oxide in eggs. Lipids 15:124–128, 1980.
77. Aringer L, Eneroth P: Formation and metabolism *in vitro* of 5,6-epoxides of cholesterol and β-sitosterol. J Lipid Res 15:389–398, 1974.
78. Sporer A, Brill DR, Schaffner CP (in preparation).
79. Petrakis NL: Breast secretory activity in nonlactating women, post partum breast involution, and epidemiology of breast cancer. Natl Cancer Inst Monogr 47:161–164, 1977.
80. Petrakis NL, Maack CA, Lee RE, Lyon M: Mutagenic activity in nipple aspirates of human breast fluid. Cancer Res 40:188–189, 1980.
81. Ames BN, McCann J, Yamasaki E: Method for detecting carcinogens and mutagens with the *Salmonella*/ mammalian-microsome mutagenicity test. Mutat Res 31:347–363, 1975.
82. Petrakis NL, Gruenke LD, Craig JC: Cholesterol and cholesterol-α-epoxide in human breast secretions. Cancer Detect Prevent 3:133, 1980.
83. Petrakis NL, Gruenke LD, Craig JC: Cholesterol and cholesterol epoxides in nipple aspirates of human breast fluid. Cancer Res 4:2563–2565, 1981.
84. Bischoff F: Carcinogenic effects of steroids. Adv Lipid Res 7:165–244, 1969.
85. Black HS, Lo W-B: Formation of a carcinogen in human skin irradiated with ultraviolet light. Nature 234:306–308, 1971.
86. Lo W-B, Black HS: Formation of cholesterol-derived photoproducts in human skin. J Invest Dermatol 58:278–283, 1972.
87. Black HS, Douglas DR: A model system for the evaluation of the role of cholesterol α-oxide in ultraviolet carcinogenesis. Cancer Res 32:2630–2632, 1972.
88. Chan JT, Black HS: Skin carcinogenesis: Cholesterol-5α-epoxide hydrase activity in mouse skin irradiated with ultraviolet light. Science 186:1216–1217, 1974.
89. Imai H, Werthessen NT, Subramanyam V, LeQuesne PW, Soloway AH, Kanisawa M: Angiotoxicity of oxygenated sterols and possible precursors. Science 207:651–653, 1980.
90. Gray MF, Lawrie TDV, Brooks CJW: Isolation and identification of cholesterol α-oxide and other minor sterols in human serum. Lipids 6:836–843, 1971.
91. Kadis B: Steroid epoxides in biologic systems: A review. J Steroid Biochem 9:75–81, 1978.
92. Smith LL, Smart VA, Ansari GAS: Mutagenic cholesterol preparations. Mutat Res 68:23–30, 1979.
93. Parsons PG, Goss P: Chromosome damage and DNA repair induced in human fibroblasts by UV and cholesterol oxide. Austr J Exp Biol Med 56:287–296, 1978.

94. Blackburn GM, Rashid A, Thompson MH: Interaction of 5α, 6α-cholesterol oxide with DNA and other nucleophiles. Chem Commun 1979:420–421.
95. Kelsey MI, Pienta RJ: Transformation of hamster embryo cells by cholesterol α-epoxide and lithocholic acid. Cancer Lett 6:143–149, 1979.
96. Reddy BS, Watanabe K: Effect of cholesterol metabolites and promoting effect of lithocholic acid in colon carcinogenesis in germ-free and conventional F344 rats. Cancer Res 39:1521–1524, 1979.
97. Fioriti JA, Buide N, Sims RJ: Deposition of dietary epoxides in tissues of rats. Lipids 4:142–146, 1969.
98. Fioriti JA, Kanuck MJ, George M, Sims RJ: Metabolic fate of epoxycholesterol in the rat. Lipids 5:71–75, 1970.
99. Bowden JP, Muschik GM, Kawalek JC: The metabolic fate of cholesterol-5α, 6α-epoxide *in vivo*. Lipids 14:623–629, 1979.
100. Sevanian A, Mead JF, Stein RA: Epoxides as products of lipid autoxidation in rat lungs. Lipids 14:634–643, 1979.
101. Assmann G, Fredrickson DS, Sloan HR, Fales HM, Highet RJ: Accumulation of oxygenated steryl esters in Wolman's disease. J Lipid Res 16:28–38, 1975.
102. Hwang K-K, Kelsey MI: Evidence of epoxide hydrase activity in human intestinal microflora. Cancer Biochem Biophys 3:31–35, 1978.
103. Fraley EE, Ecker S: Spontaneous *in vitro* neoplastic transformation of adult human prostatic epithelium. Science 170:540–542, 1970.
104. Chen TT, Heidelberger C: Cultivation *in vitro* of cells derived from adult C3H mouse ventral prostate. J Natl Cancer Inst 42:903–914, 1969.
105. Heidelberger C, Iype PT: Malignant transformation *in vitro* by carcinogenic hydrocarbons. Science 155:214–217, 1967.
106. Chen TT, Heidelberger C: *In vitro* malignant transformation of cells derived from mouse prostate in the presence of 3-methylcholanthrene. J Natl Cancer Inst 42:915–925, 1969.
107. Daley JW, Jerina DM, Witkop B: Arene oxides and the NIH shift: the metabolism, toxicity and carcinogenicity of aromatic compounds. Experientia 28:1129–1264, 1972.
108. Glatt HR, Oesch F, Frigerio A, Garattini S: Epoxides metabolically produced from some known carcinogens and from some clinically used drugs. I. Differences in mutagenicity. Int J Cancer 16:787–797, 1975.
109. Bürki K, Stoming TA, Bresnick E: Effects of an epoxide hydratase inhibitor on *in vitro* binding of polycyclic hydrocarbons to DNA and on skin carcinogenesis. J Natl Cancer Inst 52:785–788, 1974.
110. Greenwald P, Kirmss V, Polan AK, Dick VS: Cancer of the prostate among men with benign prostatic hyperplasia. J Natl Cancer Inst 53:335–340, 1974.
111. Greenwald P, Damon A, Kirmss V, Polan AK: Physical and demographic features of men before developing cancer of the prostate. J Natl Cancer Inst 53:341–346, 1974.
112. Armenian HK, Lilienfeld AM, Diamond EL, Bross IDJ: Relation between benign prostatic hyperplasia and cancer of the prostate. Lancet 2:115–117, 1974.
113. Rotkin ID: Benign prostatic hyperplasia, prostatic cancer, and carcinogenesis. Lancet 2:359–360, 1975.
114. Fraley EE, Paulson DF: Morphological and biochemical studies of virus (SV40) transformed prostatic tissue. J Urol 101:735–739, 1969.
115. Sanford EJ, Geder L, Laychock A, Rohner TJ Jr, Rapp F: Evidence for the association of cytomegalovirus with carcinoma of the prostate. J Urol 118:789–792, 1977.
116. Rich RA: On the frequency of occurrence of occult carcinoma of the prostate. J Urol 33:215–223, 1935.

117. Edward CN, Steinthorsson E, Nicholson D: An autopsy study of latent prostatic carcinoma. Cancer 6:531–554, 1953.
118. Franks LM: Latent carcinoma. Ann R Coll Surg Engl 15:236–249, 1954.
119. Gittes RF, McCullough DL: Occult carcinoma of the prostate: An oversight of immune surveillance—a working hypothesis. J Urol 112:241–244, 1974.

The Prostatic Cell: Structure and Function
Part A, pages 325–336

A Growth Factor in Extracts of Human Prostatic Tissue

Russell K. Lawson, Michael T. Story, and Stephen C. Jacobs

Numerous reports have appeared in the literature describing the effect of many different steroid hormones on prostate tissue both in the intact animal and man, as well as in tissue culture and organ culture systems. These studies have failed to establish a definite link between the hormonal concentration in vitro and cell proliferation or the hormonal milieu in man and the development of benign prostatic hyperplasia [1–5]. Glandular/stromal interaction in the prostate is similarly thought to play an important role in the genesis of BPH, but little definite information exists regarding the mechanisms of such interaction [6–8]. As early as 1939, Deming suggested that a growth-promoting factor caused BPH [9]. Growth factors have been found in the prostate of animals, but two current reports state that nerve growth factor (NGF) and epidermal growth factor (EGF) are not present in the human prostate [10,11]. We have recently reported the presence of a growth factor in crude extracts of human prostatic tissue [12,13]. We have determined some of the biological and physiochemical properties of this factor. A summary of our work to date is the basis of this report. Some of the data have previously been published, while that portion which deals with the effect of human prostate extract on thymidine pool and mitotic index in the standard fibroblast assay has not been previously presented.

MATERIALS AND METHODS

Tissue Source

Fresh specimens from men who have undergone prostatectomy for obstructing BPH, normal postpubertal prostates from male cadaver kidney donors, and specimens of metastatic prostatic carcinoma have been utilized to prepare the extracts. Control extracts were also prepared from normal human kidney and muscle tissue in an identical manner.

Extract Preparation

The specimens are transported to the laboratory in cold salt-poor albumin. All steps in preparing the extract are carried out at 0–4°C. The tissue is washed in Hank's balanced salt solution (HBSS) and stored at –80°C or is minced into small pieces for extract preparation (no loss of activity can be detected with one year of storage). The minced tissue is weighed and placed in a sterile steel mortar. Liquid nitrogen is added and as soon as boil-off is completed, the tissue is powdered with a steel pestle. The powder is taken up with an equal volume (weight/volume) of HBSS and allowed to stand overnight at 4°C. The preparation is then centrifuged at 3,000 rpm for 30 minutes and the supernatant removed and saved. The pellet is resuspended in an equal volume of HBSS and centrifuged again at 3,000 rpm for 30 minutes. The second supernatant is added to the first and the extract is centrifuged at 105,000g for 40 minutes. The supernatant is then decanted through glass wool to remove floating lipids and sterilized by passage through a 0.22 μm Millipore filter. The extract is then stored at –80°C.

Standard Assay

Human foreskin fibroblasts are maintained in stock culture in 75 cm^2 flasks using MEM Eagle's with 10% newborn calf serum (MEM_{10}). These cells are used for assay only between the second and eighth passages. The cells are dispersed with 0.25% trypsin solution and seeded into 24-well culture plates (Falcon) at a density of 2×10^5 cells per well. The cells are incubated in a humidified atmosphere of 5% CO_2–95% air until confluent monolayers are obtained (3–4 days). They are then washed with HBSS and nutritionally downshifted by the addition of 0.8 ml of MEM with 0.5% newborn calf serum

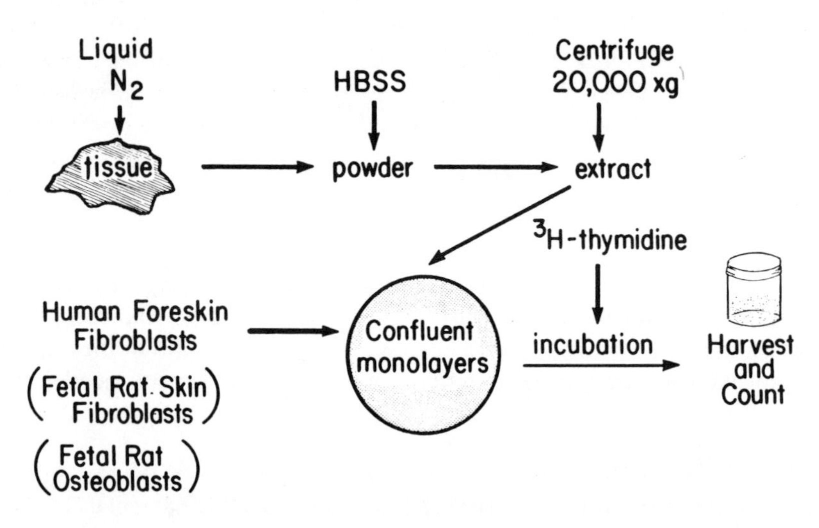

Fig. 1. Scheme for extract preparation and growth factor assay system.

($MEM_{0.5}$). After three days of incubation, 0.2 ml of the test sample is added to each well. Controls consist of a standard amount of crude BPH extract that has been determined by previous dose response studies to elicit a maximum incorporation of ^3H-thymidine (positive control) and HBSS (negative control). After 24 hours incubation of the test sample with the cells, ^3H-thymidine (0.1 μCi, 6.7 Ci/mmole, NEN) is added in 10 μl of HBSS to all wells. After a 1-hour pulse the medium is removed and the cells are washed three times with cold phosphate buffered saline (PBS). Trypsin/EDTA solution, 0.3 ml (0.25% trypsin, 0.01% EDTA in Ca^{++} and Mg^{++}-free HBSS) is added to each well. The plates are incubated for 10 minutes at 37°C and the cells collected on glass fiber filters using a multiple sample harvester fitted with a suction delivery head to accommodate the 24-well Falcon culture plates. The filters are air dried and transferred to counting vials and incubated at 60°C for 30 minutes with 0.25 ml of Protosol (NEN) tissue solubilizer. Econofluor scintillation cocktail (5 ml) is added and the ^3H-thymidine uptake determined by liquid scintillation counting. The mean ± SD of quadruplicate samples is determined and the relative mitogenic activity (RMA) calculated (Fig. 1):

$$RMA = \frac{\text{CPM (test sample)} - \text{CPM (negative control)}}{\text{CPM (positive control} - \text{CPM (negative control)}}$$

During the initial phase of this work extracts of normal human kidney and muscle tissue were also used as controls. These extracts repeatedly produced very little increased uptake of ^3H-thymidine over HBSS and are, therefore, no longer used in the standard assay system. Prior to conversion to the 24-well plate system, all studies were carried out using confluent monolayers in 25 cm^2 Falcon flasks.

Cells that have been tested in this assay system are: fetal rat osteoblasts (obtained from 19-day fetal rat calvaria and grown in Fitton-Jackson modified BGJ_b medium (Gibco) with 10% fetal calf serum), fetal rat skin fibroblasts, human foreskin fibroblasts, human fibroblast strain BUD8, and human cervical carcinoma cell line, DoT.

Our initial data showing an increased uptake of ^3H-thymidine by the cultured cells were interpreted as demonstrating the presence of a mitogen. However, two alternative explanations were possible: 1) that the cell thymidine pool was increased by some factor in crude extract, or 2) that a factor in the extract caused damage to DNA with the resultant DNA repair accounting for the ^3H-thymidine uptake. We carried out experiments to rule out these latter two possibilities.

Thymidine Pool

In order to determine if the crude extract affected the cell thymidine pool, human foreskin fibroblasts were grown in 25-cm^2 flasks (Falcon) in 5 ml MEM_{10}. When the cells reached confluence, the medium was changed to MEM_{10} with

20% HBSS (control) and MEM_{10} with 20% HBSS that contained 1.5 mg BPH extract. After 23 hours of incubation 1.0 μCi of ^{3}H-thymidine was added to each flask. The specific activity of ^{3}H-thymidine (64 Ci/mmole, NEN) was adjusted as indicated by the addition of stock solution of unlabelled thymidine (Sigma) standardized spectrophotometrically ($E_{260} = 7.4 \times 10^{-3}$ mole/liter). After a 1-hour pulse, the medium was removed and the cells were washed three times with cold PBS. Two ml of distilled water were added to each flask and the cultures were freeze thawed two times. The radiolabel incorporated in the cold 10% TCA insoluble fraction was determined after collecting and washing the precipitate on glass fiber filters supported on a manifold filtration device. The filters were washed with ethanol and transferred to vials and counted by liquid scintillation counting as previously described. Cell protein was determined by the Lowry method with bovine serum albumin used as a standard.

DNA Synthesis

Studies were carried out to determine the mitotic index and percent of labelled nuclei present in human fibroblast cultures in the presence and absence of BPH extract. To determine mitotic index the fibroblasts were grown to confluence on cover slips in 2-ml Leighton tubes using MEM_{10}. For the labelled mitosis experiments, the medium was changed to MEM_{10} with 20% HBSS (control) or MEM_{10} with 20% HBSS that contained 1.6 mg BPH extract. After 22 hours of incubation 0.5 μCi ^{3}H-thymidine (6.7 Ci/mmole) was added to each tube. Following 1 hour of pulse the cells were washed three times in HBSS and fresh control medium and medium containing BPH extract were added. Duplicate control and BPH cultures (to be stopped at the first time point) received 0.1 μg of Colcemid (Gibco). At each subsequent time point Colcemid was added to the control and BPH cultures (to be stopped at the next time point) and the Colcemid arrested cultures were washed three times with PBS and fixed with acetic alcohol. Following 15 minutes of fixation, the cells were washed three times with 80% ethanol followed by three washes with water. The coverslips were removed from the tube, air dried, and mounted cells side up on microscope slides. The cells were acid hydrolyzed and stained with Schiff's reagent and then coated with NTB 2 liquid emulsion (Kodak) diluted 1:1 with water. Following 24-hour development the slides were processed in Dektol (Kodak). The autoradiographs were viewed at 400× magnification and 20 fields per slide (2,620 ± 620 cells) were scored by counting labelled mitoses. The values from duplicate slides were averaged.

To determine the percent of labelled nuclei in BPH stimulated cultures the medium in the Leighton tubes was changed to MEM_{10} with 20% HBSS (control) or MEM_{10} with 20% HBSS that contained 1.6 mg BPH extract and 1 μCi of ^{3}H-thymidine was added to each tube. At each subsequent time point control and BPH cultures were washed three times with PBS and fixed in acetic alcohol.

After staining the cell number for representative fields was determined (2,424 ± 600/20 fields), the cover slips were then autoradiographed as described above. Twenty fields per slide were scored for labelled nuclei. The percent of cells in the field with labelled nuclei was determined from the mean of triplicate slides.

Physiochemical Characterization: Heat and Trypsin Sensitivity

Extracts of BPH were exposed to trypsin 100 mg/ml for varying periods of time up to 24 hours. At each time point in the experiment the trypsin activity was stopped by the addition of 500 mg/ml of soy trypsin inhibitor. The digested specimens were then tested in the standard fibroblast assay system. Soy trypsin inhibitor was used as a control and was shown not to effect the uptake of ^{3}H-thymidine by the fibroblasts.

Extracts of BPH were exposed to 60°C for 10, 20, and 30 minutes and the mitogenic activity of the extract was then determined using the standard fibroblast assay system. Extracts were also kept at room temperature and at 4°C for 24 hours prior to assay.

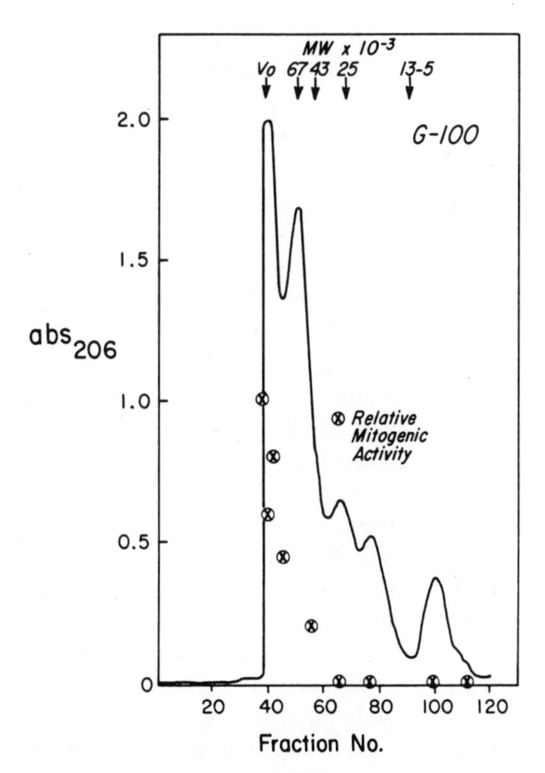

Fig. 2. BPH extract elution profile on Sephadex G-100.

RESULTS

Physiochemical Properties

Treatment of BPH extract with 100 mg/ml of trypsin for 24 hours resulted in an 83% reduction in mitogenic activity [13]. We have concluded from these experiments that the factor is a protein or contains a protein moiety.

Extracts exposed to 60°C showed a loss of mitogenic activity at a constant rate of 2% per minute. The extract, however, lost no activity in 24 hours at room temperature or at 4°C [13].

Sephadex G-100 Elution Profile

BPH extract (5 ml, 415 mg) was applied to a 2.6 × 95 cm column of Sephadex G-100 equilibrated with PBS at pH 7.4. The column was eluted (4°C) at 24 ml per hour and absorbance at 206 nm was recorded (LKB). Five-ml fractions corresponding to peaks of Abs_{206} were filtered through a 0.22 μm Millipore filter and tested for activity in the fibroblast assay system. The results of this study are shown in Figure 2. The void volume of the column was determined with blue dextran. The elution position of BSA (67,000), ovalbumin (43,000), chymotrypsinogen (25,000), and ribonuclease (13,500) are shown in Figure 2. It can be seen that a majority of the mitogenic activity eluted at or near the void volume indicating that the apparent molecular weight of the growth factor or growth factor/carrier complex is at least 67,000.

Biologic Properties

Extracts prepared from BPH, normal postpubertal prostate, and well-differentiated adenocarcinoma of the prostate all stimulate human foreskin fibroblasts, fetal rat skin fibroblasts, fetal rat osteoblasts, human cell strained BUD8, and human cell line DoT to undergo mitosis in culture (Table I). Human foreskin fibroblasts, fetal rat skin fibroblasts, and fetal rat osteoblasts showed only slight increase in ^{3}H-thymidine uptake above controls when treated with extracts of normal human muscle and kidney tissue (Table II). The typical dose response of human fibroblasts, growth inhibited by serum shift-down, to BPH extract and serum is shown in Table III. These data show a decrease in ^{3}H-thymidine uptake with decreasing concentrations of BPH extract. This study also demonstrates that 60 μg of BPH extract is as effective as 10.5% serum in stimulating the uptake of ^{3}H-thymidine. A study of the effects of BPH extract over time, on confluent cultures of fibroblasts, has shown that ^{3}H-thymidine incorporation is detectable at 12 hours, reaches a peak at 18 hours, remains elevated until 30 hours, and disappears by 36 hours after addition of the extract.

Growth factor activity has been found in every extract prepared from human prostatic tissue (normal prostate, BPH, and carcinoma of the prostate). A total

TABLE I. Stimulation of ^{3}H-thymidine incorporation by tissue extracts

	Fetal rat osteoblasts		Fetal rat skin fibroblasts		Human foreskin fibroblasts		DoT		BUD-8	
	n[a]	% stimulation[b]	n	% stimulation	n	% stimulation	n	% stimulation	n	% stimulation
BPH	40	550 ± 28*	54	586 ± 25*	19	254 ± 6*	7	723 ± 45*	9	753 ± 22*
Normal postpubertal prostate	4	385 ± 15*	8	328 ± 19*	5	313 ± 22*				
Well-differentiated adenocarcinoma prostate			4	459 ± 19*						
Muscle	4	186 ± 28	12	130 ± 9	8	109 ± 6	2	64 ± 19%		
Kidney	4	122 ± 10	8	131 ± 91						

Data are shown as percent stimulation over control cultures.

[a]Number of cultures.

[b]^{3}H-thymidine incorporation/control ^{3}H-thymidine incorporation × 100.

*$P < 0.001$.

TABLE II. Effect of extract additives on the incorporation of ^{3}H-thymidine by fetal rat skin fibroblasts

Extract	n	^{3}H-thymidine
Well-differentiated adenocarcinoma prostate	4	36,250 ± 1480*
BPH	4	24,920 ± 1060*
Normal postpubertal prostate	4	23,570 ± 1290*
Normal muscle	4	10,980 ± 1100
Control medium (HBSS)	4	8290 ± 370

Values are expressed as mean ± SEM.
*$P < 0.01$.

TABLE III. Dose response of human fibroblasts to BPH extract and serum in standard assay system

Serum (%)	BPH (μg)	CPM × 10^{-3} ± SD (n = 3) Serum	BPH	Serum/control	BPH/control
10.5	120	2.42 ± 0.15	3.74 ± 0.29	22	34
3.0	60	1.53 ± 0.03	2.84 ± 0.22	13.9	25.8
1.0	30	0.37 ± 0.01	1.27 ± 0.15	3.3	11.5
0.5	15	0.11 ± 0.01	0.76 ± 0.03	1.0	6.9

Cell growth is inhibited, after confluent monolayer present, by serum shift down to $MEM_{0.5}$.

TABLE IV. Growth factor activity of representative BPH preparations

Preparation number[a]	Wet weight (gm)	Crude extract total protein (mg)	Amount required for maximum activity[b] (mg)
77	16	112	0.07
92	63	504	0.16
93	16	192	0.12
96	25	375	0.15
102	32	266	0.10
106	17	666	0.24

Maximum activity is shown as mg of protein extract/ml culture medium.
[a]Number 106 was from tissue obtained by transurethral prostatectomy. All other preparations were from tissues obtained at open prostatectomy.
[b]Determined by dose-response studies in the standard fibroblast assay.

TABLE V. Effect of BPH extract on the incorporation of ^{3}H-thymidine by fibroblasts under conditions of varying precursor-specific radioactivity

Experiment number	^{3}H-thymidine (Ci/mmole)	CPM × 10^{-3}/mg protein[a] BPH	Control	Ratio of BPH to control
1	64	131.6 ± 16.1	26.0 ± 2.3	5.0
	6.4	120.2 ± 8.1	23.4 ± 1.7	5.1[b]
	0.64	84.2 ± 13.4	17.6 ± 1.5	4.7[b]
	0.064	15.5 ± 0.5	3.1 ± 0.2	5.0[b]
2	64	56.9 ± 3.2	14.2 ± 0.2	4.0
	0.064	4.7 ± 0.4	1.5 ± 0.4	3.1[b]

Total amount of radiolabel added to each culture was 1 μCi.
[a]Values are the mean ± SD of triplicate cultures.
[b]Not significantly different ($P > 0.05$) from the ratio at ^{3}H-thymidine (64 Ci/mmole).

of 20 separate extracts have been tested and six representative preparations are shown in Table IV. Crude BPH extracts contain an average of 10 mg/ml of protein with a range of 7–15 mg. Dose-response studies have shown that an average of 0.12 mg/ml of BPH extract is required for maximum activity in the standard human fibroblast assay system.

Studies on the incorporation of ^{3}H-thymidine by fibroblasts under conditions of varying precursor specific radioactivity are shown in Table V. Dilution of specific activity of the thymidine precursor by a factor of 1000 reduced the incorporation of labelled material by approximately 89%. As can be seen from Table V, as the size of the thymidine pool is increased (decreasing precursor specific activity), the ratio of response of BPH-stimulated cells to controls remains the same. These observations show that large changes in the thymidine pool are not occurring in BPH responding cells compared to control cells and, therefore, the response to BPH extract cannot be accounted for by alterations in thymidine pool size.

Autoradiographic studies were undertaken to differentiate between BPH stimulated DNA repair and mitogenesis. Time-course studies show only occasional cells with labelled mitosis in both control and BPH treated cultures at 29 hours. However, fibroblasts treated with BPH extract for 36 hours showed a 15-fold increase in labelled mitosis over control cultures (Fig. 3). A 7–8-fold increase of labelled mitosis in BPH-treated cultures over control cultures was sustained for the duration of the study (51 hours). The enhanced mitotic activity observed 36 hours after BPH treatment is consistent with the observed increase in ^{3}H-thymidine incorporation occurring at 18–30 hours after BPH stimulation and is indicative of cells completing S-phase and transversing G-phase before arrested in M-phase by Colcemid.

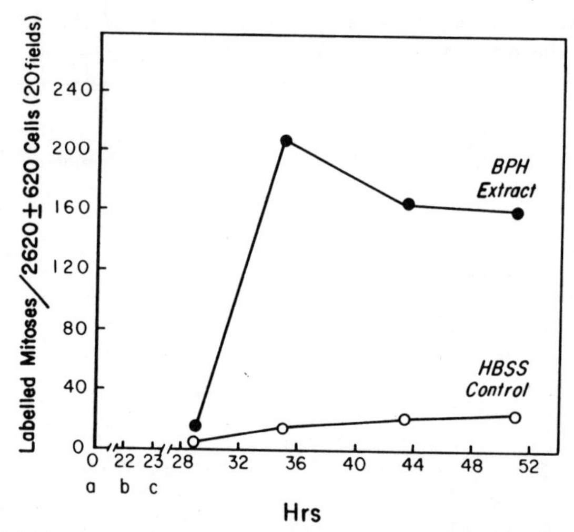

Fig. 3. Time vs labelled mitoses in the presence and absence of BPH extract. a) Addition of BPH extract to confluent cultures. b) Addition of 0.5 μCi ^{3}H-thymidine. c) ^{3}H-thymidine removed and fresh control and BPH medium added. First set of cultures received colcemid 0.1 μg at point C. Duplicate control and BPH cultures harvested at each time point after addition of colcemid at previous time point.

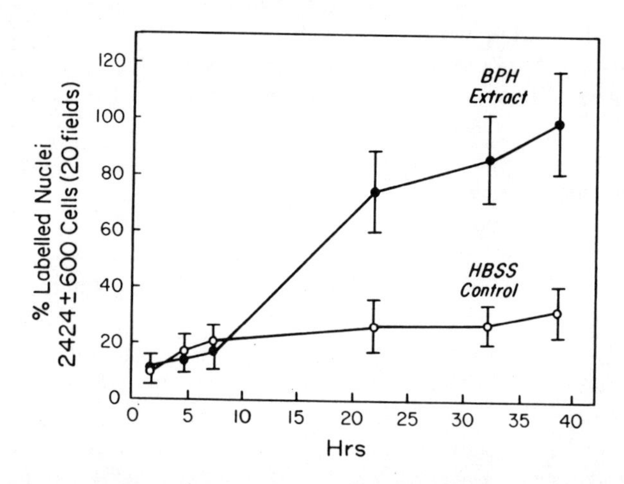

Fig. 4. Time vs the percent of the cell population with ^{3}H-thymidine labelled nuclei, in the presence and absence of BPH extract. Values are the mean of triplicate slides. The vertical bars represent the SD.

To assess the fraction of fibroblasts that were actively participating in the proliferative process, autoradiography was performed on the cells following continuous labelling with ^{3}H-thymidine. Figure 4 shows that 100.6 ± 18.2% of the nuclei of treated fibroblast cultures incorporated the thymidine label 38.5 hours after BPH addition when compared to control cultures which showed 33.3 ± 8.9% labeling. In separate incubations, cultures treated three days with BPH extract showed a 152 ± 15% increase in cell protein and a 194 ± 15% increase in cell number over control culture. These studies indicate that nearly the entire confluent fibroblast population participates in the proliferative process as a result of stimulation by the growth factor.

DISCUSSION

Our initial studies have all been carried out using crude extracts of prostatic tissue. For that reason, interpretation of our experimental results has been difficult. A major concern has been whether the increased uptake of ^{3}H-thymidine actually indicates new DNA synthesis and mitosis. The experiments with labelled precursor of varying specific activity demonstrate that there is no major change in cell thymidine pool that could account for our results. The labelling studies that have shown a total increase in the number of cells and increased labelled metaphase chromosomes have demonstrated that a mitogenic substance is present in the extracts. The concentration of spermine, spermidine, putrescine,* and acid phosphatase has been determined in the crude extracts, and we have added each of these substances to the culture assay system in the same concentration as found in the extracts and found no effect on cell proliferation [13]. We have dialyzed the extracts using a membrane with an exclusion size of 50,000 and retained all mitogenic activity demonstrating that low molecular weight nutrients such as amino acids and sugars do not account for the mitogenic effect. Initial separation on Sephadex G-100 shows that the activity is retained in the high molecular weight fractions. The finding suggests that the factor or factor/carrier complex has a MW of at least 67,000. This observation is consistent with the findings of growth factor/carrier complexes seen with other known growth factors. Initial attempts (data not shown) to separate a smaller molecular weight polypeptide from a carrier protein by lowering the pH to 1.5 before application to the column has resulted in complete loss of activity. We are currently carrying out experiments to determine the stability of crude extracts at various pHs. It may be that a more purified factor will be stable at low pH when separated from the many contaminants that are present in the crude extract. The studies with trypsin digestion suggest that the factor is a protein or contains a protein moiety. Initial studies of heat stability suggest that unlike epidermal growth factor this

*Courtesy of Dr. D.H. Russell.

substance is heat labile. These studies again must be interpreted with caution because they have been carried out with crude extract and contaminants may have effected the results.

The factor has been found in all prostatic tissue tested (young adult, BPH, and carcinoma of the prostate). If one assumes that purified prostatic growth factor is approximately equal in mitogenic potency to mEGF, then the amount of growth factor per gm of prostate is about 1,000 times less than the amount of mEGF per gm of mouse salivary gland [14].

Our studies are now directed at purification and physiochemical characterization of the factor from large quantities of BPH. We wish to determine if the factor is one of the known growth factors or is a factor unique to the human prostate. Biological characterization studies are being carried out to determine if there is any synergistic or antagonist effect of androgen and estrogen in growth factor stimulated cell systems. If such an interaction can be demonstrated, it may be important in the genesis of BPH.

REFERENCES

1. Schrodt GR, Foreman CD: In vitro maintenance of human hyperplastic prostate tissue. Invest Urol 9:85–94, 1971.
2. Wojewski A, Przeworska-Kaniewicz D: The influence of stilbesterol and testosterone on the growth of prostatic adenoma and carcinoma of tissue culture. J Urol 93:721–724, 1965.
3. Robel P, Lasnitzki L, Baulieu EE: Hormone metabolism and action: Testosterone and metabolites in prostate organ culture. Biochemie 53:81–96, 1971.
4. Siiteri PK, Wilson JD: Dihydrotestosterone in prostatic hypertrophy. I. The formation and content of dihydrotestosterone in the hypertrophic prostate of man. J Clin Invest 49:1737–1745, 1970.
5. Geller J, Albert J, Lopez D, Geller S, Niwayama G: Comparison of androgen metabolites in benign prostatic hypertrophy (BPH) and normal prostate. J Clin Endocrinol Metab 43:686–688, 1976.
6. Lowsley L: Injuries and disease of prostate gland. Clin Urol 1:829–831, 1944.
7. Pradhan BK, Chandra K: Morphogenesis of nodular hyperplasia—prostate. J Urol 113:210–213, 1975.
8. McNeal JE: Origin and evolution of benign prostatic enlargement. Invest Urol 15:340–345, 1978.
9. Deming CL, Neumann C: Early phases of prostatic hyperplasia. Surg Gynecol Obstet 68:155–160, 1939.
10. Hirata Y, Orth DN: Epidermal growth factor (urogastrone) in human tissues. J Clin Endocrinol Metab 48:667–672, 1979.
11. Elder JB, Williams G, Lacey E, Gregory H: Cellular localization of human urogastrone/epidermal growth factor. Nature 271:466–467, 1978.
12. Jacobs SC, Pikna D, Lawson RK: Prostatic osteoblastic factor. Invest Urol 17:195–198, 1979.
13. Jacobs SC, Lawson RK: Mitogenic factor in human prostate extracts. Urology 16:488–491, 1980.
14. Cohen S, Carpenter G: Human epidermal growth factor: Isolation and chemical and biological properties. Proc Natl Acad Sci USA 72:1317–1321, 1975.

UNIQUE PROSTATIC PROTEINS

The Prostatic Cell: Structure and Function
Part A, pages 339–350

Prostatic Binding Protein and Its Hormonal Regulation

W. Heyns, B. Peeters, J. Mous, D. Bossyns, W. Rombauts, and P. De Moor

Little is known about the functional significance of the rat ventral prostate, although its anatomical situation points to a role in male reproductive physiology. This role is probably not essential for fertility, since removal of this gland does not produce a major effect on fertility [1].

During the last few years, several groups have demonstrated that the ventral prostate contains and secretes large quantities of abundant proteins, such as "prostatic binding protein" [2,3], "prostatein" [4,5] and "estramustine-binding protein" [6,7]. These proteins have been characterized in some detail [3,5,7], and the reported properties are very similar suggesting that they are identical.

In view of the quantitative importance of these proteins in the rat ventral prostate, it seems very likely that they are important functional parameters for this gland. The function of these proteins, however, is still unknown. Their most prominent functional characteristic is the binding of various nonpolar hormonal steroids [2] and of the synthetic estradiol derivative estramustine [7]. To what degree this steroid binding is functionally important remains to be elucidated, but it seems likely that it is related to the previously reported nonreceptor binding of androgens to α-protein [8] and the so-called "pregnenolone receptor" binding [9] in the ventral prostate.

In this communication we will summarize our studies on "prostatic binding protein" or PBP. This name was chosen because of the marked steroid-binding properties of this protein. We will primarily present our own results, since other speakers at this meeting will report on similar proteins. A first section of this presentation deals with the general characteristics and binding properties of PBP. In the second section various physiological aspects are treated, with particular emphasis on hormonal regulation. The molecular biology of the synthesis of PBP and of its hormonal regulation forms the subject of the third section.

GENERAL CHARACTERISTICS AND BINDING PROPERTIES OF PROSTATIC BINDING PROTEIN

Demonstration of a Major Binding Protein in the Rat Ventral Prostate

During studies on DHT receptor binding in the rat ventral prostate, we were surprised by the marked degree of nonreceptor binding in this organ [2]. We originally believed that this was due to a high degree of contamination with plasma proteins and the observation of a prominent protein band at the position of rat serum albumin after polyacrylamide gel electrophoresis seemed to confirm this hypothesis. An immunological measurement of rat serum albumin in prostatic cytosol, however, produced very low values. This discrepancy prompted us to study this problem more in detail. It soon became apparent that there were marked kinetic differences between the nonspecific binding in the prostate and in rat serum. Furthermore, an electrophoretic analysis at different gel concentrations revealed that the major protein band in prostatic cytosol was somewhat smaller than serum albumin. These observations led us to believe that a particular "prostatic binding protein" was responsible for the nonspecific binding of androgens in the vental prostate.

Purification of PBP

Since PBP constitutes the major component of prostatic cytosol, its purification is relatively easy. DEAE cellulose chromatography with linear salt gradients for elution provides an efficient purification step [2,3]. It should be noted that this procedure actually resolves two forms of PBP with somewhat different properties (Fig. 1). As we demonstrated recently [10], the first eluted peak of PBP consists of a complex of PBP with a small protein (see below). The relative proportion between both forms depends on the experimental procedure. A more alkaline pH or previous "delipidation" [11] of the sample both favor the second form. Additional purification of PBP can be obtained by gel filtration.

General Characterization of PBP

When the molecular weight of PBP was estimated by gel filtration on Sephadex, a value of 51,000 was obtained. This value is in good agreement with a sedimentation coefficient of 3.7 S found by ultracentrifugation in sucrose density gradients [2,3]. An isoelectric point of 5.2 was obtained by isoelectric focusing in sucrose density gradients, but some heterogeneity was observed and PBP tended to precipitate in the neighborhood of its isoelectric point.

Polyacrylamide gel electrophoresis of PBP in the absence of SDS produced some peculiar results. Indeed, PBP tended to dissociate at alkaline pH. In addition to the major PBP band two other bands were observed, one with a markedly

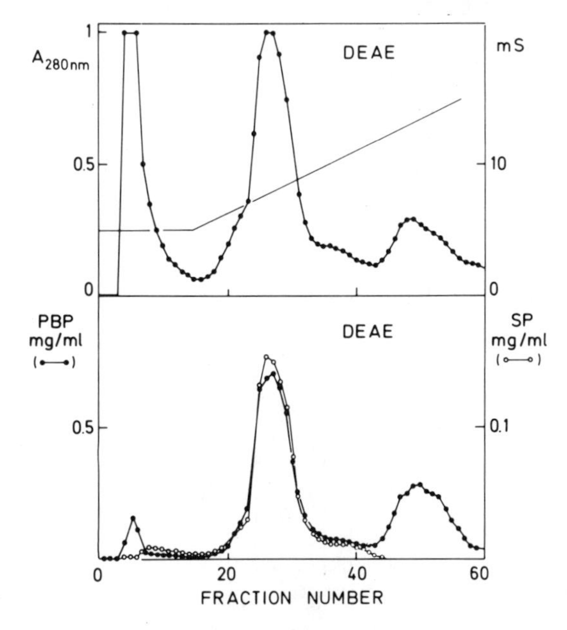

Fig. 1. DEAE cellulose chromatography of prostatic cytosol. Prostatic cytosol was applied at 4°C on a DEAE cellulose column (15 × 1.5 cm) and eluted with a linear KCl gradient (25–200 mM; 2 × 100 ml) in Tris (50 mM), EDTA (5 mM) buffer at pH 6.5. The upper part of the figure represents the absorbancy at 280 nm and the conductivity; the lower part the concentrations of PBP and SP measured by radial immunodiffusion.

higher mobility and another one with a slightly lower mobility. This dissociation can be prevented by electrophoresis at lower pH [3].

Polyacrylamide gel electrophoresis in the presence of SDS reveals that PBP is composed of two different subunits with estimated molecular weights of 18,500 (F subunit) and 19,500 (S subunit). After reduction of disulfide bridges three different bands were observed with estimated molecular weights of 8000 (C_1), 11,000 (C_2), and 13,000 (C_3). We have shown that the F subunit is composed of component C_1 and C_3 and the S subunit of component C_2 and C_3. Since the common component C_3 is glycosylated, PBP and its two subunits are glycoproteins.

A tentative model of PBP, derived from these data, is shown in Figure 2. We propose that PBP is a dimer composed of two different subunits, which are linked together by noncovalent forces. Each subunit contains the common glycosylated component C_3 linked by disulfide bridges to C_1 in subunit F and to C_2 in subunit S.

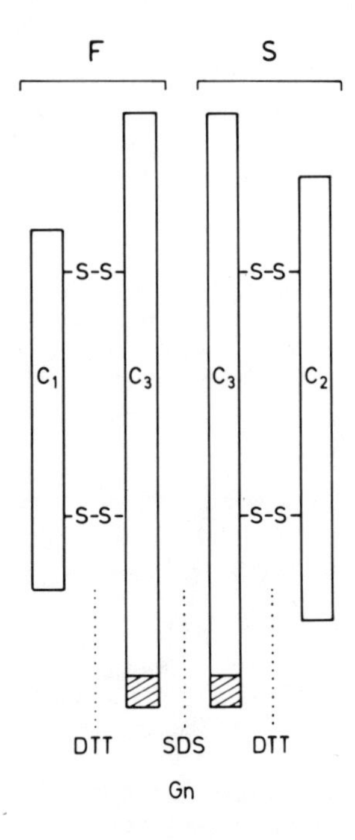

Fig. 2. Tentative structure of PBP. PBP is composed of two different subunits, linked together by non-covalent forces. In the F-subunit the glycosylated component C_3 is linked to component C_1 by disulfide bridges; in the S-subunit the same C_3-component is linked to component C_1 also by disulfide bridges.

Purification of Subunits and Components

The F and S subunit can be separated by hydroxyapatite chromatography in the presence of SDS (3) or by DEAE cellulose chromatography in the presence of 8 M urea (unpublished results). After reduction and alkylation of the purified subunits the same techniques can be used for the purification of the 3 components.

Amino Acid Composition

The amino acid composition of PBP, of both subunits and of the three components is given in Table I. The amino acid composition of PBP is nearly identical to the amino acid composition of the estramustine binding protein described by Forsgren et al, [7], but differs somewhat from the results of Lea, Petrusz, and French for prostatein [5]. As shown in Table I, the F and S subunit have a rather similar amino acid composition. This is not unexpected in view of the presence of the common C_3 component in both subunits. As expected, the amino acid composition of C_{3-S} and C_{3-F} is identical. More marked differences are observed between C_1, C_2, and C_3, in particular for tyrosine, which is higher in C_1, for arginine, which is more elevated in C_2, and for serine and threonine, which are more abundant in C_3.

Amino Acid Sequence of the Components

Very recently the amino acid sequence of the common C_3 component has been elucidated [12]. This sequence is shown in Table II. The oligosaccharide chain is attached to the peptide by an N-glycosidic bond to the asparagine residue 17. The three cysteine residues are localized at both ends and in the middle of the molecule. The peptide chain of C_3 contains 77 amino acids, corresponding to a molecular weight of 8653. This value is much lower than the value of 13,000 estimated by SDS gel electrophoresis. This discrepancy is due to the glycosylation

TABLE I. Amino acid composition of PBP and its purified subunits and components

		Composition (nmole/100 nmole recovered)					
		Subunits		Components			
Amino acid	PBP	F	S	C_1	C_2	C_{3-S}	C_{3-F}
Cys	3.59	3.46	4.13	3.43	2.83	4.14	4.13
Asp	9.25	8.86	10.09	9.23	10.1	9.89	9.94
Thr	6.15	5.13	5.96	3.19	4.65	7.38	7.00
Ser	5.45	6.35	6.42	4.59	3.63	7.83	7.49
Glu	15.62	17.16	15.59	18.57	14.46	13.92	14.62
Pro	3.27	3.45	3.24	3.01	5.60	2.63	2.79
Gly	4.68	3.78	5.11	2.70	5.35	5.30	4.78
Ala	4.53	4.79	4.19	6.76	6.01	2.67	2.93
Val	7.96	9.25	7.26	8.85	6.34	8.57	8.62
Met	2.93	3.28	3.14	4.89	3.27	4.12	3.84
Ile	5.02	5.30	5.27	4.24	5.84	4.61	4.43
Leu	8.42	7.82	9.04	9.06	10.82	6.22	6.85
Tyr	3.26	4.58	1.97	6.66	1.57	2.55	2.69
Phe	4.95	4.29	5.14	3.12	5.24	4.93	4.94
His	2.31	1.72	1.19	1.10	N.D.	2.58	2.62
Lys	6.89	6.81	6.43	6.85	6.39	7.60	7.53
Arg	2.53	1.60	3.14	2.33	6.11	1.21	1.35
Trp	0.85	0.65	1.13	1.28	1.51	N.D.	N.D.
GlcN	2.29	1.67	1.57	N.D.	N.D.	3.53	3.62
GalN	N.D.	N.D.	N.D.	N.D.	N.D.	N.D.	N.D.

N.D., not detectable.

TABLE II Primary structure of the C_3 Component

Ser-Gly-Ser-Gly-Cys-Ser-Ile-Leu-Asp-Glu[10]-Val-Ile-Arg-Gly-Thr-Ile-Asn(CHO)-Ser-Thr-Val[20]-Thr-Keu-His-Asp-Tyr-
Met-Lys-Leu-Val-Lys[30]-Pro-Tyr-Val-Gln-Asp-His-Phe-Thr-Glu-Lys[40]-Ala-Val-Lys-Gln-Phe-Lys-Gln-Cys-Phe-Leu[50]-Asp-Gln-
Thr-Asp-Lys-Thr-Leu-Glu-Asn-Val-Gly-Val[60]-Met-Glu-Ala-Ile-Phe-Asn-Ser-Glu-Ser-Cys[70]-Gln-Gln-Pro-Ser

TABLE III. Structural homology in components C_1 and C_2

												U					
	A		A		U	U						C	A		G		
	GAG	CUN	GAG	AUG	UAC	AAC	GCN	CCN	CCN	GCN	GCN	GUA	GAG	GCN	AAA		
C_1-T_5	Glu -	Leu -	Glu -	Met -	Tyr -	Asn -	Ala -	Pro -	Pro -	Ala -	Ala -	Val -	Glu -	Ala -	Lys		
C_2-T_{15}	Glu -	Leu -	Glu -	Glu -	Phe -	Asp -	Ala -	Pro -	Pro -	Glu -	Ala -	Val -	Glu -	Ala -	Asn -	Leu -	Lys
	GAG	CUN	GAG	GAG	UUC	GAC	GCN	CCN	CCN	GAA	GCN	GUA	GAG	GCN	AAC		
	A		A	A	U	U				G		C	A		U		
												U					

Comparison of the amino acid sequences of the tryptic peptide C_1-T_5, obtained from C_1, and of the tryptic peptide C_2-T_{15}, obtained from C_2. Table also shows the marked similarity of the encoding nucleotides.

of C_3, which not only increases its molecular weight, but also leads to excessive estimations by this technique.

The amino acid sequence of C_1 and C_2 have been partially elucidated. The available data indicate that these two components are completely different from C_3, but that they show marked similarities between them [13]. Table III, for instance, compares the amino acid sequence of analogous peptides found respectively in C_1 and C_2. It is obvious that there is a marked similarity between both peptides, a similarity that becomes even more striking at the nucleotide level.

Steroid-Binding Properties of PBP

Our original interest in PBP concerned its steroid-binding properties [2,11]. The essential features of these studies may be summarized as follows. PBP binds a number of nonpolar steroids, such as pregnenolone, 5α-dihydrotestosterone, and testosterone, with a relatively low affinity, but dissociation of the bound steroid occurs rather slowly at low temperature. Furthermore, there are some indications that the steroid-binding site is largely occupied by unknown endogenous substances, as is suggested by the marked effect of "delipidation" on binding.

The description by Forsgren et al [6,7] of an estramustine-binding protein with nearly identical properties prompted us to compare the binding by PBP of pregnenolone and estramustine. For estramustine we found an association constant of $2.5 \times 10^7 M^{-1}$, a value comparable to the value of $5.88 \times 10^7 M^{-1}$ described by Forsgren et al, [14] and much higher than the value of $1.1 \times 10^6 M^{-1}$ we found for pregnenolone under the same conditions. Forsgren et al, have noted that they could only very partially suppress the binding of estramustine, even with very high concentrations of competing steroids. In similar experiments (unpublished results) we found complete inhibition of pregnenolone binding by estramustine, but only incomplete suppression of estramustine binding by pregnenolone. This discrepancy can be explained by preliminary data, which indicate that both subunits bind estramustine, whereas pregnenolone binds to the S subunit only.

Binding of a Small Protein (SP) to PBP

Recently, we have shown that a small protein (SP) in prostatic cytosol binds to PBP [10]. As shown in Figure 1, the presence of SP explains the findings of two forms of PBP in prostatic cytosol by DEAE cellulose chromatography. Indeed, the PBP-SP complex is eluted before PBP. SP dissociates from PBP at alkaline pH and also in the presence of urea and detergents. SP has been purified and partially characterized.

The molecular weight of SP, estimated by gel filtration, was 5200. Its amino acid composition is characterized by a particularly high proline content. SP can be visualized by SDS gel electrophoresis, but attention should be paid during destaining, since this component stains relatively weakly and is destained rapidly.

The association with SP does not affect the binding of estramustine to PBP but seems to be favorable for the binding of pregnenolone. Indeed, the observed affinity for pregnenolone was 3.7 times higher for the PBP.SP complex than for PBP.

PHYSIOLOGICAL ASPECTS

Location of PBP in the Rat Ventral Prostate

Our initial binding studies strongly suggested that PBP is a characteristic feature of the rat ventral prostate [2,11]. This hypothesis was confirmed by measurement of PBP by radial immunodiffusion in cytosols prepared from a number of rat organs. Only the ventral prostate contained large amounts of PBP, while small amounts were found in the dorsal and lateral prostate [15]. It should be noted, however, that Forsgren et al, [7] found low amounts of material reacting in a radioimmunoassay for "estramustine binding protein" in various other organs of male rats.

Within the prostate PBP is localized for the largest part in the acinar lumen, and also at the apical border of the epithelial cells. This localization indicates that PBP is secreted by the prostate. It can be detected also in male rat urine, in rat semen, and after copulation in the female genital tract. These observations strongly suggest that PBP plays a role in reproductive physiology.

Effect of Age on PBP

PBP is present in low but detectable amounts in the prostate of 5-day-old rats. From day 10 on its concentration increases gradually in a biphasic way, with maximal increases between days 15 and 30 and days 50 and 80. Androgens probably are the stimulating factor for this increase [15]. In fact, the presence of high amounts of androgens in rat prostates of these age groups has been demonstrated by Corpéchot, Baulieu, and Robel [16].

In adult rats the relative concentration of PBP is very high, and may reach up to 60% of the total cytosolic protein. It should be noted, however, that most of this PBP is localized extracellularly and included in the cytosol fraction during homogenization.

Effect of Hormonal Treatment on PBP

Androgens are clearly the major stimulatory factor for PBP synthesis by the ventral prostate. Indeed, castration of adult rats produces a strong decrease of the prostatic PBP content and also of the relative concentration of PBP in this gland. These changes occur rather slowly and it takes several days before they become pronounced [15].

Administration of androgens (testosterone or 5α-dihydrotestosterone), on the other hand, increases the concentration of PBP in castrated rats. This stimulation, too, is rather slow. Actually, 1 day after castration a moderate but consistent drop of the prostatic PBP content is observed. This is probably due to an increased removal of stored PBP, since the prostatic mRNAs for PBP and the rate of synthesis of PBP are increased already at that time [17,18].

Other hormones, such as oestradiol and progesterone are without effect. They do not stimulate PBP in castrated rats and also do not interfere with the effect of androgens. The antiandrogen cyproterone acetate, on the other hand, produces marked inhibition of the effect of androgens.

Effect of Hormonal Treatment on SP

As for PBP, androgens are the major regulatory factor for SP. In fact, castration and androgen treatment produce a more pronounced effect on SP than on PBP [10]. Ten days after castration the amount of SP in the prostate decreases from precastration levels (1105 ± 267 μg/prostate) to undetectable levels ($<$ 1 μg/prostate). A clear-cut stimulation is already observed after 1 day of androgen treatment and further stimulation occurs during the following days. Other hormones, such as estradiol and progesterone do not stimulate the level of SP in castrated rats.

MOLECULAR BIOLOGY OF PBP SYNTHESIS AND ITS REGULATION BY ANDROGENS

Characterization of PBP mRNAs

Since PBP is composed of three different peptides one may expect that three different mRNAs are required for its synthesis. In fact, after translation of mRNA from the rat ventral prostate in a cell-free translation system derived from wheat germ three different peptide bands are observed in the immunoprecipitate with anti-PBP-antiserum. The molecular weights of these peptides, however, do not agree with those of the components of PBP. By use of specific antisera to each of these components their relation to the products formed in vitro has been elucidated [17]. The "in vitro" product with a molecular weight of 9000 corresponds to C_1 (MW 8000) and the "in vitro" product with a molecular weight of 12,000 to C_2 (MW 11,000). In both cases the products formed by in vitro translation are thus somewhat larger than the native products. As for other secreted proteins, the precursors probably contain an N-terminal signal peptide [19]. For C_3, on the other hand, the "in vivo" product (MW 13,000) is much larger than its precursor (MW 11,000). This discrepancy is due to glycosylation of this component. In fact, the amino acid sequence of the peptide part of C_3 corresponds to a molecular weight of 8653. In this case, too, the mRNA seems thus to encode a precursor protein, which is converted into a smaller peptide and glycosylated.

The mRNA activity of prostatic RNA has also been studied by microinjection in Xenopus Oocytes. In this case the injected mRNA is not only translated, but the formed peptide seems to be processed and glycosylated. Consequently, the products have a similar mobility as the native components and even are assembled in corresponding F and S subunits [20].

Androgenic Regulation of These mRNAs

It is generally assumed that steroid hormones exert their effect at the transcriptional level. The influence of androgens on PBP probably occurs by a similar mechanism, since these hormones produce a marked effect on the corresponding mRNAs. Castration, for instance, results after 6 days in a 14-fold decrease of the PBP directed mRNA activity of prostatic RNA. Inversely, a rapid and marked increase of this mRNA is observed after administration of androgens to castrated rats [17].

The presence of an androgen-dependent abundant class of mRNAs in the rat ventral prostate has been demonstrated by Parker et al [21] and confirmed by Mansson et al [22]. This class most probably includes the mRNAs of PBP, and its "in vitro" translation leads to the formation of peptides with similar molecular weights.

Recently Parker, White, and Williams [23] have purified and amplified ds-cDNA to some of those mRNAs by cloning. One of the obtained clones contains a DNA-sequence complementary to the mRNA of the peptide, which probably corresponds to the C_3 component of PBP. By hybridization of prostatic mRNA with this probe the same authors found already marked stimulation of this mRNA after 4 hours of androgen treatment.

CONCLUSIONS

Although it is now well established that the rat ventral prostate secretes large amounts of a specific protein, we are still puzzled by its functional significance. The observation that a protein with binding properties is found in the secretion of the prostate suggests that it exerts a carrier function, eg, for steroids or for other unidentified substances, which may have an influence in the female reproductive system. There is no real proof, however, for such a role.

Another attractive hypothesis is that PBP plays a role in the formation or removal of the copulation plug. Our experiments on an interference in this process were negative, however, and we also could not find protease activity or protease inhibitory activity associated with PBP.

Shyr and Liao [24] have shown that a protein factor in the prostate, which probably corresponds to the F subunit of PBP, inhibits the "in vitro" binding of androgen receptor to nuclear chromatin. Whether such a role occurs "in vivo" may be questioned, however, in view of the high amounts required of this factor and in view of the predominantly extracellular location of PBP.

We may conclude that we can only speculate at the present time on the function of PBP. Nevertheless, it is clear already that this protein constitutes an important biochemical marker for the epithelial cells of the rat ventral prostate [25] and an interesting end point for studies on the mechanism of action of androgens in this organ.

REFERENCES

1. Pang SG, Chow PH, Wong TM: The role of the seminal vesicles, coagulating glands and prostate glands on the fertility and fecundity of mice. J Reprod Fertil 56: 129–132, 1979.
2. Heyns W, Verhoeven G, De Moor P: A comparative study of androgen binding in rat uterus and prostate. J Steroid Biochem 7: 987–991, 1976.
3. Heyns W, Peeters B, Mous J, Rombauts W, De Moor P: Purification and characterization of prostatic binding protein and its subunits. Eur J Biochem 89: 181–186, 1978.
4. Lea OA, Petrusz P, French FS: Isolation and characterization of prostatein, a major secretory protein of rat ventral prostate. Fed Proc 36: 780 (abstr), 1977.
5. Lea OA, Petrusz P, French FS: Prostatein, a major secretory protein of the rat ventral prostate. J Biol Chem 254: 6196–6202, 1979.
6. Forsgren B, Högberg B, Gustafsson JA, Pousette A: Binding of estramustine, a nitrogen mustard derivative of estradiol-17β, in cytosol from rat ventral prostate. Acta Pharmaceut Suec 15: 23–32, 1978.
7. Forsgren B, Björk P, Carlström K, Gustafsson JA, Pousette A, Högberg B: Purification and distribution of a major protein in rat prostate that binds estramustine, a nitrogen mustard derivative of estradiol-17β. Proc Nat Acad Sci USA 76: 3149–3153, 1979.
8. Fang S, Liao S: Androgen receptors. Steroid and tissue specific retention of 17β-hydroxy-5α-androstan-3-one protein complex by the cell nuclei of ventral prostate. J Biol Chem 246: 16–24, 1971.
9. Karsznia R, Wyss R, Heinrichs L, Herrman WL: Binding of pregnenolone and progesterone by prostatic "receptor" proteins. Endocrinology 84: 1238–1246, 1969.
10. Heyns W, Bossyns D, Peeters B: Binding of a small androgen dependent protein to the prostatic binding protein of rat ventral prostate. The Prostate 1: 116, 1980.
11. Heyns W, De Moor P: Prostatic binding protein. A steroid binding protein secreted by rat prostate. Eur J Biochem 78: 221–230, 1977.
12. Peeters B, Rombauts W, Mous J, Heyns W: Structural studies on rat prostatic binding protein. The primary structure of its glycosylated component C_3. Eur J Biochem 115: 115–121, 1981.
13. Peeters B, Rombauts W, Mous J, Heyns W: Do the subunit-specific components C_1 and C_2 of

rat prostatic binding protein have a common ancestor? Arch Intern Physiol Biochim 89: B73, 1981.
14. Forsgren B, Gustafsson JA, Pousette A, Högberg B: Binding characteristics of a major protein in rat ventral prostate cytosol that interacts with estramustine, a nitrogen mustard derivative of 17β-estradiol. Cancer Res 39: 5155–5164, 1979.
15. Heyns W, Van Damme B, De Moor P: Secretion of prostatic binding protein by rat ventral prostate: influence of age and androgen. Endocrinology 103: 1090–1095, 1978.
16. Corpéchot C, Baulieu EE, Robel P: Testosterone, dihydrotestosterone and androstanediols in plasma, testes and prostates of rats during development. Acta Endocrinol 96: 127–135, 1981.
17. Peeters BL, Mous JM, Rombauts WA, Heyns WJ: Androgen-induced messenger RNA in rat ventral prostate. Translation, partial purification and preliminary characterization of the mRNAs encoding the components of prostatic binding protein. J Biol Chem 255: 7017–7023, 1980.
18. Heyns W, Peeters B, Mous J, Rombauts W, De Moor P: Androgen-dependent synthesis of a prostatic binding protein by rat prostate. J Steroid Biochem 11: 209–213, 1979.
19. Blobel G, Dobberstein B: Transfer of proteins across membranes. I. Presence of proteolytically processed an unprocessed nascent immunoglobulin light chains on membrane-bound ribosomes of murine myeloma. J Cell Biol 67: 835–851, 1975.
20. Mous J, Peeters W, Rombauts W, Heyns W: Synthesis and glycosylation of rat prostatic binding protein in Xenopus Laevis oocytes. FEBS Lett 103: 81–84, 1979.
21. Parker MG, Scrace GT: The androgenic regulation of abundant mRNA in rat ventral prostate. Eur J Biochem 85: 399–406, 1978.
22. Mansson PE, Silverberg AB, Gipson SH, Harris SE: Purification of major abundance class of poly (A^+)-RNA from rat ventral prostate. Mol Cell Endocrinol 19: 229–241, 1980.
23. Parker MG, White R, Williams JG: Cloning and characterization of androgen-dependent mRNA from rat ventral prostate. J Biol Chem 255: 6996–7001, 1980.
24. Shyr C-I, Liao S: Protein factor that inhibits binding and promotes release of androgen-receptor complex from nuclear chromatin. Proc Natl Acad Sci USA 75: 5969–5973, 1978.
25. McKeehan WL, Rosser MP, Glass HA, Fast D: Prostatic binding protein: an androgen-dependent marker for prostate epithelial cells. Biochem Biophys Res Commun 95: 674–681, 1980.

The Prostatic Cell: Structure and Function
Part A, pages 351–380

Model Systems for Studies on Androgen-Dependent Gene Expression in the Rat Prostate

Elizabeth M. Wilson, David H. Viskochil, Richard J. Bartlett, Oscar A. Lea, Claudia M. Noyes, Peter Petrusz, Darrel W. Stafford, and Frank S. French

INTRODUCTION

The rat prostate differentiates from individual buds in the urogenital sinus under the influence of androgen. As shown in Figure 1, it is composed of ventral, lateral, dorsal, and anterior (coagulating gland) lobes which together with seminal vesicles and preputial glands make up the accessory sex glands that contribute secretory products to the seminal fluid.

The prostate gland of the rat is an excellent model system for studies on androgen action at the molecular level. It contains a relatively high concentration of androgen receptor and is rigidly dependent on androgen stimulation for RNA and protein synthesis, cell division, and maintenance of metabolic functions. Thus far, studies of androgen action on the prostate have contributed to our understanding of the metabolism of androgens [1–4], functions and physico-chemical properties of the androgen receptor, [1, 5–10], and the demonstration of temporal relationships between androgen exposure and numerous cellular responses [11–16].

Progress in understanding androgen action at the nuclear level has been hindered by the complexity of the eukaryotic genome. For this reason we have undertaken to isolate and characterize specific genes known to be under androgen control. Androgen-dependent proteins of ventral and dorsal prostate have been purified and antisera prepared for use in the identification of specific messenger RNA (mRNA) translation products. DNAs complementary to these mRNAs (cDNA) have been isolated for use as hybridization probes in purification and characterization of cellular genes. We have found that the natural abundance of mRNAs coding for these major secretory proteins eliminates the necessity of mRNA purification. Thus cDNAs for these mRNAs can be synthesized from total poly(A)RNA and isolated by recombinant DNA and cloning methods.

Herein, we also report the lack of expression of major androgen-dependent dorsal prostate proteins in the Dunning androgen-dependent prostate adenocarcinoma (R3327) and describe a high content of transferrin in this tumor.

MATERIALS

RNA extraction and translation materials include wheat germ (Niblac), phenol (Mallinckrodt), proteinase K (P and L Biochemicals), guanidine-HCl (Heico), hydroxyapatite (BioRad), oligo-dT_{12-18} cellulose (Collaborative Research-T3). Cloning and cDNA materials include restriction enzymes (Bethesda Research Laboratories and Boehringer Mannheim Biochemical), DNA polymerase I (Bethesda Research Labs), [^{3}H]dCTP, 14 Ci/mmole and [^{3}H]dGTP, 8 Ci/mmole (ICN Inc.), α [^{32}P]dCTP, 500 Ci/mmole (New England Nuclear), ^{125}I (Amersham IMS. 300), S1 nuclease, Terminal transferase, and unlabeled nucleotides (P and L Biochemicals) and [^{35}S]L-methionine, 1200 Ci/mmole (Amersham). Avian myeloblastosis virus reverse transcriptase was provided by Dr. J.W. Beard and the Office of Program Resources and Logistics, Viral Cancer Program, NIH. HB101 E. Coli K12 cells were used as recipient cells for plasmid transformation.

METHODS

Animals

Sprague-Dawley rats weighing ~350 gm were obtained from Zivic Miller and used for the isolation of RNA from dorsal and ventral prostate and coagulating gland. Copenhagen Fischer rats bearing the Dunning prostate tumor (R3327) were obtained from the Papanicolaou Cancer Research Institute, Inc, Miami, Fl. Tumor tissue was implanted subcutaneously at the Cancer Institute and was allowed to grow until a tumor diameter of not more than 2 cm was reached for use in RNA extraction, and 3–4 cm for protein purification.

Purification of Prostate Proteins

Ventral prostate cytosol was used for the purification and characterization of prostatein, as previously described [17]. Dorsal prostate cytosol was used for the purification and characterization of dorsal protein I, as previously described [18].

A major Dunning prostate tumor protein, identified as transferrin, was purified from Dunning prostate tumor cytosol [Wilson EM, unpublished studies]. The pellet of a 40–60% $(NH_4)_2SO_4$ fraction of tumor cytosol was resuspended in 1/10 volume of 50 mM Tris, pH 7.5, 1mM EDTA, 10 mM KCl and following dialysis was applied to a DEAE-Sepharose column (1.6 × 15 cm) equilibrated in the same buffer. The unadsorbed fraction was dialyzed against 2mM Tris, pH

7.5, overnight at 4°C and applied to a second DEAE-Sepharose column equilibrated in 2 mM Tris, pH 7.5. A 200-ml gradient from 0–0.2 M KCl in 2mM Tris, pH 7.5, was applied. The major peak eluting at approximately 0.1 M KCl was pooled, dialyzed, and lyophilized. The protein was resuspended in 50 mM Tris, pH 7.5, 1 mM EDTA and chromatographed on a Sephadex G-200 column (64 × 2.6 cm) while collecting fractions of 3.3 ml. The major peak eluting at 38 Å was pooled, dialyzed against H_2O, and lyophilized. The resuspended protein was rechromatographed on DEAE-Sepharose as described above. The protein recovered from the peak eluting at about 0.1 M KCl was considered pure by SDS polyacrylamide gel electrophoresis, as shown in Figure 13, gel 1.

Immunocytochemical Localization

Antisera prepared to prostatein and dorsal protein I were used to localize these proteins in sections of the prostate complex as previously described using the peroxidase-immunoglobulin bridge technique [19, 20].

Extraction of RNA from Tissues

Dorsal and ventral prostate and coagulating gland were obtained from Sprague-Dawley rats. Dunning prostate tumors were grown as subcutaneous transplants in Copenhagen-Fischer rats. Rats were decapitated using a guillotine. Tissues were immediately removed and frozen in liquid N_2. Total RNA was extracted as previously described using either phenol-chloroform-isoamyl alcohol [21] or guanidine-HCl [22]. The DNA content of phenol extracted RNA was reduced by batchwise treatment with hydroxylapatite as previously described [23]. Polyadenylated RNA [poly(A)RNA] was partially purified by chromatography on oligo-dT cellulose using a modification of the procedure of Aviv and Leder [24].

Translation of Poly(A)RNA in a JLS-V16 system

Tissue-specific poly(A)RNA was translated in a mouse embryo fibroblast extract essentially as previously described [25]. Briefly, cell-free protein synthesis was assayed in 25 μl containing 20mM HEPES (pH 7.5), 90 mM KCl, 1mM $Mg(OAc)_2$, 150 μM spermine, 8mM 2-mercaptoethanol, 1 mM ATP, 150 μM GTP, 10 mM creatine phosphate, 16 μg/ml creatine kinase, 400–800 μCi/ml [^{35}S] methionine (> 600 Ci/mmole), 100 μM each of unlabeled amino acids (without methionine), 5.25 μl of a nuclease-treated JLS-V16 cell extract (gift from E. Murphy, University of Texas System Cancer Center, Houston), 0.125 A_{280} of reticulocyte ribosome high-salt wash-initiation factors (gift from E. Murphy), and 0.5–1.5 μg poly(A)RNA. Protein synthesis was allowed to proceed at 32°C for 120 minutes.

Fluorography of SDS polyacrylamide gels containing ^{35}S-methionine labeled proteins was carried out as previously described [26].

Preparation of Ventral Prostate cDNAs

Complementary DNA (cDNA) was synthesized from total ventral prostate poly(A)RNA using avian myeloblastosis virus reverse transcriptase (Dr. J. W. Beard, Life Sciences Inc.), oligo-dT_{12} primer, and high levels of dNTPs [27]. The yield of single stranded cDNA was approximately 25%. Analytical S1 nuclease digestion indicated that 12% of the cDNA was a double-stranded hairpin generated by the DNA-dependent polymerase activity of reverse transcriptase. DNA polymerase I was used to extend this duplex to yield a double-stranded cDNA [28] of which 75% was protected from S_1 nuclease digestion. This cDNA was treated with S1 nuclease to generate blunt-ended, double-stranded DNA and size selected by chromatography on a Biogel A-150 column. Fractions containing cDNA greater than 200 base pairs were pooled and approximately 10–30 deoxycytosine bases were added to the 3′ end using Terminal deoxynucleotidyl Transferase in the presence of Co^{2+} [29]. This "dC tailed" double stranded cDNA was then ready to anneal with "dG tailed" Pst I cut pBR322.

The plasmid pBR322 (greater than 90% supercoiled) was prepared by cutting with the restriction enzyme Pst I and extending the 3′ end with approximately 10–20 deoxyguanosine bases using Terminal Transferase [29]. Pst I (Boehringer) cleaves pBR322 at a single site in the gene region coding for ampicillin resistance [30]. Cloning experiments were carried out under P3 containment in compliance with National Institutes of Health guidelines and the University of North Carolina Biohazards Committee.

The "tailed" cDNA and vector were annealed [Lis J, Personal communication] and used to transform $CaCl_2$ treated E. coli HB 101 cells [31]. Bacteria colonies harboring plasmids were selected by their ability to grow on agar containing tetracyline (15 μg/ml) (Table III). These colonies were toothpicked to nitrocellulose filters on tetracycline agar plates and screened with a radioactive probe [Hanahan D, Personal communication] and [32]. Colonies hybridizing to either [^{125}I]poly(A)RNA [Bartlett RJ, personal communication] or [^{32}P]cDNA [33] were selected for further analysis. Plasmids were amplified with chloramphenicol and extracted in SDS/NaOH [34, 35]. The extracted DNA was tested for its content of cDNA insert when cut with Pst I and its ability to hybridize with labeled ventral prostate poly(A)RNA sequences. cDNA extracted from pBR322 by Pst I digestion was electrophoresed on polyacrylamide gels and DNA fragments were stained with ethidium bromide and visualized under ultra-violet light. A few Pst I digests were electrophoresed on agarose gels followed by blotting to nitrocellulose [36] and hybridization with labeled ventral prostate poly(A)RNA [37]. Hybridization of inserted DNA with ventral prostate poly(A)RNA sequences encouraged the use of hybridization arrest translation (HART) [38] in selecting sequences which code for peptides in the wheat germ translation system.

Colony hybridization positives were pooled in groups of six, grown in tetracycline followed by chloramphenicol, and harvested [34, 35]. Plasmid DNA was extracted and passed over a CsCl gradient. The supercoiled DNA was collected, dialyzed, ethanol precipitated, and subsequently linearized by digestion with Eco RI, Bam HI or Hind III (Bethesda Research Laboratories). High-excess DNA (more than tenfold) to poly(A)RNA hybridizations were carried out and ethanol precipitated. Pellets were resuspended in dH_2O and half was translated in the wheat germ system with ^{35}S-methionine. Aliquots of the reaction were run on 15% SDS-polyacrylamide gels, the gel was prepared for fluorography [39] and exposed to x-ray film. The pooled colonies demonstrating HART positives were separated and the individual clones tested in an identical fashion (Fig. 7). Plasmids containing cDNA inserts were linearized with a restriction enzyme (Eco RI, Hind III, or Bam HI), bound covalently to diazobenzyloxymethyl-paper [40], and hybridized with an excess of ventral prostate poly(A)RNA [41]. After extensive washing, hybrid poly(A)RNA was eluted, ethanol precipitated, and translated in the wheat germ system. With each cDNA a high degree of purification of the specific HART positive band was observed.

Using the method of hybridization arrest translation, we have isolated cDNAs corresponding to messenger RNAs coding for the 20K, 14K, 11K, and 10K peptides in the wheat germ system. The 20K and 14K subunits were identified also by the method of hybridization selection for translation [41], which confirmed the HART analysis.

RESULTS AND DISCUSSION

Ventral Prostate

The ventral prostate consists of four lobes containing tubuloalveolar glands which secrete fluid into the urethra through several minute ducts (Fig. 1) [42]. Its major secretory protein has been identified and referred to as prostatein[1] [17]. Prostatein has been purified from ventral prostate cytosol by DEAE-Sephadex and hydroxylapatite chromatography, isoelectric focusing, gel filtration, and gel electrophoresis. It is an acidic glycoprotein with molecular weight of approximately 40,000 (Table I) and carbohydrate content of 9.1% (Table II). Prostatein contains 50% nonpolar amino acids (Table II) and binds steroids in accordance with the polarity rule [17]. The binding affinity for steroids is inversely related to steroid polarity: progesterone ($K_a = 6.9 \times 10^4$) > androstenedione > dihydrotestosterone > androsterone > estradiol > testosterone > 5α-androstane-3α, 17β-diol. Although prostatein has a low affinity for steroids, its extraordinarily high concentration may render its androgen binding property biologically relevant.

[1]It has become apparent that prostatein [17] and prostatic binding protein, PBP [43, 44], described by Heyns and co-workers are probably the same protein. It appears also to be identical to α-protein of Liao and co-workers [45] and estramustine-binding protein of Forsgren et al [46, 47].

TABLE I. Physicochemical properties of prostatein

Molecular weight[a]	42,000
Subunit structure[b]	tetrameric
Sedimentation coefficient ($S^0 20,w$)	3.2S
Frictional ratio[c]	1.22
Isoelectric point	4.8
Content of hydrophobic amino acids[d]	50.9%
Carbohydrate content[e]	9.1%
Steroid binding[f]	$Ka \leq 6.9 \times 10^4$

[a]Determined by polyacrylamide gel electrophoresis using the method of Rodbard and Chrambach [48].
[b]The 42,000 MW (42K) intact prostatein yields 22K + 20K subunits on SDS polyacrylamide gel electrophoresis corresponding to the "slow" and "fast" subunits, respectively, of Heyns and co-workers [44]. Under reducing conditions (0.2 M dithiothreitol) upon SDS gel electrophoresis, the subunit 22K→14K + 10K and the 20K→14K + 6K.
[c]Calculated from the equation $f/f_0 = a/R$, where a is the Stokes-Einstein radius and R is the unhydrated radius [48].
[d]Calculated from the amino acid composition [49].
[e]Measured by gas-liquid chromatography [50].
[f]Measured by equilibrium dialysis using prostatein purified from ventral prostate cytosol as previously described [17].

TABLE II. Amino acid and carbohydrate composition of prostatein (mole/mole protein)

Asp, Asn[a]	9.28	Met	4.45	Mannose[b]	3.4
Thr	5.06	Ile	5.15	Galactose	1.6
Ser	4.83	Leu	8.89	Glucose	1.2
Glu, Gln	19.56	Tyr	3.37	N-Ac-glucosam.	2.9
Pro	2.54	Phe	7.37	Sialic Acid	—
Gly	2.52	His	1.95		
Ala	3.17	Lys	8.01		
1/2 Cys	3.01	Arg	3.31		
Val	7.52				

[a]Protein (100 μg) was hydrolyzed in 6 N HCl in evacuated, sealed tubes for 24 hours. The hydrolysate was analyzed in a BioCal BC 200 automatic amino acid analyzer equipped with an Autolab integrator. Cysteine was also determined as cysteic acid in an independent run following performic acid oxidation. Tryptophan was not analyzed.
[b]Carbohydrate composition was determined by gas-liquid chromatography [50].

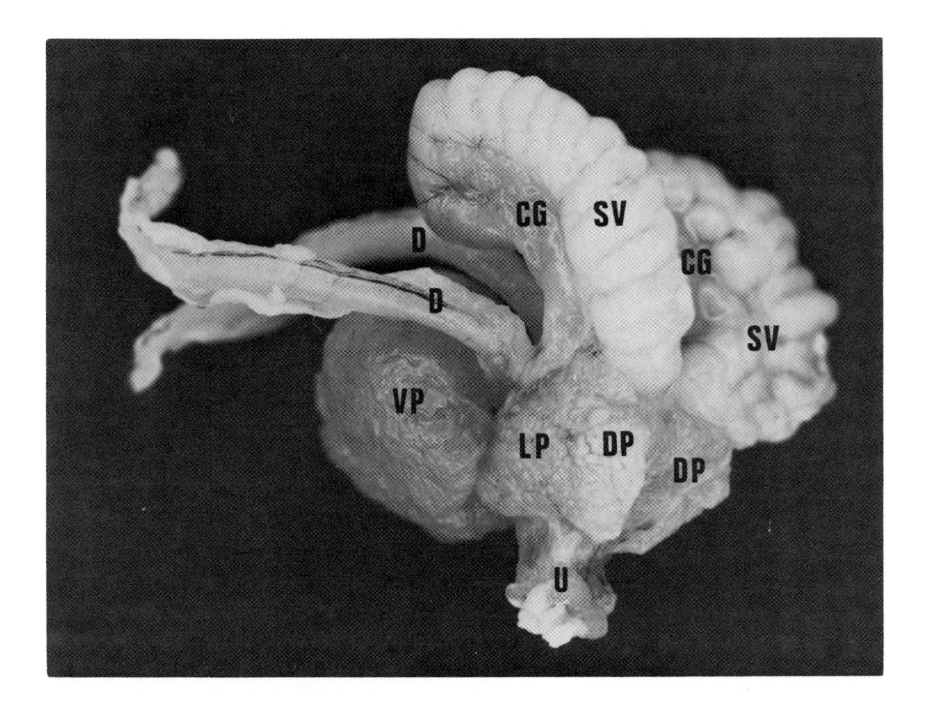

Fig. 1. Male accessory sex organs of the adult rat. The accessory sex organ complex was removed from an adult Sprague-Dawley rat by cutting the ductus deferens and urethra. The complex was fixed in formalin (10%) for 48 hours. Indicated are the ventral (VP), lateral (LP), and dorsal (DP) lobes of the prostate, the urethra (U), seminal vesicle (SV), coagulating glands (CG), and ductus deferens (D).

In agreement with Heyns and co-workers [44, 51], we have observed that partially purified prostatein (MW = 42K) yields two smaller components (22K and 20K) when fractionated by SDS polyacrylamide gel electrophoresis. Each of these components is separated further into smaller fragments by reduction and SDS gel electrophoresis (22K → 14K + 10K and 20K → 14K + 6K). The 14K peptides are thought to be identical, based on molecular weight and periodic acid-Schiff staining for glycoprotein [44]. During purification of prostatein, a protein of molecular weight 38K, estimated by Ferguson plots of electrophoretic mobility in nondenaturing gels of different pore size [48], was observed to have a mobility similar to prostatein. It could be separated, however, by polyacrylamide gel electrophoresis under nondenaturing conditions. It was found that this 38K protein forms a 22K component on SDS gel electrophoresis and this can be reduced with 0.2 M dithiothreitol to 14K and 10K fragments on SDS polyacrylamide gels. We initially believed this to be contaminating protein which could be purified away from intact prostatein [17]. However, it seems likely now that the 38K protein is formed when intact prostatein breaks up during purification under denaturing conditions to yield both the 38K protein (an aggregate of the 22K subunit) and the 20K subunit.

Immunization with prostatein, both dimer and monomer (20K), produced precipitating antibodies in three rabbits injected. The antisera were judged monospecific by immunodiffusion and crossed immunoelectrophoresis. Prostatein could be quantitated by rocket immunoelectrophoresis in 5 μl of a 1:1000 dilution of ventral prostate cytosol from adult rats (~ 35 ng total protein). It could not be detected in cytosols from dorsal prostate, seminal vesicle, epididymis, testis, skeletal muscle, levator ani muscle, lung, liver, intestine, kidney, submaxillary gland, or brain [17]. Immunocytochemical localization using the peroxidase bridge method showed specific staining in the acinar glands of the ventral prostate but not in adjacent glandular structures (Fig. 2). Secretion into the seminal fluid is indicated by dark staining in the lumen of the urethra. A saline extract of the

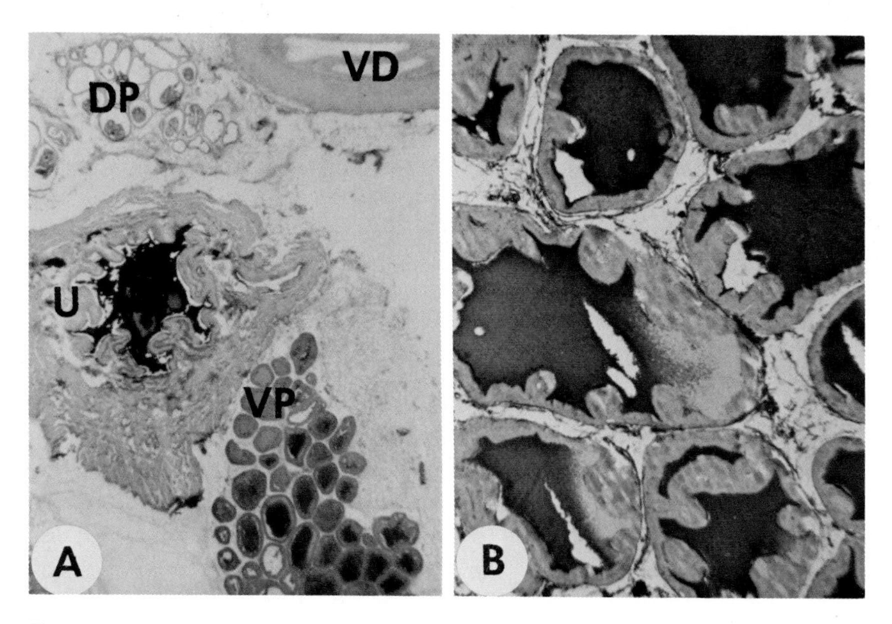

Fig. 2. Immunoperoxidase localization of prostatein in rat ventral prostate and surrounding tissues. Antiserum to prostatein [17] was diluted 1:1000. Tissues were counterstained with toluidine blue. (A) Immunoreactive prostatein is present within acinar gland lumena of ventral prostate (VP) as indicated by deposition of dark reaction product. Dark staining in the urethra indicates that prostatein is secreted into seminal fluid. The dorsal prostate (DP), vas deferens (VD), and surrounding connective tissue lack detectable amounts of prostatein. × 18. (B) Higher power (× 73) view of the ventral prostate. Note heavy accumulation of reaction product in acinar lumena with little staining in the lining epithelium.

ejaculated sperm plug contained prostatein in amounts of 32–41% of the concentration found in normal prostate when calculated per mg of soluble protein [17].

Prostatein was measured in prostates of 16-day-old rats using rocket immunoelectrophoresis. Its concentration increases during puberty and reaches 25% of total soluble protein in the mature prostate (Fig. 3). Maintenance of prostatein in the mature gland is dependent on androgen (Fig. 4). A rather slow decline following castration likely results from its high concentration and storage within acinar glands.

It has been shown by hybridization experiments following castration and readministration of androgen that the concentration of abundant mRNA and protein in the ventral prostate is regulated by androgen [53–55]. Cell-free translation of ventral prostate poly(A)RNA extracts suggested that this effect of androgens increased the abundance of mRNAs coding for subunits of prostatic binding protein [56].

The ventral prostate is an abundant source of RNA. From 12 gm of tissue 40 mg total RNA is extracted using the guanidine-HCl procedure [22], from which 3.4 mg poly(A)RNA can be selected using oligo-dT cellulose chromatography (Table III). Translation of total poly(A)RNA in a cell free system containing the wheat germ S-30 fraction [57] results in three major and two minor peptides [Viskochil DH, unpublished studies] (Fig. 5). Molecular weights

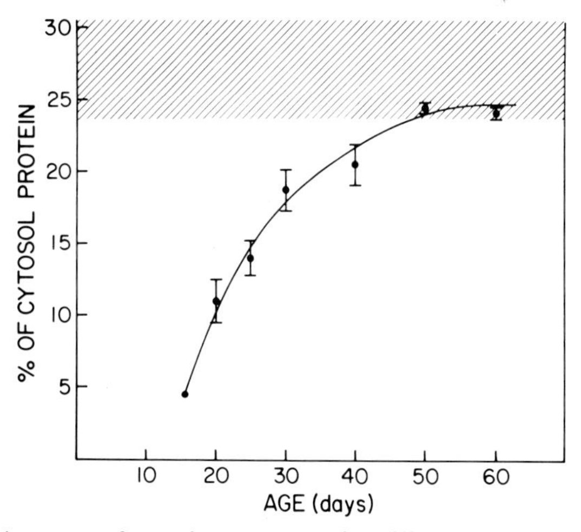

Fig. 3. Prostatein content of ventral prostate cytosol at different ages of the rat. Prostatein concentration was estimated using rocket immunoelectrophoresis [17] and is expressed as percent of total cytosol protein measured in the Lowry assay [52]. Data are expressed as mean ± SD of five individual determinations, except for the 16-day-old, which was a pooled sample. The shaded area indicates the range in prostatein content in adult male rat prostate.

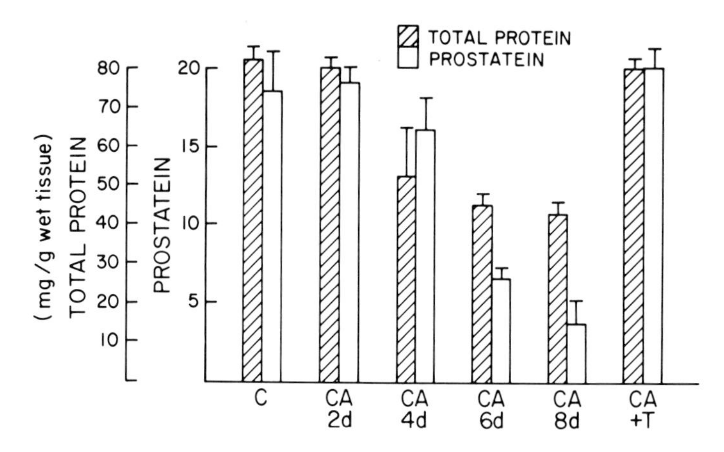

Fig. 4. Effect of castration and androgen replacement on total cytosol protein and prostatein content in rat ventral prostate. Adult Sprague-Dawley rats (~ 450 gm) were castrated in groups of four (CA) for different periods of time from 2–8 days. Another group (CA + T) was castrated and immediately administered testosterone propionate (1 mg in 0.1 ml sesame oil) intramuscularly. Control (C) and untreated castrated rats received injections of vehicle. Injections were continued every other day for 8 days. Ventral prostates were removed and cytosols prepared. Prostatein concentration (open bars) was determined by rocket immunoelectrophoresis [17] and total protein (hatched bars) by the Lowry assay [52]. Bars indicate means ± SD.

TABLE III. RNA isolation from prostate

	Total crude RNA[a] (mg)	Poly(A)RNA[b] (mg)
Dorsal prostate	8	0.6
Coagulating gland	31	2.0
Ventral prostate	40	3.4
Dunning tumor	12	0.3

[a]Total nucleic acid extracted using guanidine-HCl [22] or phenol [21] from 12 gm tissue.
[b]Poly(A) RNA was selected on oligo-dT cellulose as previously described [24].

of the major peptides correspond to 14K, 11K, and 10K, while the minor species are 20K and 34K. The three major translation products represent approximately 70% of the total protein synthesized in vitro as measured using either [^{35}S]methionine or [^{14}C]leucine.

Antibody to the 20K component of prostatein (14K + 6K subunits) selectively precipitates the 11K peptide translated in the wheat germ ribosome system suggesting that this peptide corresponds to either the 14K or 6K subunit of prostatein. In the wheat germ system, translated peptides may differ in size from proteins synthesized in vivo since post translational processing of peptides by signal

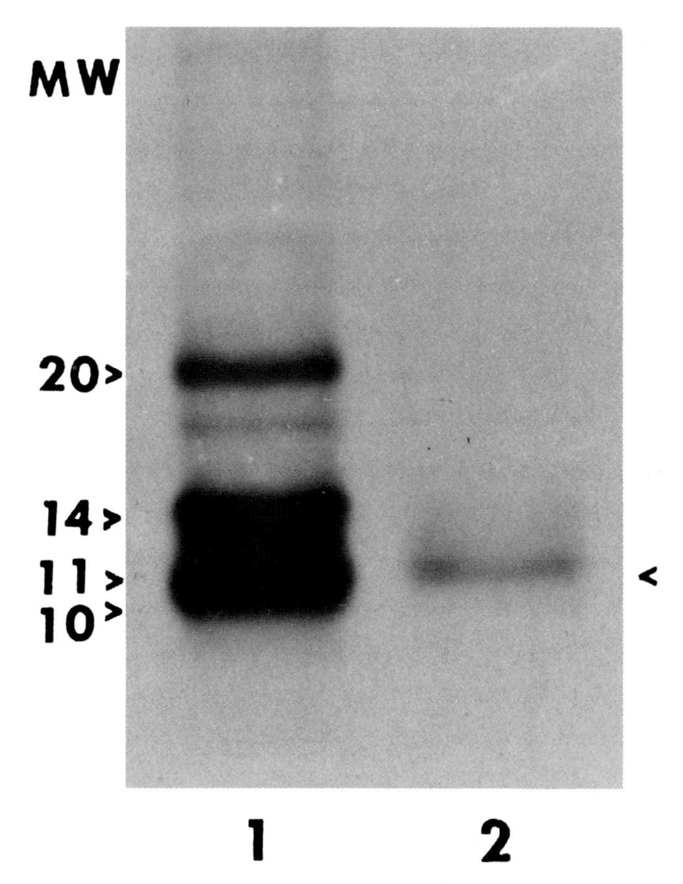

Fig. 5. Fluorogram of an SDS polyacrylamide gel containing ^{35}S-methionine-labeled proteins synthesized in the wheat germ system [38] using total poly(A)RNA isolated from rat ventral prostate. Poly(A)RNA was extracted using guanidine-HCl and selected on oligo dT-cellulose as described in Methods. Synthesized proteins were treated with 10 mM dithiothreitol, heated to 100°C for 5 minutes and 50,000 cpm were electrophoresed in a 15% polyacrylamide gel containing SDS [58] (lane 1). An aliquot of labeled proteins was incubated with an antiserum (diluted 1/300) against the 20K subunit of prostatein [17]. Protein A was used to precipitate the antigen-antibody complex and the sample was treated with dithiothreitol and electrophoresed as above (lane 2). Molecular weight markers used to calibrate the gel were lysozyme (14K), carboxypeptidase B (35K), and ovalbumin (43K). Indicated are the approximate MWs of the major in vitro synthesized ventral prostate proteins.

peptide cleavage and glycosylation does not occur. Heyns and co-workers [59] have reported that the 11K peptide translated in the wheat germ system corresponds to the 14K subunit of prostatic binding protein which is larger as a result of glycosylation. Our results indicate also that most of the carbohydrate is attached to the 14K subunit [Lea OA, unpublished studies].

The abundance of the three prostate mRNAs led us to clone the cDNA synthesized from total poly(A)RNA (Fig. 6) as described in Methods. E. coli colonies containing pBR322 plasmids with ventral prostate cDNA inserts were tested for their ability to hybridize with either [^{125}I] poly(A)RNA or [^{32}P]cDNA. Strong hybridization was observed with approximately 10% of the 800 tetracycline-resistant colonies. These results encouraged us to use hybridization arrest of translation (HART) [38] in selecting recombinant cDNAs which correspond to messenger RNAs coding for specific peptides in the wheat germ translation system. Loss of a radioactive peptide band indicates arrest of translation due to hybridization of a specific mRNA with its complementary DNA (Fig. 7). We have isolated cDNAs corresponding to mRNAs coding for the 20K, 14K, 11K, and 10K peptides in the wheat germ system [Viskochil DH, unpublished studies].

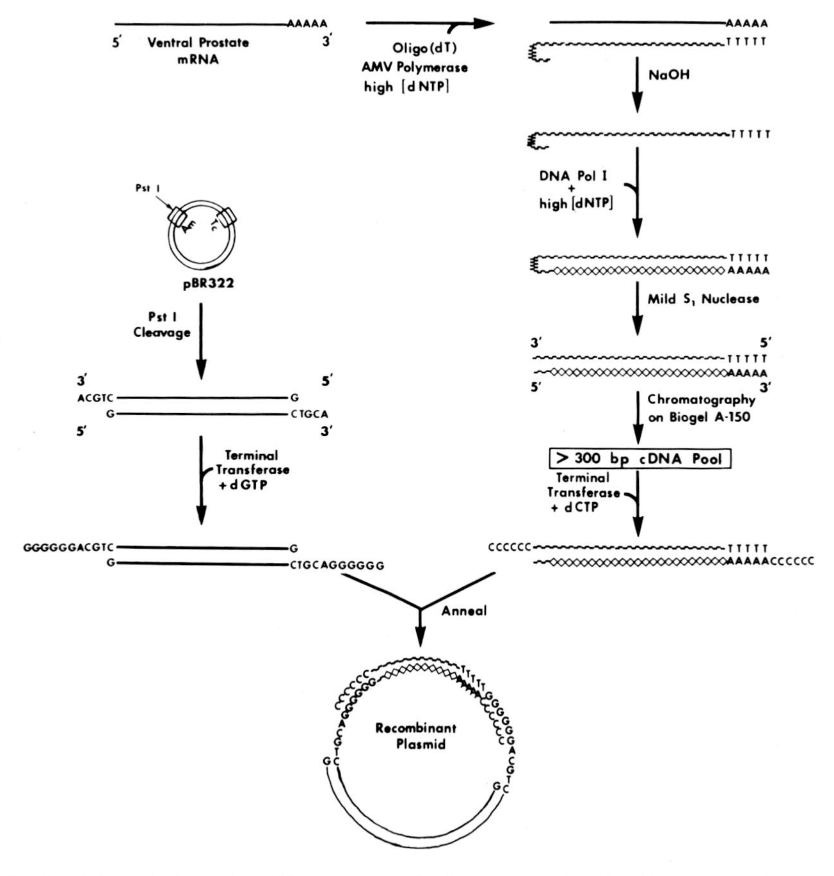

Fig. 6. Schematic illustration of in vitro synthesis of double stranded DNA from rat ventral prostate poly(A)RNA and construction of cDNA-plasmid hybrids. (AMV polymerase = reverse transcriptase).

These cDNAs were identified also by the method of hybridization selection for translation [41] as described in Methods. The majority of inserted cDNA sequences could be separated from pBR322 using the restriction enzyme Pst I since this cleavage site is usually regenerated by the G-C "tailing" method of cDNA insertion. Pst I digestion released cDNAs ranging in size from 300–700 base pairs as determined by electrophoresis in 6% polyacrylamide gels.

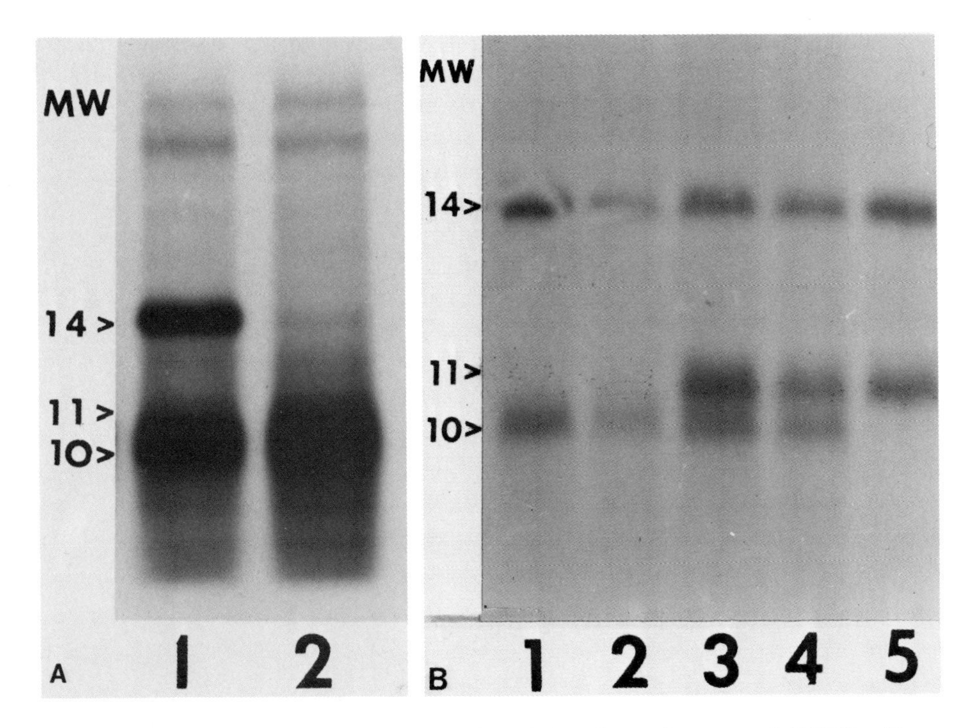

Fig. 7. Fluorograms of hybridization arrest of translation of ventral prostate poly(A)RNA with various cDNA inserts. A) Poly(A)RNA (200 ng) isolated from rat ventral prostate using guanidine-HCl and oligo-dT selection (see Methods) was hybridized to linearized plasmid DNA containing the cDNA insert designated BB 34 (20 μg) as described in Methods. The hybridization mixture was split and one half boiled for 3 minutes to melt all hybrids (lane 1). The other was not boiled (lane 2) prior to in vitro translation in the wheat germ system. [^{35}S]-Methionine labeled translated peptides were treated with 10 mM dithiothreitol, heated to 100°C for 5 minutes, and separated on 15% polyacrylamide SDS gels [58]. Indicated are the labeled 14K, 11K and 10K peptides. Note the loss of the 14K fragment in lane 2, indicating that cDNA BB34 selectively hybridized with and thus prevented the translation of poly(A)RNA coding for this peptide. B) Poly(A)RNA from rat ventral prostate was hybridized with cloned cDNA and translated as described above. Shown are samples not boiled following hybridization with linearized plasmids extracted from clones designated αE7 (lane 1), αE45 (lane2), no cDNA (lane 3), α E52 (lane 4), and αE58 (lane 5). Note the identification of cDNAs corresponding to mRNA for 11K peptide (lane 1 and 2) and the 10K peptide (lane 5).

Heynes et al [59] purified and raised antibodies to three different subunits (8K, 11K, and 13K) which make up the 22K and 20K components of prostatic binding protein. Antiserum to 8K subunit recognized the 9K peptide synthesized in vitro, 11K subunit antiserum bound to the 12K peptide, and 13K antiserum bound the 11K peptide (see chapter by Heyns and co-workers). These findings together with observations that each cDNA sequence hybridizes with mRNA coding for a single peptide (Viskochil DH, unpublished studies) and [60] suggest that prostatein is composed of three unique subunits synthesized from three cellular genes.

A complication of this interpretation, however, is our finding of only two different N-terminal sequences in intact prostatein (Fig. 8). If it is assumed that the 14K peptides of the 20K and 22K subunits are identical, one possible explanation for detection of only two N-terminal sequences is that one of the peptide chains has a blocked animo-terminus. Since both N-terminal sequences could be obtained from the 20K component (14K and 6K subunits) of prostatein, the blocked amino-terminus should be on the 10K subunit. This possibility will be tested by attempting to sequence the purified 10K subunit. Another possibility is that two of the mRNAs coding for prostatein are products of duplicated genes differing only in regions near their 3′ ends; base sequences coding for the N-

Chain 14K

Ser-Gly-Ser-Gly-Cys-Ser-Ile-Leu-Asp-Glu-

Val-Ile-Arg-Gly-Thr-Ile-Asn-Ser/Cys-Thr-Val-
CHO

Thr-Leu-?-Asp-Tyr-Met-?-Leu-Val-?-Pro-Tyr-

Chain 6K

Ser-Gln-Ile-Cys-Glu-Leu-Val-Ala-His-Glu-

Thr-Ile-Cys-Phe-Leu-Met-?-Ser/Cys-Gly-?-Glu-Leu-

Fig. 8. Partial N-terminal amino acid sequences of prostatein. Prostatein was purified as described by Lea et al [17]. Automated Edman degradations were performed by a Beckman 890C sequencer [61]. The phenylthiohydantoin amino acids produced were identified by gas chromatography [62], high-performance liquid chromatography [63], and thin-layer chromatography [64, 65]. Both intact prostatein (40K) and the 20K (fast) subunit yielded the two sequences indicated above. A single N-terminal sequence, noted as 14K, was obtained from analysis of the purified 14K component of the 20K subunit.

terminal regions of their peptide products could thus be identical. Final proof of the quaternary structure of prostatein may be established by matching the base sequences of isolated cDNAs with purified fragments of the intact protein.

Dorsal Prostate and Coagulating Gland

The dorsal prostate, also known as dorsocaudal prostate, surrounds the dorsal side of the urethra near the bladder and is in close juxtaposition to the lateral prostate (Fig. 1). It consists of two lobes, smaller than the ventral, that have the same tubuloalveolar structure as the ventral prostate. Dorsal prostate is anatomically separate from the coagulating gland, and can be distinguished from the lateral prostate along a connective tissue plane of cleavage. The coagulating glands are tubular glands with luminal compartments containing fluid of high protein concentration (~ 300 mg/ml). They lie free of the urethra and are in close contact with the concave sides of the seminal vesicles (Fig. 1). As they approach the urethra, each forms a single small duct through which it secretes the fluid contents of its lumen into the urethra. Despite their anatomical differences the pattern of dorsal prostate cytosol proteins is the same as that of the coagulating gland (Fig. 9) and is distinct from the lateral and ventral prostate [18]. In addition to two major secretory proteins, referred to as DP I and II, dorsal prostate and coagulating gland are major sites of fructose secretion [66, 67]. The tenfold higher prostate-specific transglutaminase activity reported in coagulating gland as opposed to dorsal prostate [68] is likely due to the large pool of enzyme stored in the lumen of the coagulating gland. Moreover, lateral prostate was included with the dorsal prostate and could have caused a dilution of dorsal prostate transglutaminase since lateral prostate proteins differ from those of the dorsal gland.

Dorsal protein I (DP I) has been purified from the dorsal prostate and partially characterized [18]. It is a dimer composed of two identical subunits. Each monomer is 71,000 molecular weight when estimated from its sedimentation coefficient 4.6 S and Stokes radius 32 Å (Table IV). A monomer MW of 62,000 is observed by SDS polyacrylamide gel electrophoresis. The 150,000 MW dimer has a sedimentation coefficient of 6.8 S, Stokes radius of 46 Å. The dimer dissociates to the monomer in the presence of 0.5 M KCl. DP I is a basic protein that is retained by phosphocellulose, but not by DEAE-Sepharose at pH 7.5. It has a small carbohydrate content, as revealed by periodic acid-Schiff staining. Rocket immunoelectrophoresis using an antibody specific to DP I revealed that DP I is a protein unique to the dorsal prostate and coagulating gland (Table V). It is antigenically undetectable in ventral and lateral prostate, seminal vesicle cytosol or fluid, testis, epididymis, liver, or kidney. Localization using the immunoperoxidase method [19] also indicates that DP I is a secretory protein of dorsal prostate and coagulating glands (Fig. 10). The tubular nature of the coagulating gland facilitates the collection of fluid from its luminal compartment.

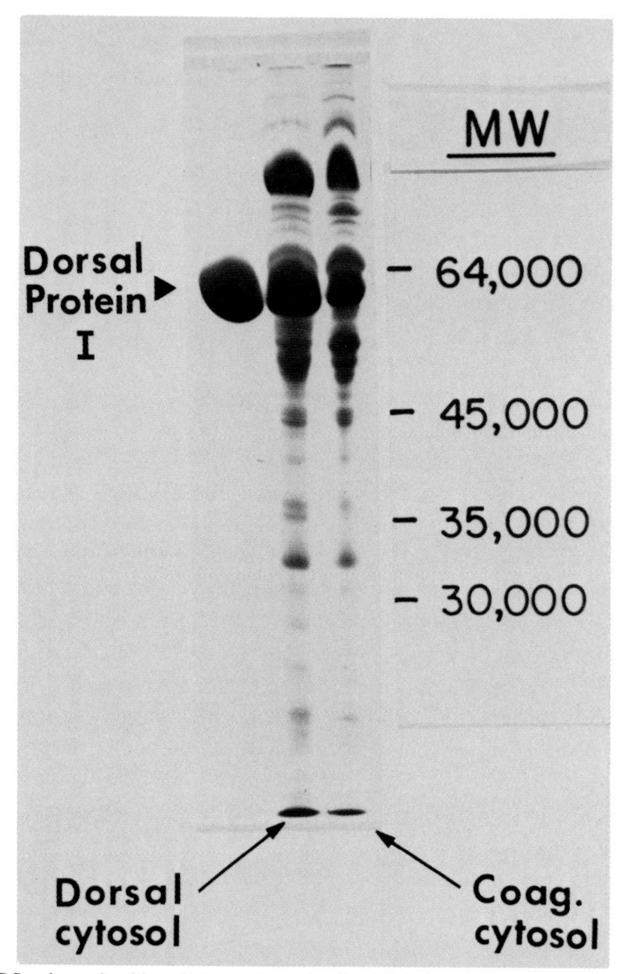

Fig. 9. SDS polyacrylamide gel electrophoresis of purified dorsal protein I and dorsal prostate and coagulating gland cytosol proteins. An SDS slab gel of 9% acrylamide prepared as previously described [18] illustrates purified dorsal prostate protein I (10 μg) (left), dorsal prostate cytosol (80 μg total protein) (middle), and coagulating gland cytosol (65 μg) (right). Molecular weight marker proteins are rat serum albumin, 64,000; ovalbumin, 45,000; carboxypeptidase-B, 35,000; and chymotrypsinogen, 30,000 MW.

DP I comprises as much as 25% of cytosol protein; however, it represents only 6% of total protein in coagulating gland fluid and seminal fluid (Table V). This disparity between DP I concentration in cytosol and secreted fluid suggests that it might be sequestered and stored within the cell.

Dorsal protein II is a larger protein (MW~80,000 by SDS gel electrophoresis) with a high carbohydrate content. Under nondenaturing conditions it has a Stokes radius of > 200 Å, corresponding to MW above 300,000. While dorsal protein II composes a smaller proportion of total cytosol protein than DP I, it is the

TABLE IV. Molecular properties of dorsal protein I

	Monomer	Dimer
Sedimentation coefficient[a] (S)	4.6	6.8
Stokes radius[b] (Å)	32	46
Molecular weight		
SDS-polyacrylamide gel[c]	62,000	
Hydrodynamic[d]	71,000	150,000
Frictional ratio[e] (f/f_o)	1.16	1.3

[a]Determined on linear 5–20% (w/v) sucrose gradients in 1 mM EDTA, 50 mM Tris, pH 7.5, containing no KCl for the dimer and 0.15 M KCl for the monomer. Gradients were centrifuged in a Beckman SW 50.1 rotor at 44,000 rpm for 18 hours at 2°C. Purified dorsal protein samples of 200 μg in 0.2 ml were applied. Sedimentation coefficients were estimated by centrifuging standard proteins in parallel gradients: ovalbumin (3.6 S), bovine γ-globulin (7S) and catalase (11.3 S). The S designates Svedberg units.

[b]Determineed by Sephadex G-200 chromatography in a column (65 × 2.6 cm) equilibrated in 1 mM EDTA, 50 mM Tris, pH 7.5. The column was calibrated with blue dextran to indicate the void volume (V_o), bovine γ-globulin (52Å), and ovalbumin (27.3 Å). The equation used $K_{av} = [(V_e—V_o)/(V_t—V_o)]$, where V_o is the void volume, V_e is the elution volume, and V_t is the total column volume. A semilogarithmic plot of $K_{av}{}^{1/3}$ versus Stokes radius was used to estimate the Stokes radii of monomer and dimer.

[c]Determined on SDS polyacrylamide (9%) gels as shown in Figure 9, using the marker proteins: rat serum albumin, 64,000; ovalbumin 45,000; carboxypeptidase B, 35,000; and chymotrypsinogen, 30,000. Molecular weight was plotted on a semilogarithmic scale versus relative mobility.

[d]Estimated as previously described [69] using the equation $M_r = 6 \pi \eta NaS/(1—\bar{v}\rho)$, where η is viscosity of medium, 0.01 gm/sec/cm; N is Avogadro's number, 6.02×10^{23}/gm-mole; a is Stokes radius, 10^{-8} cm; S is Svedberg unit in 10^{-13} S; $\bar{v}$ is partial specific volume, 0.743 cm^3/gm; and ρ is density, 1.03 gm/cm^3. The partial specific volume was calculated from the amino acid composition, $\bar{v} = (\Sigma_i \bar{v} w_i)/(\Sigma_i w_i)$ where $\bar{v}$ is the partial specific volume of each residue [70] and w is the weight fraction.

[e]Estimated using the equation $f/f_o = a/(3\bar{v}M_r/4 \pi N)^{1/3}$ with abbreviations as indicated above.

TABLE V. Distribution of dorsal protein I in rat cytosols and fluids

	Percent of total protein[a]
Dorsal prostate	25
Coagulating gland	
cytosol	27
fluid	6
Ejaculated seminal fluid	5
Dunning prostate tumor (R3327)	ND[b]
Ventral prostate	ND
Lateral prostate	<2
Seminal vesicle	
cytosol	ND
fluid	ND
Serum	ND
Testis, epididymis, liver, or kidney	ND

[a]Dorsal protein I concentration was determined by rocket immunoelectrophoresis [18] and total protein by the Lowry assay [52].

[b]ND designates "not detectable" by rocket immunoelectrophoresis.

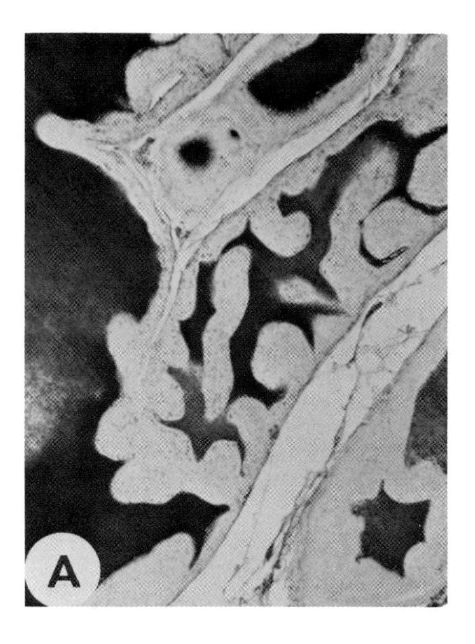

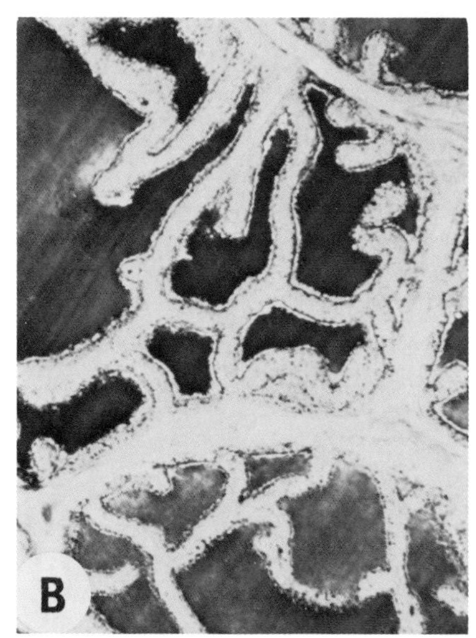

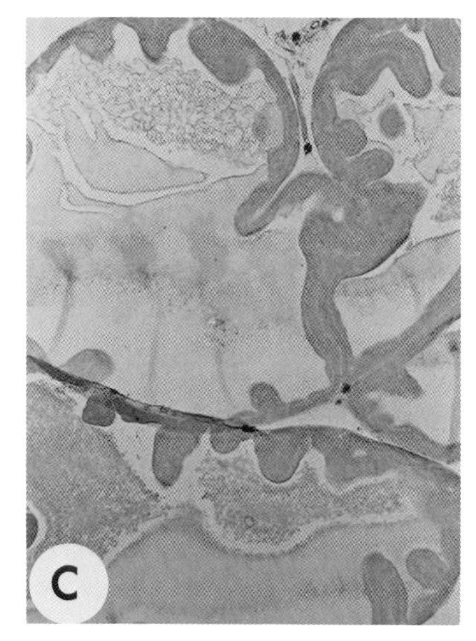

Fig. 10. Immunoperoxidase staining of Dorsal Protein I in rat dorsal prostate and coagulating gland. Antiserum to dorsal protein I (DP I) [18] was diluted 1:1000. Tissues were counterstained with toluidine blue. All magnifications are ×91. Immunoreactive DP I is present within acini and, to a lesser extent, in the epithelia of dorsal prostate (A) and coagulating glands (B). Staining is undetectable in ventral prostate (C). Dark spots in the interstitial space are mast cells stained with toluidine blue.

major protein of both coagulating gland and seminal fluid. An appreciation of the significance of the distribution of these proteins may come with an understanding of their function, which is as yet unknown.

As shown in Figure 11, dorsal protein I is an androgen-dependent protein. Its concentration increases linearly after 20 days of age in both the dorsal prostate and coagulating gland, the time when a surge in gonadotropin stimulates androgen production and the onset of puberty. Castration of the adult rat caused a gradual decrease to near undetectable levels at 4 weeks postcastration. The relatively slow loss in dorsal protein I likely reflects stored pools of the protein within the glands. A similar time scale was noted for both the age-dependent appearance of prostatein (Fig. 3) and its gradual loss after castration in rat ventral prostate (Fig. 4).

Because of the abundance and androgen dependence of dorsal protein I, we isolated and translated dorsal prostate poly(A)RNA in the mouse embryo fibroblast cell-free system as described in Methods (Fig. 12). Using either [^{35}S]methionine or [^{3}H]tyrosine as precursor, three abundant peptides were identified. The 62,000 molecular weight peptide corresponding in size to DP I was selectively precipitated with specific DP I antiserum. Two smaller peptides (MW~50,000 and 20,000) are as yet unidentified; however, their abundance implies that they may represent subunits of dorsal protein II. Comparison of peptides translated from dorsal prostate and coagulating gland mRNA reveal identical radioactive bands on SDS gel electrophoresis supporting the biochemical homology between these glands. There is, however, a quantitative difference in

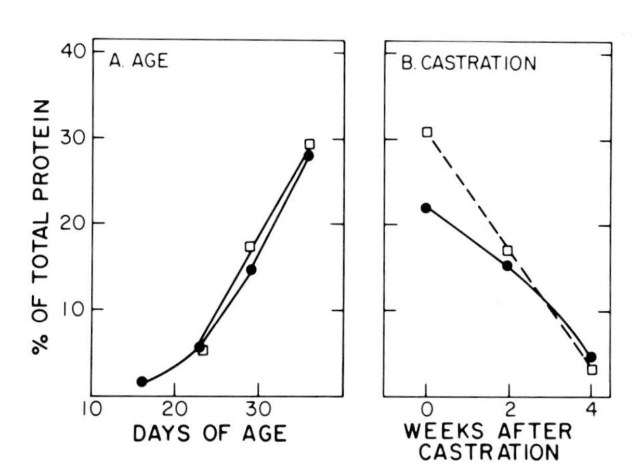

Fig. 11. Effects of age and castration on the concentration of dorsal protein I. Rocket immunoelectrophoresis was carried out as previously described [18] to quantitate dorsal protein I in cytosols from rats of differing ages (A) and in adult rats at 2 and 4 weeks after castration (B). Cytosols (100,000 g supernatants) were prepared from dorsal prostate (●) or coagulating gland (□). A rocket height of 58 mm corresponded to approximately 1 μg pure dorsal protein I. Total protein was measured by the procedure of Lowry [52].

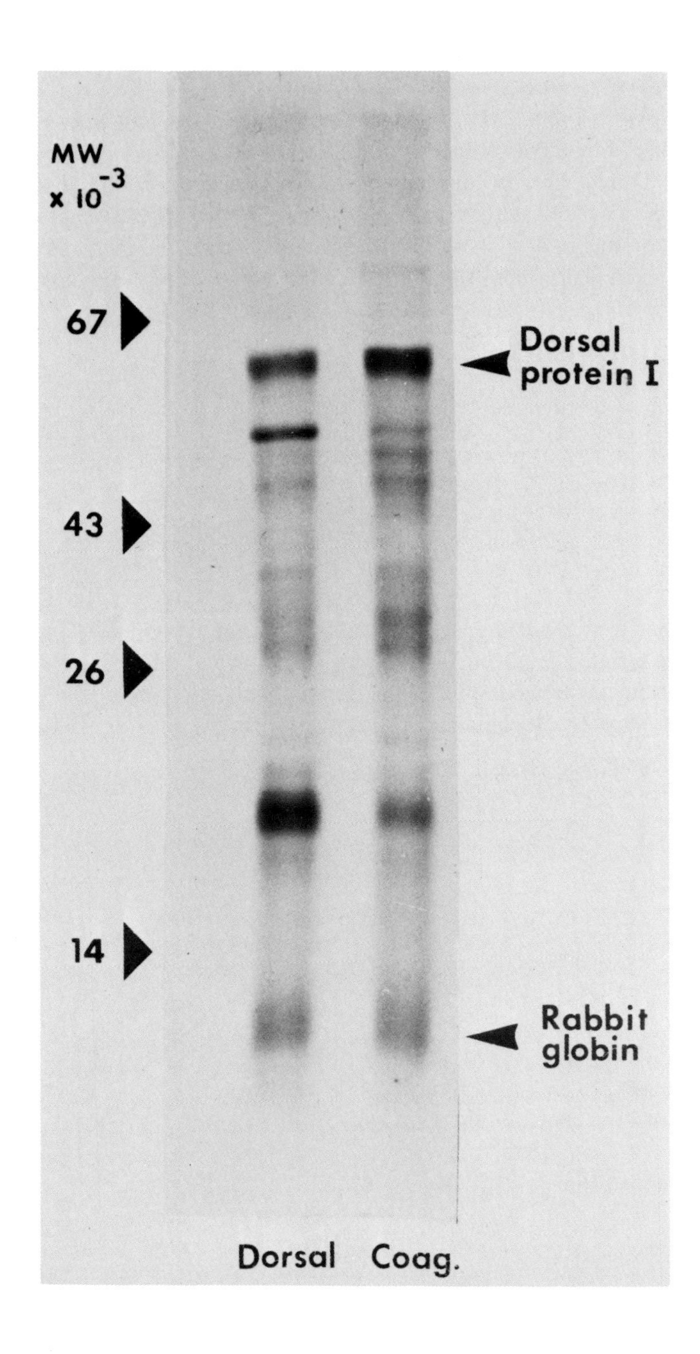
MW
x 10^{-3}
67
43
26
14
Dorsal
protein I
Rabbit
globin
Dorsal
Coag.

the relative amounts of each of the three major peptides (Fig. 12). Of the in vitro synthesized peptides, DP I is found to predominate in the coagulating gland, while the 20K and 50K peptides predominate in the dorsal prostate.

The coagulating gland is known to secrete the enzyme vesiculase [72]. It catalyzes the coagulation of a seminal vesicle protein through a transamidation reaction [73–75]. The secretion of rat coagulating gland contains two unique transglutaminases that are active in the clotting of semen. These enzymes utilize aliphatic amines such as spermidine, spermine, and putrescine as acceptor substrates and incorporates them into seminal vesicle fluid proteins in the form of peptide bond-γ-glutamyl derivatives. The free primary amine group can then react with other peptide bond glutamic residues, resulting in bis-(γ -glutamyl) polyamine cross bridges, forming a highly insoluble, high-molecular-weight protein complex that is part of the seminal clot [68]. The transglutaminase activity of coagulating gland fluid is not retained by DEAE-cellulose, but is retained by carboxymethyl-cellulose at neutral pH [68] in a manner similar to dorsal protein I. DP I also has properties similar to a 4.7 S protein described by Joshi et al [76] that causes gelation of uterine fluid post coitus. The gel matrix consisted of a 17 S protein similar to dorsal protein II. However, the possible enzyme activity of dorsal protein I or II remains to be established.

Androgen-Dependent Rat Prostate Tumor (Dunning R3327)

The Dunning prostate tumor is an androgen-dependent adenocarcinoma that has been propagated since 1963 at the Papanicolaou Cancer Research Institute in Miami by subcutaneous implantation into Copenhagen-Fischer rats. This tumor (R3327) is a well-differentiated adenocarcinoma that arose spontaneously in an old rat [77]. It has a normal concentration of androgen receptor [9, 78, 79]. The site of origin of the tumor is believed to be the dorsal prostate [77] as supported by the distribution of several enzymes [80, 81].

Fig. 12. SDS polyacrylamide gel electrophoresis of ^{35}S-methionine-labeled peptides translated in the JLS-V16 system from dorsal prostate and coagulating gland RNA. Poly(A)RNA (1.5 μg) from dorsal prostate (left) and coagulating gland (right) was translated as described in Methods. Trichloracetic acid-precipitable radioactivity (40,000 cpm in 7–18 μl) from each translation was combined with 5% SDS–0.5M dithiothreitol (10 μl) and dH_2O to a final volume of 30 μl. Samples were heated to 95°C for 10 minutes, cooled for 2 minutes, and combined with 3 μl of 0.5% bromophenol blue, 0.5% xylene cylanol, and 70% glycerol. Gels of 1% agarose, 12% acrylamide crosslinked with diallyltartardiamide as previously described [71] were pre-electrophoresed for 20 minutes prior to sample application. Molecular weight standards were bovine serum albumin (67,000), ovalbumin (43,000), chymotrypsinogen (26,500), and lysozyme (14,000). The electrophoretic position of purified native dorsal protein I and in vitro synthesized rabbit globin are indicated. Rabbit globin appears in all translations due to the addition of globin mRNA present in the fraction containing reticulocyte translation factors.

We have examined the protein pattern of Dunning prostate tumor cytosol. A somewhat surprising finding was that dorsal protein I could not be detected in the tumor either by rocket immunoelectrophoresis or SDS polyacrylamide gel electrophoresis. Dorsal protein II was also absent on SDS polyacrylamide gel electrophoresis of tumor cytosol. These results suggest that androgen-controlled gene expression is altered in the tumor despite its well differentiated appearance.

A major protein of tumor cytosol evident on SDS polyacrylamide gels (Fig. 13, gel 2) was purified (see Methods). This protein was found to have a sedimentation coefficient of 5.5 S, Stokes radius of 38 Å, and corresponding MW of 86,800. The MW on SDS polyacrylamide gels was estimated at 70,000 (Fig. 13, gel 1). The tumor protein had characteristics similar to those reported for transferrin (Table VI), and the amino acid composition was similar to that reported for transferrin by Schreiber et al [85]. Furthermore, the protein formed a single precipitin line with antiserum to authentic rat transferrin. Thus, transferrin appears to be a major protein of the Dunning prostate tumor cytosol. The concentration of transferrin in tumor fluid collected from cysts within the tumor is 4–6 times greater than that of serum, suggesting that the presence of transferrin in tumor fluid and cytosol is not due simply to serum contamination. The total protein concentration of tumor fluid varies from 5–14 mg/ml. Transferrin represents 30–40% of total tumor cyst fluid protein. The electrophoretic pattern of total proteins of the fluid on SDS polyacrylamide gels indicate that transferrin and albumin are predominant proteins (Fig. 13). Albumin, however, is present in tumor fluid at a concentration lower than in serum.

Transferrin is the plasma carrier for iron. Its function is to bind and deliver iron to cells for a variety of metabolic processes. Transferrin is a single polypeptide glycoprotein with a molecular weight of about 76,500 [85]. Membrane receptors exist on cells with high iron requirements, such as reticulocytes, immature erythroid cells of the bone marrow, and the placenta. Each molecule of transferrin has two equivalent sites for iron (Fe^{3+}) with a very high binding affinity of 10^{24} M^{-1} [88]. Iron enters cells through a mechanism involving endocytosis of the receptor-transferrin-iron complex [89]. Entry of transferrin into cells is a prerequisite for the assimilation of iron bound to transferrin [90]. Intracellular iron release appears to result during exposure of endocytic vesicles to the lysosome, while iron-free transferrin appears to be recycled intact to the outside of the cell [91]. Transferrin has been found to be a primary factor required for growth of cells in serum-free medium [92]. Lactoferrin is similar to transferrin in its molecular weight (85,000) and its ability to bind iron; it is however, immunologically distinct from transferrin [93].

We have used immunocytochemistry to localize transferrin within the prostate tumor and in normal rat prostate. Histologically, the Dunning tumor is well-differentiated in that it contains acinar glands characteristic of the rat prostate. The distribution of peroxidase staining in Figure 14 indicates that transferrin is

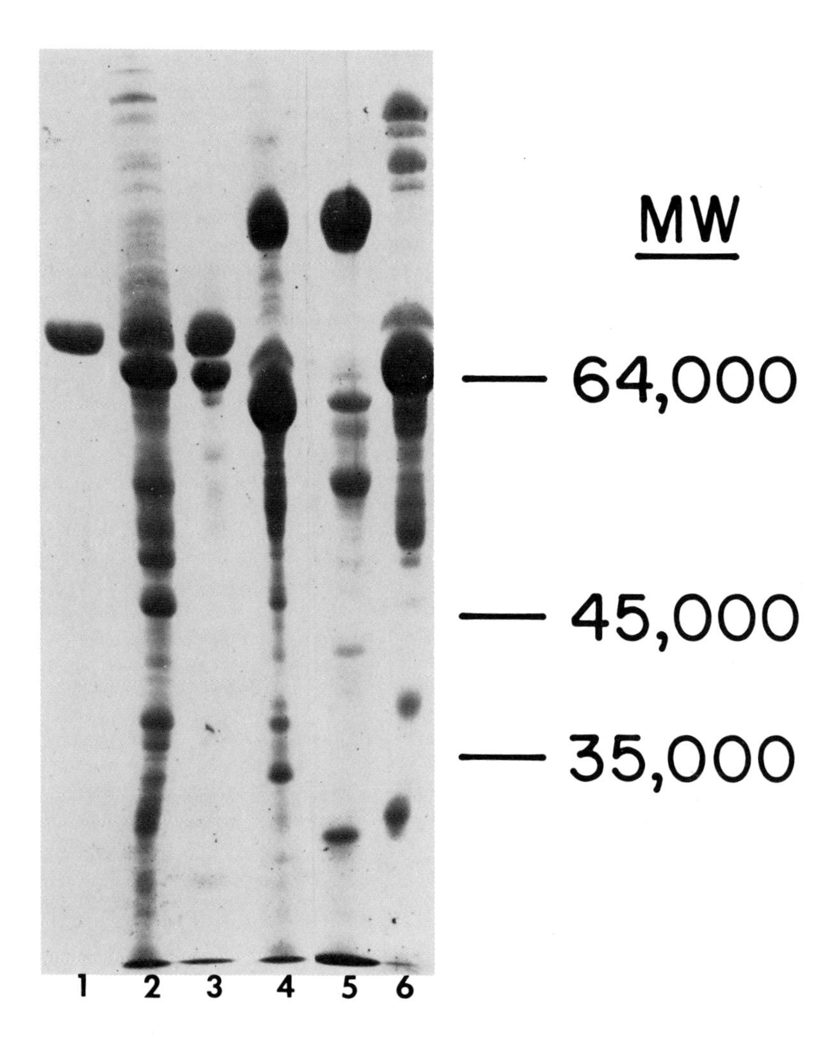

Fig. 13. SDS polyacrylamide gel electrophoresis of transferrin purified from the Dunning tumor, tissue cytosols, and fluids. SDS gel containing 8% acrylamide was prepared as previously described [58] with some modifications [18]. Shown are protein patterns for 1) Dunning prostate tumor protein (transferrin) purified as described in Methods, 6μg; 2) Dunning prostate tumor cytosol prepared as previously described [9], 46μg; 3) Dunning tumor fluid (15.5 mg/ml) collected from a fluid-filled cyst in the tumor, 20 μg protein; 4) dorsal prostate cytosol, 40 μg protein; 5) supernatant of a homogenate of ejaculated rat seminal fluid and sperm plug centrifuged 100,000g for 30 minutes, 75 μg protein; and 6) rat serum, 97 μg protein. Marker proteins are indicated for rat albumin (MW 64,000), ovalbumin (MW 45,000), and carboxypeptidase B (MW 35,000).

TABLE VI. Comparison of purified Dunning tumor protein with rat transferrin

	Dunning tumor[a] protein	Transferrin
Sedimentation coefficient (S)	5.3	5.1[b]
Stokes radius (Å)	38	40[c]
Molecular weight		
SDS-polyacrylamide gel	70,000	76,500[d]
hydrodynamic	86,800	
Frictional Ratio (f/f_o)	1.3	1.4[e]
Anti-rat transferrin[f]	+	+
Amino acid composition (mole/mole protein)		
Lys	48[g]	49[d]
His	16	16
Arg	20	22
Tryp		7
Asp/Asn	66	64
Thr	34	32
Ser	41	38
Glu/Gln	74	57
Pro	38	40
Gly	64	51
Ala	57	50
Cys		30
Val	43	40
Met	4	4
Ile	22	20
Leu	53	51
Tyr	4	19
Phe	32	28
Glucosamine		3

[a]Sedimentation coefficient, Stokes radius, molecular weights and frictional ratio were determined as described in Table IV.
[b]Reported for rat transferrin [82, 83].
[c]Reported for transferrin [84].
[d]Reported for rat transferrin [85].
[e]Reported for conalbumin of chicken egg white [86], the protein portion of which is identical to transferrin [87].
[f]Immunoreactivity determined by rocket immunoelectrophoresis [18].
[g]Determined by Dr. D.G. Klapper of the University of North Carolina at Chapel Hill and Dr. J.D. Capra of Texas Health Science Center in Dallas.

present within acinar glands of the tumor and in the interstitial spaces. Highest concentrations appear present in those glands closest to the periphery of the tumor (Fig. 14). This distribution may be accounted for by the increased blood supply of the peripheral regions. Staining for transferrin was noted also in the

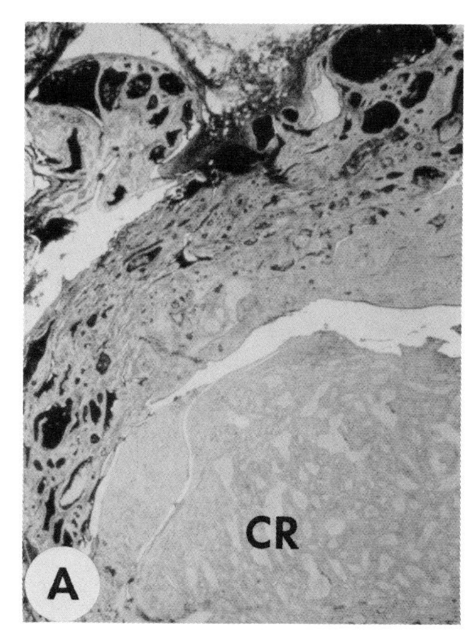

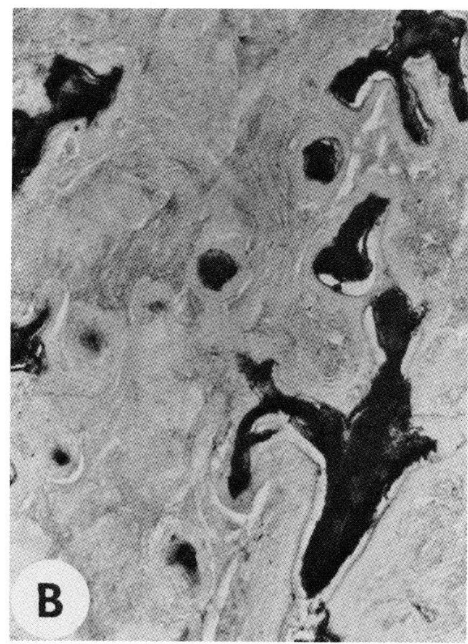

Fig. 14. Immunoperoxidase localization of transferrin in the androgen-dependent Dunning tumor (R-3327) with anti-rat transferrin serum. Antiserum (Cappel Laboratories, Cochranville, PA) was diluted 1:2000. Tumors (~ 2 cm diameter) were counterstained with toluidine blue. A) Low-power (× 23) photomicrograph showing heavy accumulation of immunoreactive transferrin in peripheral acini and undetectable staining in the central region (CR) of the Dunning tumor. B) High-power (× 227) detail from the peripheral region of the tumor indicates dense accumulation of reaction product within prostate-like acini of variable size and shape. Lighter staining is present in the interstitial spaces.

normal dorsal and lateral prostate (not shown), but was essentially undetectable in acinar glands of the coagulating gland and ventral prostate. Levels of transferrin assayed by rocket immunoelectrophoresis, however, were at least 200 times lower in all normal rat prostate glands than in the tumor.

Elevated levels of transferrin have been reported in the prostatic fluid in human patients with prostate cancer [94]. Greater than 90% of these patients had levels of transferrin in the prostatic fluid that were 4–5 times higher than controls. This increase is similar to the increase (4- to 6-fold) in transferrin over serum observed in Dunning tumor fluid. Both in the human [94] and the rat, no statistical elevation was noted between sera of controls and in prostate cancer.

It is not clear at this time whether the high levels of transferrin in the tumor are due to an increase in the number of membrane receptors for transferrin or to the induction of synthesis of the protein. Our preliminary results with the in vitro translation of poly(A)RNA isolated from the tumor indicate that transferrin is not being produced by the tumor; we have not observed a major or minor in vitro translation product that corresponds with transferrin. The more likely possibility is that transferrin is taken up from blood via the transferrin receptor. Elevated levels of transferrin within the tumor may reflect elevated receptors for transferrin. The presence of transferrin within the lumen of acinar glands (Fig. 14) may be due to recycling and release of iron-free transferrin from endocytotic vesicles, as recently suggested [91]. In agreement with this hypothesis, it has long been known that gallium-67 has an affinity for certain soft-tissue neoplasms [95]. Recently it has been shown that tumors take up iron-59 and gallium-67 by the same mechanism, ie, via the transferrin receptor [96].

ACKNOWLEDGMENTS

The authors wish to thank Dr. Roger L. Lundblad, Dental Research Center, University of North Carolina, and Dr. K. Sletten, Biochemical Institute, University of Oslo, Norway, for amino acid analysis of prostatein; Dr. T. Christensen, Biochemical Institute, University of Oslo, for carbohydrate analysis of prostatein; Dr. David G. Klapper of the University of North Carolina and Dr. F. D. Capra of the Texas Health Science Center for amino acid analyses of dorsal protein I and rat (Dunning tumor) transferrin. We are grateful also to Dr. Henry S. Kingdon for helpful discussions on the amino acid sequencing of prostatein. Dr. Norman H. Altman and Marion L. Stevens of the Papanicolaou Cancer Research Institute, Miami, Florida, kindly supplied the Dunning dorsal prostate tumor-bearing rats (with support of the National Prostatic Cancer Project).

This work was supported by United States Public Health Service Grants HD04466, HD10306, the University of North Carolina Cancer Center Grant 5-P30-CA16086, and Department of Energy Grant DE-026688.

REFERENCES

1. King RJB, Mainwaring WIP: Steroid Cell Interactions. London: Butterworths, 1974.
2. Bruchovsky N, Wilson JD: The conversion of testosterone to 5α-androstan-17β-ol-3-one by rat prostate in vivo and in vitro. J Biol Chem 243:2012–2021, 1968.
3. Tveter KJ, Attramadal A: Selective uptake of radioactivity in rat ventral prostate following administration of testosterone-1, 2-^{3}H. Methodological considerations. Acta Endocrinol 59:218–226, 1968.
4. Wilson JD: Metabolism of testicular androgens. In Greep RO, Astwood EB (eds): "Handbook of Physiology." Washington, D.C.: American Physiological Society, Vol 5, 1975. pp 491–508.
5. Bruchovsky N, Wilson JD: The intranuclear binding of testosterone and 5α-androstan-17β-ol-3-one by rat prostate. J Biol Chem 243:5953–5960, 1968.
6. Fang S, Anderson KM, and Liao S: Receptor proteins for androgens: On the role of specific proteins in selective retention of 17β-hydroxy-5α-androstan-3-one by rat ventral prostate in vivo and in vitro. J Biol Chem 244:6584–6595, 1969.
7. Hansson V, Tveter KJ, Unhjem O, Djoseland O, Attramadal A, Reusch E, Torgersen O: Androgen binding in male sex organs, with special reference to the human prostate. In Goland

M (ed): "Normal and Abnormal Growth of the Prostate. Springfield: C. C. Thomas, 1975, pp 676–711.

8. Wilson EM, French FS: Binding properties of androgen receptors: Evidence for identical receptors in rat testis, epididymis and prostate. J Biol Chem 251:5620–5629, 1976.
9. Wilson EM, French FS: Effects of proteases and protease inhibitors on the 4.5 S and 8 S androgen receptor. J Biol Chem 254:6310–6319, 1979.
10. Lea OA, Wilson EM, French FS: Characterization of different forms of the androgen receptor. Endocrinology 105:1350–1360, 1979.
11. Williams-Ashman HG: Metabolic effects of testicular androgens. In Greep RO, Astwood EB (eds): "Handbook of Physiology." Washington, D. C.: American Physiological Society, Vol 5, 1975, pp 473–490.
12. Coffey DS, Sloan WR: Biochemical changes in prostatic tissue associated with DNA synthesis. In Goland M (ed): "Normal and Abnormal Growth of the Prostate." Springfield: Charles C. Thomas, 1973, pp 240–274.
13. Bruchovsky N, Lesser B, van Doorn E, Craven S: Hormonal effects on cell proliferation in rat prostate. Vitam Horm 33:61–102, 1975.
14. Johnsonbaugh RE, Dalldorf FG, French FS, Nayfeh SN: Androgen action in the rat ventral prostate: Effect of castration and testosterone treatment on polyribosomes. J Steroid Biochem 7:73–79, 1976.
15. Liao S: Molecular actions of androgens. In Litwack G (ed): "Biochemical Actions of Hormones." New York: Academic Press Vol IV, 1977, pp 351–406.
16. Davies P, Thomas P, Giles MG, Boonjawat J, Griffiths K: Regulation of transcription of the prostate genome by androgens. J Steroid Biochem 11:351–360, 1979.
17. Lea OA, Petrusz P, French FS: Prostatein: A major secretory protein of the rat ventral prostate. J Biol Chem 254:6196–6202, 1979.
18. Wilson EM, French FS: Biochemical homology between rat dorsal prostate and coagulating gland: Purification of a major androgen-induced protein. J Biol Chem 255:10946–10953, 1980.
19. Petrusz P, DiMeo P, Ordronneau P, Weaver C, Keefer DA: Improved immunoglobulin-enzyme bridge method for light microscopic demonstration of hormone-containing cells of the rat adenohypophysis. Histochemistry 46:9–26, 1975.
20. Petrusz P, Sar M, Ordronneau P, DiMeo P: Specificity in immunocytochemical staining. J Histochem Cytochem 24:1110–1115, 1976.
21. Rosen JM, Woo SLC, Holder JW, Means AR, O'Malley BW: Preparation and preliminary characterization of purified ovalbumin messenger RNA from the hen oviduct. Biochemistry 14:69–78, 1975.
22. Deeley RG, Gordon JI, Burns ATH, Mullinix KP, Bina-Stein M, Goldberger RF: Primary activation of the vitellogenin gene in the rooster. J Biol Chem 252:8310–8319, 1977.
23. Meinke W, Goldstein DA, Hall MR: Rapid isolation of mouse DNA from cells in tissue culture. Anal Biochem 58:82–88, 1974.
24. Aviv H, Leder P: Purification of biologically active globin messenger RNA by chromatography on oligothymidylic acid-cellulose. Proc Natl Acad Sci USA 69:1408–1412, 1972.
25. Murphy EC, Arlinghaus RB: Cell-free synthesis of Rauscher Murine Leukemia Virus "gag" and "gag-pol" precursor polyproteins from virion 35 S RNA in a mRNA-dependent translation system derived from mouse tissue culture cells. Virology 86:329–343, 1978.
26. Laskey RA: The use of intensifying screens or organic scintillators for visualizing radioactive molecules resolved by gel electrophoresis. Methods Enzymol 65:363–371, 1980.
27. Maniatis T, Gek Kee S, Efstratiadis A, Kafatos FC: Amplification and characterization of a β-globin gene synthesized in vitro. Cell 8:163–182. 1976.
28. Buell GN, Wickens MP, Payvar F, Schimke RT: Synthesis of full length cDNAs from four partially purified oviduct mRNAs. J Biol Chem 253:2471–2482, 1978.

29. Nelson T, Brutlag D: Addition of homopolymers to the 3′-ends of duplex DNA with Terminal Transferase. Methods Enzymol 68:41–50, 1979.
30. Bolivar F, Rodriguez RL, Greene PJ, Betlack MC, Heyneker HL, Boyer HW, Crosa JH, Falkow S: Construction and characterization of new cloning vehicles II. A multipurpose cloning system. Gene 2:95–113, 1977.
31. Mandel M, Higa A: Calcium-dependent bacteriophage DNA infection. J Mol Biol. 53:159–162, 1970.
32. Grunstein M, Wallis J: Colony hybridization. Methods Enzymol 68:379–389, 1979.
33. Monahan JJ, Harris SE, O'Malley BW: Analysis of cellular messenger RNA using complementary DNA probes. In O'Malley BW (ed): "Receptors and Hormone Action." New York: Academic Press, vol I, 1977, 297–329.
34. Blin N, Sperrazza JM, Wilson FE, Bieber DG, Mickel FS, Stafford DW: Organization of the ribosomal RNA gene cluster in Lytechinus variegatus: Restriction analysis and cloning of restriction fragments. J Biol Chem 254:2716–2721, 1979.
35. Birnboim HC, Doly J: A rapid alkaline extraction procedure for screening recombinant plasmid DNA. Nucleic Acid Res 7:1513–1523, 1979.
36. Southern EM: Detection of specific sequences among DNA fragments separated by gel electrophoresis. J Mol Biol 98:503–517, 1975.
37. Wahl GM, Stern M, Stark GR: Efficient transfer of large DNA fragments from agarose gels to diazobenzyloxymethyl-paper and rapid hybridization by using dextran sulfate. Proc Natl Acad Sci USA 76:3683–3687, 1979.
38. Paterson RM, Roberts BE, Kuff EL: Structural gene identification and mapping by DNA·mRNA hybrid-arrested cell-free translation. Proc Natl Acad Sci USA 74:4370–4374, 1977.
39. Laskey RA, Mills AD: Quantitative film detection of ^{3}H and ^{14}C in polyacrylamide gels by fluorography. Eur J Biochem 56:335–341, 1975.
40. Alwine JC, Kemp DJ, Parker BA, Reiser J, Renart J, Stark GR, Wahl GM: Detection of specific RNAs or specific fragments of DNA by fractionation in gels and transfer to diazobenzyloxymethyl-paper. Methods Enzymol 68:220–242, 1979.
41. Goldberg ML, Lifton RP, Stark GR, Williams JG: Isolation of specific RNAs using DNA covalently linked to diazobenzyloxymethyl cellulose or paper. Methods Enzymol 68:206–220, 1979.
42. Price D, Williams-Ashman HG: The accessory reproductive glands of mammals. In Young WC (ed): "Sex and Internal Secretions." Baltimore: Williams and Wilkins, 1961, pp 366–448.
43. Heyns W, DeMoor P: Prostatic binding protein: A steroid-binding protein secreted by rat prostate. Eur J Biochem 78:221–230, 1977.
44. Heyns W, Peeters B, Mous J, Rombauts W, DeMoor P: Purification and characterisation of prostatic binding protein and its subunits. Eur J Biochem 89:181–186, 1978.
45. Chen C, Hiipakka RA, Liao S: Prostate α-protein: Sub-unit structure, polyamine binding and inhibition of nuclear chromatin binding of androgen-receptor complex. J Steroid Biochem 11:401–405, 1979.
46. Forsgren B, Björk P, Carlström K, Gustafsson JA, Pousette A, Högberg B: Purification and distribution of a major protein in rat prostate that binds estramustine, a nitrogen mustard derivative of estradiol-17β. Proc Natl Acad Sci USA 76:3149-3153, 1979.
47. Forsgren B, Gustafsson JA, Pousette A, Höberg B: Binding characteristics of a major protein in rat ventral prostate cytosol that interacts with estramustine, a nitrogen mustard derivative of 17β-estradiol. Cancer Res 39:5155–5164, 1979.
48. Rodbard D, Chrambach A: Estimation of molecular radius, free mobility and valence using polyacrylamide gel electrophoresis. Anal Biochem 40:95–134, 1971.
49. Bigelow CC: On the average hydrophobicity of proteins and the relation between it and protein structure. J Theor Biol 16:187–211, 1967.

50. Chambers RE, Clamp JR: An assessment of methanolysis and other factors used in the analysis of carbohydrate-containing materials. Biochem J 125:1009–1018, 1971.
51. Mous J, Peeters B, Rombauts W, Heyns W: Synthesis of rat prostatic binding protein in xenopus oocytes and in wheat germ. Biochem Biophys Res Commun 79:1111–1116, 1977.
52. Lowry OH, Rosebrough NJ, Farr AL, Randall RJ: Protein measurement with the folin phenol reagent. J Biol Chem 193:265–275, 1951.
53. Parker MG, Mainwaring WIP: Effects of androgens on the complexity of poly(A)RNA from rat prostate. Cell 12:401–407, 1977.
54. Parker MG, Scrace GT, Mainwaring WIP: Testosterone regulates the synthesis of major proteins in rat ventral prostate. Biochem J 170:115–121, 1978.
55. Parker MG, Scrace GT: The androgenic regulation of abundant mRNA in rat ventral prostate. Eur J Biochem 85:399–406, 1978.
56. Heyns W, Peeters B, Mous J: Influence of androgens on the concentration of prostatic binding protein (PBP) and its mRNA in rat prostate. Biochem Biophys Res Commun 77:1492–1499, 1977.
57. Roberts BE, Paterson BM: Efficient translation of tobacco mosaic virus RNA and rabbit globin 9 S RNA in a cell-free system from commercial wheat germ. Proc Natl Acad Sci USA 70:2330-2334, 1973.
58. Laemmli UK: Cleavage of structural proteins during the assembly of the head of bacteriophage T4. Nature 227:680–685, 1970.
59. Peeters BL, Mous JM, Rombauts WA, Heyns WJ: Androgen-induced messenger RNA in rat ventral prostate: Translation, partial purification, and preliminary characterization of the mRNAs encoding the components of prostatic binding protein. J Biol Cehm 255:7017--7023, 1980.
60. Parker MG, White R, Williams JG: Cloning and characterization of androgen-dependent mRNA from rat ventral prostate. J Biol Chem 255:6996–7001, 1980.
61. Edman P, Begg G: A protein sequenator. Eur J Biochem 1:80–91, 1967.
62. Pisano JJ, Bronzert TJ, Brewer HB: Advances in the gas chromatographic analysis of amino acid phenyl- and methylthiohydantoins. Anal Biochem 45:43–59, 1972.
63. Lominac GD, Kingdon HS: A simple and inexpensive high pressure liquid chromatographic system as an adjunct to gas chromatography in identification of amino acid phenylthiohydantoins. Arch Biochem Biophys 173:320–325, 1976.
64. Inagami T, Murakami K: Identification of phenylthiohydantoins of amino acids by thin-layer chromatography on a plastic-backed silica-gel plate. Anal Biochem 47:501–504, 1972.
65. Inagami T: Simultaneous identification of PTH derivatives of histidine and arginine by thin-layer chromatography. Anal Biochem 52:318–321, 1973.
66. Humphrey GF, Mann T: Studies on the metabolism of semen, 5. Citric acid in semen. Biochem J 44:97–105, 1949.
67. Mann T: The Biochemistry of Semen and of the Male Reproductive Tract. London: Methuen, 1964.
68. Williams-Ashman HG, Beil RE, Wilson J, Hawkins M, Grayhack J, Zunamon A, Weinstein NK: Transglutaminases in mammalian reproductive tissues and fluids: Relation to polyamine metabolism and semen coagulation. Adv Enz Regul 18:239–258, 1980.
69. Siegel LM, Monty KJ: Determination of molecular weights and frictional ratios of proteins in impure systems by use of gel filtration and density gradient centrifugation. Application to crude preparations of sulfite and hydroxylamine reductases. Biochim Biophys Acta 112:346–362, 1966.
70. Cohn EJ, Edsall JT: Proteins, Amino Acids and Peptides. New York: Reinhold, 1941.
71. Renart J, Reiser J, Stark GR: Transfer of proteins from gels to diazobenzyloxymethyl-paper and detection with antisera: A method for studying antibody specificity and antigen structure. Proc Natl Acad Sci USA 76:3116–3120, 1979.

72. Gotterer GS, Williams-Ashman HG: Some factors which influence vesiculase action. Proc Soc Exp Biol Med 94:60–64, 1957.
73. Notides AC, Williams-Ashman HG: The basic protein responsible for the clotting of guinea pig semen. Proc. Natl Acad Sci USA 58:1991–1995, 1967.
74. Williams-Ashman HG, Notides AC, Pabalan SS, Lorand L: Transamidase reactions involved in the enzymic coagulation of semen: Isolation of γ-glutamyl-ε-lysine dipeptide from clotted secretion protein of guinea pig seminal vesicle. Proc Natl Acad Sci USA 69:2322–2325, 1972.
75. Beil RE, Hart RG: Cowper's gland secretion in rat semen coagulation II. Identification of the potentiating factor secreted by the coagulating glands. Biol Reprod 8:613–617, 1973.
76. Joshi MS, Yaron A, Linder HR: Intrauterine gelation of seminal plasma components in the rat after coitus. J Reprod Fertil 30:27–37, 1972.
77. Dunning WF: Prostate cancer in the rat. Natl Cancer Inst Monogr 12:351–369, 1963.
78. Markland FS, Lee L: Characterization and comparison of the estrogen and androgen receptors from the R-3327 rat prostatic adenocarcinoma. J Steroid Biochem 10:13–20, 1979.
79. Lea OA, French FS: Androgen receptor protein in the androgen-dependent Dunning R-3327 prostate carcinoma. Cancer Res 41:619–623, 1981.
80. Smolev JK, Heston WDW, Scott WW, Coffey DS: Characterization of the Dunning R-3327H prostatic adenocarcinoma: An appropriate animal model for prostatic cancer. Cancer Treat Rep 61:273–287, 1977.
81. Müntzing J, Saroff J, Sandberg AA, Murphy GP: Enzyme activity and distribution in rat prostatic adenocarcinoma. Urology 11:278-282, 1978.
82. Charlwood PA: Ultracentrifugal characterisics of human, monkey and rat transferrins. Biochem J 88:394–398, 1963.
83. van Eijk HG, Van Noort WL: Isolation of rat transferrin using CNBr-activated Sepharose-4B. J Clin Chem Clin Biochem 14:475-478, 1976.
84. Ackers GK: Molecular exclusion and restricted diffusion processes in molecular sieve chromatography. Biochemistry 3:723–730, 1964.
85. Schreiber G, Dryburgh H, Millership A, Matsuda Y, Inglis A, Phillips J, Edwards K, Maggs J: The synthesis and secretion of rat transferrin. J Biol Chem 254:12013–12019, 1979.
86. Fuller RA, Briggs DR: Some physical properties of hen's egg conalbumin. J Am Chem Soc 78:5253–5257, 1956.
87. Williams J: A comparison of conalbumin and transferrin in the domestic fowl. Biochem J 83:355–364, 1962.
88. Aisen P, Leibman A, Pinkowitz RA, Pollack S: Exchangeability of bicarbonate specifically bound to transferrin. Biochemistry 12:3679–3684, 1973.
89. Hemmaplardh D, Morgan EH: The role of endocytosis in transferrin uptake by reticulocytes and bone marrow cells. Br J Haemotol 36:85–96, 1977.
90. Hemmaplardh D, Morgan EH: Transferrin and iron uptake by human cells in culture. Exp Cell Res 87:207–212, 1974.
91. Karin M, Mintz B: Receptor-mediated endocytosis of transferrin in developmentally totipotent mouse teratocarcinoma stem cells. J Biol Chem 256:3245–3252, 1981.
92. Rizzino A, Sato G: Growth of embryonal carcinoma cells in serum-free medium. Proc Natl Acad Sci USA 75:1844–1848, 1978.
93. Groves ML: In McKenzie HA (ed): "Milk Proteins, Chemistry and Molecular Biology. New York: Academic Press, 1971, pp 367–376.
94. Grayhack JT, Wendel EF, Oliver L, Lee C: Analysis of specific proteins in prostatic fluid for detecting prostatic malignancy. J Urol 121:295–299, 1979.
95. Edwards CL, Hayes RL: Tumor scanning with ^{67}Ga citrate. J Nucl Med 10:103–105, 1969.
96. Larson SM, Rasey JS, Allen DR, Nelson NJ, Grumbaum Z, Harp GD, Williams DL: Common pathway for tumor cell uptake of gallium-67 and iron-59 via a transferrin receptor. J Natl Cancer Inst 64:41–53, 1980.

The Prostatic Cell: Structure and Function
Part A, pages 381–389

Cellular Dynamics of Androgen Receptor and Protein Induction in Rat Ventral Prostate

Shutsung Liao, Richard A. Hiipakka, Karen Schilling, Amy K. Oberhauser, Chawnshang Chang, and Sheila M. Judge

Our working model for the major steps involved in the intracellular cycling of the androgen receptor and protein induction in the rat ventral prostate is shown in Figure 1. In this hypothetical scheme an intracellular receptor protein in a form (R°) that cannot bind androgens is activated by an energy-dependent process into a form (R) that can bind active androgens. The androgen-receptor complex (AR) is then transformed by a temperature-dependent step to the form (AR*) that can bind to nuclear chromatin. As the result of this interaction the synthesis of RNA is enhanced. The newly synthesized RNA is utilized in the production of certain early proteins that mediate later androgenic responses, such as reconstruction of cellular organelles and secretion of major proteins.

For the prostate cells to grow and function normally these processes must be regulated properly. Besides the obvious controlling factors, such as the availability of androgens and the levels of receptor proteins in the prostate cells, we have investigated, as the possible steps of control, the activation of inactive receptor protein and the interaction of the androgen-receptor complex with chromatin.

CELLULAR ENERGY SUPPLY

The importance of energy supply in the receptor binding of androgens was first recognized during our initial study of 5α-dihydrotestosterone (DHT) retention by prostate nuclei. We found that androgen retention could be virtually abolished if minced prostate was incubated with radioactive DHT in the presence of respiratory poisons, such as NaCN, 2,4-dinitrophenol, or NaN_3 [1,2]. Subsequently, we found that the amount of androgen-binding receptor as measured by a gradient centrifugation assay was greatly diminished by these inhibitors of cellular energy production [3]. These inhibitors did not affect the stability of the DHT-receptor complex in the cell-free system. The removal of the respiratory

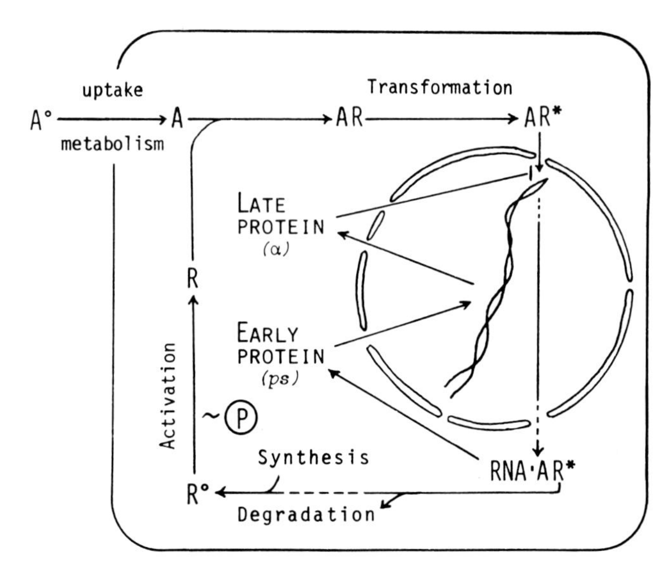

Fig. 1. A schematic view of intracellular androgen receptor cycling and action. A°, an androgen that can be metabolized to an active androgen (A), such as DHT; R°, a protein that can be activated by an energy-dependent process to a receptor (R) that can bind androgen; *ps*, a prostate spermine-binding protein induced within 1 hour of androgen treatment; α, a major secretory protein induced several hours after the initial androgen responses. See text for further details.

poison rapidly restores the androgen binding activity of the receptor protein in the incubated prostate and both inhibition and restoration occurred in the presence of cycloheximide [4]. These processes, therefore, appeared to represent a reversible inactivation and an energy-dependent activation and not degradation and resynthesis of the receptor protein.

Although not necessarily related to receptor activation, we also found that ATP and GTP at 1–5 mM can enhance the DHT-binding activity of the cytosol receptor fraction prepared from rat ventral prostate. These nucleoside triphosphates can stabilize the DHT-receptor complex at 20°C and can shift the sedimentation coefficient of the receptor complex [5]. Toft et al [6] also demonstrated that the chick oviduct progesterone-receptor complex, if activated to the nuclear form, can bind to ATP covalently linked to Sepharose.

The energy-dependent control of receptor binding of steroids has been the concern of several investigators. In 1968, Munck and his associates [7] showed, by adjusting the glucose and oxygen in the culture medium, that the extent of cortisol uptake by thymocytes was correlated with the ATP level in the cells. In 1972, they also suggested that ATP may be involved in the transformation of an inactive receptor protein to the glucocorticoid-binding form. Working on L-cells, Ishii et al [8] reached a similar conclusion.

More recently, Pratt and his associates [9–11] were able to show that the glucocorticoid receptor from L-cells or lymphocytes which were not bound to a glucocorticoid could be inactivated by a mechanism that may involve dephosphorylation. This inactivation could be prevented by a phosphatase inhibitor, such as molybdate. They also succeeded in reactivating the inactive form by incubation with ATP in the presence of dithiothreitol and a heat stable factor prepared from thymocytes, L-cells, or liver. According to Toft, molybdate can also inhibit the transformation of the chick progesterone-receptor complex to the form that can be retained by nuclei [6]. These studies support the view that a phosphorylation process is required to maintain the steroid-binding activity of the receptor, but that a dephosphorylation process may be needed before the steroid-receptor complex can be retained by the target cell nuclei.

The same mechanism may exist in rat prostate for the androgen receptor. We have been able to use molybdate to stabilize the DHT binding activity of the prostate cytosol receptor and also to inhibit the nuclear retention of DHT-receptor complex in a cell-free system or during incubation of minced prostate [3,4]. It should be emphasized that no direct evidence is available at present to show whether the suggested phosphorylation or dephosphorylation process directly involves the receptor proteins or other closely related molecules in the receptor preparations.

α-PROTEIN AND RECEPTOR INTERACTION WITH CHROMATIN

As a model system to study the control of receptor interaction with nuclei, we have investigated a cytosol protein that can prevent the DHT-receptor complex from binding to nuclear chromatin. The protein, named α-protein, was first isolated in 1970 [12,13] as a nonreceptor steroid-binding protein. The protein binds various sex steroids (androgens, estrogens, and progestins) well, but not glucocorticoids. We have recently found that purified α-protein has about 0.7–1.0 mole of cholesterol per mole protein. No other steroids were detected. Cholesterol, therefore, may be a natural ligand [14].

α-Protein (Mr: about 50,000) can be dissociated by sodium dodecyl sulfate into two different subunits (A and B). As shown in Figure 2, subunit A is composed of components I (Mr: 10,000) and III (Mr: 15,000), and the B unit is composed of components II (Mr: 13,000) and III (Mr: 15,000). The two polypeptide chains in the individual subunits appear to be linked by disulfide bonds and can be dissociated from each other in the presence of β-mercaptoethanol. We have purified all components to homogeneity. Component III isolated from subunit A and that from subunit B are antigenically identical and have the same amino terminal sequences (Ser-Gly-Ser-Gly), suggesting that they are the same polypeptide. Of the three components only component III has carbohydrate (19%). The protein has no detectable sialic acid [14,15]. Although there

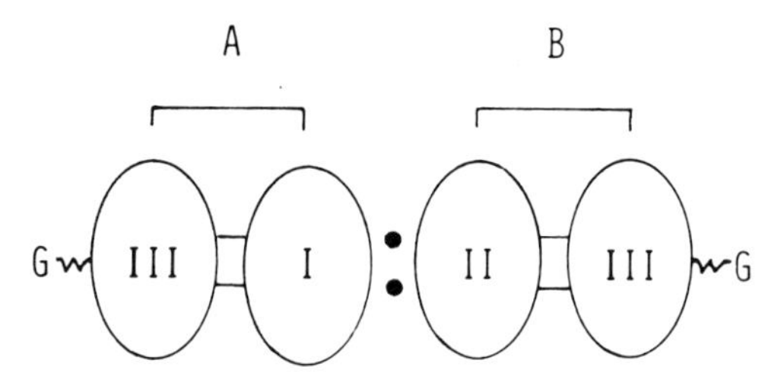

Fig. 2. A diagrammatic representation of the arrangement of subunits (A and B) and polypeptide component (I, II, and III) in α-protein of rat ventral prostate. Carbohydrate (G) is attached to component III. One mole of cholestrol can bind to 1 mole of α-protein.

are some distinct disagreements in the estimated sizes of the protein components, α-protein is probably identical to the "prostatein" of Lea et al [16], the "prostate-binding protein" of Heyns et al [17], and the estramustine binding protein of Forsgren et al, [18]. (See articles in this book by Wilson et al, Heyns et al, and Forsgren et al.)

To show inhibition of receptor interaction with chromatin, a prostate α-protein fraction is mixed with the androgen receptor complex and prostate cell nuclei. The inhibitor did not appear to cause irreversible destruction of the receptor complex or damage to the nuclear binding site. Besides acting as an inhibitor, α-protein can promote the release of the androgen-receptor complex already attached to chromatin. To show this, we first allowed the radioactive receptor complex to bind to prostate nuclei. The nuclei were then washed to removed the excess receptor complex and were incubated again either with or without the inhibitor. At a low concentration of the inhibitor, a significant loss of radioactivity occurred at 20°C, but not at 0°C. At a high concentration of the inhibitor, the release of radioactivity from the chromatin was evident even at 0°C, but was more obvious at 20°C. Without the inhibitor, there was no temperature-dependent loss of radioactivity released from the chromatin. By gradient centrifugation, we found that all radioactivity released from the nuclei was associated with protein that sedimented as 3S [19].

Of the two subunits, only subunit A was inhibitory. Component I was at least five-fold more active than subunit A, when the concentrations required to show 50% inhibition were compared. Components II and III were inactive. Component I, therefore, may be the inhibitory component of α-protein [14,15].

Figure 3 shows the complete amino acid sequence of component I [20]. This component is rich in acidic amino acids. Most of the glutamic acid and lysine are localized in the amino terminal half, whereas all aspartic acid and almost all aromatic amino acids are in the carboxyl terminal half of the protein. These

Amino acid sequence

```
                                             10                                                   20
NH2- Ser-Gln-Ile-Cys-Glu-Leu-Val-Ala-His-Glu-Thr-Ile-Ser-Phe-Leu-Met-Lys-Ser-Glu-Glu-Glu-Leu-
                                    30                                                   40
     Lys-Lys-Glu-Leu-Glu-Met-Tyr-Asn-Ala-Pro-Pro-Ala-Ala-Val-Glu-Ala-Lys-Leu-Glu-Val-Lys-Arg-
                                    50                                                   60
     Cys-Val-Asp-Gln-Met-Ser-Asp-Gly-Asp-Arg-Leu-Val-Val-Ala-Glu-Thr-Leu-Val-Tyr-Ile-Phe-Leu-
                    70                                                   80                   88
     Glu-Cys-Gly-Val-Lys-Gln-Trp-Val-Glu-Thr-Tyr-Tyr-Pro-Glu-Ile-Asp-Phe-Tyr-Tyr-Asp-Met-Asn-OH
```

Amino acid composition:

Glu_{13}, Gln_{3}, Asp_{5}, Asn_{2}, Lys_{6}, Arg_{2}, His_{1},

Val_{9}, Leu_{8}, Ala_{6}, Ser_{4}, Ile_{4}, Thr_{3}, Gly_{2},

Tyr_{6}, Phe_{3}, Pro_{3}, Trp_{1}, Met_{4}, Cys_{3}

Molecular weight:

10,191

Fig. 3. Complete amino acid sequence of component I of α-protein of rat ventral prostate.

features may be important in the inhibition but this activity may simply be due to a small oligopeptide stretch and not dependent on a complex structure.

INTERACTION OF RNA WITH ANDROGEN-RECEPTOR COMPLEX

Another aspect we have explored is the interaction of RNA with steroid-receptor complexes. In 1969, we suggested that RNA made in the nuclei may bind to the receptor complex and facilitate the release of the complex from nuclei [2]. We proposed that the receptor complex, in turn, may play an important role in processing, stabilization, and/or utilization of RNA [2,21]. Although direct evidence supporting this idea is still lacking, our studies have shown that both the estrogen- and androgen-receptor complexes can bind to certain ribonucleoprotein particles in the uterus and in the prostate [22,23].

Since the proposed scheme suggests that certain RNA molecules can promote the release of DHT-receptor complex from DNA or chromatin, we have tested this possibility by using DNA-cellulose column chromatography [24]. These studies indicated that for a polynucleotide to be active in releasing the receptor complex from DNA-cellulose the polymer appears to need nonhydrogen-bonded bases with an oxygen or a sulfur atom at C-6 of purines or C-4 of pyrimidines. Thus, poly(U), poly(G), poly(X), and poly(I) were active but poly(C) and poly(A) were inactive. Poly(U,G) was more active than poly(G), poly(U), or equivalent mixtures of poly(G) and poly(U), indicating that the activity was dependent on the nucleotide sequence. The minimum length of the oligonucleotide needed to show activity appeared to be about 10–20 nucleotides but this may be dependent on the type of nucleotide in the oligomer.

The RNA-dependent release of the steroid-receptor complex from DNA could also be demonstrated by gradient centrifugation. As shown in Figure 4, the radioactive androgen-receptor complex stayed near the top of the tube after gradient centrifugation if no nucleic acid was present. If SV-40 DNA was added to the tube, a large quantity of the radioactivity was found to associate with DNA that sedimented at the bottom of the tube. When poly(U_1,G_1) (5S) was added to the receptor complex and SV-40 DNA before centrifugation, the radioactivity was not found with DNA in the bottom of the tube, but was found associated with poly(U_1,G_1). Poly(A,C) was able to bind to the receptor complex if no DNA was present; however, it could not release the receptor complex from the viral DNA.

We have also found that radioactive estradiol-receptor and progesterone-receptor complexes from rat or calf uterus and dexamethasone-receptor complex

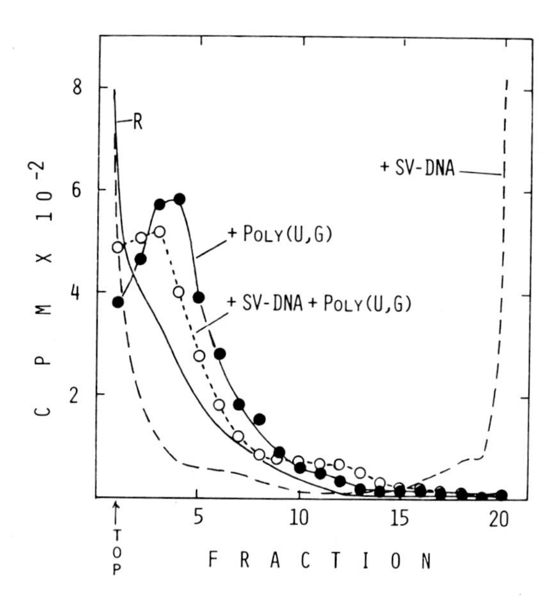

Fig. 4. Effect of poly(U,G) on binding of the [^{3}H]-DHT-receptor complex to SV-40 DNA. The radioactive receptor complex (5,000 cpm) was mixed with 3 μg of SV-40 DNA. Poly(U,G) (3 μg) was then added (o) and the mixture incubated at 0°C for 10 minutes. The incubated mixture was layered on top of the sucrose gradient and centrifuged at 50,000 rpm for 105 minutes at 0°C. After centrifugation, the contents of the tube were fractionated and the radioactivity in the individual fractions was determined and is shown on the ordinate. Parallel tubes contained receptor complex alone (R) or the complex mixed with SV-40 DNA (---) or with poly(U,G) (●). Monitoring the absorbance at 260 nm showed that after centrifugation SV-40 DNA sedimented to the bottom of the tube, whereas poly(U,G) was found near the top (fractions 2 to 5) of the tube.

from rat liver could also be removed from DNA by various polyribonucleotides as discussed above. Although we have not been able to demonstrate polymer specificity toward different receptor complexes, it is conceivable that certain natural RNA with specific nucleotide sequences may be more active than the synthetic polymers we have tested and can demonstrate such a specificity.

Since the concentration of RNA needed (1–5 μg/ml) to release receptor from DNA may be within the range expected in intact cell nuclei, preferential RNA binding of the steroid-receptor complexes in the nuclei is not inconceivable. Such a process may be important in the recycling of the receptor protein from nuclei to cytoplasm. The removal of RNA from DNA may also make the genetic template available for further transcription while receptor binding of RNA may be involved in post transcriptional control processes [2,21–24]. In this scheme, different RNA molecules may contain identical or similar nucleotide sequences so that more than one RNA species can be selected, although with some preference, by the same steroid-receptor complex. These diversified specificities together with other cellular factors may provide the selectivity and multiplicity observed in the induction of different proteins by steroid hormones.

CONCLUSIONS

Various steroid hormones can induce specific proteins in target cells. Hormonal induction of many of these proteins has been found to follow increases in the level of mRNA molecules specific for these proteins. Nevertheless, it has not been possible to prove that steroid or the steroid-receptor complexes can act directly on the genes for these protein products. In some well-studied cases there are reasons to believe that such inductions may not represent the primary effect of steroid hormones on the target cells. For example, increases in the cellular levels of chick oviduct ovalbumin mRNA by estrogen and rat liver α_{2u} globulin mRNA by androgen were seen after a lag phase and a protein synthesis inhibitor could inhibit the mRNA accumulation, suggesting that stimulation of mRNA synthesis or accumulation may be secondary to the synthesis of certain 'early' proteins [25]. In the rat ventral prostate, it is not clear whether spermine binding protein and α-protein represent an "early" mediatory protein and a "late" protein, respectively. Further studies are also necessary to determine whether a component of a "late" protein has a role in maintaining the chromatin interaction with androgen-receptor complex at a normal level as we have suggested.

REFERENCES

1. Anderson KM: Selective retention of dihydrotestosterone by prostatic nuclei in vivo and in vitro. PhD thesis, University of Chicago, 1969.
2. Liao S, Fang S: Receptor proteins for androgens and the mode of action of androgens on gene transcription in ventral prostate. Vitam Horm 27:17–90, 1969.

3. Liao S, Rossini GP, Hiipakka RA, Chen C: Factors that can control the interaction of the androgen-receptor complex with the genomic structure in the rat prostate. In Bresciani F (ed): "Perspectives in Steroid Receptor Research," New York: Raven Press, 1980, pp 99–112.
4. Rossini GP, Liao S: unpublished observation.
5. Liao S, Tymoczko JL, Castaneda E, Liang T: Androgen receptors and androgen-dependent initiation of protein synthesis in the prostate. Vitam Horm 33:297–313, 1975.
6. Nishigori H, Toft DO: Inhibition of progesterone receptor activation by sodium molybdate. Biochemistry 19:77–83, 1980.
7. Munck A, Wira C, Young DA, Mosher KM, Hallahan C, Bell PA: Glucocorticoid-receptor complexes and the earliest steps in the action of glucocorticoids on thymus cells. J Steroid Biochem 3:567–578, 1973.
8. Ishii DN, Pratt WB, Aronow L: Steady-state level of the specific glucocorticoid binding component in mouse fibroblasts. Biochemistry 11:3896–3904, 1972.
9. Sando JJ, LaForest AC, Pratt WB: ATP-dependent activation of L cell glucocorticoid receptors to the steriod binding form. J Biol Chem 254:4772–4778, 1979.
10. Sando JJ, Hammond ND, Stratford CA, Pratt WB: Activation of thymocyte glucocorticoid receptors to steroid binding form. J Biol Chem., 254:4779–4789, 1979.
11. Wheeler RH, Leach KL, LaForest AC, O'Toole TE, Wagner R, Pratt WB: Glucocorticoid receptor activation and inactivation in cultured human lymphocytes. J Biol Chem 256:434–441, 1981.
12. Liao S, Fang S: Factors and specificities involved in the formation of 5α-dihydrotestosterone-nuclear receptor protein complex in rat ventral prostate. In Griffiths K, Pierrepoint CG (eds): "Some Aspects of the Aetiology and Biochemistry of Prostate Cancer." Cardiff: Alpha Omega Alpha Publishing, 1970, pp 105–108.
13. Fang S, Liao S: Androgen receptors: Steroid- and tissue-specific retention of a 17β-hydroxy-5α-androstan-3-one-protein complex by cell nuclei of ventral prostate. J Biol Chem 246:16–24, 1971.
14. Chen C, Schilling K, Hiipakka RA, Huang I-Y, Liao S: Prostate α-protein: Isolation and characterization of the polypeptide components and cholesterol binding. J Biol Chem (in press).
15. Chen C, Hiipakka RA, Liao S: Prostate α-protein: Subunit structure, polyamine binding, and inhibition of nuclear chromatin binding of androgen-receptor complex. J Steroid Biochem 11:401–405, 1979.
16. Lea OA, Petruz P, French FS: Prostatein, a major secretory protein of the rat ventral prostate. J Biol Chem 254:6196–6202, 1979.
17. Heyns W, Peeters B, Mous J, Rombaut W, DeMoor P: Purification and characterization of prostatic binding protein and its subunits. Eur J Biochem 89:181–186, 1978.
18. Forsgren B, Bjork P, Carlstrom K, Gustafsson J-A, Pousette A, Hogberg B: Purification and distribution of a major protein in rat prostate that binds estramustine, a nitrogen mustard derivative of estradiol-17β. Proc Natl Acad Sci USA, 76:3149–3153, 1979.
19. Shyr C-I, Liao S: A protein factor that inhibits binding and promotes the release of the androgen-receptor complex. Proc Natl Acad Sci USA 75:5969–5973, 1978.
20. Liao S, Chen C, Huang I-Y: Prostate α-protein: Complete amino acid sequence of the component that inhibits nuclear retention of androgen receptor complex. J Biol Chem (in press).
21. Liao S, Tymoczko JL, Howell DK, Lin AH, Shao T-C, Liang T: Interaction of ribonucleoprotein particles and sex-steroid-receptor complexes: A model for receptor cycling and possible function. Int Congr Ser Excerpta Med 219:434–440, 1970.
22. Liao S, Liang T, Tymoczko JL: Ribonucleoprotein binding of steroid-receptor complexes. Nature New Biol 241:211–213, 1973.
23. Liang T, Liao S: Association of the uterine 17β-estradiol-receptor complex with ribonucleoprotein in vivo and in vitro. J Biol Chem 249:4671–4678, 1974.

24. Liao S, Smythe S, Tymoczko JL, Rossini GP, Chen C, Hiipakka RA: RNA-dependent release of androgen and other steroid-receptor complexes from DNA. J Biol Chem 245:5545--5551, 1980.
25. Liao S, Hiipakka RA: Mechanism of action of steroid hormones at the subcellular level. In Makin HLJ (ed): "Biochemistry of Steroid Hormones." Oxford: Blackwell Scientific Publications (in press).

The Prostatic Cell: Structure and Function
Part A, pages 391–407

The Presence in Rat and Human Prostate of Proteins That Bind Steroid-Cytostatic Complexes

Björn Forsgren, Per Björk, Kjell Carlström, Jan-Åke Gustafsson, Åke Pousette, and Bertil Högberg

INTRODUCTION

Studying the pharmacokinetic properties of estramustine phosphate (Estracyt^R), a nor-nitrogen mustard carbamate derivative of 17β-estradiol-17β-phosphate (Fig. 1) introduced in 1966 as a therapeutic agent in the treatment of prostatic carcinoma, Plym Forshell and Nilsson [1] found considerably higher levels of radioactivity in the rat prostate following intravenous administration of the drug tritiated in the estradiol moiety than after administration of tritiated 17β-estradiol-17β-phosphate or 17β-estradiol (1–10 mg/kg body weight). The main metabolite of estramustine phosphate in the rat prostate was identified as its dephosphorylated metabolite, estramustine (Fig. 1). Confirming the uptake of estramustine after a single intravenous injection of estramustine phosphate Høisaeter [2], after administration of the drug for 3 days (100 mg/kg body weight), also found high amounts of the 17-dehydrogenated congener of estramustine, the estrone nitrogen mustard complex estromustine (Fig. 1), in the rat ventral prostate. These findings initiated more detailed studies on the uptake of the nitrogen mustard derivatives of 17β-estradiol and estrone by the rat ventral prostate as part of the work directed toward an understanding of the biological effects of estramustine phosphate in man.

RAT

Distribution studies in rats using tritiated estramustine with high specific radioactivity (80–110 Ci/mmole, 0.8 μg/kg body weight) instead of the low-labeled estramustine phosphate used earlier (1–10 mCi/mmole, 10 mg/kg body

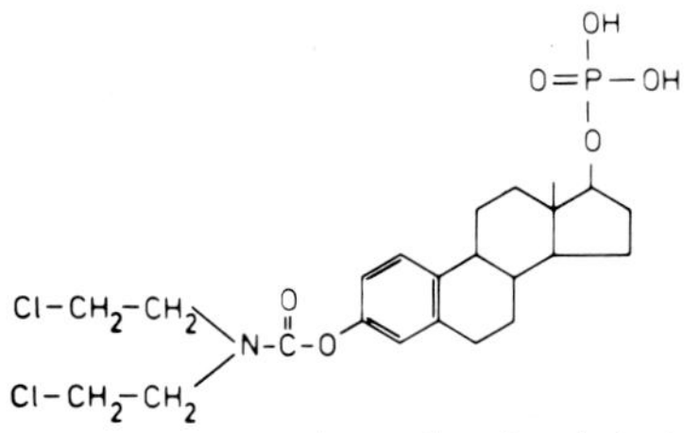

estramustine phosphate, Leo 299

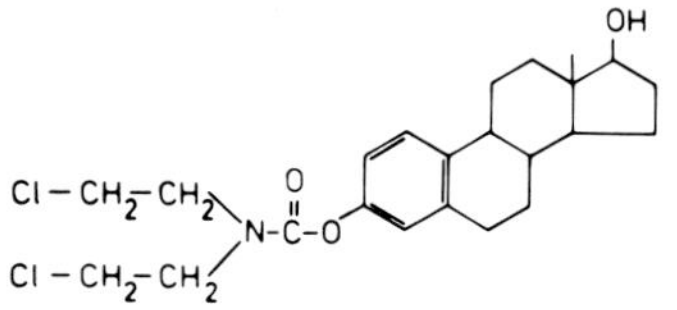

estramustine, Leo 275

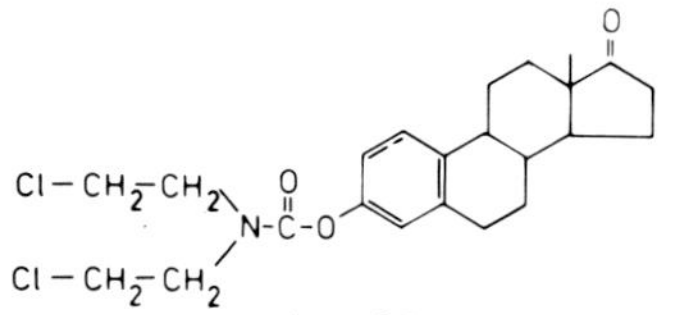

Leo 271

Fig. 1. Structure of estramustine phosphate (Leo 299), estramustine (Leo 275), and 17-dehydro-estramustine or estromustine (Leo 271).

weight) confirmed the earlier findings and also showed a time-dependent concentration of radioactivity in the ventral prostate that did not occur in most other tissues examined [3] (Fig. 2). Using autoradiography Appelgren et al [4] found radioactivity in the epithelial cells of the ventral prostate 5 minutes after [^{3}H]-estramustine had been intravenously administered to the rat. Fifteen minutes later the ventral prostate had an increased content of radioactivity mainly confined to the epithelial cells. Four hours after injection of [^{3}H]-estramustine radioactivity was also localized in the secretory contents of the lumina of the gland. In another experimental series, this observation was also made at 2 hours after an intramuscular injection of [^{3}H]-estramustine. These results indicated that estramustine is taken up by the epithelial cells of the ventral prostate, passed through the cells into the lumina and most probably excreted together with the prostatic secretory contents. Gel chromatography (Ultrogel AcA-54) of prostate cytosol (105,000g supernatant) recovered from rats 2 hours after administration of [^{3}H]-estramustine showed a major radioactive peak eluted at a position corresponding to a molecular weight of 40,000–50,000. The ethyl ether extract of the pooled fractions comprising this peak was analyzed by thin-layer chromatography. The main radioactivity had a mobility corresponding to that of estramustine. A smaller amount of radioactivity travelled as the estramustine-congener, Leo 271 [3].

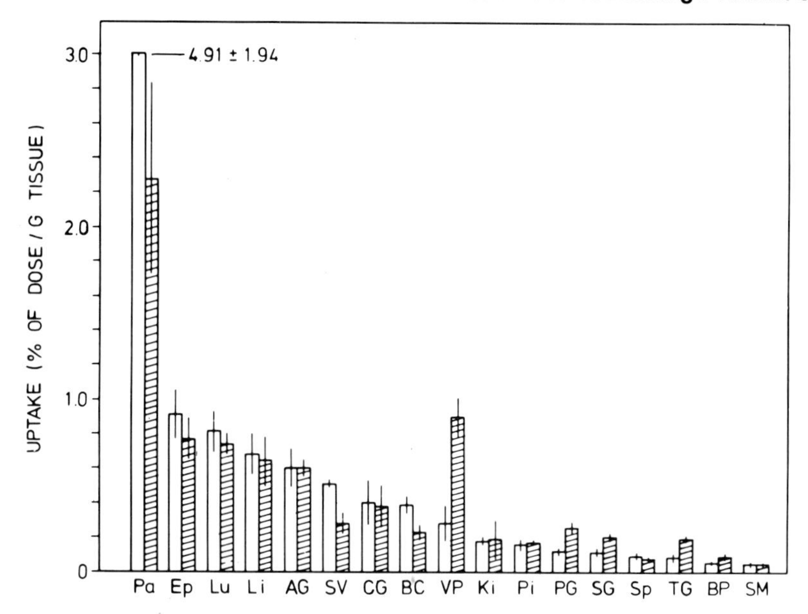

Fig. 2. Uptake of [^{3}H]-estramustine in various tissues of the male rat, expressed as percentage of dose ±S.E. (bars) (n = 5) per gram tissue, wet weight, 30 minutes (white columns) and 2 hours (hatched columns) after administration of 0.44 nmoles of [^{3}H]-estramustine to orchiectomized rats. The tissues examined were (left to right) pancreas (Pa), epiphysis (Ep), lung (Lu), liver (Li), adrenal gland (AG), seminal vesicle (SV), coagulating gland (CG), brain cortex (BC), ventral prostate (VP), kidney (Ki), pituitary gland (Pi), preputial gland (PG), submaxillary gland (SG), spleen (Sp), thyroid gland (TG), blood plasma (BP), and skeletal muscle (SM).

The physicochemical properties of the estramustine-binding agent in the rat ventral prostate were further studied in vitro using cytosol preparations [3,5]. Estramustine was bound to a much higher extent and to other macromolecular species (Fig. 3) than 17β-estradiol or 5α-dihydrotestosterone [5]. The protein nature of the estramustine-binding agent was demonstrated by the susceptibility of the binding to proteases. Subtilopeptidase A completely destroyed the estramustine-macromolecular complex and Streptomyceus griseus and pancreatic crude protease decreased the binding by 85% and 45%, respectively. On the other hand, DNase and RNase had no significant effect on the binding. The binding of estramustine decreased by 50% when labeling of the cytosol was performed in the presence of 1–2 mM of N-bromosuccinimide or *p*-hydroxymercuribenzoate. Dithiothreitol also influenced the binding of estramustine giving a 35% decrease at 5 mM and a 55% to 60% decrease at 10 mM. However, the binding was not influenced by 10% ethanol or 0.6 M KC1 [3].

The in vitro binding of estramustine by rat ventral prostate cytosol occurs with a broad pH optimum between pH 7 and 8.5 with a maximum binding at pH 7.8. The association rate of estramustine with the estramustine-binding protein is very high at 37°C (Fig. 4) and almost as high at 30°C. At 37°C, however,

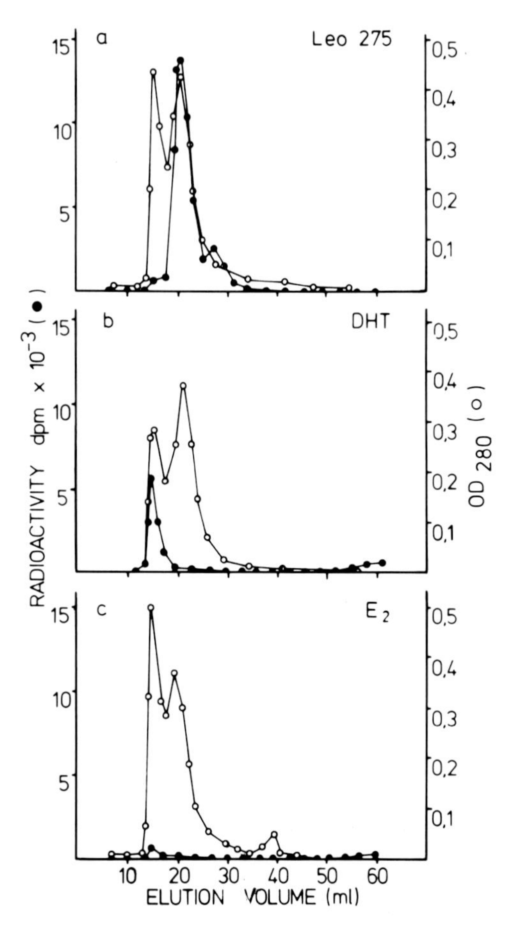

Fig. 3. Ultrogel AcA-54 chromatography of the macromolecular fraction obtained after Sephadex G-25 filtration of rat ventral prostate cytosol incubated for 4 hours at 0–4°C with a) [^{3}H]-estramustine (1.2 nM), b) 5α-[^{3}H]-dihydrotestosterone (1.4 nM), and c) 17β-[^{3}H]-estradiol (2.0 nM). Protein concentrations were 13 mg (a,b) and 16 mg(c) per ml cytosol. Absorbance at 280 nm (o); radioactivity (●).

the estramustine/protein complex is very rapidly degraded, which creates a sharp maximum in bound estramustine after 10 minutes of incubation. At 30°C, binding starts to decrease after 2 hours. The association rate decreases with decreasing temperature. At 22°C equilibrium is reached after 2 hours, at 15°C after 8–12 hours, and at 0°C after 20 hours. At 0°C, however, only 25% of the maximal cytosol binding is achieved [3].

The rate of dissociation of the estramustine/protein complex increases rapidly with temperature with half-lives of about 210, 80, 9, and 4 minutes at 15°C, 22°C, 30°C, and 37°C, respectively. At 0°C no dissociation is found even after 24 hours. Since the dissociation rates are high compared to the degradation rates

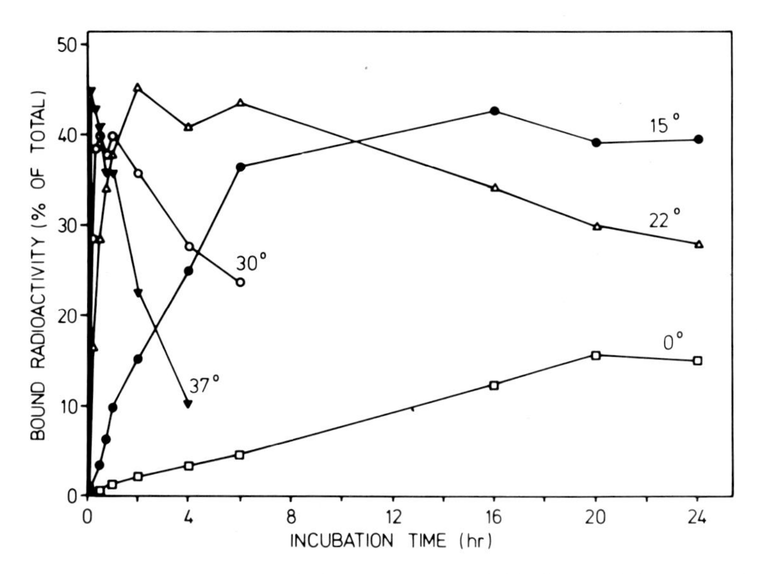

Fig. 4. Rate of association between [^{3}H]-estramustine and the binding protein in rat ventral prostate cytosol at various temperatures. The concentrations of ligand and total cytosol protein were 10 nM and 10μg/ml, respectively. At each time, protein-bound [^{3}H]-ligand was determined by dextran-coated charcoal technique. Corrections for dissociation and degradation were not made.

(see below), no corrections have been made for the latter. The estramustine-binding protein in rat ventral prostate cytosol degrades with half-lives of about 80, 30, 6, and 1.5 hours at 15°C, 22°C, 30°C, and 37°C, respectively. At 0°C no sign of degradation is found even after 24 hours [3].

Analysis of the binding of estramustine by rat ventral prostate cytosol yielded a mean apparent K_d of about 17 nM. The mean value of the maximal binding capacity (B_{max}) was about 5 nmoles/mg cytosol protein using cytosol from ventral prostates of 8–10-week-old rats orchiectomized 24 hours before dissection of the glands [3] (Fig. 5).

Using rat ventral prostate cytosol labeled with [^{3}H]-estramustine the estramustine/protein complex was shown to concentrate at pH 5 during isoelectric focusing in a sucrose gradient. Sucrose density gradient centrifugation at low ionic strength indicated a sedimentation coefficient of 3.7 S. Using this value and a Stokes radius of 2.9 nm obtained by gel chromatography on a calibrated column (Ultrogel AcA-44), the molecular weight of the ligand/protein complex was calculated to be 44,000. Using the linear correlation of the ratio of elution volume to void volume with the logarithm of the molecular weight, the molecular weight of the complex was determined to be 50,000 [5]. Later, during purification of estramustine-binding protein on a calibrated Sephadex G-100 Superfine column, the molecular weight of the ligand/protein complex using the same correlation was calculated to be 46,000 [6].

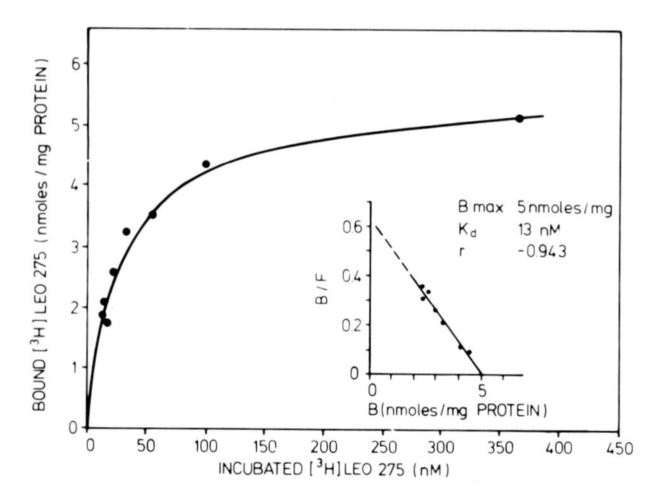

Fig. 5. Saturation and Scatchard analysis of binding of [^{3}H]-estramustine to rat ventral prostate cytosol. Each point represents the mean of duplicate samples. The Scatchard plot (inset) shows the specific binding after correction for nonspecific binding. Maximal specific binding was 8 nM giving 5 nmoles per mg cytosol protein (1.6 μg cytosol protein per ml incubate) with an apparent K_d of 13 nM (r = –0.943).

The efficiency of various steroids and steroid derivatives to displace estramustine from the estramustine-binding protein was examined by incubating rat ventral prostate cytosol with 10 nM [^{3}H]-estramustine in the presence of various unlabeled steroids, steroid conjugates, and steroid nitrogen mustard derivatives in concentrations ranging from 1 nM to 45 μM [3]. None of the steroids or steroid conjugates inhibited the binding of [^{3}H]-estramustine by more than 35% even at 45 μM concentration. The most efficient steroidal inhibitor at this concentration (4,500-fold excess versus the tracer) was progesterone (35% inhibition) followed by estrone (30%), pregnenolone (25%), androstenedione (20%), and dehydroepiandrosterone (10%). All other steroids or steroid conjugates tested decreased the binding of the tracer by less than 10% when added in 4,500-fold excess (Table I). Those steroids and steroid conjugates were: 17β-estradiol, 5α-dihydrotestosterone, testosterone, 19-nortestosterone, 5α-androstane-3β,17β-diol, corticosterone, cortisol, dexamethasone, ethinylestradiol, estriol, diethylstilbestrol, estrone sulfate, 17β-estradiol-3-sulfate, 17β-estradiol-3,17-disulfate, estrone glucuronide, and 17β-estradiol-17-glucuronide. In contrast, several of the nitrogen mustard derivatives tested inhibited the binding of 10 nM [^{3}H]-estramustine by 50% at concentrations ranging from 15–25 nM to 6–8 μM, ie, from twofold to 700-fold excess of the unlabeled competitor versus the tracer (Fig. 6).

Using cytosol prepared from ventral prostates of 100 rats, 8–10 weeks old, estramustine-binding protein was purified to homogeneity by a four-step pro-

TABLE I. Effect of various steroids and steroid conjugates on the binding of [^{3}H]-estramustine by rat ventral prostate cytosol

Competitor (45μM)	Bound [^{3}H]-estramustine % of control
No competitor	100
Progesterone	65
Estrone	70
Pregnenolone	75
Androstenedione	80
Dehydroepiandrosterone	90
Other steroids or steroid conjugates	>90

Cytosol samples (200 μl, 1.6 μg protein per ml) were incubated at 15°C for 18 hours with 10 nM [^{3}H]-estramustine in the presence of varying amounts (1 nM to 45 μM) of unlabeled steroids and steroid conjugates. After treatment with dextran-coated charcoal the radioactivity bound in the presence of competitor was expressed as percentage of radioactivity bound in the absence of competitor. Table shows the cytosol binding of [^{3}H]-estramustine in the presence of 45 μM competitor, ie, a 4500-fold excess of competitor in proportion to [^{3}H]-estramustine. Unlabeled estramustine gave 50% inhibition in twofold excess.

cedure [6]. After labeling of crude cytosol with [^{3}H]estramustine the [^{3}H]estramustine/protein complex eluted from DEAE-cellulose at 0.2 M KCl was chromatographed on Sephadex G-100 Superfine. The radioactive peak recovered with an elution volume corresponding to a molecular weight of 46,000 was applied onto a column of Octyl-Sepharose. The [^{3}H]estramustine/protein complex, interacting with the hydrophobic sidechains of the Octyl-Sepharose at high ionic strength conditions, could be eluted with low-salt buffer containing ethylene glycol. Polyacrylamide gel electrophoresis (PAGE) in the absence of sodium dodecyl sulfate (SDS) and 2-mercaptoethanol turned out to be a convenient last step in the purification scheme showing a single radioactively labeled protein band, indicating a homogeneous preparation of the estramustine-binding protein (EMBP).

Amino acid analysis of EMBP (Table II) showed that acidic amino acids constitute about 26% (molar basis) and that sulfur-containing amino acids account for about 6% (molar basis) of the total amino acids. The presence of glucosamine shows that EMBP is a glycoprotein. A minor content (1–2%) of other carbohydrate components was indicated by the trace(s) of furfural(s) in the amino acid chromatogram.

When analyzed by SDS-PAGE in the absence of 2-mercaptoethanol, purified EMBP labeled with ^{125}I was found to be composed of two subunits with almost similar electrophoretic mobilities corresponding to molecular weights of about 20,000 and 18,000, respectively (Fig. 7A). The band migrating faster during

$R = -\overset{O}{\overset{\|}{C}}-N-(CH_2CH_2Cl)_2$

Structure	Leo no.	RBA
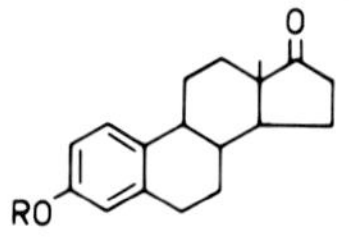 RO, O	Leo 271	1.16
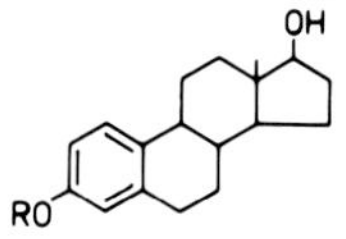 RO, OH	Leo 275	1.00
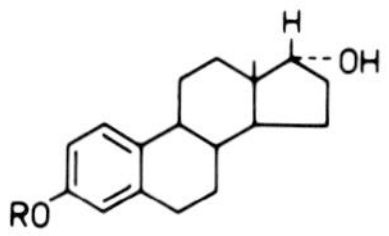 RO, H, OH	Leo 2179	1.00
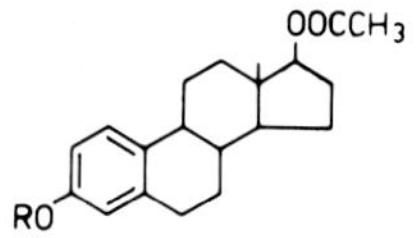 RO, OOCCH$_3$	Leo 289	0.77
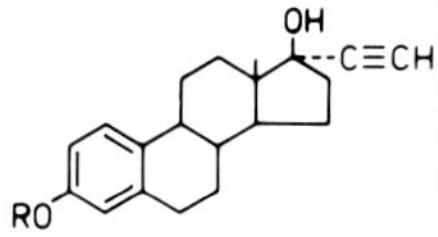 RO, OH, C≡CH	Leo 675	0.44
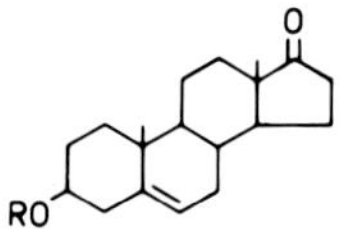 RO, O	Leo 452	0.23
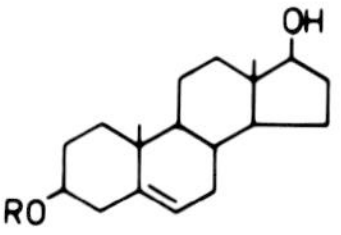 RO, OH	Leo 524	0.16
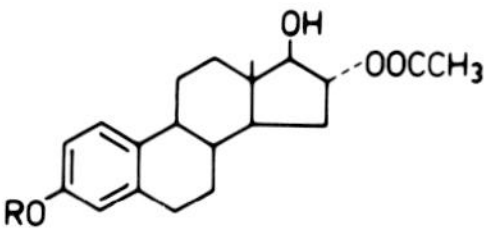 RO, OH, OOCCH$_3$	Leo 2035	0.02
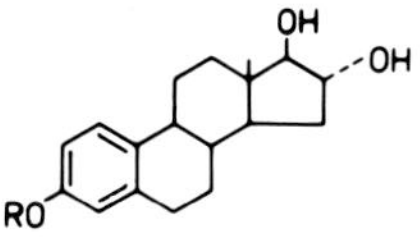 RO, OH, OH	Leo 1611	0.01
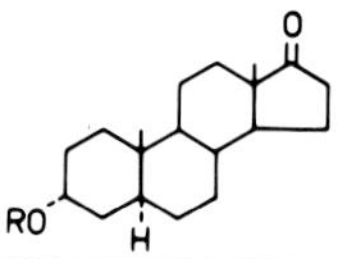 RO, H, O	Leo 451	0.007
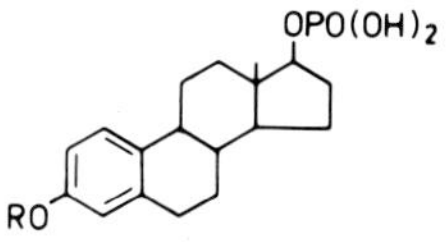 RO, OPO(OH)$_2$	Leo 299	0.002

Fig. 6. Relative binding affinity (RBA) of some estrogen and non-estrogen nitrogen mustard derivatives for the estramustine-binding protein in rat ventral prostate. Cytosol samples (200 μl, 1.6 μg protein per ml) were incubated at 15°C for 18 hours with 10 nM [^{3}H]-estramustine in the presence of varying amounts (1 nM to 45 μM) of unlabeled estrogen nitrogen mustard derivatives. After treatment with dextran-coated charcoal, the radioactivity bound in the presence of competitor was expressed as percentage of radioactivity bound in the absence of competitor. RBA is calculated as the ratio excess of estramustine required for 50% inhibition to excess of competitor required for 50% inhibition. Under the experimental conditions used, the concentration of estramustine required for 50% inhibition was 20 nM, ie, twofold excess to the concentration of [^{3}H]-estramustine.

electrophoresis contained larger amounts of ^{125}I than did the more slowly migrating band. When disulfide bridges were reduced prior to analysis, the two subunits decomposed into three components with molecular weights of about 14,000, 11,000, and 8,000, respectively (Fig. 7B). The smallest component contained practically all the ^{125}I indicating a high content in this peptide of amino acids susceptible to iodination (principally tyrosine, histidine, and phenylala-

TABLE II. Amino acid composition of the estramustine-binding protein from rat ventral prostate

Amino acid	nmole/100nmoles Protein
Glutamic acid	15.97
Aspartic acid	9.78
Leucine	8.91
Valine	8.62
Lysine	6.82
Serine	6.31
Threonine	5.93
Isoleucine	5.23
Alanine	4.71
Glycine	4.54
Phenylalanine	4.33
Proline	3.63
Cysteic Acid	3.57
Tyrosine	2.90
Methionine	2.51
Arginine	2.46
Histidine	1.23
Tryptophan	0.60
Glucosamine	1.96
Total	100.01

nine). Intact disulfide bridges seemed to be prerequisite for the protein to bind estramustine because incubation with 0.3 M 2-mercaptoethanol led to total abolishment of estramustine binding.

Antibodies against the purified protein were raised in rabbits and a radioimmunoassay was developed using ^{125}I-labeled protein as a standard [6]. By means of this radioimmunoassay cytosol preparations of various male and female rat tissues were analyzed for EMBP. In male rats EMBP was found in high levels in the ventral prostate (18–20% of the total cytosol protein content) and in lower amounts in the lateral and dorsal lobes of the prostate(0.8 and 0.2% of total cytosol protein, respectively). In addition, EMBP was found in lower amounts in other androgen-dependent tissues of the male rat (Table III). In male rats no EMBP was detected in the epiphysis, lung, liver, kidney, spleen, testis, skeletal muscle, or plasma. In female rats no EMBP was found in the epiphysis, pituitary gland, thyroid gland, lung, liver, adrenal gland, uterus, ovary, oviduct, vagina, preputial gland, skeletal muscle, or plasma, and in very small amounts in the kidney and spleen (4 and 3 ng/mg of total cytosol protein, respectively). Cytosol preparations from pancreas of both sexes contained minor amounts of EMBP but no parallelism between the sample curves and the standard curve was obtained, possibly due to proteolytic enzyme activities. With the exception of

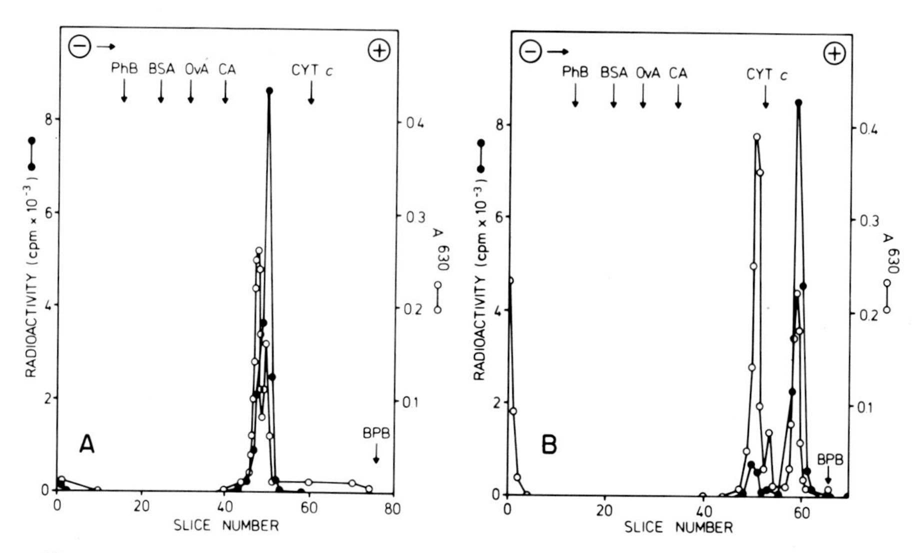

Fig. 7. Polyacrylamide gel electrophoresis performed in the presence of 0.1% sodium dodecyl sulfate. ^{125}I-labeled purified protein was incubated for 5 minutes at 90°C in 0.01 M sodium phosphate buffer, pH 7.4, containing 0.1% sodium dodecyl sulfate, in the absence (A) or the presence (B) of a disulfide bridge reducing agent. In addition, [^{14}C]methyl-labeled protein standards were run to calibrate the gels for molecular weight determination: PhB, phosphorylase B (≈92,500); BSA, bovine serum albumin (67,000); OvA, ovalbumin (45,000); CA, carbonic anhydrase (30,000); and Cyt *c*, cytochrome *c* (12,300). BPB, position of the marker, bromophenol blue.

pancreas, the only tissue in female rats containing appreciable amounts of EMBP was the cerebral cortex.

The presence of EMBP in androgen-dependent tissues especially initiated studies on the androgen-dependency of EMBP. Using radioimmunoassay, Pousette et al [7] found that being rather low before puberty the concentration of EMBP in rat ventral prostate cytosol increases significantly at puberty. After orchiectomy of mature rats, prostatic EMBP decreases totally and more rapidly than the total proteins do. Subsequent androgen treatment restores precastration levels of EMBP. Estrogen treatment of male rats decreases the EMBP concentration of the ventral prostate. When castrated rats are given both estrogen and androgen the effects on the prostate and EMBP are the same as when only androgen is given, showing that the effect of estrogen is completely counteracted by androgen. Treatment with progesterone tended to somewhat decrease the weight of the ventral prostate as well as the total amount of EMBP, but had no effect on the specific content of EMBP in the prostate cytosol.

The presence of EMBP in the prostate and other male sex accessory glands of the rat also initiated a comparative study on the presence of EMBP in the prostate of different species [8]. As comparison, seminal vesicles were also

TABLE III. Concentration of estramustine-binding protein in cytosol preparations from various rat tissues

Tissue	ng/mg of total cytosol protein			
	Male		Female	
Ventral prostate	177,000	+		
Lateral prostate	8,350	+		
Dorsal prostate	1,817	+		
Coagulating gland	503	+		
Seminal vesicle	394	+		
Submaxillary gland	278	+	6	+
Adrenal gland	210	+	ND	–
Preputial gland	184	+	ND	–
Pancreas	167	–	167	–
Pituitary gland	63	+	ND	–
Epididymis	50	+		
Thyroid gland	48	+	ND	–
Cerebral cortex	28	+	99	+

Within-assay variation was ±5.8% in samples ranging from 98–300 ng/ml cytosol ($\bar{x}$ = 166.3 ng/ml, n = 14), ±12.2% in samples ranging from 50–116 ng/ml cytosol ($\bar{x}$ = 74.6 ng/ml, n = 11), and ±16.1% in samples ranging from 11–56 ng/ml ($\bar{x}$ = 31.1 ng/ml, n = 14). Between-assay variation calculated as SD for a sample containing 75.5 ng/ml analyzed in six different assays was ±10.8%. The least detectable dose was 2.5 ng/ml cytosol. Values below 2.5 ng/ml cytosol are indicated by ND. Tissues giving dose-response curves of shape similar to those for ventral prostate are indicated by +; those giving curves of other shapes are indicated by –.

analyzed (Table IV) . Although the rat prostate was the richest source of EMBP, still significant amounts of it or of immunochemically similarly reacting proteins were found in prostate tissues from rabbit, boar, mouse, and man, as well as in the seminal vesicles analyzed. These lower amounts may reflect a truly smaller content or may be due to insufficient cross reactivity between the tissue protein and the rat EMBP antibody resulting in a falsely low value. However, the important finding is that a protein similar to EMBP is present in all prostate tissues investigated, including the human prostate.

Several reports have been published on the binding of steroids to rat ventral prostate cytosol proteins sedimenting at 3–5 S and with molecular weights of 45,000–70,000 [9–16]. In 1969 Karsznia et al [17] found a pregnenolone- and progesterone-binding protein in rat ventral prostate sedimenting at 3.5 S and with a molecular weight of 45,000–50,000. Simultaneously, Liao et al [18,19] reported on a dihydrotestosterone-binding protein designated as "α-protein" in rat ventral prostate cytosol sedimenting at 3–3.5 S that was distinct from the androgen receptor ("β-protein"). Further studies on the α-protein have been

TABLE IV. Changes in free plasma testosterone[a] and salivary testosterone with age

Age	TBG × 10^{-8}M (± SE)	% Free T (± SE)	Free T pmole/l	Range pmole/l
20–50	5.2 ± 0.07	2.08 ± 0.08	402.7 ± 24.3	191–694.4
50–70	6.5 ± 0.8	1.72 ± 0.12	298.6 ± 34.7	
70–85	8.9 ± 1.5	1.26 ± 0.14	156.3 ± 27.8	

Age	Saliva/plasma % (± SD)	T In saliva pmole/l (± SD)	Range pmole/l
18–35	1.6 ± 0.42	368 ± 166 (AM)	104–781
		212 ± 131 (PM)	35–538
40–60		158 ± 68 (AM)	51–292
61–80		103 ± 53 (AM)	38–208

[a]Vermeulen, Stoica, and Verdonck, J Clin Endocrinol 33: 759, 1971, with permission.

published recently [20–22]. In a series of publications Heyns et al [23–28] and Peeters et al [29] have extensively described a major protein in rat ventral prostate cytosol called "prostatic binding protein" or PBP that has a molecular weight of 51,000, an isolectric point of 5.2, a sedimentation coefficient of 3.7 S, and low binding affinity for steroids of which pregnenolone is bound with highest affinity ($K_a \approx 10^6 M^{-1}$). In 1977 Lea et al [30] also reported the isolation and characterization of a major protein ("prostatein") in rat ventral prostate cytosol with a molecular weight of 46,000 and an isoelectric point of 4.8, and which bound 5α-dihydrotestosterone with low affinity and high capacity. In a later publication [31] the molecular weight of prostatein is stated to be in the range of 38,000–46,000 and the steroid binding affinity to be inversely related to steroid polarity with progesterone being bound with the highest affinity ($K_a \approx 7 \times 10^4 M^{-1}$).

All data published to date on α-protein, prostatic binding protein, prostatein, and estramustine-binding protein from the rat ventral prostate strongly indicate that these names designate one and the same protein. They are all major, androgen dependent, secretory proteins in the rat ventral prostate cytosol with approximately the same molecular weight, sedimentation coefficient, isoelectric point, and subunit structure to mention only some of their common properties. The physiological role of this (these) protein(s), however, is not known. According to Fang and Liao [18] α-protein strongly inhibits the DNA or chromatin retention of the androgen-receptor complex, most probably through its A-subunit [21], that corresponds to the 20,000 dalton subunit of prostatic binding protein and estramustine-binding protein, respectively. Recent studies [32] have shown that purified estramustine-binding protein inhibits the in vitro uptake by rat ventral prostate nuclei of the androgen receptor labeled with [^{3}H]-methyltrienolone, and that it also inhibits the binding of this androgen-receptor complex to DNA-cellulose. These results together with the known androgen dependency of the protein in question may indicate that its role may possibly be as a regulator of the activity of the prostate cell. Its presence in the prostate secretion and in other male sex accessory glands also may indicate a role in fertilization, possibly as a sperm protective agent. Prostatein has been reported to bind to the plasma membrane of spermatozoa [31]. The protein may also act as a carrier of steroids and/or other compounds. Besides binding steroids, α-protein has been reported to bind polyamines under certain conditions [21], and using cultures of isolated rat ventral prostate epithelial cells, McKeehan et al [33] have found that PBP binds carcinogens. In this connection, it may be worthwhile to mention the reported uptake and secretion by the rat ventral prostate of various carcinogens such as chlorinated hydrocarbon insecticides [34,35], 3-methylcholanthrene [36,37], 2-acetylaminofluorene [38], and N-hydroxyurethane [39]. It is tempting to speculate that this uptake and secretion by the prostate of various exogenous compounds is due to the multi-named major secretory protein that binds steroid nitrogen mustard complexes with higher affinity than steroids. Further studies on this protein in rat ventral prostate are in progress in several laboratories.

MAN

The discovery of the uptake and binding by rat ventral prostate of estramustine and estromustine, the estrogen mustard complexes found circulating in patients treated with estramustine phosphate [40], aroused great interest in studying the possible presence of a corresponding estramustine-binding protein in the human prostate, especially in the prostatic cancer tissue.

Initial studies on the binding of estramustine by the human prostate showed radioactive peaks at about the same positions as for rat EMBP when samples of [^{3}H]-estramustine-labeled cytosol from a specimen of human benign prostatic hyperplasia (BPH) were analyzed by gel chromatography, sucrose density gradient centrifugation, and isoelectric focusing [41]. The binding affinity of estramustine for the BPH cytosol was about the same as for rat prostate cytosol (K_d = 35 nM). The concentration of binding sites, however, was considerably lower in the human prostate cytosol, about 1 pmole per mg cytosol protein compared to 5 nmoles/mg protein in the rat prostate cytosol. Examination of different cell fractions after incubation of minced human BPH tissue with [^{3}H]-estramustine or [^{3}H]-estromustine showed the concentration of both total and specifically protein-bound radioactivity to be highest in the Triton X-100 washings of the buffer-washed crude 800g sediment after homogenization (unpublished observations). However, high pressure liquid chromatography of detergent and 0.6 M KC1 extracts of such sediments as well as of cytosol from human prostate tissue show major binding of radioactivity after incubation with [^{3}H]-estramustine to molecular species with higher molecular weights than rat EMBP [42]. In the cytosol preparations, binding to human serum albumin (HSA) may disguise a

TABLE V. Amount of proteins immunochemically similar to rat EMBP in cytosol preparations from human BPH specimens

Tissue no.	ng Estramustine-binding protein per ml cytosol	mg cytosol protein	
264	28.0	1.8	+
265	38.0	5.8	+
266	32.5	3.9	–
272	52.0	2.6	+
274	1,162.5	108.6	+
279	104.0	10.8	+?
290	25.5	6.9	+
291	65.0	13.8	–
295	23.0	0.8	+
296	64.5	1.5	–
297	932.8	98.2	+
298	33.0	1.9	–

See footnote to Table III.

possible binding to a protein of the same molecular weight as rat EMBP if HSA is present in large excess to the latter.

Radioimmunoassay of cytosol preparations from human BPH tissue showed a large response range from values corresponding to less than 1 ng to more than 100 ng of EMBP per mg of cytosol protein [43] (Table V). Although the concentrations of EMBP obtained in cytosols from BPH were significantly lower than in rat prostate cytosol, which may be due to insufficient cross reaction, the congruency of most sample dilution curves with the standard curve indicated the presence in these samples of a protein identical or immunologically similar to EMBP in rat ventral prostate. Analyses of different human tissues showed that proteins immunochemically similar to EMBP were found in prostate, seminal vesicles, and epididymis (98, 35, and 92 ng per mg cytosol protein, respectively), while in cytosols from testis, submaxillary gland, and kidney as well as in plasma, no such proteins were detected [8].

A recent compilation of radioimmunological analyses of some fifty human prostate cytosol samples (to be published elsewhere) shows that most samples gave rise to dose-response curves similar to the standard curve. In ten cases no cross-reacting material was found. In five of these cases the tissue specimens had been stored lyophilized and three samples were obtained by electroresection. On the other hand, other tissue specimens obtained by electroresection gave positive results and so did autopsy material excised three days post-mortem. Interestingly, extraction with a detergent of the sediment obtained after centrifugation of tissue homogenates either at 800g or at 105,000g gave extracts showing dose-response curves similar to that of EMBP when analyzed by radioimmunoassay (unpublished observations). This is especially interesting in connection with the pronounced specific uptake of estramustine by this fraction mentioned earlier. Further studies are under way on the uptake and binding of estramustine (Leo 275) and its 17-dehydrogenated congener, estromustine (Leo 271), by the human prostate, as well as on the nature of the binding agent(s) and its (their) isolation, in order to develop a species-specific radioimmunoassay.

SUMMARY

During studies on the uptake and distribution of estramustine phosphate (Estracyt^{R}) in the rat, a major protein in the rat ventral prostate was found that binds estramustine, estromustine, and several other steroid nitrogen mustard complexes. This protein, called estramustine-binding protein, shares many physicochemical characteristics with α-protein, prostatic-binding protein, and prostatein, each reported to constitute a major steroid-binding protein in the rat ventral prostate. There is every indication that these four names designate one and the same protein, the binding properties of which favor the binding of lipophilic compounds, and which has shown an affinity for estramustine and closely structure-related compounds that is 100- to 1000-fold higher than for the natural steroids.

Also, the human prostate has been shown to take up and bind estramustine and estromustine. However, the binding entity (or entities) is still under intense investigation.

ACKNOWLEDGMENTS

The authors are indebted to Dr. Torgny Nilsson and to Drs. Lars-Eric Tisell and Håkan Salander for providing the electroresected and autopsy tissues referred to, respectively. The invaluable assistance by Mrs. Diane Smith in preparing this review is gratefully acknowledged.

REFERENCES

1. Plym Forshell G, Nilsson H: The distribution of radioactivity after administration of labelled estramustine phosphate (Estracyt^{R}), estradiol-17β-phosphate and estradiol to rats. Acta Pharmacol Toxicol 35(Suppl I):28, 1974 (abstr).
2. Høisæter PA: Studies on the conversion of oestradiol linked to a cytostatic agent (Estracyt^{R}) in various rat tissues. Acta Endocrinol 82:661–672, 1976.
3. Forsgren B, Gustafsson J-Å, Pousette Å, Högberg B: Binding characteristics of a major protein in rat ventral prostate cytosol that interacts with estramustine, a nitrogen mustard derivative of 17β-estradiol. Cancer Res 39:5155–5164, 1979.
4. Appelgren L-E, Forsgren B, Gustafsson J-Å, Pousette Å, Högberg B: Autoradiographic studies of ^{3}H-estramustine in the rat ventral prostate. Acta Pharmacol Toxicol 43:368–374, 1978.
5. Forsgren B, Högberg B, Gustafsson J-Å, Pousette Å: Binding of estramustine, a nitrogen mustard derivative of estradiol-17β, in cytosol from rat ventral prostate. Acta Pharm Suec 15:23–32, 1978.

6. Forsgren B, Björk P, Carlström K, Gustafsson J-Å, Pousette Å, Högberg B: Purification and distribution of a major protein in rat prostate that binds estramustine, a nitrogen mustard derivative of estradiol-17β. Proc Natl Acad Sci USA 76:3149–3153, 1979.
7. Pousette Å, Björk P, Carlström K, Forsgren B, Högberg B, Gustafsson J-Å: Influence of sex hormones on prostatic secretion protein, a major protein in rat prostate. Cancer Res 41:688–690, 1981.
8. Pousette Å, Björk P, Carlström K, Forsgren B, Gustafsson J-Å, Högberg B: On the presence of "Prostatic Secretion Protein" in different species. Acta Chem Scand B34:155–156, 1980.
9. Fang S, Liao S: Dihydrotestosterone binding by androphilic proteins of rat ventral prostate. Fed Proc 28:846, 1969 (abstr).
10. Fang S, Anderson KM, Liao S: Receptor proteins for androgens. On the role of specific proteins in selective retention of 17β-hydroxy-5α-androstan-3-one by rat ventral prostate in vivo and in vitro. J Biol Chem 244:6584–6595, 1969.
11. Mainwaring WIP: A soluble androgen receptor in the cytoplasm of rat prostate. J Endocrinol 45:531–541, 1969.
12. Unhjem O, Tveter KJ, Aakvaag A: Preliminary characterization of an androgen-macromolecular complex from the rat ventral prostate. Acta Endocrinol 62:153–164, 1969.
13. Unhjem O: Metabolization and binding of oestradiol-17β by rat ventral prostate in vitro. Res Steroids 4:139–143, 1970.
14. Baulieu E-E, Jung I: A prostatic cytosol receptor. Biochem Biophys Res Commun 38:599–606, 1970.
15. Mainwaring WIP, Peterken BM: A reconstituted cell-free system for the specific transfer of steroid-receptor complexes into nuclear chromatin isolated from rat ventral prostate gland. Biochem J 125:285–295, 1971.
16. Mainwaring WIP, Irving R: The use of deoxyribonucleic acid-cellulose chromatography and isoelectric focusing for the characterization and partial purification of steroid-receptor complexes. Biochem J 134:113–127, 1973.
17. Karsznia R, Wyss RH, LeRoy Heinrichs W, Herrmann WL: Binding of pregnenolone and progesterone by prostatic "receptor" proteins. Endocrinology 84:1238–1246, 1969.
18. Fang S, Liao S: Androgen receptors: steroid- and tissue-specific retention of a 17β-hydroxy-5α-androstan-3-one-protein complex by the cell nuclei of ventral prostate. J Biol Chem 246:16–24, 1971.
19. Liao S, Tymoczko JL, Liang T, Anderson KM, Fang S: Androgen receptors: 17β-hydroxy-5α-androstan-3-one and the translocation of a cytoplasmic protein to cell nuclei in prostate. Adv Biosci 7:155–163, 1971.
20. Shyr CI, Liao S: Protein factor that inhibits binding and promotes release of androgen-receptor complex from nuclear chromatin. Proc Natl Acad Sci USA 75:5969–5973, 1978.
21. Chen C, Hiipakka RA, Liao S: Prostate α-protein: subunit structure, polyamine binding, and inhibition of androgen-receptor complex. J Steroid Biochem 11:401–405, 1979.
22. Liao S, Mezzetti G, Chen C, Smythe S, Hiipakka RA, Loor R, Schilling K, Rossini GP: Alpha protein and spermine-binding protein of rat ventral prostate. In Murphy GP, Sandberg AA (eds): "Prostate Cancer and Hormone Receptors." New York: Alan R. Liss, Inc., 1979, pp 3–11.
23. Heyns W, DeMoor P: Prostatic binding protein. A steroid-binding protein secreted by rat prostate. Eur J Biochem 78:221–230, 1977.
24. Heyns W, Peeters B, Mous J: Influence of androgens on the concentration of prostatic binding protein (PBP) and its mRNA in rat prostate. Biochem Biophys Res Commun 77:1492–1499, 1977.
25. Heyns W, Peeters B, Mous J, Rombauts W, DeMoor P: Purification and characterization of prostatic binding protein and its subunits. Eur J Biochem 89:181–186, 1978.

26. Heyns W, Van Damme B, DeMoor P: Secretion of prostatic binding protein by rat ventral prostate. Influence of age and androgen. Endocrinology 103:1090–1095, 1978.
27. Heyns W, Peeters B, Mous J, Rombauts W, DeMoor P: Androgen-dependent synthesis of a prostatic binding protein by rat prostate. J Steroid Biochem 11:209–213, 1979.
28. Heyns W, Bossyns D, Peeters B: Binding of a small androgen-dependent protein to the prostatic binding protein of rat ventral prostate. The Prostate 1:116, 1980 (abstr).
29. Peeters BL, Mous JM, Rombauts WA, Heyns WJ: Androgen-induced messenger RNA in rat ventral prostate. Translation, partial purification and preliminary characterization of the mRNAs encoding the components of prostatic binding protein. J Biol Chem 255:7017–7023, 1980.
30. Lea OA, Petrusz P, French FS: Isolation and characterization of prostatein, a major secretory protein of rat ventral prostate. Fed Proc 36:780, 1977((abstr).
31. Lea OA, Petrusz P, French FS: Prostatein. A major secretory protein of the rat ventral prostate. J Biol Chem 254:6196–6202, 1979.
32. Pousette Å, Björk P, Carlström K, Forsgren B, Högberg B, Gustafsson J-Å: Influence of prostatic secretion protein on uptake of androgen-receptor complex in prostatic cell nuclei. The Prostate 2:23–33, 1981.
33. McKeehan WL, Rosser MP, Glass HA, Fast D: Prostatic binding protein: an androgen-dependent marker for prostate epithelial cells. Biochem Biophys Res Commun 95:674–681, 1980.
34. Wakeling AE, Visek WJ: Insecticide inhibition of 5α-dihydrotestosterone binding in the rat ventral prostate. Science 181:659–661, 1973.
35. Wakeling AE, Schmidt TJ, Visek WJ: Effects of dieldrin on 5α-dihydrotestosterone binding in the cytosol and nucleus of the rat ventral prostate. Toxicol Appl Pharmacol 25:267–275, 1973.
36. Lasnitzki I, Bard DR, Franklin HR: 3-Methylcholanthrene uptake and metabolism in organ culture. Br J Cancer 32:219–229, 1974.
37. Smith ER, Hagopian M: The uptake and secretion of 3-methylcholanthrene by the prostate gland of the rat and dog. J Natl Cancer Inst 59:119–122, 1977.
38. Smith ER, Hagopian M, Reister HC: The uptake and secretion of 2-acetylaminofluorene by the rat and dog prostate. Toxicol Appl Pharmacol 40:185–191, 1977.
39. Smith ER, Hagopian M, Norlin RD: The penetration of N-hydroxyurethane into the prostate and prostatic secretion of the rat and dog. Toxicol Appl Pharmacol 40:335–345, 1977.
40. Andersson SB, Gunnarsson PO, Nilsson T, Plym Forshell G: Metabolism of estramustine phosphate (Estracyt[R]) in patients with prostatic carcinoma. Eur J Drug Metab Pharmacokinet 1981 (in press).
41. Högberg B, Björk P, Carlström K, Forsgren B, Gustafsson J-Å, Hökfelt T, Pousette Å: The interaction of steroidal alkylating agents with binding components in the soluble fraction of the prostate. In Murphy GP, Sandberg AA (eds): "Prostate Cancer and Hormone Receptors." New York: Alan R. Liss, Inc., 1979, pp 181–199.
42. Kirdani RY, Corrales JJ, Høisæter PA, Karr JP, Murphy GP, Sandberg AA: Estramustine binding in rat, baboon and human prostate measured by high pressure liquid chromatography. Steroids 37:471–484, 1980.
43. Forsgren B, Björk P, Carlström K, Ekman P, Gustafsson J-Å, Pousette Å, Högberg B: Radioimmunoassay of a protein in human prostatic tissue that binds estramustine, the dephosphorylated metabolite of estramustine phosphate (Estracyt[R]). Cancer Treat Rep 63:1186, 1979 (abstr).

The Prostatic Cell: Structure and Function
Part A, pages 409-415

Immunocytochemistry of Prostatic Binding Protein in the Rat Ventral Prostate

Gerhard Aumüller and Walter Heyns

As shown by Heyns et al [1–4], Forsgren et al [5–7], and Lea et al [8], the rat ventral prostate contains a large amount of a steroid binding protein that has been named prostatic binding protein (PBP) [2], estramustine binding protein [6,7], or prostatein [8]. The synthesis of this protein is androgen dependent [4] and it is secreted into the acinar lumen of the prostate [4]. Although the molecular subunits of this protein have been purified [8], the intracellular pathways of the protein and its precursors during the process of secretion are unknown.

In this paper the binding of an antiserum against PBP is described which was used to localize the protein within the accessory sex glands of the rat. At the electron microscopic level it was found that PBP is present in the secretory granules of the rat ventral prostatic epithelium. The molecule has also been localized within the condensing vacuoles surrounding the Golgi apparatus.

MATERIALS AND METHODS

Tissue Processing

Adult male rats (2 Wistar, 2 Sprague-Dawley) weighing 250–280 gm were perfusion fixed in deep ether anesthesia. After laparotomy, a polyethylene tubing connected to a syringe was inserted into the abdominal aorta, the vena cava was severed, and about 50 ml of a precooled (4°C) fixative (5% paraformaldehyde, 0.5% glutaraldehyde, 0.5% $CaCl_2$, and 2000 IU heparin sulphate dissolved in

Abbreviations used: DAB, diaminobenzidine hydrochloride; PAP, soluble horseradish peroxidase anti-peroxidase complex; PBP, prostatic binding protein; PBS, phosphate-buffered saline; PBS-NSS, phosphate buffered saline containing normal swine serum; FITC, fluorescein thioisocyanate.

100 ml cacodylate buffer, 0.05 M, pH 7.3) were injected. The accessory sex glands were dissected, cut into small cubes, and rinsed in cacodylate buffer (0.1 M, pH 7.3). Part of the tissue was osmicated (1% OsO_4 in cacodylate buffer, 0.1 M, pH 7.3). Specimens were dehydrated in a graded series of ethanol, transferred to propylene oxide, and embedded in an Epon/Araldite mixture. After polymerization (24 hours at 60°C), semithin sections were cut with glass knives and ultrathin sections with a diamond knife. Semithin sections were mounted on glass slides, and ultrathin sections were collected on uncoated 200 mesh gold grids. The embedding resin was removed from the semithin sections by treatment with sodium alcoholate [9,10]. Ultrathin sections were etched with H_2O_2 for 7 minutes [11]. The sections were then processed with different immunocytochemical techniques.

Immunocytochemistry

An antiserum was raised in rabbits with purified PBP as previously described [1,4], and specificity was checked using an immunodiffusion test [1]. An aliquot of this antiserum was conjugated with horseradish peroxidase (courtesy of Dr. Grenner, Behringwerke, Marburg, FRG).

For light microscopic studies, semithin sections were incubated with PBS-NSS after removal of the resin to minimize nonspecific adsorption of proteins [12]. Sections were then incubated with the antiserum (dilution 1:2000) for 36 hours at 4°C. After rinsing with PBS and PBS-NSS, the sections were incubated with either FITC-conjugated IgG (goat, anti-rabbit, Boehringer, Ingelheim) diluted 1:50, for 20 minutes at room temperature, or with unlabeled IgG, diluted 1:200 (20 minutes, room temperature), rinsed, and treated for 5 minutes at room temperature with PAP (Boehringer, Ingelheim) [13] diluted 1:150. Peroxidase activity was visualized by incubation in PBS containing 20 mg/100 ml DAB and 7 μl/100 ml H_2O_2. Sections were then covered with a drop of 80% glycerol in PBS and photographed in a Zeiss Axiomat photomicroscope (with fluorescence microscopy equipment).

For electron microscopy, ultrathin sections were processed with either an immunoferritin method or with peroxidase-labeled antibody. After etching with diluted H_2O_2, sections were transferred on drops of antiserum (dilution 1:2000), rinsed with PBS-NSS, and incubated for 20 minutes with ferritin-labeled IgG (goat, anti-rabbit, Miles, Frankfurt) diluted 1:100. After rinsing, sections were stained with lead citrate [14] for 2 minutes.

Sections incubated with perioxidase-conjugated antiserum (diluted 1:200, 1 hour at room temperature) were developed in the DAB/H_2O_2 medium mentioned above and osmicated for 30 minutes. They were then examined in a Zeiss EM 10 electron microscope at a current voltage of 60 kV and magnifications between 5000 and 25,000.

For specificity controls [12], sections were processed with the procedures mentioned above with the exception that the antiserum was replaced by non-immune rabbit serum or a previously immunoabsorbed antiserum (adsorption of the antiserum with PBP, fivefold excess of the antigen). Controls were negative if not otherwise stated.

RESULTS

The ventral prostate was the only tissue with strong intraepithelial fluorescence in immunofluorescence studies using anti-PBP antiserum (Fig. 1a). Fluorescence of lesser intensity was seen within the acini of the dorsal and lateral prostates (Fig. 1b) and also in the lumen of the seminal vesicles, but not of the coagulating gland. Unlike the ventral prostate no intraepithelial fluorescence was found in these areas.

Using the peroxidase-labelled antiserum at the ultrastructural level, the secretory granules of the ventral prostate were clearly stained as well as the intraluminal secretion. No staining was seen at the Golgi level or in the cisternae of the rough endoplasmic reticulum (Fig. 2). For a better resolution of structural details in the electron microscope, sections were processed with anti-PBP antiserum and ferritin-labelled IgG.

Although some background staining was present, the secretory granules of the prostatic epithelial cells were densely convered with ferritin granules (Figs. 2,3). There was no difference between secretory granules of differing structure and size. In addition to the secretory granules, the condensing vacuoles surrounding the Golgi apparatus were stained (Figs. 4, 5), while the Golgi apparatus was not. The same was true for the rought endoplasmic reticulum. In individual cells ferritin-labelled lysosomes were seen.

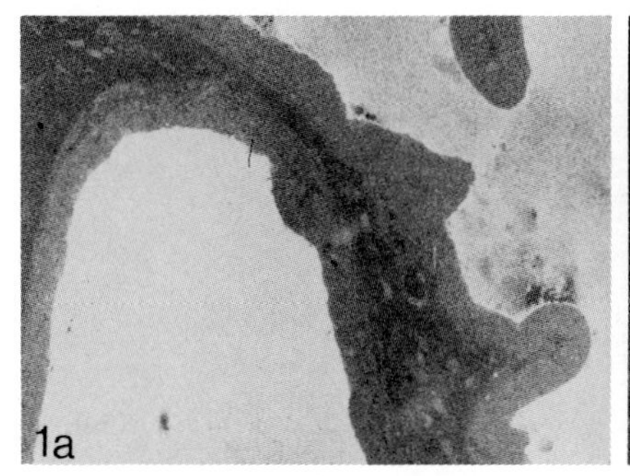

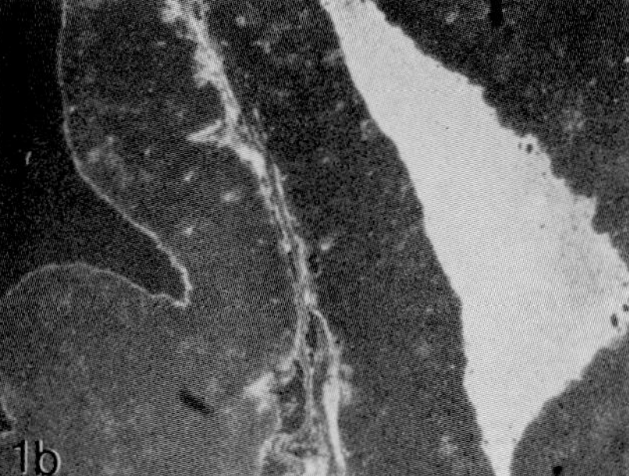

Fig. 1. Immunofluorescence of PBP. a) Survey light micrograph of acini of the ventral prostate containing fluorescent material within the lumen × 160. b) The lateral prostate shows a heterogeneous distribution of PBP in different acini. Background staining of individual epithelial cells. × 250.

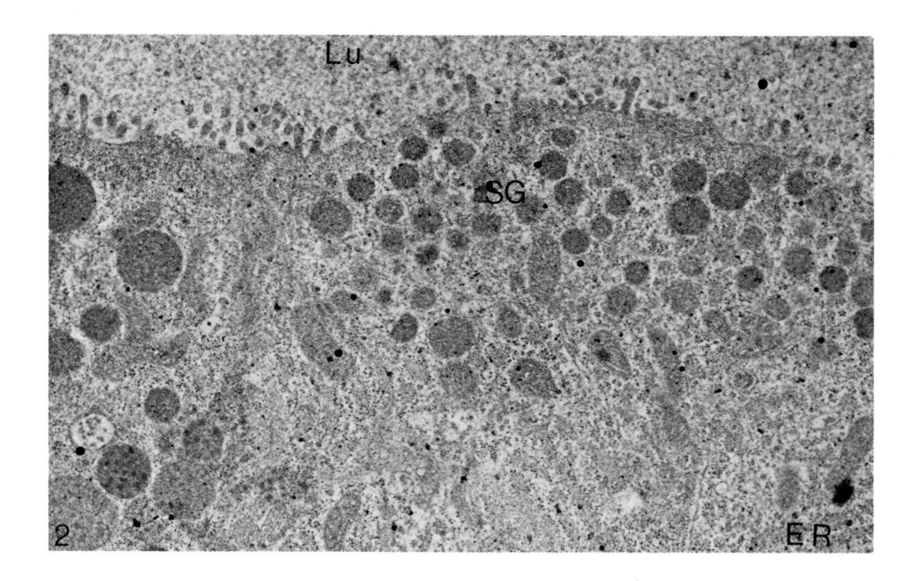

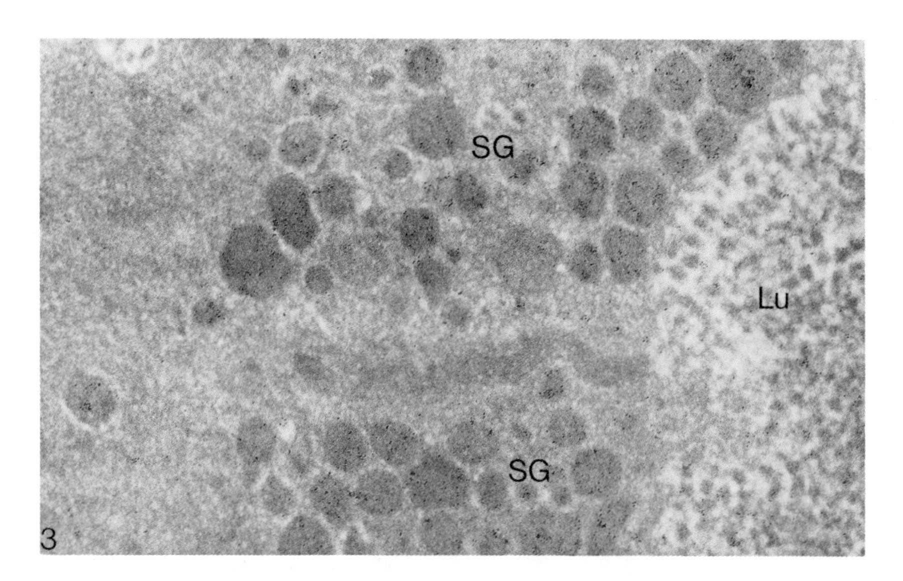

Fig. 2. Electron micrograph of rat ventral prostate epithelial cells containing numerous secretory granules (SG) stained with peroxidase-conjugated anti-PBP antiserum. The luminal contents (Lu) react rather weakly. There is no reaction within the cisternae of the rough endoplasmic reticulum (ER). × 4000.

Fig. 3. Electron micrograph of a rat ventral prostate epithelial cell. Immunoferritin-labeled secretory granules (SG) and luminal secretion (Lu) indicate the presence of PBP. × 10,000.

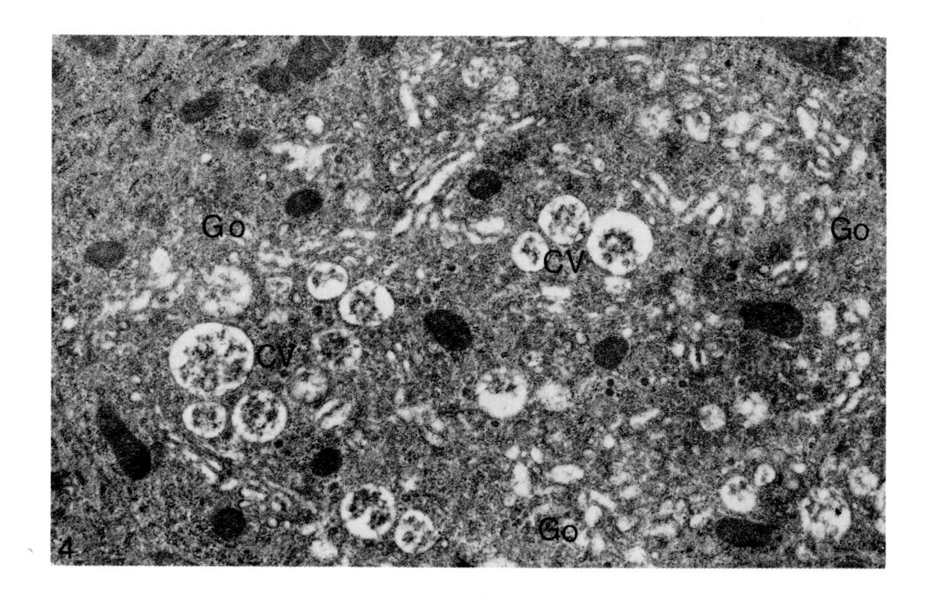

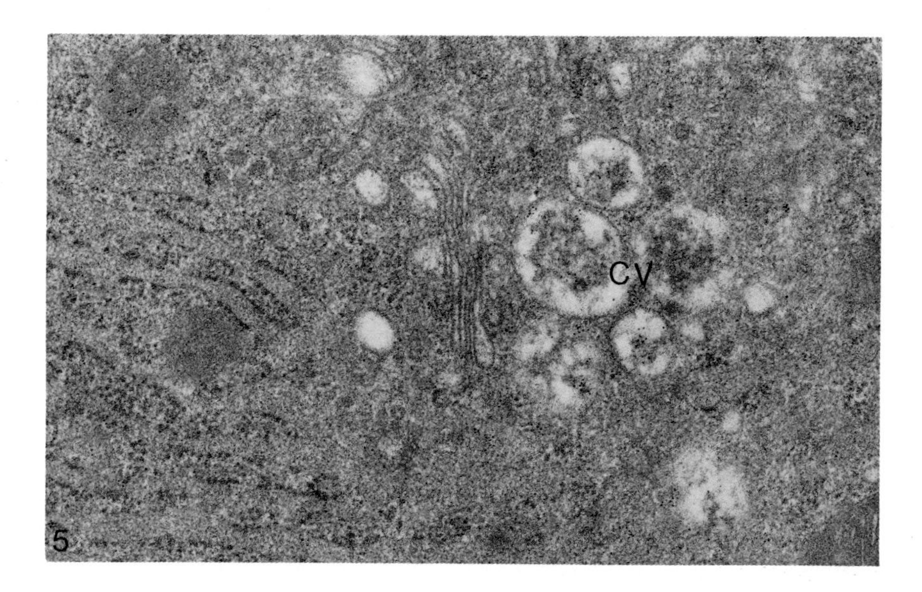

Fig. 4. Golgi area of a prostatic epithelial cell with numerous stacks of Golgi cisternae (Go), vesicles, and condensing vacuoles (CV). × 10,000.

Fig. 5. Immunoferritin labeling of condensing vacuoles (CV) where PBP precursors presumably combine to form the definite molecule. × 25,000.

DISCUSSION

In the present study PBP-immunoreactive secretory granules were exclusively found in the secretory cells of the ventral prostate. Intraluminal secretion was stained to varying degrees also in the seminal vesicles and the dorsal and lateral prostates. A possible explanation for this phenomenon is the redistribution of secretory material of the prostate via the excretory ducts back into the adjacent glands. Another explanation would be that very low amounts of PBP are secreted also by glands other than the ventral prostate.

The latter explanation is in accordance with biochemical findings [6] that estramustine binding protein is present in small amounts in some other tissues. However, the concentration of the protein is presumably very low in those tissues and therefore difficult to detect at the ultrastructural level.

At the electron microscopic level, the secretory granules of the ventral prostatic epithelium were clearly labeled, indicating the presence of PBP within these granules. No clear-cut differences in the number of ferritin grains present in the different types of secretory granules were observed; particularly there were no differences of labeling between the mature secretory granules and the condensing vacuoles. The Golgi stacks, however, and the rough endoplasmic reticulum were unlabeled. This labeling pattern seems to indicate that the subunits or precursors of PBP unite within the condensing vacuoles to form the definite immunoreactive PBP molecule.

This is an interesting aspect both with respect to the intracellular transport of secretory proteins in the prostatic epithelial cells and the formation of the PBP molecule. Regarding the latter, it has been shown biochemically to dissociate into two subunits, named S and F [3]. Upon reduction of disulfide bridges each subunit dissociates further into two components: One of these components is the same in both subunits. The subunits have an amino acid composition very similar to that of PBP. In a previous study [9] it was shown that both subunits react immunologically with the antiserum against the complete protein with a pattern of partial identity. It is therefore unclear whether the positive immunoreaction found in the condensing vacuoles is due to the definitive molecule and/or to the subunits. The present immunocytochemical results stress the importance of the condensing vacuoles in the formation of the PBP molecule. As has been previously shown [15], newly synthesized proteins move through prostatic cells rather slowly. Autographic labeling of the condensing vacuoles was observed by Flickinger [15] for up to 2 hours, indicating a prolonged presence of newly synthesized proteins within this compartment of the prostatic cell.

CONCLUSIONS

Our immunocytochemical studies of PBP at the ultrastructural level have clearly demonstrated the secretory nature of this protein by localizing it within the secretory granules of the glandular epithelium. Moreover, they have provided insight into the intracellular formation of the definite protein molecule which possibly takes place within the condensing vacuoles surrounding the Golgi apparatus. Comparing the labelling of the secretory granules within different cells, no indication of a secretory cycle of the prostatic acinar cells was found. PBP therefore represents an excellent model for the study of prostatic secretion in the rat.

REFERENCES

1. Heyns W: Immunochemical measurement of prostatic binding protein. FEBS Lett 81:43–47, 1977.
2. Heyns W, de Moor P: Prostatic binding protein. A steroid-binding protein secreted by rat prostate. Eur J Biochem 78:221–230, 1977.
3. Heyns W, Peeters B, Mous J, Rombauts W, de Moor P: Purification and characterization of prostatic binding protein and its subunits. Eur J Biochem 89:181–186, 1978.
4. Heyns W, van Damme B, de Moor P: Secretion of prostatic binding protein by rat ventral prostate: Influence of age and androgen. Endocrinology 103:1034–1090, 1978.
5. Forsgren B, Högberg B, Gustafsson J-Å, Pousette Å: Binding of estramustine, a nitrogen mustard derivative of estradiol-17β, in cytosol from rat ventral prostate. Acta Pharm Suec 15:23–32, 1978.
6. Forsgren B, Björk P, Carlström K, Gustafsson J-Å, Pousette Å, Högberg B: Purification and distribution of a major protein in rat prostate that binds estramustine, a nitrogen mustard derivative of estradiol-17β. Proc Natl Acad Sci USA 76:3149–3153, 1979.
7. Forsgren B, Gustafsson J-Å, Pousette Å, Högberg B: Binding characteristics of a major protein in rat ventral prostate cytosol that interacts with estramustine, a nitrogen mustard derivative of 17β-esradiol. Cancer Res 39:5155–5164, 1979.
8. Lea OA, Petrusz P, French FS: Isolation and characterization of prostatein: a major secretory protein of rat ventral prostate Fed Proc 36:780, 1977.
9. Baskin DG, Erlandsen SL, Parsons JA: Immunocytochemistry with osmium-fixed tissue. I. Light microscopic localization of growth hormone and prolactin with the unlabelled antibody-enzyme method. J Histochem Cytochem 27:867–872, 1979.
10. Lane BP, Europa DL: Differential staining of ultrathin sections of epon-embedded tissues for light microscopy. J Histochem 13:579–582, 1965.
11. Baskin D, Erlandsen SL, Parsons JA: Influence of hydrogen peroxide or alcoholic sodium hydroxide on the immunocytochemical detection of growth hormone and prolactin after osmium fixation. J Histochem Cytochem 27:1290–1292, 1979.
12. Sternberger LA: Immunocytochemistry. Second Ed, New York: John Wiley, 1979.
13. Sternberger LA, Hardy PH, Cuculis JJ, Meyer HG: The unlabelled antibody-enzyme method of immunohistochemistry. Preparation and properties of soluble antigen-antibody complex (horseradish peroxidase-anti horseradish peroxidase) and its use in identification of spirochetes. J Histochem Cytochem 18:315–333, 1970.
14. Venable JH, Coggeshall R: A simplified lead citrate stain for use in electron microscopy. J Cell Biol 25:407, 1965
15. Flickinger CJ: Protein secretion in the rat ventral prostate and the relation of Golgi vesicles, cisternae and vacuoles, as studied by electron microscopic radioautography. Anat Rec 180:427–447, 1974.

The Prostatic Cell: Structure and Function
Part A, pages 417–434

Steroid Binding Proteins in Rat and Human Prostate

A.M. Traish, R.E. Muller, M.E. Burns, and H.H. Wotiz

INTRODUCTION

The mechanism by which steroid hormones elicit their action has been extensively studied. Briefly, upon entry of the hormones into their target cells they bind to specific cytoplasmic proteins termed receptors. These receptors bind steroids with specificity, high affinity, and limited capacity. Upon binding in the cytoplasm the steroid receptor complexes undergo physicochemical changes that lead to translocation of the complexes to the nuclei, where they trigger a chain of biochemical events leading to the observed physiological response. Other steroid binding proteins such as sex steroid binding globulin (SSBG), cortisol binding globulin (CBG), α-acid glycoprotein, and serum albumin are thought to play an important role at the extracellular level in preventing metabolism of the bound steroid during transport to the target tissue. While considerable information on the function of the intracellular receptors and plasma steroid binding proteins exists, very little is known of a third class of steroid binding proteins found in several sex steroid target tissues. In the prostate several such binding entities have been described. Among those are the α-protein described by Fang and Liao [1], the pregnenolone binding protein [2], and the prostatic binding protein which requires delipidation to unmask its binding activity [3]. Additionally, Lea et al [4] have described a binding protein in the prostate which binds progesterone. All of these proteins have been observed in the rat prostate or prostatic fluid. In human prostate a binding protein for the drug estramustin has been described by Forsgren et al [5].

In attempting to develop a reliable method for the assay of the specific androgen receptors in human prostatic tissue, we observed that treatment of cytosol with dextran-coated charcoal (DCC) revealed the existence of a new steroid binding protein distinct from the androgen receptor. The work described here deals with the partial characterization of this protein.

MATERIALS AND METHODS

Isotopes and Chemicals

17β-Hydroxy-17α-methyl(^{3}H)-estra-4,9,11-trien-3-one ([^{3}H]-R1881) (87 Ci/mmol), dihydrotestosterone [1,2,4,5,6,7-^{3}H(N)] 110 Ci/mmol, and radioinert R1881, were obtained from New England Nuclear. All other nonradioactive steroids were obtained from Steraloids. All reagents were reagent grade obtained from commerical sources.

Dextran-Coated Charcoal (DCC)

Acid-washed charcoal (5gm) was suspended in a liter of Tris-EDTA buffer (0.05 M Tris 1.5mM EDTA pH 7.4) and dextran T-70 was added (0.5gm). The suspension was stirred overnight at 4°C and stored in the presence of 0.02% sodium azide.

Hydroxylapatite (HAP)

Hydroxylapatite slurry was prepared in Tris-phosphate buffer (Tris 0.05M, KH_2PO_4, 0.001M, pH 7.2, at 0°C). The slurry was washed several times by resuspension and decantation until the pH of the wash was 7.2. The final slurry was reconstituted to 0.7 cc HAP/ml buffer.

Human Tissue

Tissue samples of human prostate were obtained during the course of both transurethral and open prostatectomy carried out in the management of patients with both benign prostatic hypertrophy and adenocarcinoma of the prostate. In the case of transurethral prostatectomy a random sampling of tissue chips was frozen after a midportion of the chip was sent for histologic confirmation of diagnosis. In the case of open prostatectomy, if there was a nodule of suspected cancer present, a segment of tissue was obtained from the midpoint of the tissue and an adjacent segment of prostate was submitted for histologic confirmation. All human prostate samples were freshly obtained and if not used immediately were stored frozen in liquid nitrogen.

Animals

Male Sprague Dawley rats (200–300gm) were castrated 18–24 hours before use. Animals were sacrificed by cervical dislocation and ventral prostates were excised and immediately used for experimentation or stored frozen in liquid nitrogen for 1–3 weeks.

Preparation of Cytosol Fraction From Prostatic Tissue

Unless otherwise stated all manipulations were carried out at 0–4°C. Frozen tissue samples were pulverized using a Thermovac tissue pulverizer submerged in liquid nitrogen. Fresh tissue or the tissue powder was quickly weighed and homogenized in 3–4 volumes of buffer TEDG (Tris 0.05M, EDTA 1.5mM, DTT 0.5mM, glycerol 10% (v/v) and Na_2MoO_4 10mM pH 7.4 at 25°C) using a glass-glass homogenizer with motor driven pestle. The homogenate was cetrifuged at 100,000g for 45 minutes to yield the high speed supernatant (cytosol).

Assay of Cytoplasmic Androgen Receptor

One volume of cytosol (0.1–0.3 ml) was incubated with an equal volume of buffer containing the desired concentrations of [^{3}H]-R1881 and a 500-fold excess of nonradioactive triamcinolone acetonide (TA) to prevent binding of R1881 to putative progesterone receptors. Parallel incubations were made with [^{3}H]-R1881, 500-fold excess TA, and a 100-fold excess unlabeled R1881 to determine nonspecific binding.

The incubations remained at 0°C for the specified length of time. The protein-bound radioactivity was assayed by HAP binding. Briefly, a slurry of HAP (0.5 ml) was added to the cytosol; after 15 minutes at 0°C with intermittent vortexing, the samples were washed three times with 3 ml of buffer (Tris 0.05M, pH 7.2) by resuspension and centrifugation. The final HAP pellet was extracted with 2 ml of ethanol at 22°C, and the total slurry was transferred to counting vials, mixed with 10 ml of Betafluor (National Diagnostics), and counted.

Specifically bound [^{3}H]-R1881 was determined from the difference between the total bound [^{3}H]-R1881 and the [^{3}H]-R1881 bound in the presence of a 100-fold excess unlabeled R1881.

Treatment of Prostatic Tissue Cytosol With DCC Pellet

DCC suspension (equal in volume to the cytosol sample to be treated) was centrifuged at 800g for 5 minutes at 0°C, and the supernatant was removed. The prostatic cytosol was then mixed with this pellet and kept in suspension by frequent vortexing for 30 minutes at 0°C. The charcoal was removed by centrifugation at 800g × 10 minutes and the supernatant ("DCC-treated cytosol") used for steroid binding experiments.

Assay of Human and Rat Prostatic Steroid Binding Protein

Single point assay. Cytosol samples were equally divided and one half of the cytosol was treated with DCC. Both samples were incubated with [^{3}H]-R1881 ($2–4 \times 10^{-8}$M) and a 500-fold excess TA with or without a 100-fold excess unlabeled R1881. The incubations remained on ice for 16–24 hours, and the bound radioactivity was assayed with HAP. The specifically bound [^{3}H]-R1881 in the native cytosol incubation represents the androgen bound receptor. The [^{3}H]-R1881 specifically bound in the DCC-treated sample represents both the androgen receptor and the steroid binding protein.

TABLE I. Competition for [^{3}H]-R1881 binding by various steroids (fmol/mg protein)

Specimen			Untreated cytosol				DCC-treated cytosol		
		No Competitor	Pregnenolone	Androstenedione	Epitestosterone	No Competitor	Pregnenolone	Androstenedione	Epitestosterone
Cancer	1	88	57	28	12	360	80	8	23
	2	57	55	26	21	243	68	0	0
	3	42	29	14	9	66	22	19	0
BPH	4	30	31	0	15	115	26	6	18
	5	28	26	18	14	96	36	14	20
	6	15	15	10	9	83	16	15	20

Samples 1, 2, 3: From patients with adenocarcinoma, 4, 5, 6: from patients with BPH. DCC-treated or native cytosol were incubated with 3×10^{-8}M [^{3}H]-R1881 and a 500-fold excess unlabeled TA. Parallel incubations with 3×10^{-6}M unlabeled R1881 were performed to determine nonspecific binding.

TABLE II. Androgen receptor and HPSBP in human prostate ([^{3}H]-R1881 bound [fmol/mg protein])

	Specimen no.	Untreated cytosol	DCC-Treated cytosol
BPH	1654	19	255
	1639	30	358
	1678	27	175
Cancer	1551	78	720
	15661	41	530
	1562	30	420
	1592	44	580
	1730	14	438
	1685	22	293
	1700	23	515
	1716	19	281
	1724A	22	156
	1724B	33	169
	1761	31	446
	1730	22	422
	1733	0	100
	1784	28	189
	1803	18	90
	1804	18	213
	1811	9	49
	1816	0	166
	1826	63	1218
	1823	13	74
	1835	9	196
	1840	0	375
	2130	7	530
	2131	8	624
	2133	13	555

Native or DCC-treated human prostatic cytosol was incubated with [^{3}H]-R1881 and unlabeled TA, with or without a 100-fold excess of nonradioactive R1881. Incubation conditions were as in Figure 3, and binding was measured with HAP. Data of the first 8 specimens were obtained from Scatchard analysis. The remaining binding data were measured after incubation with a single concentration of [^{3}H]-R1881 (4×10^{-8}M).

Equilibrium binding of [^{3}H]-R1881. Native or DCC-treated cytosol was incubated with increasing concentration of [^{3}H]-R1881 (1×10^{-9} to 5×10^{-8}M) in the presence of 500-fold excess TA. Parallel incubations were made with [^{3}H]-R1881, 500-fold excess TA, and a 100-fold excess of unlabeled R1881. The incubations were kept at 0–4°C for 16 hours and the bound radioactivity was assayed by HAP.

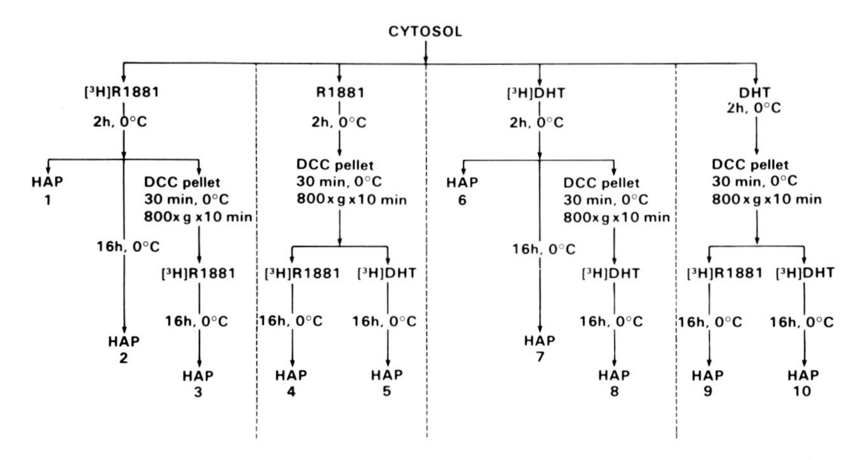

Fig. 1. Schematic representation of the experimental protocol used to compare the binding of [^{3}H]-R1881 and [^{3}H]-DHT to native and DCC-treated cytosol of the prostate. Results in Figure 2 have been numbered according to incubation numbering in this figure.

Protein Determination

Protein determination was performed by the procedure of Lowry et al [6].

RESULTS

Effect of DCC Treatment of Native Cytosol on Subsequent Binding of Androgens

One of the problems frequently associated with the measurement of steroid hormone receptors by radioligand assay is the interference by the unlabeled steroids of endogenous origin. Thus, depending on the hormonal milieu prior to surgery, prostatic tissue may contain considerable amounts of free and protein-bound steroids. In the case of the uterine estrogen receptor it has been shown [7] that treatment of cytosol with DCC facilitates quantitation of free and occupied receptors by exchange assay. This procedure has also been applied [8, 9] to the measurement of the androgen receptor in prostate, a tissue which normally contains significant concentrations of endogenous steroids. We have found that specific binding of [^{3}H]-R1881 was increased greatly in DCC treated cytosols (Table II). This increased binding is unlikely to be associated with SSBG, since we utilized the synthetic androgen R1881, a ligand of little affinity for plasma binding proteins [10]. This observation was further substantiated by steroid specificity data presented in Table I.

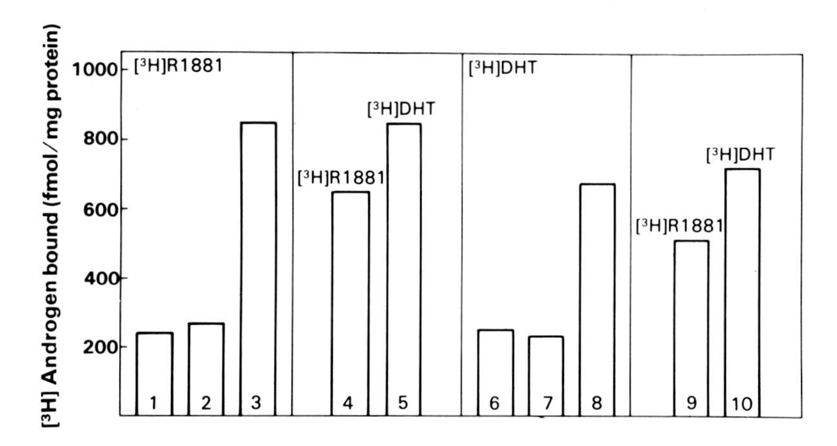

Fig. 2. Binding of [^{3}H]-R1881 and [^{3}H]-DHT to native and DCC-treated rat prostatic cytosol. Aliquots of prostatic cytosol (10 mg protein/ml) were mixed with an equal volume of TEDGM buffer containing 4×10^{-8}M [^{3}H]-R1881 and a 500-fold excess TA in the presence or absence of a 100-fold excess unlabeled R1881 (incubations 1,2, and 3). Similarly, aliquots of cytosol were incubated with an equal volume of TEDG buffer containing 4×10^{-8}M [^{3}H]-DHT and a 500-fold excess TA with or without a 100-fold excess unlabeled DHT (incubations 6,7, and 8). Cytosols containing 1×10^{-5}M TA were also incubated with 2×10^{-8}M unlabeled R1881 (incubations 4 and 5) or 2×10^{-8}M unlabeled DHT (incubations 9 and 10). All samples were kept at 0°C for 2 hours. Triplicate samples (0.2 ml) of the incubations with [^{3}H]-R1881 and [^{3}H]-DHT were either assayed for bound radioactivity by HAP technique (incubations 1 and 6) or kept at 0°C for an additional 16 hours and then treated with HAP (incubations 2 and 7) or treated with a DCC pellet for 30 minutes at 0°C, centrifuged at 800g for 10 minutes, and the supernatants were reincubated with [^{3}H]-R1881 (incubation 3) or [^{3}H]-DHT (incubation 8). After 16 hours at 0°C the bound radioactivity was assayed with HAP. Samples which had been incubated with unlabeled R1881 were treated with DCC and reincubated with [^{3}H]-R1881 or [^{3}H]-DHT for 16 hours at 0°C (incubations 4 and 5). Those samples which had been incubated with unlabeled DHT were treated with DCC and reincubated with [^{3}H]-R1881 or [^{3}H]-DHT (incubations 9 and 10). Binding was measured with HAP. Data represent only specific binding.

To exclude the possibility that this increased binding may be unique for R1881, the binding characteristics of the natural 5α-dihydrotestosterone (DHT) and the synthetic ligand R1881 were compared. These experiments were performed with castrated rat prostatic cytosol as outlined in Figure 1. Figure 2 shows the results obtained. Aliquots of untreated cytosol were incubated with [^{3}H]-R1881 or [^{3}H]-DHT (incuations 1 and 6, Fig. 1) at 0°C for 2 hours and specific binding measured by the hydroxylapatite (HAP) technique. No significant difference in binding was observed (Fig. 2, bars 1 and 6).

That equilibrium had been obtained at this short period of time can be seen from the fact that no significant increase in binding was observed when the incubation was extended to 16 hours (Fig. 2, bars 2 and 7). Since the prostatic tissue used was obtained from castrated rats, the concentration of endogenous androgens in this cytosol preparations can be assumed to be negligible. In order to mimic the situation encountered with prostatic tissue specimens from untreated patients, aliquots of the above cytosol which had been labeled with [^{3}H]-R1881 or [^{3}H]-DHT for 2 hours at 0°C were added to a DCC pellet and incubated for 30 minutes at 0°C. (As described above, binding prior to this treatment was measured in incubations 1 and 6, Fig. 1; data presented in Fig. 2, bars 1 and 6.) DCC was removed by centrifugation and the sample reincubated for 16 hours at 0°C with [^{3}H]-R1881 or [^{3}H]-DHT (Fig. 1, incubations 3 and 8). Specifically bound ligand was determined by the HAP assay. A comparison of binding in incubations 1 and 3 shows (Fig. 2, bars 1 and 3) that upon DCC treatment, reincubation with [^{3}H]-R1881 results in a 3–4-fold increase in binding (240 fmol/mg protein vs 850 fmol/mg protein). A similar effect was observed with [^{3}H]-DHT (incubations 6 and 8, Fig. 1; 250 fmol/mg protein vs 670 fmol/mg protein). This increased binding was caused by DCC treatment and not simply by the second exposure to [^{3}H]-DHT, since reincubation of untreated cytosol for 16 hours did not increase specific binding (in Fig. 1, compare incubation 2 with 1, 260 vs 240 fmol; and incubation 7 with 6, 230 vs 250 fmol). Thus, DCC treatment of prostatic cytosol promotes androgen binding to a specific class of sites which cannot be labeled by direct incubation with hormone for up to 16 hours at 0°C. It is possible that either DCC removes an inhibitor of binding to this type of site or these sites were occupied with steroid of nontesticular origin which was removed by charcoal treatment.

When the same cytosol preparation used to obtain the above data was first incubated with nonradioactive R1881 (Fig. 1) to saturate the androgen receptor and then treated with DCC and reincubated with [^{3}H]-R1881 or [^{3}H]-DHT (Fig. 1, incubations 4 and 5), significant binding was again observed (Fig. 2, bars 4 and 5, 650 fmol R1881, 850 fmol DHT). Similar data were obtained when the native cytosol was preincubated with nonradioactive DHT, stripped with DCC, and reincubated with [^{3}H]-R1881 or [^{3}H]-DHT (Fig. 1, incubations 9 and 10; Fig. 2, bars 9 and 10, 520 fmol R1881, 710 fmol DHT).

The concentration of androgen receptor reported here ranges from 230–260 fmol/mg protein (Fig. 1, incubations 1, 2, 6, and 7). These values are in good agreement with those previously reported by other investigators [11]. The increased binding observed after DCC treatment could not be evaluated quantitatively since the ligand concentration used was insufficient to achieve saturation of this second set of binding sites (see below). Furthermore, when cytosol, preincubated with unlabeled steroid to saturate the androgen receptor, is treated with DCC and then incubated for 16 hours with tritiated ligand, partial exchange of androgen receptor complexes also occurs, a reaction which interferes with quantitation of these nonreceptor binding sites.

Characterization of Androgen Receptor and "Nonreceptor" Androgen Binding Protein: Equilibrium Binding of [^{3}H]-R1881 to Rat and Human Prostatic Cytosol

Having established that the prostatic cytosol of human and castrated rats contains an androgen binding protein which is only measurable in DCC-treated samples, we examined the binding characteristics of this protein.

Rat tissue. Rat prostatic tissue cytosol from 24-hour castrated animals was incubated with increasing concentrations of [^{3}H]-R1881 at 0°C for 16 hours and the bound radioactivity representing the androgen receptor was measured by HAP (Fig. 3, upper panel, lower curve). Another portion of the same cytosol was first incubated with DCC at 0°C for 30 minutes, centrifuged, and the supernatant incubated at 0°C for 16 hours with increasing concentrations of [^{3}H]-R1881. Parallel incubations in the presence of an excess of unlabeled R1881 were performed to determine nonspecific binding. Figure 3 (upper panel) shows that untreated cytosol contains a single binding moiety with the characteristics of the androgen receptor: $K_D = 2.5 \times 10^{-9}$M and 100 fmol of binding sites/mg protein. When the same cytosol was first treated with DCC and then incubated with [^{3}H]-R1881 a biphasic binding curve was obtained. The first part of this binding curve represents R1881 bound to both receptor and nonreceptor androgen binding sites. The increment in binding at molarities higher than 1×10^{-8}M represents exclusively binding to the second component, ie, the nonreceptor binding protein with K_D of approximately 5×10^{-8}M and a concentration of approximately 1160 fmol/mg protein. These data taken from the Scatchard Plot have not been corrected for the androgen-receptor contribution.

Human tissue. Human prostatic tissue cytosol was first treated with DCC and then incubated with increasing concentrations of [^{3}H]-R1881 in the presence or absence of a 100-fold excess of unlabeled R1881 at 0°C for 16 hours; binding was measured with HAP. As shown in Figure 3 (lower panel), a biphasic binding curve was obtained indicating the presence of more than one component, as previously described for rat tissue. The high affinity component (androgen receptor) was saturated at concentrations below 1×10^{-8}M [^{3}H]-R1881, while the second entity required concentrations beyond 4×10^{-8}M for saturation. On Scatchard plot analysis the first component displayed a $K_D = 5 \times 10^{-9}$M and a binding capacity of 50 fmol/mg protein. The second binding component had a K_D of 2.5×10^{-8}M and a binding capacity of 200 fmol/mg protein.

Is the Human Prostatic Steroid Binding Protein (HPSBP) Identical With SSBG?

Because of the potentially significant contamination of prostatic tissue with SSBG it was thought essential to verify that the second R1881 binding component

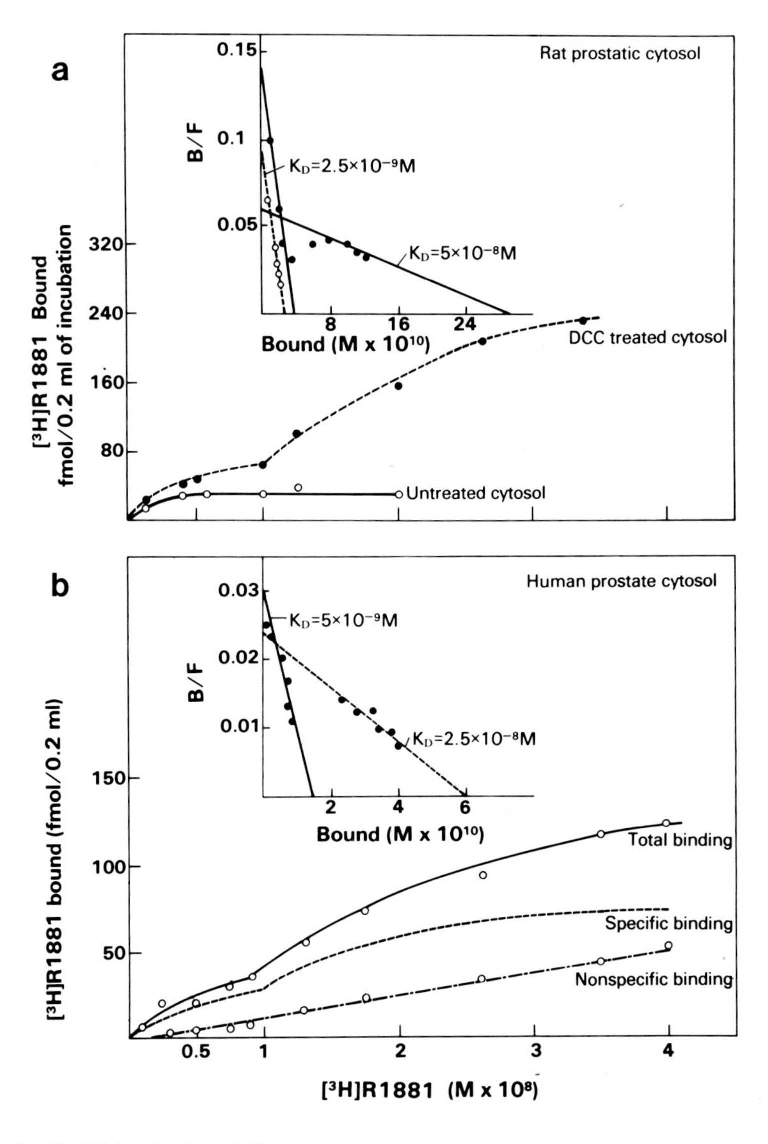

Fig. 3. Equilibrium binding of [^{3}H]-R1881 to rat and human prostatic cytosol. a) Native or DCC-treated rat cytosol (5 mg protein/ml) was incubated with an equal volume of buffer containing [^{3}H]-R1881 and a 500-fold excess of unlabeled TA. Parallel incubations with [^{3}H]-R1881, TA, and a 100-fold excess of unlabeled R1881 were performed to determine nonspecific binding. Data represent specific binding determined with the HAP technique. A Scatchard plot is shown in the inset. b) Human prostatic cytosol (6 mg protein/ml) from a patient with BPH was treated with DCC and incubated with steroids as described above.

was not a plasma contaminant. Although R1881 is known not to bind significantly to plasma proteins, further evidence was sought by measuring the binding of pregnenolone, androstenedione, and epitestosterone to this prostatic protein. These steroids are known not to interact with SSBG [12, 13], and their ability to compete for those [^{3}H]-R1881 binding sites exposed by DDC pretreatment would then suggest that they do not represent SSBG. Prostatic cytosol from patients with adenocarcinoma of the prostate and prostatic benign hypertrophy were used in this experiment. The cytosols were divided equally and either treated with DCC or kept untreated at 0°C. Each sample was then incubated for 16 hours at 0°C with 3×10^{-8}M [^{3}H]-R1881 in the presence or absence of a 100-fold excess of nonradioactive R1881, pregnenolone, androstenedione, or epitestosterone, and the bound radioactivity was measured by HAP. The high R1881 molarity was required to partially saturate HPSBP, as shown in Figure 3. The results are summarized in Table I. Specific binding of R1881 in untreated cytosol representing androgen receptor ranged from 15–88 fmol/mg protein. Addition of a 100-fold excess of pregnenolone resulted in little or no decrease in the specific binding, while androstenedione and epitestosterone significantly inhibited [^{3}H]-R1881 binding. When the same experiment was performed on the DCC-treated cytosols, there was a marked increase in the total number of R1881 binding sites. In the presence of pregnenolone, binding was depressed to that found in native cytosol, suggesting that pregnenolone competes for R1881 binding to HPSBP without affecting [^{3}H]-R1881 binding to the specific androgen receptor. Similar observations were made for androstenedione and epitestosterone except that some competition for R1881 binding to the specific receptor was observed as before. These findings obviate the possibility that the R1881 binding observed upon DCC treatment represents binding to SSBG, since these steroids do not interact with this plasma protein.

HPSBP Binds Androgens, Estrogens, Progestins but not Glucocorticoids

Human prostatic tissue cytosol was treated with DCC and incubated with [^{3}H]-R1881 (4×10^{-8}M) in the presence of increasing concentrations of nonradioactive steroids. The incubations were kept at 0°C for 16 hours and the bound radioactivity was measured by HAP. The difference between ligand bound in the incubation with [^{3}H]-R1881 (total binding) and [^{3}H]-R1881 and a 100-fold excess of unlabeled R1881 (nonspecific binding) represents specific binding (224 fmol/mg protein) and was defined as 100% binding (Fig. 4). The percentage of specific R1881 binding was plotted as a function of the concentration of the nonradioactive competitors.

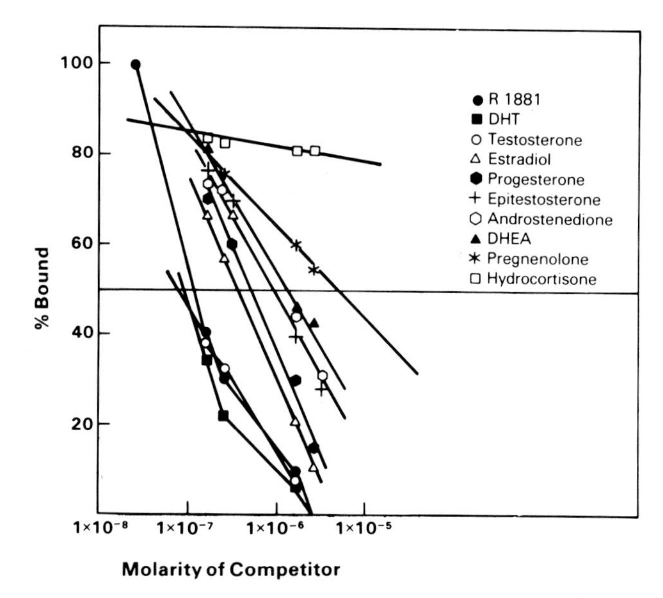

Fig. 4. Binding specificity of the human prostatic steroid binding protein (HPSBP). Cytosol was treated with DCC and reincubated for 16 hours at 0°C with 4×10^{-8} [^{3}H]-R1881 and 1×10^{-6}M TA. The final protein concentration was 2.8 mg/ml. Parallel incubations in the presence of increasing concentrations of nonradioactive competitor were performed. Binding was measured by the HAP technique. All data points have been corrected for nonspecific binding by subtracting the value measured in the sample containing a 100-fold excess of unlabeled R1881.

DHT, R1881, and testosterone were the best competitors with 50% inhibition achieved at concentrations of 1×10^{-7}M. For estradiol and progesterone higher concentrations (5×10^{-7}M) were required to obtain similar inhibition. Epitestosterone, androstenedione, dehydroepiandrosterone, and pregnenolone were much weaker inhibitors ($1–8 \times 10^{-6}$M); cortisol had no inhibitory effect. These results indicate that the human prostatic steroid binding protein has broad steroid specificity although androgens bind to it most effectively. It should also be noted that some of the binding in this preparation represents androgen receptor sites (55 fmol of the 224 fmol/mg protein which were defined as 100%).

Tissue Specificity of Rat and Human Prostatic Steroid Binding Protein

Tissue specificity of the nonreceptor androgen binding protein was assessed by examining cytosols from human prostatic and breast cancer tissue, rat kidney and plasma, calf uterus, and human plasma. All cytosols and plasmas were first

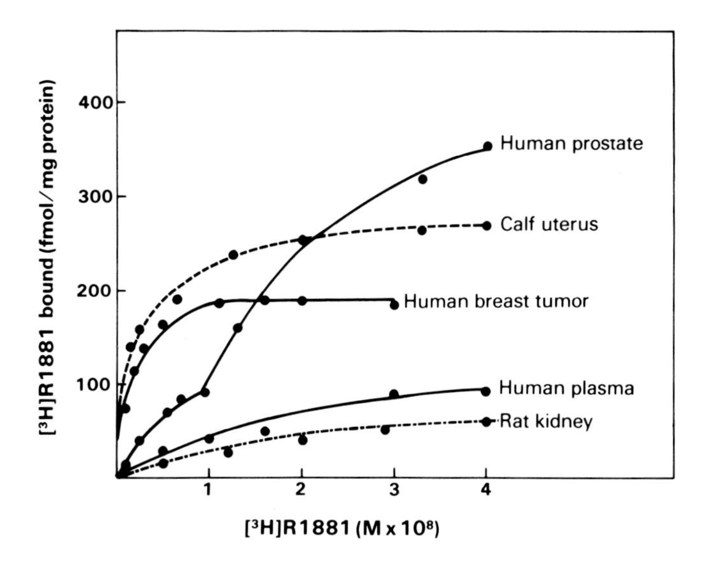

Fig. 5. Tissue specificity of the human prostatic steroid binding protein (HPSBP). Tissue cytosol or plasma was treated with DCC and incubated as described in Figure 3. Data represent specifically bound [^{3}H]-R1881.

treated with DCC and incubated at 0°C for 16 hours with increasing concentrations of [^{3}H]-R1881 in the presence or absence of a 100-fold excess of unlabeled R1881. The bound radioactivity was assayed by HAP. As shown in Figure 5 human plasma had very little binding and it displayed one component of relatively high affinity. Rat plasma showed no specific binding (data not shown). Rat kidney cytosol had a specific high affinity component, probably rat kidney androgen receptor [14]. Human breast cancer and calf uterine cytosols showed a single high affinity binding component suggesting that these tissues have androgen receptors. R1881 binding to progesterone receptors was not measurable, since, as in all other experiments described in this paper, cytosols contained 10^{-6}M triamcinolone acetonide [15, 16]. Only prostatic tissue displayed a biphasic binding curve with both a high and a low affinity component.

Effects of Trypsin Digestion and Heating on HPSBP

Human prostatic cytosol was first treated with DCC and then incubated at 0°C with [^{3}H]-R1881 to allow binding to the androgen receptor and to HPSBP. Tryptic digestion was then performed at 0°C for 16 hours in the presence of 200 μg/ml trypsin and 5mM $CaCl_2$. These incubation conditions effectively eliminated 80% of estradiol binding of calf uterine estrogen receptor and 85% of [^{3}H]-R1881 binding to human prostatic cytosol. Since in the latter, 15% of the total

R1881 is bound to the androgen receptor, the loss of 85% binding suggests that HPSBP is, at least in part, a protein.

Another of the characteristics typical for prostatic androgen receptors is their thermal instability. When human prostatic cytosol was first heated for 1 hour at 37°C, subsequent incubation with R1881 did not show specific binding. However, when heated cytosol was DCC treated and then incubated with R1881, specific binding was 200 fmol/mg protein. This binding is comparable to that obtained in parallel incubations to unheated DCC treated cytosol (180 fmol/mg protein), demonstrating that HPSBP is a more thermostable protein than the receptor.

HPSBP Is Present in Human Prostatic Cancer and BPH

Prostatic cytosol prepared from specimens of patients with adenocarcinoma or BPH was processed for androgen receptor and HPSBP measurement. Table II shows the number of binding sites representing the androgen receptor (RA) obtained when the native cytosol was incubated with [^{3}H]-R1881. The number of binding sites obtained after treatment with DCC represents both the androgen receptor and the steroid binding protein (RA + HPSBP). In all tumors tested so far, this nonreceptor steroid binding protein was present.

Preliminary Characterization of HPSBP

Further characterization of this prostatic steroid binding protein is presently underway in this laboratory. Preliminary observations suggest that HPSBP is a macromolecule excluded by Sephadex-G25 and that on sucrose gradient analysis it sediments in the 4–5 S region. In contrast to the androgen receptor, this protein appears to be insensitive to the mercurial reagent mersalyl acid [17].

DISCUSSION

The observations reported here were incidental to our search for a reliable exchange assay for cytoplasmic androgen receptor [18,19]. The presence of unlabeled androgens of endogenous origin interferes with receptor quantitation by direct [^{3}H]-R1881 binding assay either by occupying receptor sites or by diluting the specific activity of the radioactive ligand. It has been proposed that brief treatment of freshly prepared cytosol with DCC will remove these interfering androgens to allow subsequent labeling of receptors by exchange assay [8,9]. In evaluating this procedure we observed that this treatment results in a dramatic increase in [^{3}H]-R1881 binding sites (Table II). This was found to be true for both malignant and benign hypertrophic prostates, as well as rat prostate. The same increase in binding was observed with the natural steroid DHT (Fig. 2) demonstrating that this binding is not unique to the synthetic ligand R1881. This increase in binding is not attributable to androgen receptors, since the cytosol was treated with DCC at 0°C for only 30 minutes, a technique which does not cause dissociation of receptor-bound endogenous androgens.

An additional reason to exclude that the DCC treatment unmasked occupied receptors is the nature of the equilibrium binding curve shown in Figure 3. It is well established that hormone receptors are present in low concentrations and bind with high affinity to their steroid ligands. Thus in the samples pretreated with DCC only the first part of the curve represents binding to the androgen receptor.

Finally, the specificity data presented in Table I show that pregnenolone competes with [^{3}H]-R1881 for binding to the component revealed by DCC treatment, while it has no effect on untreated cytosol. Since pregnenolone does not bind to androgen receptors, these data indicate that the DCC pretreatment allows measurement of a second set of R1881 binding sites, distinct from the androgen receptor. The biphasic binding curve shown in Figure 3 resembles that obtained by Clark and his associates [20] for the estrogen binding to uterine cytosol. In contrast to the uterine "binding site II," however, these prostatic binding components can only be observed in cytosols pretreated with charcoal.

Stein et al [21] observed a similar increase in DHT binding in cytosols pretreated with charcoal, but the authors did not pursue this observation further, nor did their experimental design allow discrimination between SSBG and other androgen binding proteins.

That this second binding component may represent SSBG is unlikely, since 1) binding is observed with R1881, a ligand of low affinity for SSBG, and 2) pregnenolone, androstenedione, and epitestosterone (steroids which do not bind to SSBG [12,13] effectively compete for [^{3}H]-R1881 binding to this protein (Table 1, Fig. 4). Preliminary characterization of this binding entity suggests that it is a protein which sediments on sucrose density gradients as a 4–5 S molecule. It is excluded on Sephadex G-25 chromatography, is sensitive to trypsin digestion, and insensitive to concentrations of mercurial reagents which destroy steroid binding to the androgen, progesterone, and glucocorticoid receptors [17]. These latter characteristics together with the described heat stability further distinguish this protein from the classical androgen receptor. Tissue specificity (Fig. 5) indicates that this protein is present only in human and rat prostatic tissue but not in human breast cancer tissue, calf uterus, rat kidney, or human plasma (Fig. 5). It is also absent from rat plasma and rat uterus (data not shown). We have not yet tested for its presence in prostatic fluid or seminal vesicles.

A number of different binding proteins for steroids—particularly androgens—have been described in the literature [22,23]. One of these is so called "androgen receptor" which has characteristics resembling those of a number of other receptors for steroids. In addition, other binding proteins, different from those found predominantly in plasma, have also been reported to occur in prostatic tissue of the rat [1–3]. The physicochemical characteristics of these various proteins are compiled in Table III for comparison. The human prostatic steroid binding protein we have described here shows many similar properties such as relative heat stability, broad steroid specificity, tissue specificity, and magnitude

TABLE III. Steroid binding proteins in prostatic tissues

	References				
	[28]	[4]	[29]	[2]	*
K_A (M^{-1})	1.2×10^6	6.9×10^4	1×10^7	$1–5 \times 10^7$	$1–2 \times 10^7$
Ligand:	pregnenolone	progesterone	DHT	pregnenolone	R-1881
S value:	3.7	3.2	4	3.4	3.5–4 rat 4.6 human
Stable at 37°C:	X	X	X	X	X
MW:	51,000	40,000	45–50,000	45–50,000	ND
$\%NH_4SO_4$ pptn.:	50–70	ND	55–70	ND	ND
Binds: DHT	+	+	+	ND	+
TST	+	+	pl	—	+
R-1881	—	ND	ND	ND	+
A-dione	+	+	ND	+	+
Epi-TST	+	ND	ND	+	+
Progesterone	+	+	+	+	+
Pregnenolone	+	+	ND	+	+
Estradiol	+	+	+	—	+
Cortisol	—	—	—	—	—
Tissues					
Rat prostate	+	+	+	+	+
liver	—	ND	ND	—	ND
kidney	—	ND	ND	ND	—
uterus	—	ND	ND	ND	ND
plasma	—	ND	ND	ND	—
prostatic fluid	+	+	ND	ND	ND
Calf uterus	ND	ND	ND	ND	—
Human prostate	ND	ND	ND	ND	+
breast tumor	ND	ND	ND	ND	—
plasma	ND	ND	ND	ND	—

X, Yes.
+, Present.
—, Absent.
ND, Not determined.
*Data presented in this paper.

of affinity for androgens. It differs, however, in requiring treatment with DCC prior to steroid binding. The latter property has been described for a binding protein in rat prostate [3]. In that study no stringent criteria to determine displaceable binding, such as parallel incubations with an excess of unlabeled ligand, were used.

While there is good reason to assume that the steroid receptor interaction is a prerequisite to specific cellular growth and physicologic functions, no specific role in cellular function has as yet been assigned to the various other binding proteins.

Several studies have shown that higher concentrations of DHT are found in human BPH [24,25], while others have suggested that CBG and SSBG are preferentially accumulated in prostatic tissue [26]. More interestingly, Wilson [27] has calculated that the amount of DHT present in hypertrophic tissue far exceeds the number of androgen receptor sites. Since free hormone is not only readily metabolized by cytoplasmic enzymes but is rapidly cleared from the cell, the observed high levels of DHT may reflect association with other binding moieties. Thus, the binding protein described here may be responsible (perhaps among others) for retaining uniquely high concentrations of androgens (and possible other steroids) in the prostate for as yet unknown purposes. Its high affinity for DHT and relatively high concentrations in prostatic cytosol are characteristics which suggest that this protein could modulate androgen interaction with its target cells by influencing uptake, accumulation, and storage.

ACKNOWLEDGMENTS

Publication No. 21 from the Hubert H. Humphrey Cancer Research Center of Boston University. These studies were supported by research grants CA-23666 and CA-28856 from the National Cancer Institute.

REFERENCES

1. Fang S, Liao S: Androgen receptors. Steroid and tissue specific retention of 17β-hydroxy-5α-androstan-3one protein complex by the cell nuclei of ventral prostate. J Biol Chem 246: 16–24, 1971.
2. Karszina R, Wyss RH, Leroy-Heinriches WM, Hermann WL: Binding of pregnenolone and progesterone by prostatic receptor proteins. Endocrinology 84: 1238–1246, 1969.
3. Heyns W, DeMoor P: Prostatic binding protein. A steroid-binding protein secreted by rat prostate. Eur J Biochem 78: 221–230, 1977.
4. Lea OA, Petrusz P, French F: Prostatein. A major secretory protein of the rat ventral prostate. J Biol Chem 254: 6196–6202, 1979.
5. Forsgren B, Bjork P, Carlstrom K, Ekman P, Gustafsson JÅ, Pousette A, Hogberg P: Radioimmunosassay of a protein in human prostatic tissue that binds estramustine, the diphosphorylated metabolite of estramustine phosphate (Estracyt^R). Cancer Treat Rep 63: 1186, 1975.
6. Lowry OH, Rosebrough NJ, Farr AL, Randall RJ: Protein measurement with the folin phenol reagent. Chemistry 193: 265–275, 1951.
7. Katzenellenbogen AA, Johnson JH Jr, Carlson KE: Studies on the uturine, cytoplasmic estrogen binding protein: Thermal stability and ligand dissociation rate. An assay of empty and filled sites by exchange. Biochemistry 12: 4092–4099, 1973.
8. Shain SA, Boesel RW, Lamm D, Radwin HM: Characterization of unoccupied (R) and occupied (RA) androgen binding components of the hyperplastic human prostate. Steroids 31: 541–556, 1978.
9. Ghanadian R, Auf G, Chaloner PJ, Chisholm GD: The use of methyltrienolone in the measurement of the free and bound cytoplasmic receptors for dihydrotestosterone in benign hypertrophied human prostate. Biochemistry 9: 325–330, 1978.
10. Bonne C, Raynaud JP: Methyltrienolone, a specific ligand for cellular androgen receptors. Steroids 26: 227–232, 1975.
11. Baulieu EE, Atger M, Best-Belpomme M, Carvol P, Courvalin JC, Mester J, Milgrom E, Robel P, Rochefort H, DeCataloyne D: Steroid hormone receptors. Vitam Horm 33: 649–736, 1975.

12. Mercier-Bodard C, Alfsen A, Baulieu EE: "Sex Steroid Binding Plasma Protein." 2nd Symposium: Steroid Assay by Protein Binding, Geneva, 1970, pp 204–224.
13. Vermeulen A, Verdonck L: "Testosterone Assay by Competitive Protein Binding." 2nd Symposium: Steroid Assay by Protein Binding. Geneva, 1970, pp 239–256.
14. Gustafsson JÅ, Pousette A: Demonstration and partial characterization of cytosol receptors for testosterone. Biochemistry 14: 3094, 1975.
15. Zava DT, Landrum B, Horwitz KB, McGuire WL: Androgen receptor assay with [^{3}H]-methyltrienolone (R1881) in the presence of progesterone receptor. Endocrinology 104: 1007–1012, 1979.
16. Asselin J, Melancon R, Gourdeau Y, Labrie F, Bonne C, Raynaud JP: Specific binding of [^{3}H]-methyltrienolone to both progestin and androgen binding components in the human benign prostatic hypertrophy. J Steroid Biochem 10: 483–486, 1979.
17. Traish AM, Müller RE, Wotiz HH: A new procedure for the quantitation of nuclear and cytoplasmic receptors. J Biol Chem (in press).
18. Wotiz HH, Traish AM, Müller RE, Olsson CA: Evaluation of procedures for the measurement of nuclear and cytoplasmic steroid receptors in human prostate. Cancer Treatment Rep 63: 1146, 1979.
19. Olsson CA, deVere White R, Goldstein I, Traish AM, Müller RE, Wotiz HH: A prelimenary report on the measurment of cytosolic and nuclear prostatic tissue steroid receptors. In Murphy GP, Sandberg AA (eds): 1979, "Prostate Cancer and Hormone Receptors." New York: Alan R. Liss, Inc., pp 209–221.
20. Eriksson H, Upchurch S, Hardin JW, Peck EJ Jr, Clark JH: Heterogeneity of estrogen receptors in the cytosol and nuclear fraction of the rat uterus. Biochem Biophys Res Commun 81: 1–7, 1978.
21. Steins P, Krieg M, Hollmann HJ, Voight KD: In vitro studies of testosterone and 5α-dihydrotestosterone binding in benign prostatic hypertrophy. Acta Endocrinol (Copenh) 75: 773–784, 1974.
22. Mainwaring WIP: Steroid hormone receptors: A survey. Vitam Horm 33: 223–244, 1975.
23. Ritzen E, Hagenas L, Hanssson VG, Weddington SC, French FS, Nayfeh SN: Androgen binding and transport in testis and epididymis. Vitam Horm. 33: 283–294, 1975.
24. Siiteri PK, Wilson JD: Dihydrotestosterone in prostatic hypertrophy. The formation and content of dihydrotestosterone in the hypertrophic prostate of man. J Clin Invest 49: 1737–1745, 1970.
25. Geller J, Albert J, Lopez D, Geller S, Niwayama G: Comparison of androgen metabolites in benign prostatic hypertrophy (BPH) and normal prostate. J Clin Endocrinol Metab 43: 686–688, 1976.
26. Cowan RA, Cowan SK, Giles CA, Grant JK: Prostatic distribution of sex hormone binding globulin and cortisol binding globulin in benign hyperplasia. J Endocrinol 71: 121–131, 1976.
27. Wilson JD: Pathogenesis of benign prostatic hyperplasia. Am J Med 68: 745–756, 1980.
28. Heyns W, Peeters B, Mous J, Rombauts W, DeMoor P: Purification and characterization of prostatic binding protein and its subunits. Eur J Biochem 89: 181–186, 1978.
29. Liao S, Tymoczo JL, Castaneda E, Liang T: Androgen receptors and androgen dependent initation of protein synthesis in the prostate. Vitam Horm 33: 297–318, 1975.

The Prostatic Cell: Structure and Function
Part A, pages 435–443

Human Prostate Epithelial Cell-Specific Antigen

Lawrence D. Papsidero, Ming C. Wang, Manabu Kuriyama, Julius S. Horoszewicz, Susan S. Leong, Gary A. Croghan, Luis A. Valenzuela, Gerald P. Murphy, and T. Ming Chu

INTRODUCTION

Considerable efforts have been made in recent years to identify enzyme or antigen markers for various types of cancers with the view toward developing specific diagnostic reagents. Among other characteristics, the ideal tumor marker would exhibit organ-site or cell-type specificity. Such markers are of interest for several reasons: 1) Cell-type specific antibodies may allow for the identification of the tissue origin of a cell, which can aid, for example, in the determination of the primary site of an isolated metastasis with unknown origin. 2) Studies on the variation in expression of cell-specific antigens during development of pre-neoplastic and neoplastic lesions may provide insight into their role in regulation of growth and possible metastatic ability of malignant cells. 3) If released by tumor cells, such antigens would represent valuable indicators of neoplasia.

We have recently developed antiserum with which we have detected and isolated a prostate-specific antigen which is distinct from acid phosphatase [1]. Evidence suggests that this antigen may represent a valuable indicator for the presence of pathological involvement of the prostate [2,3]. Additionally, it is presented in this report that this antigen may be considered as a cell-type-specific product of prostate, some aspects of which have been previously noted [4].

MATERIALS AND METHODS

Cultured Cells

All human cell cultures were grown in plastic culture dishes under standard conditions in RPMI-1640 medium plus 10% fetal bovine serum with penicillin/

streptomycin and 5 μg bovine insulin/ml. Cell lines used for these studies included LNCaP [5], PC-3 [6], DU-145 [7] RT-4 [8], MCF-7 [9], HT-29 [10], BT-20 [11], PaCa-2 [12], Daudi [13], and Raji cells [14]. Spent culture fluids were centrifuged for 1 hour at 40,000 g and stored at –20°C. Cells were mechanically harvested, washed three times with PBS buffer, and extracted in cold PBS using a Ten-Broeck homogenizer. The 40,000 g supernatant was adjusted to 5 mg protein/ml PBS and stored at –20°C.

Antiserum

Antiserum to PA was prepared in rabbits with the use of purified antigen preparations prepared as described previously [1]. Anti-PA demonstrated a single immunoprecipitin reaction versus crude prostate extracts as determined by double immunodiffusion in agarose and failed to react with a panel of extracts from nonprostate tissues [1].

Rocket-Immunoelectrophoresis (R-IEP)

Semiquantitative measurements of PA using the R-IEP technique were performed as described previously [2]. Briefly, anti-PA at a final concentration of 1% (v/v) was incorporated into 1% agarose maintained at 55°C, and the mixture was plated onto cellulose acetate membranes or glass plates. Agarose gel and running buffer consisted of 80 mM Tris-24 mM tricine-24 mM sodium barbital (pH 8.8) containing 0.3 mM calcium lactate and 0.02% sodium azide. Samples of various human tissue extracts (25 μl) were electrophoresed at 5V/cm for 18 hours at 4°C.

Enzyme-Linked Immunosorbent Assay (ELISA)

For the quantitative measurement of PA, an ELISA assay has been developed [3,4]. Briefly, antigen-containing samples were allowed to react with solid-phase anti-PA (IgG fraction) for 3 hours. Following a washing procedure, the immobilized antibody with bound antigen was incubated with peroxidase-conjugated anti-PA for a further 18 hours. The amount of bound enzyme activity was related to antigen concentration which can be extrapolated from a standard curve using known PA samples as described [3,4].

Immunoperoxidase and Immunofluorescence Cytological Techniques

These procedures have been described in detail previously [4,15,16]. For the evaluation of routinely fixed and paraffin-embedded tissues or fixed culture cells, anti-PA serum was used at a 1:50 or 1:8 dilution, respectively. Following a 1-hour incubation period, washed specimens were treated with either fluorescein or peroxidase conjugates of goat antiserum to rabbit γ-globulin to reveal sites of PA activity.

Hybridoma Cultures Producing Monoclonal Antibodies

Spleen cells were obtained from Balb/c mice which were hyperimmune to purified prostate antigen. Immune splenocytes were fused to murine plasmacytoma cells (P3X63AG8.653) using polyethylene glycol [20]. Hybrid cultures were maintained in selective media containing hypoxanthine/aminopterin/thymidine [21]. Culture fluids were screened for specific antibodies using an enzyme immunoassay procedure. Antibodies reacting with solid-phase prostate antigen in microtiter wells were detected after incubation with peroxidase-labeled antisera to mouse immunoglobulins. Suitable cultures were cloned by limiting dilution in the presence of mouse peritoneal exudate cells. Clones producing antibody were grown in mass culture and frozen in the presence of 10% dimethylsulfoxide.

RESULTS

Our prototype antiserum was raised against crude extracts of prostate tissue and extensively absorbed with other human tissues. Using immunodiffusion analyes, this antibody preparation demonstrated specific reactivity with prostate gland [1]. Inasmuch as prostatic acid phosphatase contains a prostate-specific fraction (PAP), efforts were made to evaluate the relationship between the two antigens. Immunodiffusion analyses clearly demonstrated absence of cross reactivity of these antigens and their respective heteroantisera [1,2]. Monoclonal antibodies to PA were also unable to be neutralized by absorption with purified PAP. Further, enzymatic analyses of homogenous PA preparations failed to demonstrate acid phosphatase activities. From the physical characteristics determined for both antigens, it can be seen that these two proteins are distinct prostate-specific constituents (Table I).

TABLE I. Characteristics of purified PA and PAP antigens[a]

Parameter	PA	PAP
M_r	34,000 (monomer)	100,000 homodimer (M_r 50,000 subunit)
Isoelectric point value(s)	6.9	4.2–5.5 (multiple bands)
Percent of total soluble prostatic protein	0.2	1.0
Electrophoretic mobility	β	α–β
Lectin binding activity	+	+
Optimal salt precipitability (% saturated ammonium sulfate)	35–55	50–70
Cellular localization	prostate ductal cells	prostate ductal cells

[a]See [1,2,4,17–19].

A more extensive study regarding PA tissue specifically has been performed using the technique of rocket-immunoelectrophoresis. Data derived from this procedure, which can detect 13 ng (0.5 μg/ml) of antigen, have revealed the presence of PA only in soluble extracts of prostate gland (Table II). All prostate samples examined to date, whether normal, benign hypertrophic, or malignant in nature have demonstated antigen activity. Reactivities of extracts prepared from tissues of nonprostatic origins have been consistently negative. Using this approach, we calculate that PA occurs in prostate tissue at a level of approximately 2 mg/gm soluble extract. This mean value of antigen concentration is similar regardless of tissue pathology, and no statistical differences in antigen levels have been observed between normal, benign, and malignant prostate specimens. This observation was not unexpected, since in strictest terms, we are not dealing with a tumor-specific neoantigen but, rather, a tissue-specific or "differentiation" antigen.

To evaluate whether PA may further be classified as a cell-type specific product, immunohistochemical localization experiments were conducted using PA antiserum and human tissue sections. At dilutions between 1:50 and 1:100, PA antiserum strongly reacted with ductal cells of prostate glands (Fig. 1), as detected by peroxidase conjugate of antiglobulin antibodies. Peroxidase reaction product was evident in the cytoplasmic portion of ductal epithelial cells and also on secretions within many ductal lumina. Nuclei of these cells and prostatic stromal elements were consistently negative for antibody binding. Binding of PA antiserum to ductal cells could be abrogated by preabsorption of antiserum with purified PA preparations, indicating the specificity of the observed reaction. Prostate sections treated under identical conditions with preimmune rabbit serum showed no reaction. Once optimal conditions for the indirect immunoperoxidase histochemical technique were determined for detection of PA in prostate glandular tissue sections, specimens of other histotypes were examined. To date, all have been antigen-negative, including bladder, testes, ureter, kidney, seminal

TABLE II. Occurrence of prostate antigen in human tissue extracts[a]

Tissue[b]	Pathology	Specimens positive/ specimens examined
Prostate	Normal	6/6
	Benign hypertrophy	10/10
	Adenocarcinoma	9/9
Other[c]	Normal/carcinoma	0/26

[a]Antigen was detected using a rocket-immunoelectrophoresis procedure.
[b]Each soluble extract was adjusted to 10 mg protein/ml prior to analysis.
[c]Including specimens of human bladder, 1; kidney, 1; liver, 5; spleen, 1; lung, 5; breast, 6; intestine, 4; and pancreas, 3.

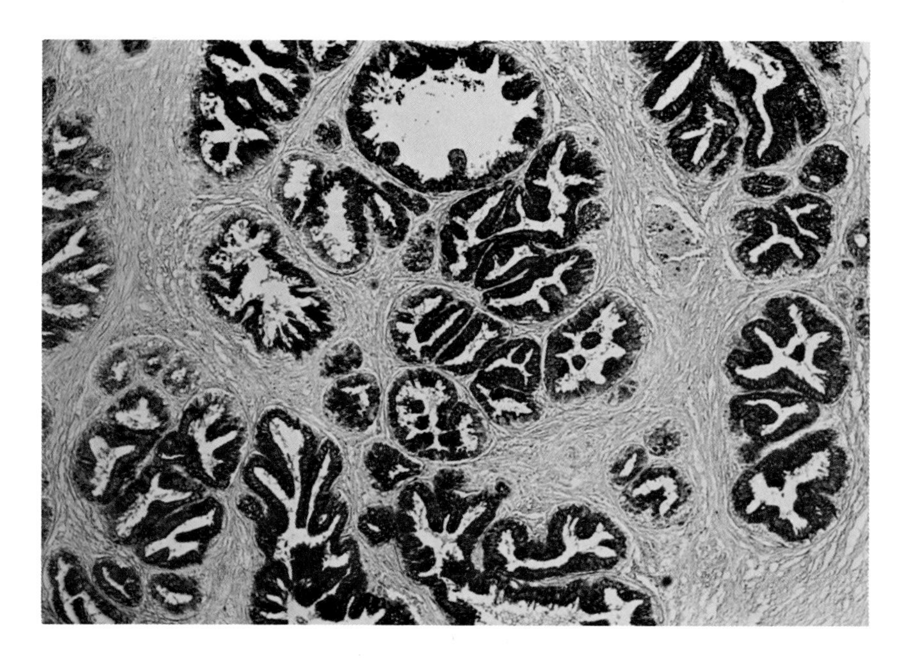

Fig. 1. Indirect immunoperoxidase demonstration of PA in paraffin-embedded prostate tissue (hyperplastic). Sections were treated with PA antiserum (1:50) and second antibody (peroxidase-conjugated antiserum to rabbit γ-globulins, 1:20) and enzyme activity revealed using diaminobenzidine: H_2O_2 [16]. Dense regions of peroxidase reaction product were found within the cytoplasm of ductal epithelial cells and in some instances on free secretory material within ductal lumina. No counterstain (200 ×).

vesicles, liver, spleen, and other soft tissues. However, metastatic deposits of prostate cancer cells (eg, to lymph nodes or liver) retain the expression of PA and may be detected in these extraprostatic sites (Table III). As indicated in the following section, prostatic cell lines derived from metastatic sites also retain antigen expression.

Although human organ and tissue preparations have been used to evaluate antigen specificity, it is of importance to analyze cultured cells for antigen expression. Since continuous cell lines represent more homogeneous populations of cell types than do parental tissues, more absolute types of specificity data can be accrued from their examination. For this purpose a sensitive enzyme immunoassay has been developed which is capable of detecting nanogram amounts of PA [3,4]. A panel of continuous cell lines of several histotypic origins has been examined with this assay. Included were adenocarcinoma cells of human prostate, breast, colon, pancreas, thyroid, and bladder origins, among others. Results using soluble extracts of these cells are presented in Table IV. Cell strains of nonprostatic origins demonstrated no detectable levels of PA activity.

TABLE III. Immunohistologic demonstration of prostate antigen in adenocarcinoma tissues[a]

Tumor	No. positive/No. examined[b]
Primary prostatic adenocarcinoma	73/73
Metastatic prostatic adenocarcinoma	49/49
Nonprostatic malignancies	0/78[c]

[a]See [22].
[b]Prostate antigen was evaluated using immunoperoxidase histochemical procedures.
[c]These included 17 tumors of the urinary bladder with extension to the prostate gland.

TABLE IV. Prostate antigen levels in homogeneous cell cultures[a]

		PA ng/ml	
Culture	Histologic origin	Cells[b]	Media
LNCaP	Prostate carcinoma	700	100
PC-3	Prostate carcinoma	50	15
DU-145	Prostate carcinoma	ND[c]	ND
HT-29	Colon carcinoma	ND	ND
MCF-7	Breast carcinoma	ND	ND
BT-20	Breast carcinoma	ND	ND
TT-4	Thyroid carcinoma	ND	ND
RT-4	Bladder carcinoma	ND	ND
BG-9	Fibroblast	ND	ND
Daudi	Lymphoblastoid	ND	ND
Raji	Lymphoblastoid	ND	ND

[a]Average of three specimens assayed.
[b]Cell extracts as prepared in Methods.
[c]ND, not detectable by enzyme immunoassay procedure.

Of three prostate tumor lines evaluated, two exhibited easily detectable antigen levels, with the LNCaP and PC-3 cell lines presenting with high and low levels, respectively. Rapidly growing cultures of LNCaP and PC-3 cells also shed significant amounts of antigen into the culture fluid milieu, as compared with other cell lines of nonprostate derivations (Table IV). Once implanted into athymic mice, LNCaP prostate tumors also released PA into the systemic circulation of these animals at a mean level of 17 ng/ml (tumor mass 1.2–1.8 gm).

LNCaP prostate tumor cells have been further examined using indirect immunofluorescence. After treatment of these fixed cells with PA antiserum and fluoroscein-labeled antiglobulin reagents, PA activity was observed. Fluorescence occurred as diffusely appearing regions of the cell cytoplasm. This staining pattern was visible in both paranuclear and apical regions of the cytoplasm. No staining of peripheral or internal membranes was observed, nor were nuclear components reactive with the antiserum. LNCaP cells treated as above with preimmune rabbit sera showed no specific fluorescent staining pattern.

DISCUSSION

The immunologic specificity and anatomic distribution of a newly described prostate antigen (PA) have been investigated. Epitopes of PA are carried on a glycoprotein of M_r of 34,000 which is biochemically and immunologically distinct from prostatic acid phosphatase [1,2]. Regardless of histopathological diagnosis, soluble extracts of prostate tissues contain high levels of PA which are easily detectable using immunoprecipitation techniques. Constituting approximately 0.2% of the total soluble proteins of prostate, PA represents a major product of this gland. Since antigen cannot be detected in other tissue types, PA may be considered as a prostate tissue-specific protein.

Results from immunoperoxidase experiments using tissue sections have provided corroborative data on the tissue specificity of PA. In addition, observations on the antibody staining patterns have revealed the specific occurrence of antigen within, and confined to, ductal epithelial cells. Since PA was originally identified in the soluble portion of prostate tissues, it was not unexpected to locate it within the cytoplasm of these cells and also associated with free secretory material of ductal lumina. Immunofluorescence experiments, providing a further measure of cytological resolution, also have revealed the presence of PA as a cytoplasmic component of prostate cells in culture.

Of these established prostate tumor cell lines examined, two have been shown to retain the expression of PA, with LNCaP and PC-3 cell strains exhibiting high and low levels, respectively. These data provide further evidence on the ability of metastatic prostate cells to produce antigen, since LNCaP cells were derived from supraclavicular lymph nodal tissue [5], while PC-3 cells were isolated from brain metastasis [6]. Although DU-145 cells, as grown in cutlure, had no detectable PA, extracts prepared from nude mouse-supported DU-145 solid tumors have been shown to contain low levels of antigen. Reasons for the observed variation in antigen levels have not been defined, but may be a reflection of the pathological or developmental status of these cells. Studies on the variation in expression of PA may provide insight into the biologic behavior of prostate tumor cells.

Based upon the experimental data available, the PA represents a valuable marker for prostate epithelial cells of normal and neoplastic origins. The specificity of the antigen is of clinical import, inasmuch as PA antisera may allow for the immunohistologic diagnosis of metastatic prostate disease. This application appears promising in light of our preliminary observations showing the retention of PA expression by metastatic prostate cells in culture. Also, and by virtue of the specific anatomic association of the antigen, the presence of elevated serum PA levels may be considered as pathognomonic of prostatic disease involvement. Our initial observations provide considerable support for this contention, as increased levels of serum PA have been found to be associated with the occurrence of prostatic neoplasia [2,3].

In view of the information available, efforts have been made to produce hybridoma cell lines which produce antibodies defining PA. Clonal derivatives of these cultures, exhibiting stable antibody production, may represent sources of diagnostically valuable reagents which circumvent problems associated with the use of conventional antisera.

ACKNOWLEDGMENTS

Mouse-supported DU-145 tumor tissue was kindly provided by Dr. Karen S. Webb, Duke University Medical Center. Dr. Mukta M. Webber, University of Colorado Health Sciences Center, provided valuable consultation on the evaluation of PA localization in tissue sections. Dr. Richard B. Bankert, Roswell Park Memorial Institute, generously provided cultures of murine plasmacytoma cells. We also thank Ms Joan Ogledzinski for secretarial assistance. This work was supported in part by a research grant CA-15437, awarded by the National Cancer Institute.

REFERENCES

1. Wang MC, Valenzuela LA, Murphy GP, Chu TM: Purification of a human prostate specific antigen. Invest Urol 17:159–163,1979.
2. Papsidero LD, Wang MC, Valenzuela LA, Murphy GP, Chu TM: A prostate antigen in sera of prostatic cancer patients. Cancer Res 20:2428–2432,1980.
3. Kuriyama M, Wang MC, Papsidero LD, Killian CS, Shimano T, Valenzuela LA, Nishiura T, Murphy GP, Chu TM: Quantitation of prostate-specific antigen in serum by a sensitive enzyme immunoassay. Cancer Res 40:4658–4662,1980.
4. Papsidero LD, Kuriyama M, Wang MC, Horoszewicz JS, Leong SS, Valenzuela LA, Murphy GP, Chu TM: Prostate antigen: A marker for human prostate epithelial cells. J Natl Cancer Inst 66:37–42,1981.
5. Horoszewicz JS, Leong SS, Chu TM, Wajsman Z, Friedman M, Papsidero LD, Kim U, Chai LS, Kakati S, Arya SK, Sandberg AA: The LNCaP cell line—a new model for studies on human prostatic carcinoma. In Murphy GP (ed): "Models for Prostate Cancer." New York: Alan R. Liss, 1980, pp 115–132.
6. Kaighn ME, Narayan KS, Ohnuki Y, Lechner JF, Jones LW: Establishment and characterization of a human prostatic carcinoma cell line (PC-3). Invest Urol 16:16–23,1979.
7. Stone KR, Mickey DD, Wunderli H, Mickey GH, Paulson DF: Isolation of a human prostate carcinoma cell line (DU-145). Int J Cancer 21:274–281,1978.
8. Rigby CC, Franks LW: A human tissue culture cell line from a transitional cell tumor of the urinary bladder: Growth, chromosome pattern and ultrastructure. Br J Cancer 24:746–754,1970.
9. Soule DH, Vasquez J, Long A, Albert S, Brennan M: A human cell line from a pleural effusion derived from a breast carcinoma. J Natl Cancer Inst 51:1409–1416,1973.
10. Fogh J, Trempe G: New human tumor cell lines. In Fogh J (ed): "Human Tumor Cells In Vitro." New York: Plenum Press, 1975, pp 115–153.

11. Lasfargues EY, Ozzello L: Cultivation of human breast carcinomas. J Natl Cancer Inst 21:1131–1147,1958.
12. Yunis AA, Arimura GK, Russin DJ: Human pancreatic carcinoma (MIA PaCa-2) in continuous culture: Sensitivity to asparaginase. Int J Cancer 19:128–135,1977.
13. Klein E, Klein G, Nadakarni JS: Surface IgM-kappa specificity on a Burkitt lymphoma cell in vivo and in derived culture lines. Cancer Res 28:1300–1310,1968.
14. Pulvertaft FJ: A study of malignant tumors in Nigeria by short-term tissue culture. J Clin Pathol 18:261–273,1965.
15. Papsidero LD, Wojcieszyn JW, Horoszewicz JS, Leong SS, Murphy GP, Chu TM: Isolation of prostatic acid phosphatase-binding immunoglobulin G from human sera and its potential use as a tumor-localizing reagent. Cancer Res 40:3032–3035,1980.
16. Heyderman E, Neville AM: A shorter immunoperoxidase technique for the demonstration of carcinoembryonic antigen and other cell products. J Clin Pathol 30:138–143,1977.
17. Vihko P, Kontturi M, Korhonen LK: Purification of human prostatic acid phosphatase by affinity chromatography and isoelectric focusing. Part 1. Clin Chem 24:466–470,1978.
18. Luchter-Wasyl E, Ostrowski W: Subunit structure of human prostatic acid phosphatase. Biochim Biophys Acta 365:349–359,1974.
19. Gryszkiewicz J, Dziembor E, Ostrowski W: Modification of human prostatic acid phosphatase by glutaraldehyde. Bull Acad Polon Sci Ser Sci Biol 26:215–220,1978.
20. Herzenberg LA, Herzenberg L, Millstein C: Cell hybrids of myelomas with antibody forming cells and T-lymphomas with T-cells. In Weir DM (ed): "Handbook of Experimental Immunology." Oxford: Blackwood Scientific Publications, 1978, pp 25.1–25.7.
21. Littlefield JW: Selection of hybrids from matings of fibroblasts in vitro and their presumed recombinants. Science 145:709–710,1964.
22. Nadji M, Tabei SZ, Castro A, Chu TM, Wang MC, Murphy GP, Morales AR: Prostate specific antigen: An immunohistologic marker for prostatic neoplasms. Cancer (in press).

TRACE METALS

The Prostatic Cell: Structure and Function
Part A, pages 447–457

Studies of Zinc in Normal and Neoplastic Prostatic Tissues

Betty Rosoff

Since 1921 when Bertrand and Vladesco first reported large amounts of zinc in the human prostate gland and in semen, many laboratories have confirmed the presense of high concentrations of zinc in the prostate of rat, dog, baboon, cat, and man. The distribution of zinc in different lobes of the prostate, the cellular and subcellular localization of prostatic zinc, the endocrine control of the concentration of prostatic zinc, and the differences in zinc concentration and zinc metabolism in BPH, CaP, and prostatitis have all been studied. While some better methodology has given us more reliable data, many questions still remain unanswered and particularly the most fundamental one—what is that large amount of zinc doing there in the first place?

W.F. Whitmore summarized and reviewed the early literature in 1963 [1], and David Byar reviewed the next 10 years in 1972 [2]. This paper will attempt to describe some studies by the author and co-workers as well as some selected observations from the recent literature on related aspects of zinc concentration and zinc metabolism in animal and human, normal and pathological prostate tissue.

HORMONAL CONTROL OF PROSTATIC ZINC

Hormonal control of ^{65}Zn uptake in the dorsolateral prostate of the rat has been studied by many workers beginning with the pioneer work of Gunn and Gould [3]. Rosoff and Martin [4] demonstrated that, in intact pubertal Long Evans rats, gonadotrophins as well as testosterone influence ^{65}Zn uptake in the lateral and to some extent the dorsal and ventral prostate. In the lateral prostate (Fig. 1), ^{65}Zn concentration (percent of dose per gm of tissue) was decreased by administration of FSH and of FSH plus prolactin, unaffected by prolactin alone, increased slightly by LH, and appreciably increased by HCG. In another study (Fig. 2) when the animals were thymectomized and sham thymectomized

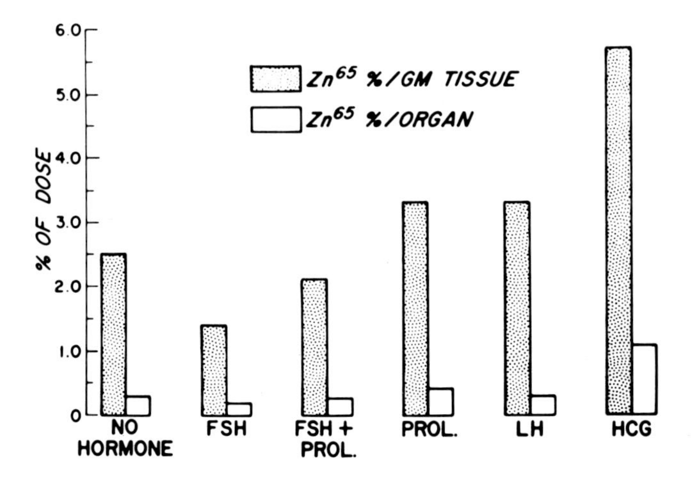

Fig. 1. Effect of gonadotrophins on ^{65}Zn uptake in the lateral prostate of Long Evans rats. Rats, 8 weeks old, were injected with the hormones for 2 weeks. ^{65}Zn was injected 24 hours before sacrifice [4].

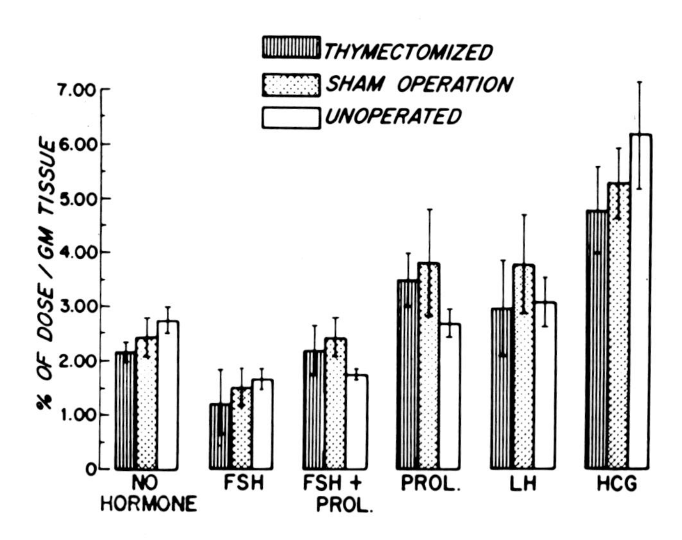

Fig. 2. Effect of thymectomy and sham thymectomy on ^{65}Zn uptake in the lateral prostate under different hormonal conditions. Surgery was performed when the rats were 6 weeks old, and the hormone injections were administered at 8 weeks as described in Figure 1 [4].

before hormone administration, the responses to gonadotrophins were modified [5]. For example, prolactin seems to have a stimulatory effect on ^{65}Zn concentration when animals undergo surgical stress. Consistent with other studies the thymus seems to play some role in response to stress because thymectomized animals all show a lower zinc uptake than sham-thymectomized rats. The weights of the lateral prostate were affected differently by the hormones than the ^{65}Zn uptake (Fig. 3). FSH increased lateral prostate weight in operated animals where it had decreased zinc uptake. The weights of the lateral prostate of thymectomized animals was generally higher than sham-operated rats except for those treated with HCG. In this study animals injected with testosterone showed a dose-dependent increase in weight and zinc uptake. Consistent with these results Byar showed that hypophysectomized and castrated rats had a decreased uptake of ^{65}Zn in the dorsolateral prostate [6].

Prolactin has been shown to have some influence on prostatic growth, metabolism, and pathology. Gunn and Gould reported its synergism with testosterone and LH in increasing ^{65}Zn uptake in castrated and hypophysectomized rats, respectively [7]. Rosoff and Martin [8] and Rosoff and Weinstein [9] showed that in orchiectomized, Long Evans rats, prolactin alone increased ^{65}Zn uptake in the lateral prostate gland (Fig. 4). In rats orchiectomized at 12 weeks and

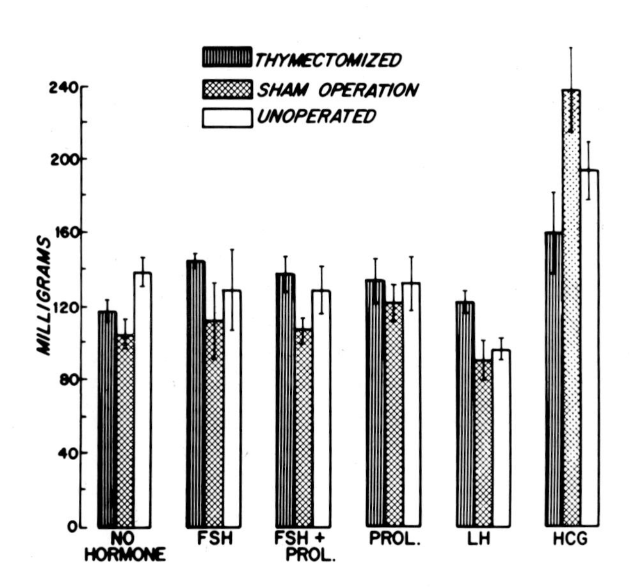

Fig. 3. Effect of thymectomy and sham thymectomy on the lateral prostate weight response to gonadotrophins [4].

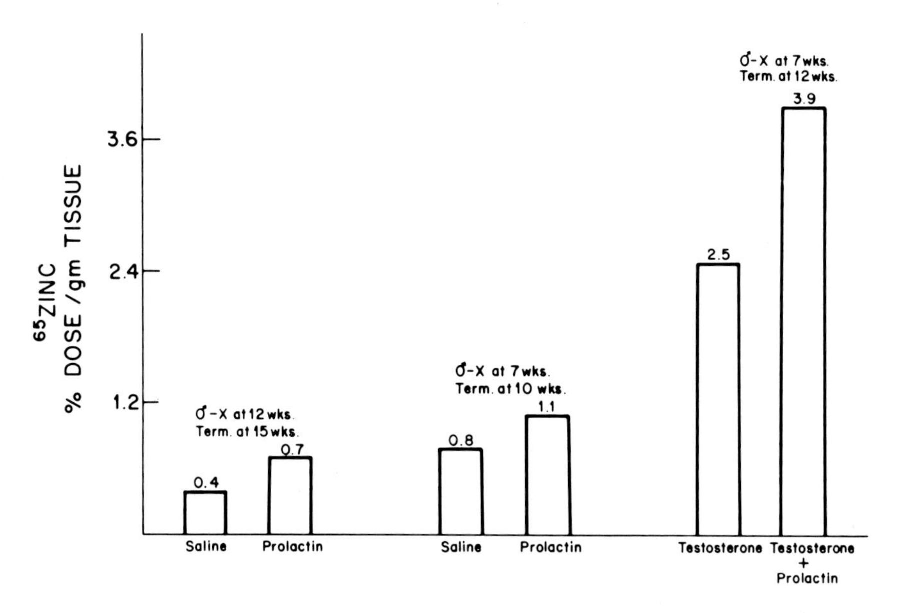

Fig. 4. Effect of prolactin on ^{65}Zn uptake in the lateral prostate of orchiectomized Long Evans rats (Rosoff, Weinstein, and Martin, unpublished observations).

sacrificed at 15 weeks, prolactin raised the ^{65}Zn uptake from 0.4% in the saline controls to 0.7% of dose per gm of tissue. In younger animals orchiectomized at 7 weeks, 3 weeks of prolaction injections increased the ^{65}Zn uptake from 0.8% of dose per gm of tissue to 1.1%. In another study, animals gonadectomized at the same age (7 weeks) were given 20 hormone injections and sacrificed after 5 weeks. When prolactin was administered with testosterone, the zinc uptake increased from 2.5 with testosterone alone to 3.9% of dose per gm of tissue with both hormones. In these studies we could not determine a clear effect of prolactin on organ weights of the prostates; in fact, the effect of the hormone seemed to be modified by the seasons. For example, in the summer prolactin administered with testosterone seemed to decrease the weight of all three prostates over testosterone alone, while in the winter study, the prostate weights were higher with prolactin and testosterone than when only testosterone was administered. Yamanaka et al [10] found that in castrated mature rats prolactin alone had no effect on ventral prostate weight and only a small effect on dorsolateral prostate weight, while testosterone administered with prolactin had a greater effect on the weight of the dorsolateral prostate. This paper [10] also summarizes the effects of prolactin on the prostate published up to 1975, and the results suggest that age, breed, length of treatment, and perhaps seasons modify the effect of prolactin on weight and zinc uptake.

Moger and Geshwind [11] measured the effect of prolactin on both ^{65}Zn uptake and stable zinc content in the dorsolateral prostate and reported that in gonadectomized rats, prolactin alone increased ^{65}Zn uptake while the stable zinc uptake was only increased when prolactin and testosterone were administered together. Schoonees et al [12] studied the effect of prolactin on ^{65}Zn uptake in the baboon and found that the caudal prostate had significant zinc uptake and that this was reduced by prolactin. It might be that the prolactin effect on zinc is dose dependent and also that it is hard to demonstrate except in castrated or stressed animals. Muntzing et al [13] found that a prolactin-release inhibitor lowered ^{65}Zn uptake in the dorsolateral prostate but had no effect on prostate weight. They also reported that in orchiectomized or immature rats, administration of estrogen increased ^{65}Zn uptake and suggested that the "estrogen effect" might really be the result of stimulating prolactin release. In this same study estrogen administered to mature animals seemed to slightly reduce zinc uptake, an effect similar to that of prolactin in mature intact rats. These studies of ^{65}Zn uptake in the dorsolateral prostate of rats, the caudal prostate of baboon, and also the dog prostate under different hormonal conditions have helped to elucidate some of the control mechanisms of prostate function and have suggested further studies in humans. In addition, ^{65}Zn uptake in the dorsolateral prostate has been used as a drug screening system by Sandberg et al [14] for agents to treat cancer of the prostate.

ANIMAL TUMOR MODELS AND ZINC

Several animal tumor models for prostatic cancer have become available, and among other parameters being studied is their zinc uptake. In a study in my laboratory the distribution of ^{65}Zn in Copenhagen × Fischer rats inoculated with R3327H tumor was determined. This tumor is a transplantable hormone-dependent rat prostatic adenocarcinoma which arose spontaneously from dorsal or dorsolateral prostate. About 6 months after inoculation of the tumor when it was well developed, ^{65}Zn was injected and the animals sacrificed 24 hours later. A control group of the same strain without tumors was also injected and radioassayed. The ^{65}Zn uptake of the tumor is more like that of the ventral prostate than the dorsolateral prostate from which it was originally derived (Table I). Muntzing et al [15] showed similar results, ie, 0.42% in the tumor compared to our 0.35%, and their dorsolateral prostate uptake was 2.2% compared to our 3.2%. In our study all the tissues in the tumor bearing animals showed a lower uptake of zinc than the controls (Fig. 5). Interestingly, the report of Muntzing shows that Estracyt is effective in decreasing tumor weight and, while it decreases ^{65}Zn concentration in the dorsolateral prostate, it has no effect on ^{65}Zn in the tumor. The low uptake of zinc in this tumor further suggests its appropriateness

TABLE I. Distribution of ^{65}Zn in Copenhagen × Fischer F_1 rats

	% Dose/gm tissue	
	Tumor	Control
Ventral prostate	0.34 ± 0.20	0.47 ± 0.26
Dorsolateral prostate	3.2 ± 2.7	4.6 ± 2.8
Tumor	0.37 ± 0.15	—
Seminal vesicles	0.24 ± 0.10	0.50 ± 0.21
Testes	0.28 ± 0.05	0.37 ± 0.07
Liver	0.67 ± 0.16	0.75 ± 0.15
Kidney	0.56 ± 0.21	0.77 ± 0.01

^{65}Zn injected 6 months after tumor innoculation (R3327H).

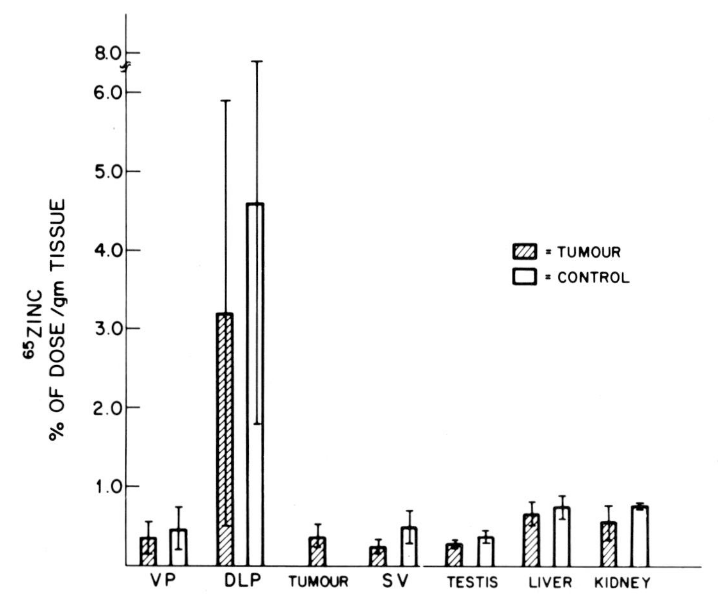

Fig. 5. Distribution of ^{65}Zn in Copenhagen × Fischer rats. Animals inoculated with R3327H tumor are compared with controls. Six months after tumor inoculation, ^{65}Zn was injected and rats sacrificed 24 hours later (Rosoff and Schwartz, unpublished observations, 1976).

as a model for human prostatic cancer because most reports show lower zinc levels in prostatic cancer tissue than in normal or BPH tissue. We are presently studying the effect of prolactin inhibition and stimulation on ^{65}Zn uptake in this tumor.

Another rat prostatic adenocarcinoma, Tumor I in Lobund Wistar rats, was also studied for its ability to accumulate ^{65}Zn [16]. This tumor also showed low zinc uptake, about 10% of that found in the dorsolateral prostate, and Estracyt did not affect the growth or zinc uptake of this tumor.

ZINC DEFICIENCY IN OLDER RATS

Since dietary changes occur in older men, it seemed of interest to us (Rosoff and Martin) to study the effect of zinc deficiency on the prostate of old rats. Long Evans rats were fed either a zinc-deficient or a control diet from age 12–16 months. Twenty-four hours before sacrifice ^{65}Zn was injected. As expected (Table II) the weights of the testes and all accessory reproductive structures were considerably lower in rats on the zinc-deficient diet. However, the ^{65}Zn concentrations (percent of dose/gm of tissue) were about the same or higher in the zinc-deficient animals except for the lateral and possibly the dorsal prostate (Table III). The lateral prostate ^{65}Zn uptake was 1.72% of dose per gm of tissue

TABLE II. Effect of zinc-deficient diet on organ weights of old rats

Organ	Zn-deficient diet (mg)	Control diet (mg)
Lateral prostate	226	304
Dorsal prostate	56	77
Ventral prostate	316	468
Seminal vesicles	589	1154
Testes	1314	1613
Coagulating gland	90	142

Long Evans rats were fed zinc-deficient and control diets from age 12–16 months, when they were sacrificed.

TABLE III. Effect of zinc-deficient diet on organ uptake of ^{65}Zn (percent of dose per gm tissue) in old rats

Organ	Zn-deficient diet (mg)	Control diet
Lateral prostate	1.72	2.12
Ventral prostate	0.32	0.25
Lateral prostate/Ventral prostate	6.14	9.91
Seminal vesicles	0.27	0.16
Testes	0.19	0.18
Coagulating gland	0.50	0.36
Dorsal prostate	0.58	0.64

Long Evans rats were fed zinc-deficient and control diets from age 12–16 months, when they were sacrificed.

compared with 2.12% in controls. The ratio of lateral prostate/ventral prostate is 6.1 in the zinc-deficient animals and 9.9 in the controls. The findings are consistent with the concept that zinc induces its own binding sites.

ZINC IN HUMAN PROSTATE—NORMAL AND PATHOLOGICAL

Concentrations of zinc in human prostatic tissues have been studied using several different methods with sometimes conflicting results, ie, ^{65}Zn uptake, histochemistry, x-ray analysis, atomic absorption spectroscopy. While there are some differences in the literature as to whether normal or BPH tissue has a higher zinc concentration, there seems to be general agreement that in tissue from carcinoma of the prostate both zinc content and concentration are always lower [16–21]. While some of the differences between groups might be methodological, some recent findings suggest that age and the general health of the individual might affect the levels of zinc in the prostate. Leissner et al [22] in a careful study showed that zinc concentration in the prostate increases with age up to 30 years and then plateaus. However, in all age groups the prostates from those suffering chronic disease had significantly lower zinc concentrations than prostates from those who died suddenly. An interesting finding is that the presence of adenomas did not affect the zinc concentration in the sudden-death group, while in those who died from chronic disease, the presence of adenomas raised the zinc concentration to normal levels.

Habib et al [23] propose that early detection of prostatic cancer might be possible by using a combination of zinc and hormone analysis. In this study, zinc concentration determined by atomic absorption spectroscopy in samples of prostate showed that carcinomatous tissue had a mean concentration of 195 μg/gm dry weight. This is less than one half the mean concentration found in tissue diagnosed as benign prostatic hypertrophy (460 μg/gm) and as normal prostate tissue (517 μg/gm). Hormone analysis of these tissues showed that DHT was increased in both BPH and CaP compared to normal prostate, but testosterone was higher only in CaP tissue. The DHT/T ratio was 1 in the normal, 3 in BPH, and 0.6 in CaP. This investigator found a strong correlation between zinc values of less than 300 μg/gm and DHT/T ratios of less than 1 in CaP, and between zinc values over 350 μg/gm and DHT/T greater than 1 in BPH. These authors [24] suggest that zinc changes precede androgen changes and that it is possible that a certain level of zinc is necessary for a normal functioning gland. Grant [25], in some in vitro studies, demonstrated that high levels of zinc inhibit DHT formation from testosterone while low levels of zinc stimulate the 5-α reductase reaction. Therefore, it seems that a critical amount of zinc might be necessary for androgen metabolism.

Zinc has been measured in plasma to determine whether there are differences in prostatic disease. Wilden and Robinson in a recent study [26] found a mean plasma zinc level of 98 μg percent in normals, 113 in CaP, and 154 in BPH. These values did not prove to be statistically significantly different, did not correlate with gland size, and therefore did not seem to be useful in diagnosis.

A study by Spencer et al [27] reports that another parameter involving zinc might be different in prostatic disease, namely zinc intestinal absorption. After administration of an oral dose of ^{65}Zn to several patients with and without prostatic disease, the ^{65}Zn absorption was determined (Table IV). Patient 1 with a diagnosis of carcinoma of the prostate had a low ^{65}Zn absorption before treatment (21%) and this absorption increased to 64% during remission due to estrogen treatment. Patient 2 with the same diagnosis had a zinc absorption of 72% before treatment and in contrast this dropped to 37% during estrogen treatment. In this patient there was no clinical response to the treatment. Two patients free of CaP showed either no change with estrogen administration or a reduction in zinc absorption. The authors propose that low ^{65}Zn absorption which is increased by estrogen administration might be a method of predicting response to this type of therapy.

These studies raise more questions than they answer, but they seem to suggest that to understand normal and abnormal prostatic physiology, more knowledge

TABLE IV. Intestinal absorption of ^{65}Zn in patients with carcinoma of prostate and in normals[a]

Patient	Diagnosis	Study conditions	^{65}Zn absorption % of dose
1	Carcinoma of prostate	Active, untreated disease	21
		Remission due to estrogen	64
		Long-term estrogen but escape	41
2	Carcinoma of prostate	Acute untreated disease	72
		Estrogen, 161 days, no clinical effect	37
		Estrogen, 752 days, no clinical effect	37
3	Normal	Control	67
		Estrogen	67
4	Normal	Control	35
		Estrogen	23

A single oral dose of ^{65}Zn was administered, and the absorption was calculated from a 12-day stool collection.

[a]Personal communication from H. Spencer.

about the role of zinc is necessary. Hormones control the concentrations of zinc in the prostate and maybe zinc also controls the metabolism of these hormones. For example, this article has mentioned some studies that involve zinc in the reduction of T to DHT. It would seem that other pathways of testosterone metabolism should be investigated as well. Low concentrations of zinc in the prostate and low absorption of zinc seem to be associated with CaP; maybe increasing zinc levels might play a role in reversing the disease. Prolactin seem to be the fine control for prostatic zinc concentrations. Further research might answer some of these questions.

REFERENCES

1. Whitmore WF Jr: Comments on zinc in the human and canine prostates. In: Biology of the Prostate and Related Tissues. Natl Cancer Inst Monogr 12: 337–340, 1962.
2. Byar DP: Zinc in male sex accessory organs: Distribution and hormonal respones. In D Brandes (ed): "Male Accessory Sex Organs." New York: Academic Press, pp 161–171, 1974.
3. Gunn SA, Gould TC: Difference between dorsal and lateral components of dorsolateral prostate of rat in ^{65}Zn uptake. Proc Soc Exp Med 92: 17–20, 1957.
4. Rosoff B, Martin C: Effect of gonadotrophins and of testosterone on organ weights and Zinc-65 uptake in the male rat. Gen Comp Endocrinol 10: 75–84, 1968.
5. Rosoff B, Martin C: The influence of thymectomy and sham operation on prostate gland responses of hooded rats to gonadotropins. Gen Comp Endocrinol 16: 484–492, 1971.
6. Byar DP, Anderson JE, Mostofi FK: The distribution of 65-zinc in the prostate and other organs in control, castrated and hypophysectomized rats. Invest Urol 7: 57–65, 1969.
7. Gunn SA, Gould TC, Anderson WA: The effect of growth hormone and prolactin preparations on the control by ICSH of uptake of Zn65 by the rat dorsolateral prostate. J Endocrinol 32: 205–214, 1965.
8. Rosoff B, Martin C: unpublished results, 1969.
9. Weinstein E, Rosoff B: Effect of prolactin on weight and zinc-65 uptake in castrated rats. Fed Proc 31: 275, 1972.
10. Yamanaka H, Kirdani Y, Saroff J, Murphy GP, Sandberg AA: Effects of testosterone and prolactin on rat prostatic weight, 5-α-reductase, and arginase. Am J Physiol 229: 1102–1109, 1975.
11. Moger WH, Geschwind II: The action of prolactin on the sex accessory glands of the male rat. Proc Soc Exp Biol Med 141: 1017–1021, 1972.
12. Schoonees R, Deklerk JN, Murphy GP: The effect of prolactin on organ weights and zinc-65 uptake in male baboons. J Surg Oncol 2: 103–106, 1970.
13. Muntzing J, Kirdani R, Murphy GP, Sandberg AA: Hormonal control of zinc uptake and binding in the rat dorsolateral prostate. Invest Urol 14: 492–495, 1977.
14. Sandberg AA, Muntzing J, Kadohama N, Karr JP, Sufrin G, Kirdani R, Murphy GP: Some new approaches to potential test systems for drugs against prostatic cancer. Cancer Treat Rep 61: 289–295, 1977.
15. Muntzing J, Kirdani RY, Saroff J, Murphy GP, Sandberg AA: Inhibitory effects of Estracyt on R-3327 rat prostatic carcinoma. Urology 10: 439–445, 1977.
16. Muntzing J, Kirdani RY, Murphy GP, Sandberg AA: A rat prostatic adenocarcinoma as a model for the human disease. Invest Urol 17: 37–41, 1979.
17. Siegel E, Graig FA, Crystal MM, Siegel EP: Distribution of 65-Zn in the prostate and other organs of man. Br J Cancer 15 Sept: 647–664, 1961.

18. Mawson CA, Fischer MI: The occurrence of zinc in the human prostate gland. Cancer J Med Sci 30: 336–339, 1952.
19. Schrodt GR, Hall T, Whitmore WF Jr: The concentration of zinc in diseased human prostate glands. Cancer 17: 1555–1566, 1964.
20. Gyorkey F, Kyung-Whan M, Huff JA, Gyorkey P: Zinc and magnesium in human prostate gland: Normal, hyperplastic and neoplastic. Cancer Res 27: 1348–1353, 1967.
21. Muntzing J, Nilsson T, Polacek J: Zinc and β-glucuronidase in the human prostate. Scand J Urol Nephrol 8: 87–90, 1974.
22. Leissner KH, Fjelkegard B, Tisell LS: Concentration and content of zinc in the human prostate. Invest Urol 18: 32–35, 1980.
23. Habib FK, Mason MK, Smith PH, Stitch SR: Cancer of the prostate early diagnosis by zinc and hormone analysis? Br J Cancer 39: 700–704, 1979.
24. Habib FK: Zinc and steroid endocrinology of the prostate. J Steroid Biochem 9: 403–407, 1978.
25. Grant JK, Fall GS, Manguell J: Zinc and the prostate in man. In: Goland M (ed): "Normal and Abnormal Growth of the Prostate." 1973, pp 494–501.
26. Wilden EG, Robinson MR: Plasma zinc levels in prostatic disease. Br J Urol 47: 295–299, 1975.
27. Spencer H, Kramer L, Osis D, Norris C, Evans C: Zinc 65 absorption in patients with carcinoma of the prostate. The Prostate 1: 239–249, 1980.

The Prostatic Cell: Structure and Function
Part A, pages 459–474

Interactions Between Protein and Heavy Metals in the Rodent Prostatic Cell

John A. Thomas, Michael P. Donovan, Michael P. Waalkes, and Karen A. Curto

The presence of various trace metals in male sex accessory organs has been investigated at some length, yet their physiologic function or their role in the pathogenesis of prostatic disease remains an enigma. Mawson and Fischer [1] reported that these organs contained much higher levels of zinc than other organs. The relationship between androgens and zinc metabolism has been known for over two decades [cf, 2–4]. Still other investigations have noted the presence of effect of other trace metals upon the male reproductive organs such as cadmium [5], copper [6], magnesium [7], lead [8], and other metals [9]. Some of these aforementioned investigations were clearly more concerned with the toxicologic actions of the metals than with any physiologic function. Few studies have actually dealt with metal-protein interactions in the prostate gland.

Recent studies from this laboratory have described the effects of several different divalent metal ions upon the binding of dihydrotestosterone (DHT) to cytosolic receptor proteins in the mouse prostate gland [10]. Estrogen [11] or progesterone [12] binding to their receptors can also be affected by metals. The present report represents an extention of some of our earlier experiments pertaining to the inhibition of DHT binding to prostate receptors by divalent ions; however, also included are some studies of non-androphilic proteins present in this organ and to what extent they are influenced by certain trace metals.

METHODS

Animals and Tissues

Sexually mature male mice (Swiss-Webster) or rats (Wistar) were obtained commercially (Hilltop Laboratories, Scottsdale, PA). Animals were acclimated in the Medical Center vivarium and were maintained on a standard laboratory diet ad libitum.

Various lobes of the rodent prostate were rapidly removed, weighed, and homogenized in appropriate buffer systems. In the mouse, anterior lobes (coagulating glands) were excised and homogenized in 10 volumes of ice-cold 0.05M Tris-HC1 (pH 7.2). It required about 30–40 mice in order to obtain sufficient amounts of cytosol for subsequent androgen receptor binding studies. In the rat, and for measurement of metallothionein (MT), prostate glands (ventral or dorsolateral lobes) or liver were homogenized at 4°C in 0.02M Tris-HC1 (pH 8.6) containing mercaptoethanol and sucrose.

Preparation of Mouse Prostate Glands

Endogenous metal ions were removed from mouse prostate gland homogenates by incubation with Dowex chelating resin (Sigma Chemical Co.). The resin was prepared by suspending in 0.05M Tris-HC1 and adjusting to pH 7.2 with 1M HC1. The resin was filtered, resuspended in Tris Buffer, the pH verified at 7.2, and refiltered. One gm of resin was added to each 3 ml of homogenate and the mixture swirled in an ice bath for 30 minutes. The mixtures were centrifuged at 100,000g for 60 minutes, removing the resin and the particular organelles. The resulting supernatants were decanted and designated as cytosols or cytoplasmic fractions. Content of zinc ion in cytosols prepared in this way was measured by atomic absorption spectroscopy and was found to be less than 10^{-6}M.

Androgen Binding in Mouse Prostate Gland Cytosols

Steroid-receptor interaction was studied using the method of Schein et al [13]. Stock solutions of [^{3}H]-DHT, 80 Ci/mmole (New England Nuclear) were dried under N_2 and redissolved in 0.05M Tris-HC1 (pH 7.2) immediately before each experiment. Purity of the radiosteroid was determined by thin-layer chromatography with chloroform:ether (7:3, v/v); solutions were used only if their radiochemical purity exceeded 95%.

The binding reaction employed a mixture containing 1-2 mg cytoplasmic protein, 0.05M Tris-HC1, pH 7.2, and [^{3}H]-DHT. Metal ions and unlabeled DHT were added as appropriate. Incubations were carried out in a total volume of 0.50 ml, at 0–4°C, and for 12 hours.

Quantitation of [^{3}H]-DHT Binding in Mouse Prostate Gland Cytosols

Dextran-coated charcoal was used to remove free steroid from the incubation mixture [14]. A suspension containing 0.25% activated charcoal and 0.025% Dextran T-70 in 0.9% NaC1 solution was stirred at 0–4°C for at least 1 hour. At the end of the incubation period, 1 ml of charcoal suspension was added to each tube and mixed for 15 minutes. Charcoal and adsorbed steroid were sedimented by centrifugation at 2000g for 10 minutes. The supernatants were decanted into 10-ml portions of scintillation counting fluid containing 0.05 gm POPOP, 4 gm PPO, and 200 ML of Beckman BioSolv® in 1 liter of toluene. All data were expressed as counts per minute of [^{3}H]-DHT per mg protein and were corrected for radiosteroid unadsorbed to charcoal by subtracting appropriate blank values derived from incubation mixtures containing [^{3}H]-DHT, but no cytosol. Nonspecific binding was determined in incubation mixtures containing unlabeled DHT in 100-fold molar excess over [^{3}H]-DHT. Specific binding was then determined by correction of total binding in tubes containing only radiosteroid [15].

Preparation and Measurement of Metallothionein in the Rat

The procedure followed was essentially that of Probst et al [16]. Rats were treated with a dose of cadmium (2 mg/kg body weight; SC) previously shown to induce hepatic metallothionein synthesis [16] and were sacrificed 48 hours later. Liver and prostatic tissue were removed and homogenized at 4°C in Tris buffer (0.02M Tris-HC1, pH 8.6; 0.005M 2-mercaptoethanol; 0.25M sucrose) with seven strokes using a Potter-Elvehjem glass homogenizer and a motor driven Teflon pestle to yield a 20% (w/v) homogenate. The homogenate was then centrifuged for 90 minutes at 70,000g (4°C), and the resulting supernatant (cytosol) was removed and stored in 6.0 ml aliquots at –20°C.

After thawing, the cytosols were mixed either with a saturating level of $CdC1_2$ (2.0 μmole in a constant volume of 0.4 ml) to permit indirect quantitation of metallothionein levels, or 0.4 ml of distilled H_2O for analysis of the endogenous metal content of metallothionein. A 5-ml aliquot of cytosol was then loaded onto a 2.6 × 52-cm calibrated column of Sephacryl S-200® (Pharmacia Fine Chemicals, Inc., Piscataway, NJ) previously equilibrated with Tris buffer (0.02M Tris-HC1, pH 8.6, at 25°C; 0.05M NaC1 and 0.005M 2-mercaptoethanol). Descending buffer flow was used (124 ml/hr), and 7.4 ml fractions were collected and analyzed for metal content using a Perkin-Elmer model 035B atomic absorption spectrophotometer. The instrument was used in the standard flame mode (acetylene-air) for measurement of cadmium and zinc in the individual fractions. Previous reports have shown that metallothionein elutes with a relative elution volume (Ve/Vo) of 1.9–2.3 with this system [17,18].

Other Procedures

Protein was estimated by the method of Lowry et al [19] using bovine serum albumin as standard. Metal solutions were standardized by titration with 0.100M Na_2EDTA using murexide or Eriochrome black T as indicator. Carrier-free radioactive zinc chloride (0.49M Ci/ml) (Amersham) was mixed with Krebs-Ringers bicarbonate buffer (pH 7.4) and used to study Zn^{65} uptake in various lobes of the rat prostate. Dextran was purchased from Pharmacia Fine Chemicals, $ZnC1_2$ and $CdC1_2$ from Apache Chemicals, charcoal and Tris from Sigma Chemical Corporation, and all other reagents from Fischer Scientific Company.

RESULTS

While trace metal concentrations in rodent sex accessory glands have been reported by a number of investigators, Table I reveals the localization of zinc,

TABLE I. Trace metal concentrations in various tissues of the rat

Tissue	Trace metal concentration[a]		
	Zinc[b]	Cadmium[c]	Copper[c]
Anterior prostate (coagulating gland)	22	0.50	0.85
Dorsal prostate	36	0.29	1.07
Lateral prostate	126	0.19	0.60
Ventral prostate	21	0.32	0.83
Seminal vesicle	29	0.32	0.87
Liver	36	0.33	2.84
Pancreas	27	—	—
Skeletal muscle	9	—	—

[a]ng/mg wet weight.
[b]Mean of 6 rats.
[c]Mean of 2 or more rats.

TABLE II. Zinc concentrations in various tissues of the mouse

Tissue	Zinc concentration (ng/mg wet weight)
Anterior prostate	26 ± 3.0[a]
Dorsolateral and ventral prostate	30 ± 2.0
Seminal vesicle (empty tissue)	26 ± 1.0
Seminal vesicle (lumen contents)	2 ± 0.4
Liver	30 ± 4.0
Pancreas	37 ± 2.0
Skeletal muscle	6 ± 1.0
Blood serum[b]	2 ± 0.2

[a]Mean ± SEM of at least 6 mice.
[b]ng Zn/μl serum.

cadmium, or copper in various lobes of the prostate. Like the earlier studies of Gunn and Gould [20], Table I reveals that the highest concentration of zinc occurs in the lateral lobe of the rate prostate. In fact, zinc levels in the lateral lobe of the rat prostate were on the average 5 to 6 times higher than any of the other lobes. Prostatic cadmium was highest in the anterior lobe (coagulating gland) while copper levels were recorded to be the highest in the dorsal lobe of the rat prostate. The seminal vesicles also contained amounts of copper (Table I). Studies by Timms et al [21] reported that the dry-weight content of cadmium was tenfold higher in the testes. Levels of copper have been measured in normal,

TABLE III. Assimilation of Zn^{65} by rat prostate gland slices in vitro[a]

Prostate lobe	Uptake (% control)	
	1 hr	2 hr
Anterior (coagulating gland) (3)	423%	639%
Dorsal (3)	527%	407%
Lateral (3)	284%	421%
Ventral (6)	41%	229%
Testes (6)	61%	147%

[a]Tissues were incubated with 2.5×10^{-3} μCi Zn^{65} in Krebs-Ringer bicarbonate buffer (pH 7.4) at 37°C. Number in parentheses indicates the number of samples.

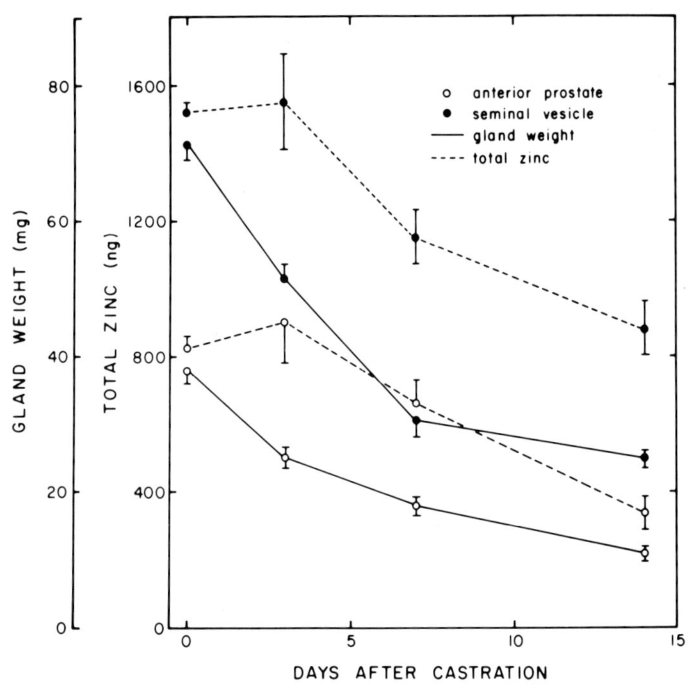

Fig. 1. Effect of castration on mouse anterior prostate gland and seminal vesicle zinc. Each point on the graph represents the mean ± SEM of 6 or more mice.

in BPH and malignant human prostates [22]. In the normal rat prostate, exclusive of specific lobes, the levels of zinc are many times greater than those overall average levels of copper. However, in the normal human prostate gland, levels of zinc and copper are very similar [22].

For a species comparison, zinc levels were measured in the normal sexually mature mouse (Table II). Due to the small sizes of the organs, and the difficulty in anatomical dissection, some lobes necessarily were removed together (viz, dorsolateral and ventral). However, a comparison of the rat's anterior lobe (Table I) with that of the mouse (Table II) indicated there were similar concentrations of zinc. While amounts of zinc in the seminal vesicles were comparable, residual seminal plasma can affect the levels of this divalent ion. In nonreproductive organ tissue (eg liver, pancreas, and skeletal muscle), zinc levels were very similar in the rat (Table I) and in the mouse (Table II).

All of the lobes of the rat prostate gland have an avidity for Zn^{65}, but clearly the ventral prostate differs in its rate of assimilation (Table III). Previous Zn^{65} distribution studies in the rat [20] have established that the large amounts of injected radioactive zinc were localized predominantly in lateral acini of the dorsolateral prostate. The ventral lobe of the prostate revealed an in vitro assimilation rate comparable to that of the testes (Table III).

While the physiologic significance of the various trace metals present in the prostate gland remain to be elucidated, several investigations have shown the relationship between androgens and sex accessory organ zinc [1,3,4]. Heretofore this relationship has been reported in the rat, but this same sort of androgen-zinc interaction is present in the mouse (Figs. 1,2). Figure 1 reveals the anterior

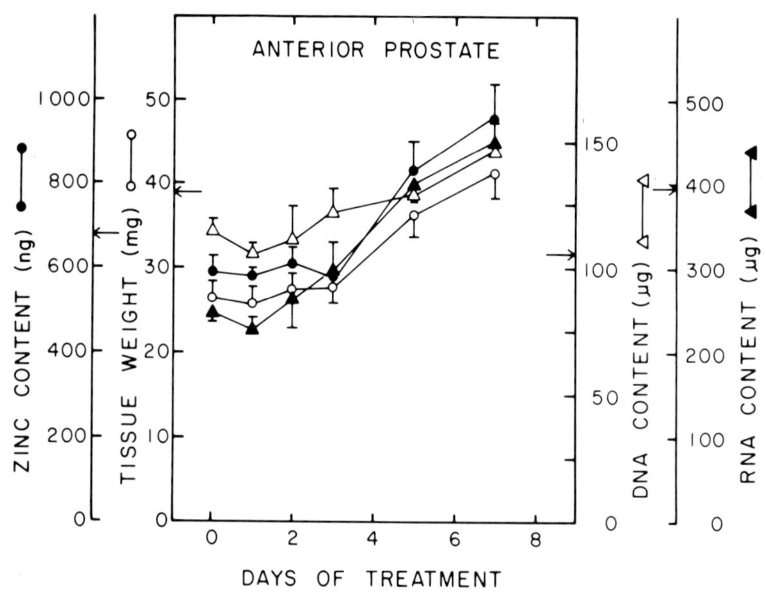

Fig. 2. Effect of dihydrotestosterone (5 mg/kg daily × 7) on anterior prostate zinc levels and upon RNA and DNA. Initial injection was 3 days post-castration. Values represent mean ± SEM of 6 or more mice.

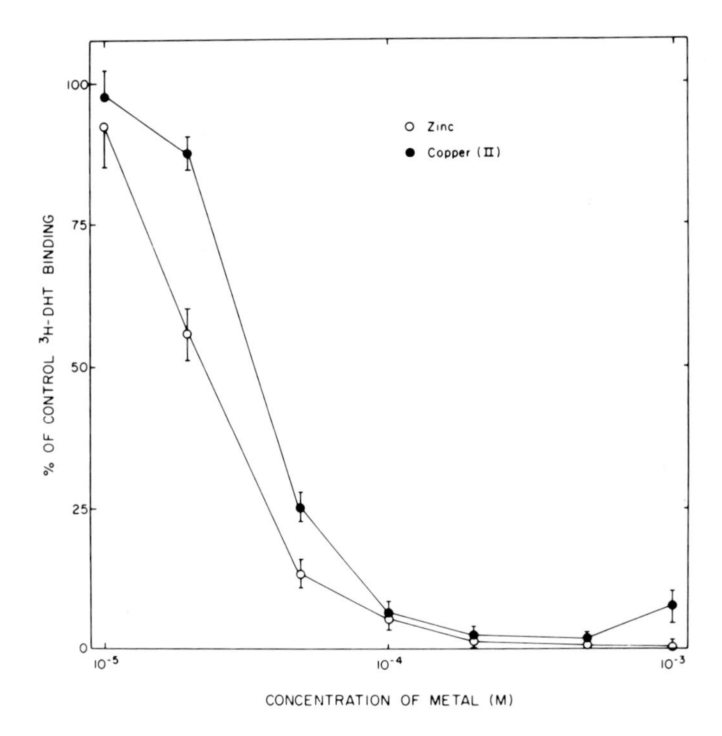

Fig. 3. Inhibition by Zn^{2+} and Cu^{2+} of specific [^{3}H]-DHT binding in mouse prostate cytosol. Cytosol protein (1–2 mg) was incubated with 5 × 10^{-9}M [^{3}H]-DHT, 0.05M Tris-HC1, pH 7.2, and metal chloride in a total volume of 0.50 ml for 12 hours at 0–4°C. Unbound [^{3}H]-DHT was removed by adsorption to 2.5 mg Dextran-coated charcoal. Values were corrected for nonspecific binding determined in identical incubation mixtures to which 5 × 10^{-7}M DHT was added. Total control binding was 500–1000 cpm of which 2–8% was nonspecific binding. Each point represents the mean of triplicate values determined for each of at least three cytosols. The bars represent the standard error of the mean. Reprinted by permission of Academic Press, Inc., New York, New York.

prostate gland zinc levels in the mouse fall rather quickly following castration. Both prostate gland zinc content and concentration are reduced by orchiectomy. Similarly, mouse seminal vesicle zinc levels were seen to decline after castration (Fig. 1). The regressive changes caused by castration in prostate gland weights and zinc can be reversed by the injection of dihydrotestosterone (Fig. 2). When mice were injected daily with dihydrotestosterone (5 mg/kg daily × 7) beginning on the third day post-castration, prostate gland zinc levels actually exceeded normal values after this week-long period of hormone administration (Fig. 2). Also seen are the stimulatory responses of prostatic RNA and DNA. Thus androgen-induced increases in prostatic zinc are paralleled by increases in sex accessory gland nucleic acid.

The mere presence of trace metals in the prostate gland, and even the fact certain of these metals can be affected by androgens, has not really clarified their physiologic or pathologic role in this organ. Steroid-receptor interactions in the presence of certain trace metals have been studied in the uterus of several species (eg rabbit, cow, human) [11,12,23,24]. Some recent reports from our laboratory have investigated dihydrotestosterone-receptor interactions in the presence of a number of divalent ions in the mouse prostate gland [10].

Both $ZnCl_2$ and $CuCl_2$ were effect inhibitors of specific [^{3}H]-DHT binding in mouse anterior prostate cytosol (Fig. 3). Neither metal inhibited binding at 10^{-5}M, but both completely abolished specific binding above 10^{-4}M. Zinc was somewhat more effective than cupric ion. Although not shown, the effects of $CaCl_2$ and $MgCl_2$ on specific [^{3}H]-DHT binding were in marked contrast to the effects of Zn^{2+} and Cu^{2+} [10]. Neither Ca^{2+} nor Mg^{2+} effectively inhibited binding and, in fact, specific binding was slightly increased with Ca^{2+} at concentrations less than 10^{-4}M. On the other hand, magnesium inhibited binding at all concentrations greater than 10^{-5}M, but the maximum inhibition was only 30% at 1 mM $MgCl_2$.

TABLE IV. Effect of metal ions on specific binding of [^{3}H]-dihydrotestosterone to mouse anterior prostate cytosol[a]

Ion	IC_{50} (M)[b]	Maximum inhibition[c]
Ca^{2+}	—	4
Mn^{2+}	—	28
Mg^{2+}	—	31
Ni^{2+}	—	41
K^+	0.2M	67
Pb^{2+}	9.0×10^{-4}M	53
Fe^{2+}	8.6×10^{-4}M	59
Co^{2+}	7.2×10^{-4}M	62
Cu^{2+}	3.5×10^{-5}M	100
Hg^{2+}	3.5×10^{-5}M	100
Zn^{2+}	2.2×10^{-5}M	100
Cd^{2+}	1.8×10^{-5}M	100

[a]Incubation mixtures contained 1–2 mg cytosol protein, 5×10^{-9}M [^{3}H]-DHT, 0.05M Tris-HCl, pH 7.2, and metal chloride in a total volume of 0.50 mg. Incubations were carried out for 12 hours at 0–4°C and were terminated by addition of 2.5 mg dextran-coated charcoal to absorb free radiosteroid.

[b]IC_{50} is the concentration of metal ion required to reduce specific [^{3}H]-DHT binding to 50% of the control level.

[c]Maximum observed percentage inhibition of control binding produced by 1.0 mM metal ion (0.3M KCl).

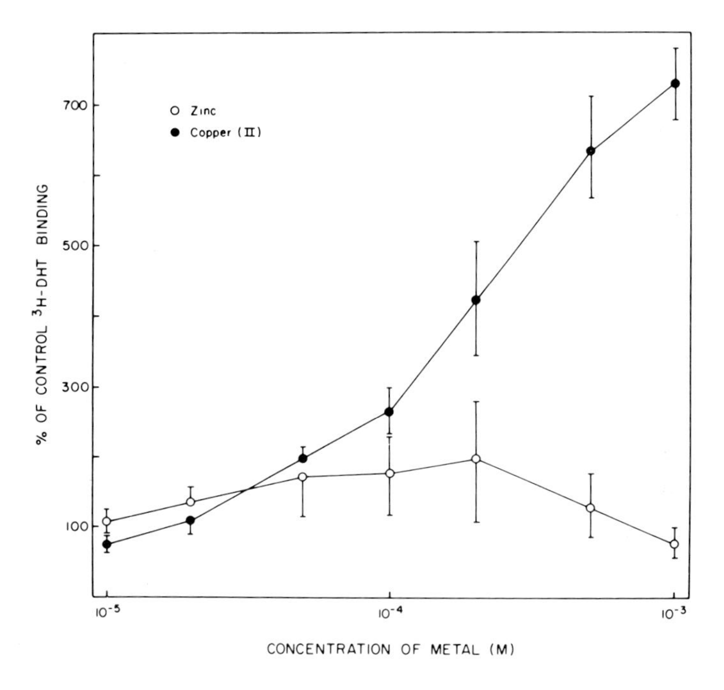

Fig. 4. Stimulation by Cu^{2+} of nonspecific binding of [^{3}H]-DHT in mouse prostate cytosol. These data represent the nonspecific component of binding in the incubations of Figure 4. Reprinted by permission of Academic Press, Inc., New York, NY.

Several metal ions were studied with respect to their ability to inhibit the specific binding of [^{3}H]-DHT to mouse anterior prostate gland cytosols. The various metals were distributed into five categories on the basis of inhibitory activity (Table IV). Calcium had no effect upon steroid binding at any concentration while magnesium, manganous and nickel ions exerted only minimal effect, causing at most 41% inhibition at 10^{-3}M $NiCl_2$. Ferric, cobalt, and lead ions were capable of inhibiting binding more than 50%, but only at concentrations near 10^{-3}M. Potassium could also produce up to 67% inhibition, but its IC_{50} was 0.2M. The most effective category of inhibitors included cadmium, copper, mercuric, and zinc ions. These metals were capable of producing complete inhibition of specific [^{3}H]-DHT binding, and had IC_{50} values ranging from 1.75×10^{-5}M (Cd^{2+}) to 3.5×10^{-5}M (Cu^{2+} and Hg^{2+}).

None of the metal ions listed on Table IV significantly inhibited nonspecific binding of [^{3}H]-DHT to mouse prostate gland cytosols. However, cupric ions substantially enhanced nonspecific binding of [^{3}H]-DHT (Fig. 4). The increase

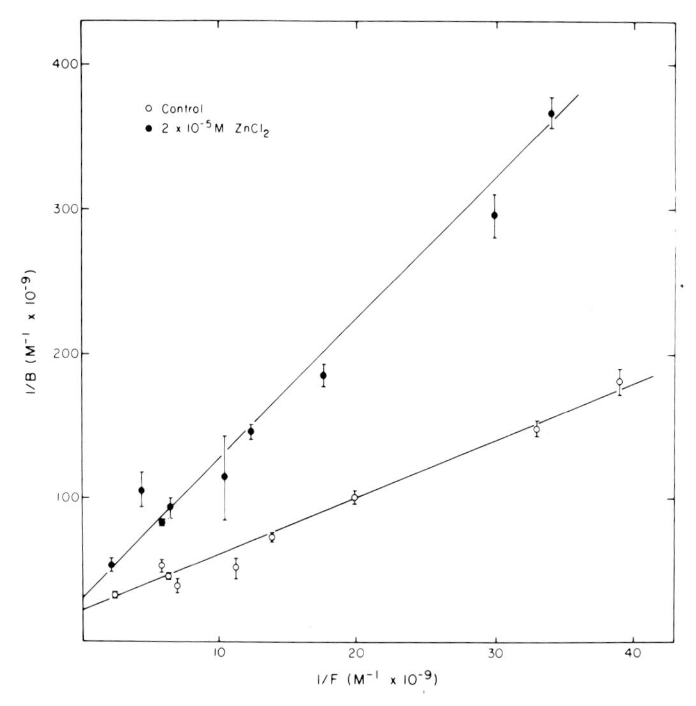

Fig. 5. Double reciprocal plot of specific binding of [^{3}H]-DHT in mouse prostate cytosol in the absence and presence of 2 × 10^{-5} $ZnCl_2$. Incubation conditions were as described in Figure 1. [^{3}H]-DHT concentration was varied from 5 × 10^{-10} to 10^{-8}M. Unlabeled DHT in the determinations of nonspecific binding was also varied to maintain a 100-fold molar excess over [^{3}H]-DHT and charcoal blanks were evaluated at each concentration of [^{3}H]-DHT. Each point represents the mean of at least two determinations on each of at least two cytosol preparations. Bars represent the standard errors of the means. The lines represent linear regression lines calculated on the individual data points. Regression lines were also calculated separately for each set of points determined on each cytosol preparation, generating a sample of estimates for each intercept. These were then compared by Student's t test. The mean value for the x-intercept in the presence of zinc differed significantly from control ($P < 0.02$), while the means for the y-intercept did not differ ($P \simeq 0.45$). Reprinted by permission of Academic Press, Inc., New York, NY.

was more than sevenfold at 10^{-3}M $CuCl_2$ and did not reach a limiting value in the concentration range studied (10^{-5}–10^{-3}M).

Figure 5 is a double reciprocal plot of the specific binding of various concentrations of [^{3}H]-DHT in the absence and presence of 2 × 10^{-5}M $ZnCl_2$. This concentration of Zn^{2+} produced approximately 50% inhibition of binding (Table IV). The presence of zinc ion did not affect the maximum binding of [^{3}H]-DHT; it was approximately 14 fmole/mg protein under both conditions (Fig. 5). However, the apparent K_a for binding, which was 5.2 × $10^9$$M^{-1}$ without zinc,

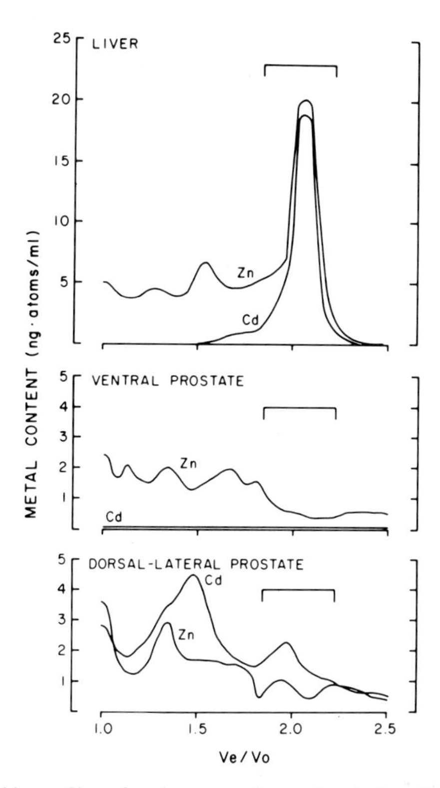

Fig. 6. Chromatographic profiles of endogenous zinc and cadmium following gel filtration of cytosols prepared from liver, ventral prostate, and dorsolateral prostate 48 hours after a single subcutaneous dose of cadmium (2 mg/kg). Brackets indicate a relative elution volume (Ve/Vo) of 1.9 to 2.3 (ie, metallothionein).

decreased to $2.9 \times 10^9\ M^{-1}$ in the presence of $2 \times 10^{-5}M\ ZnCl_2$. Although not shown, inhibition of specific [^{3}H]-DHT binding by pHMB was also studied. Complete inhibition of binding was observed at 10^{-4}M pHMB; the IC_{50} was 4×10^{-5}M. Double reciprocal analysis (Fig. 6) showed the same maximum binding (16 fmole/mg protein) in the presence and absence of 4×10^{-4}M pHMB. However, the apparent K_a of [^{3}H]-DHT binding was $5.5 \times 10^9M^{-1}$ in the absence of pHMB and was lowered to $2.0 \times 10^9M^{-1}$ when 4×10^{-5}M p-hydroxymercuribenzoate (pHMB) was present.

The presence of $2 \times 10^{-5}M\ Zn^{2+}$ did not alter the time course of the binding reaction from that previously reported [13]; binding with and without zinc ion reached maximum values by 12 hours of incubation and remained unchanged at least until 24 hours. Similarly, the presence of zinc ion did not affect the time course of removal of free steroid from the incubation mixture by charcoal. In the presence and the absence of 2 × 10^{-5}M Zn^{2+}, specific binding remained constant from 2–20 minutes of incubation with charcoal while nonspecific binding fell steadily until 15 minutes and remained unchanged at least until 20 minutes. [^{3}H]-DHT adhering to the glass tubes at the end of the incubation was extracted with scintillation cocktail after pouring out the incubation mixture and without adding charcoal. The radiosteroid remaining was unaffected by the presence of 2 × 10^{-5}M Zn^{2+} in the incubation and did not differ from the amount left by [^{3}H]-DHT in an equal volume of buffer without cytosol.

In addition to examining the protein-divalent ion interactions involving prostatic androphilic molecules and certain trace metals, studies were designed to determine whether the prostate gland contained any other specific proteins that possessed an affinity for zinc. More specifically, efforts were devoted toward isolating a prostatic metallothionein. Metallothionein is present in eukaryotic tissues and in known to bind cadmium, zinc, and copper. Metallothionein has been postulated to play a role in cadmium detoxification and in zinc and copper metabolism. In the liver, metallothionein formation is directly correlated with hepatic zinc accumulation under physiologic conditions [26]. Because few, if any, investigations have actually looked for prostatic metallothionein, a limited series of experiments were carried out to not only attempt to isolate such a protein but to also examine its localization within certain lobes of the rat prostate. Figure 6 shows representative metal elution patterns of dorsal-lateral prostate, ventral prostate and liver cytosol obtained from cadmium-treated (2 mg/kg; SC) adult rats following gel-filtration chromatography. The major metal-containing peak in the hepatic cytosol, characterized by a relative elution volume (Ve/Vo) of 1.9 to 2.3 (ie, metallothionein) corresponded to a secondary cadmium-, zinc-containing peak in the dorsal-lateral prostatic cytosol. No such peak was present in the cytosol obtained from ventral prostate, and there was no detectable cadmium in any elution fraction. Indirect quantitation of metallothionein levels were obtained by assessment of the total metal binding capacity of the protein (ie, Ve/Vo 1.9 to 2.3) following in vitro cadmium saturation and gel-filtration [16]. The metallothionein levels were 113.2 ng·atoms/gm wet weight for dorsal-lateral prostatic cytosol and 1211.8 ng·atoms/gm wet weight for hepatic cytosol. These results indicate that the lateral lobe of the rodent prostate, which is associated with high zinc levels, also contains relatively higher levels of metallothionein.

DISCUSSION

Because mammalian prostate glands are androgen dependent and because these organs contain a number of trace metals, it would seem that there should be some physiologic (or pathologic) linkage. In addition to the many and varied roles that certain trace metals may play in enzymatic functions, the presence of larger amounts of certain of these trace metals in the prostate suggests a more expanded function. It would seem that some of these divalent ions can act to enhance steroid-receptor interactions while in other concentrations endocrine states actually interfere with such hormone binding. Zinc (5 mM) can enhance the binding of estradiol in bovine endometrial cytosols [23]. On the other hand, estradiol binding in rabbit uterine cytosol reportedly is inhibited by zinc (1mM) [24]. In human endometrial cytosol a variety of divalent ions ranging in concentrations from 1 to 5 mM reportedly cause an inhibition of estradiol binding [11]. Similarly, divalent metal ions can inhibit the binding of progesterone by a protein isolated from human endometrium [12]. In the present studies, the binding of DHT to prostate cytosolic protein was inhibited by several different divalent metal ions. In the case of zinc, this inhibition was competitive.

The present study extends knowledge of the interactions of metal ions with steroid hormone receptors to the androgen receptor in male sex accessory organs. The present results in the male agree qualitatively with the previous findings of inhibition by metals of binding to estrogen receptors [11] and progesterone receptors [12] in the female. The present findings are also in agreement with the observations of these investigators that Ca^{2+}, Mg^{2+}, Mn^{2+}, and K^{+} are relatively weak inhibitors of binding; Fe^{2+} and Pb^{2+} have intermediate potency; and Cu^{2+}, Hg^{2+}, Zn^{2+}, and Cd^{2+} are very effective inhibitors.

Investigations have also noted that inhibition by metals of steroid binding to uterine cytosols could be reversed by addition of dithiothreitol [10–12]. Sulfhydryl groups of the receptor protein are involved in the processes leading to binding [25] and cations may interfere with binding by blocking the sulfhydryl groups at the binding sites [11]. Wallace and Grant [26] found the inhibition of prostate 5α-reductase by zinc was reversed by dithiothreitol, by EDTA, by o-phenanthroline, and by citrate ion. It appears that any chelating agent will reduce the concentration of free cation in the incubation and reverse inhibition. Such studies of chelation provide no information as to the identity of the affected chemical groups on the receptor. Metal ions can form stable complexes with carboxylates [27], imidazoles, terminal amino groups, and peptides [28] as well as sulfhydryl groups [29]. Therefore, it seems premature to ascribe inhibition of steroid binding to interaction of cations with any one of these chemical groups until the exact nature of the binding site is clarified.

Direct evidence against the involvement of protein sulfhydryl groups in inhibition of steroid binding has been derived from experiments using p-hydroxymercuribenzoate (pHMB) [10]. This compound forms a stable reaction product with protein sulfhydryls and can only be removed by chemical action [30]. If inhibition of steroid binding by pHMB was due to formation of such a product at the binding site, inhibition would be noncompetitive. Lineweaver-Burk analysis showed that the inhibition by pHMB was competitive and thus is not likely to be mediated by reactivity with sulfhydryl groups [10]. Finally, evidence against the involvement of sulfhydryl groups in the inhibition of steroid binding by metals comes from the relative inhibitory activity of the metals. Mercuric ion inhibits [^{3}H]-DHT binding with about the same activity as Zn^{2+}, Cu^{2+}, and Cd^{2+} (Table IV). Kontula et al [12] also found that Hg^{2+} exhibited inhibitory effects comparable to those of Cu^{2+} and Zn^{2+}. Yet the stability constants for mercuric-sulfhydryl binding are as much as 10^{10} times higher than the constants for Zn^{2+} or Cd^{2+} and sulfhydryls [29]. Similarly, Pb^{2+} complexes with sulfhydryls are much more stable than Cu^{2+} and Pb^{2+}, but all three metals are almost equal as inhibitors of binding (Table IV).

The large increase in nonspecific steroid binding resulting from the presence of Cu^{2+} might be due to conformational changes induced in some protein by the cation (Fig. 4). Such conformational changes might create new steroid binding sites on the protein surface. Extensive conformational changes have been detected in several purified proteins as a result of exposure to Cu^{2+} and other ions [33].

Wallace and Grant [26] proposed a model wherein zinc acts as a feedback inhibitor of androgen action in the prostate and they showed that zinc was a competitive inhibitor of 5α-reductase. The present study indicates another site at which zinc might function in their model, namely, the steroid-receptor interaction. Inhibition of this interaction could effectively block androgenic action and result in inhibition of secretion and cellular growth of the prostate. This mechanism might also account, in part, for the reduction in prostate size observed by Saksena et al [5] in response to administration of Cd^{2+} in vivo.

Perhaps endogenous zinc might function in a feedback loop in the prostate. Measurement of prostatic zinc content in several species average approximately 7 mmole/gm dry weight [1,3,32,33]. Assuming that tissue water is 80% and that the zinc is all free and dissolved evenly throughout the tissue water, the concentration of zinc is 1.75 mM. Thus, if as little as 1% of the tissue Zn^{2+} is free, the IC_{50}, 2×10^{-5}M, is achieved. Further, if the Zn^{2+} tends to be sequestered in the same water compartment as the receptor, this concentration can be achieved by an even smaller free/bound fraction.

Other proteins have been associated with prostate gland zinc. Early studies by Gunn et al [34] examined electrophoretic patterns using Zn^{65} and reported that the rat ventral prostatic lobe contained a single zinc-protein component while the dorsal prostatic lobe contained at least three zinc fractions. The lateral prostatic lobe secretion contained 4–5 zinc-binding proteins. The major zinc fraction in the rat lateral prostatic secretion did not appear to represent free zinc [34]. Johnson et al [35] described a zinc-associated polypeptide in the prostatic secretions of dogs. In the present studies, cadmium was used to induce prostatic metallothionein. Expectedly, cadmium caused a characteristic hepatic profile for metallothionein. Of greater interest, however, was the detection of metallothionein in the rat dorsolateral lobe of the prostate, but not in the ventral lobe. It is of related interest that cadmium can block the excretion of copper into the bile leading to an accumulation of copper in the rat liver, which in turn stimulates the synthesis of ceruloplasmin. Whether cadmium is responsible for the synthesis of prostatic metallothionein has not been entirely established from the present studies, but certainly cadmium-induced metallothionein occurs in other organs. Neither testosterone nor methyltestosterone can affect zinc accumulation in rat liver cells [25], but glucocorticoids can profoundly affect hepatic metallothionein [cf, 39]. There appear to be several unresolved questions with regard to the role of zinc and its association with androphilic and non-androphilic proteins in the rodent prostate. Only further investigations will unravel some of the complexities of sex accessory organ trace metal constituents and to what extent these divalent ions affect the glands physiology or pathology.

REFERENCES

1. Mawson CA Fischer MI: Zinc content of the genital organs of the rat. Nature 167:859, 1951.
2. Millar MJ, Fischer MI, Elcoate PV, Mawson CA: The effects of dietary zinc deficiency on the reproductive system of male rats. Can J Biochem Physiol 36:557–569, 1958.
3. Mackenzie AR, Hall T, Lo MC, Whitmore WF JR: Influence of castration and sex hormones on size histology and zinc content of canine prostate. J Urol 89:864–874, 1963.
4. Gunn SA Gould TC: The presence of an inherent reproductive cycle in the male laboratory rat. J Endocrinol 17:344–348, 1958.
5. Saksena SD, Dahlgren L, Lau IF, Chang MC: Reproductive and endocrinological features of male rats after treatment with cadmium chloride. Biol Reprod 16:609–613, 1977.
6. Oster G Salgo MP: Copper in mammalian reproduction. Adv Pharmacol Chemother 14:327–409, 1977.
7. Gyorkey F, Min KW, Huff JA, Gyorkey P: Zinc and magnesium in human prostate gland:Normal, hyperplasic and neoplastic. Cancer Res 27:1348–1353, 1967.
8. Bell JU, Thomas JA: Effects of lead on mammalian reproduction. In Singhal RL, Thomas JA (eds): "Lead Toxicity." Urban and Schwarzenberg Medical Publishers, 1980, Baltimore: pp 169–185.
9. Gunn SA, Gould TC: Cadmium and other minerals. In Johnson AD, Gomes WR, Vandemark NL (eds): "The Testis III." New York: Academic Press, Chap 10, 1970, pp 377–481.
10. Donovan MP, Schein LG, Thomas JA: Inhibition of androgen-receptor interaction in mouse prostate gland cytosol by divalent metal ions. Mol Pharmacol 17:156–162, 1980.
11. Young PCM, Cleary RE, Ragan WD: Effect of metal ions on the binding of 17β-estradiol to human endometrial cytosol. Fertil Steril 28:459–463, 1977.
12. Kontula K, Janne O, Luukkainen T, Vihko R: Progesterone-binding protein in human myometrium. Influence of metal ions on binding. J Clin Endo Metab 38:500–503, 1974.
13. Schein LG, Donovan MP, Thomas JA: Characterization of cytoplasmic binding of dihydroteststerone by the prostate gland, seminal vesicles, kidney and liver of the mouse. Toxicol Appl Pharmacol 44:147–153, 1978.
14. Binoux MA, Odell WD: Use of dextran-coated charcoal to separate antibody-bound from free hormone:A critique. J Clin Endocrinol Metab 36:303–310, 1973.
15. Robinette L, Mawhinney MG: The influence of aging on androgen dynamics in the male rat. Arch Biochem Biophys 191:503–516, 1979.
16. Probst GS, Bousquet WF, Miya TS: Correlation of hepatic metallothionein concentration with acute cadmium toxicity in the mouse. Toxicol Appl Pharmacol 39:61–70, 1970.
17. Bell JU: A metallothionein-like protein in the hepatic cytosol of the term rat fetus. Toxicol Appl Pharmacol 48:139–144, 1979.

18. Waalkes MP, Bell JU: Isolation and partial characterization of native metallothionein in fetal rabbit liver. Life Sci 27:585–593, 1980.
19. Lowry OH, Rosebrough NJ, Farr AL, Randall RJ: Protein measurement with the Folin phenol reagent. J Biol Chem 193:265–276, 1951.
20. Gunn SA, Gould TC: Difference between dorsal and lateral components of dorsolateral prostate in Zn^{65} uptake. Proc Soc Exp Biol (NY) 92:17–20, 1956.
21. Timms BG, Chandler JA, Morton MS, Groom GV: The effect of cadmium administration in vivo on plasma testosterone and the ultrastructure of rat lateral prostate. Virchows Arch Abl B Zellpathol 25:33–52, 1977.
22. Jafa A, Mahendra NM, Chowdhury AR, Kamboj VP: Trace elements in prostatic tissue and plasma in prostatic diseases of man. Ind J Canc 17:34–37, 1980.
23. Emanuel MB, Oakey RE: Effect of Zn^{65} on the binding of oestradiol-17β to a uterine protein. Nature 223:66–67, 1969.
24. Sanborn BM, Rao BR, Korenman SG: Interaction of 17-estradiol and its specific uterine receptor. Evidence for complex kinetic and equilibrium behavior. Biochemistry 10:4955–4961, 1971.
25. Failla ML, Cousins RJ: Zinc accumulation and metabolism in primary cultures of adult rat liver cells. Biochem Biophys Acta 543:293–304, 1978.
26. Wallace AM, Grant JK: Effect of zinc on androgen metabolism in the human hyperplastic prostate. Biochem Soc Trans 3:540–542, 1975.
27. Katz S, Donovan MP, Roberson LC: Structure-volume relationships. Volume effects produced by copper (II) complexing with organic acids. J Phys Chem 79:1930–1934, 1975.
28. Peters T Jr, Blumenstock FA: Copper-binding properties of bovine serum albumin and its amino-terminal peptide fragment. J Biol Chem 242:1574–1578, 1967.
29. Friedman M: The Chemistry and Biochemistry of the Sulfhydryl Group in Amino Acids, Peptides and Proteins. New York: Pergamon, 1973.
30. Hellerman L, Chinard FP, Deitz VR: Protein sulfhydryl groups and the reversible inactivation of the enzyme urease. J Biol Chem 147:443–462, 1943.
31. Katz S, Roberson LC: Protein-metal ion interaction:Volume effects produced by the interaction of proteins with metal ions. Bioinorg Chem 6:143–154, 1976.
32. Moger WH, Geschwind II: The action of prolactin on the sex accessory glands of the male rat. Proc Soc Exp Biol Med 141:1017–1021, 1972.
33. Habib FK, Hammond GL, Lee IR, Dawson JB, Mason MK, Smith PH, Stitch SR: Metal-androgen interrelationships in carcinoma and hyperplasia of the human prostate. J Endocrinol 71:133–141, 1976.
34. Gunn SA, Gould TC, Anderson WAD: Comparison of protein and zinc electrophoretic patterns of lobes of rat prostate. Proc Soc Exp Biol Med 110:32–36, 1962.
35. Johnson L Wikström S, Nylander G: The vehicle for zinc in the prostatic secretion of dogs. Scand J Urol Nephrol 3:9–11, 1969.
36. Brady FO, Bunger PC: The effect of adrenalectomy on zinc thionein levels in rat liver. Biochem Biophys Res Commun 91:911–918, 1979.

The Prostatic Cell: Structure and Function
Part A, pages 475–490

Prostate Development in Zinc-Deficient Rats

J.A. Chandler, B.G. Timms, and S. Battersby

Although the prostate has for a long time been known to accumulate high levels of zinc, the role of this metal in the gland remains uncertain. It has been considered important in reproduction as an essential component of semen [1] and is known to affect sperm cell motility [2,3]. Within the prostate zinc is considered to have a protective effect against bacterial prostatitis [4].

Interest in the possible role of the metal arises from observations that concentrations of zinc vary in human benign hyperplasia and in carcinoma of the prostate [5–7]. This paper describes a study in the rat prostate to determine whether high levels of zinc play an important role in the growth and development of the gland.

MATERIALS AND METHODS

Animals and Diet

Weanling rats (4 weeks old) bred from the Tenovus Institute Sprague Dawley colony were separated into three groups. The first group was fed a normal diet of purina chow (Pilsbury, UK) containing 10 ppm zinc and tap water ad libitum. The second group was given a glucose-based diet ad libitum containing only 0.5 ppm zinc together with deionized water (0.01 ppm zinc). The third group was pair fed to the same daily food weight as the zinc-deficient animals and with the same diet but with zinc added to the level of 40 ppm. They were also given deionized water. The zinc-deficient diet was composed of 66% sucrose; 20% dried egg albumen; 10% arachis oil; 2.5% inorganic salts and trace elements; 0.2% vitamins, and was prepared by the Rowatt Research Institute, Aberdeen.

The animals were kept in barrier-maintained conditions in stainless steel cages without sawdust or other litter. Every effort was made to avoid contamination of the environment with zinc.

In the second, zinc-deficient group some animals were given intraperitoneal injections of testosterone propionate 31 days after commencing the diet and on alternate days for a total of ten days until termination of the experiment. The testosterone propionate was made up in sesame oil and administered at levels of 0.1 mg in 0.2 ml per 100 gm body weight. Altogether the experiment ran for 40 days so that the animals were 66 days old at termination.

Histology and Electron Microscopy

The rats were killed by ether asphyxiation, the abdominal cavity opened, and the testes and accessory sex glands carefully removed. Great care was taken to identify the extremely small prostate glands in the zinc-deficient animals. The tissues were placed in 3% glutaraldehyde fixative in 0.1 M Sorensen's phosphate buffer at pH 7.4 and fixed for 3 hours. They were then washed in buffer, post fixed for 1 hour in 1.0% osmium tetroxide (Millonig's), rinsed again in buffer, dehydrated in ascending grades of alcohol, infiltrated with propylene oxide, and embedded in Araldite. Sections of 1-μm thickness were cut on an LKB III ultramicrotome, slide mounted, and stained with toluidine blue for histological assessment. Ultrathin sections (70 nm) were mounted on copper grids and examined in the EMMA-4 electron microscope (Kratos, UK).

X-ray Microanalysis

The zinc content of whole tissue was measured by x-ray microanalysis for the different groups of animals. Fresh untreated tissue taken from the animals was immediately pressed between glass slides and allowed to dry for 30 minutes. The flat tissue pieces were mounted in a grid-specimen holder and transferred to the EMMA-4 microscope for complete elemental analysis.

The subcellular distribution of zinc in prostatic tissue was performed on tissues specially prepared for analysis.

The prostate glands were removed from the animals as above and fixed in a solution of 1% osmium tetroxide containing 2% potassium pyroantimonate for 1 hour at pH 8.0. This fixative precipitated unbound zinc in situ and allowed retention of bound zinc within the subcellular locations ready for analysis. Dehydration and embedment was as described above. Sections (100 nm) were cut and mounted on aluminium grids and carbon coated for analysis.

Elemental analysis of plasma was prepared by allowing 100-μl droplets to dry onto pure carbon supporting discs which were then placed in the specimen holder and transferred to the microscope. Microprobe analysis was performed on the opaque samples in several different areas for Na, Mg, P, S, Cl, K, Ca, and Zn.

X-ray microanalysis was performed on both whole tissue and ultrathin sections using the electron microscope microanalyser EMMA-4 as described elsewhere [8]. Spatial resolution of analysis in thin sections was 0.1 μm such that individual organelles could be readily analysed for all elements quantitatively and in a matter of seconds. Analytical conditions for thin sections were 80 kV accelerating voltage and 0.05 μA probe current. For whole tissue and plasma analysis the electron energy was 40 kV and the current 0.01 μA. Quantitation was performed by comparison with resin standards [9], the minimum detectable limit being 10^{-19} gm for zinc.

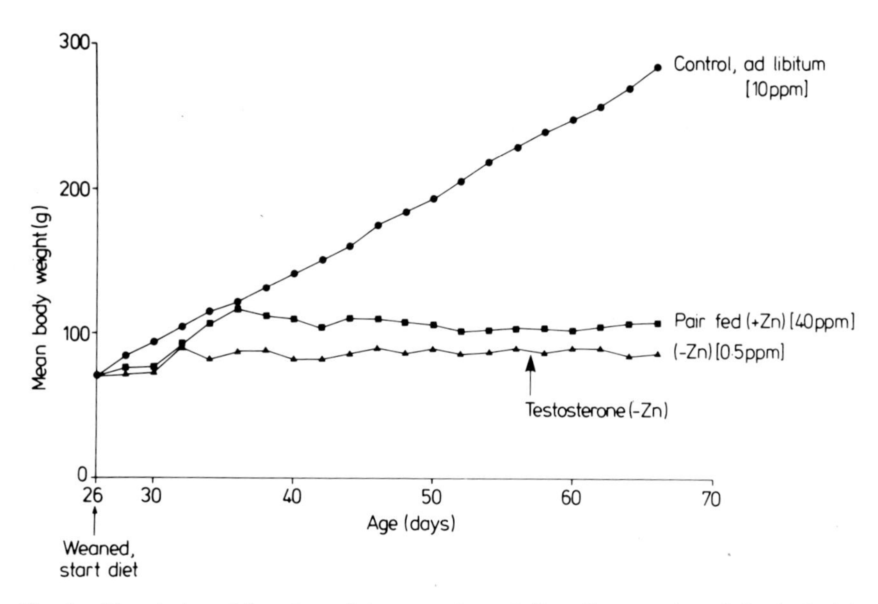

Fig. 1. Mean body weights of rats fed on experimental diets. Concentration of zinc in food is shown on each curve. The pair-fed rats were given the same weight as the zinc-deficient rats had eaten the previous day. Some of the zinc-deficient rats were injected with testosterone for the final 10 days of the experiment.

Plasma Testosterone

Circulating levels of testosterone (bound and free) were determined by radioimmunoassay using methods developed in the steroid laboratories of the Tenovus Institute. For these assays the animals were bled under light ether anaesthesia before termination. All animals were sacrificed during late morning.

RESULTS

Body Weight

The mean growth rate of each group of animals is shown in Figure 1. The control ad libitum fed animals (10 ppm zinc) increased in weight steadily throughout the experiment. The zinc deficient animals, however, suffered from inappetence and increased by only 10 gm in the first 6 days, thereafter maintaining a steady weight. The experiment was terminated when the animals became moribund, having a number of nonhealing sores on the limbs and head and loss of fur across the body.

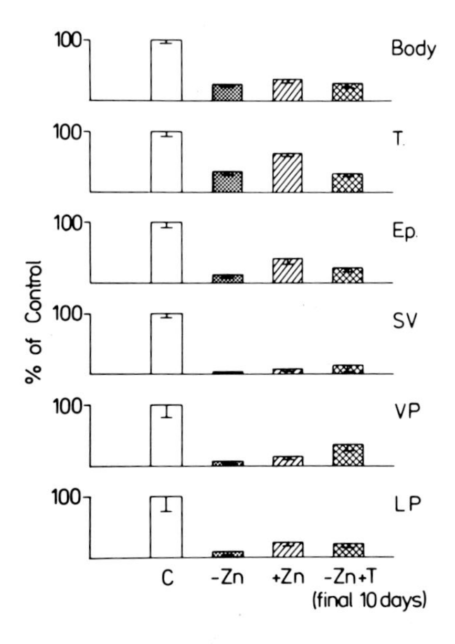

Fig. 2. Tissue weights of rats at the end of the experimental diets. C, control; –Zn, zinc deficient; + Zn, pair fed; (– Zn + T), zinc deficient with androgen supplementation. Bars represent 1 SD of mean and all weights are expressed as a percentage of the controls. T, testes; Ep, epididymis; SV, seminal vesicles; VP, ventral prostate; LP, lateral prostate.

The third group, pair fed with 40 ppm zinc added, also increased in weight but only until the tenth day, after which their weights remained constant and just 10% greater than the zinc-deficient animals. They were, however, quite healthy, lively, and without the moribund features of the previous group.

The administration of testosterone to the zinc-deficient animals for the final 10 days of the experiment did not alter the mean body weight, neither did the animals appear to recover in health after this time.

Tissue Weights

The weights of body, testes, and accessory sex organs are shown in Figure 2 for the four groups. All weights were reduced in all three experimental groups compared with controls, the most significant reductions being in the seminal vesicles, lateral and ventral prostates. Pair-fed, zinc-supplemented animals suffered less retardation in growth, especially in the testes and epididymis, but the seminal vesicles and prostate lobes were all still very much reduced. The administration of testosterone to the zinc-deficient animals caused a significant increase in the weights of lateral and ventral prostate and seminal vesicles while the total weight of the testes appeared unchanged.

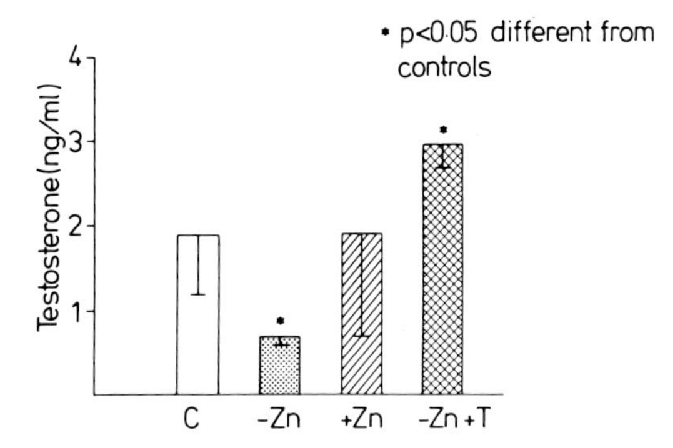

Fig. 3. Plasma testosterone levels in rats at the end of the experimental diets. Notations as in Figure 2.

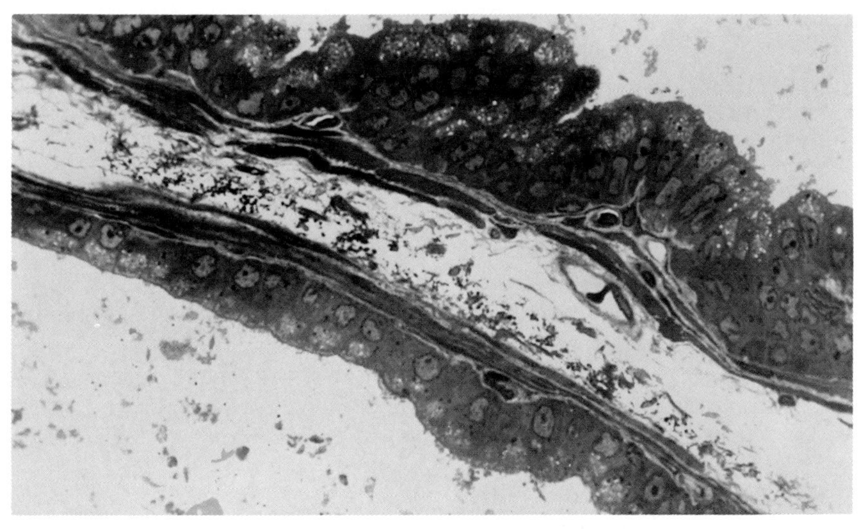

Fig. 4. Semi-thin resin section of control lateral prostate showing well formed epithelium with cuboidal shape, clear Golgi apparatus, surrounded by layers of smooth muscle.

Testosterone Levels

The levels of circulating testosterone are shown in Figure 3. Zinc-deficient animals had levels which were less than 50% of controls, while pair-fed, zinc-supplemented animals had similar testosterone values to the control animals. In these zinc deficient rats administered with testosterone propionate the levels were 50% higher than control values.

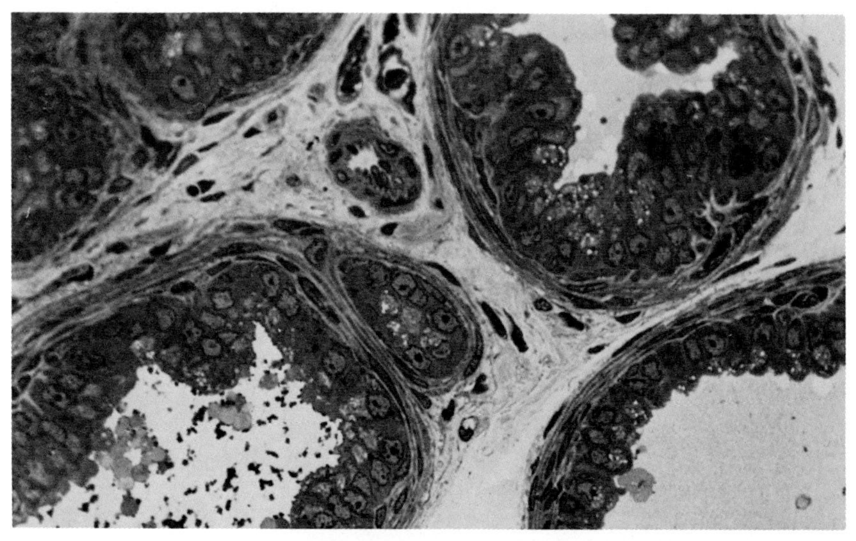

Fig. 5. Semi-thin sections of zinc deficient lateral prostate indicating partly differentiated epithelium in smaller acini than in controls but with basal nuclei and cuboidal shape. Smooth muscle cells and stromal components are also well developed.

Testicular Spermatozoa

Despite the overall difference in testicular size, spermatozoa were seen to be present in the seminiferous tubules of all animal groups. In the zinc-deficient and pair-fed groups the tubules were half the size of the control group and had fewer sperm cells. The interstitial cells were also much less prominent in these groups.

Morphology and Ultrastructure of Lateral Prostate

The morphology of the lateral prostate for these four groups of animals is shown in Figures 4–7. Control prostates had large acini with well differentiated cuboidal epithelial cells surrounded by 3–4 layers of smooth muscle cells (Fig. 4). Zinc-deficient animals exhibited smaller acini with less well organized smooth muscle but having differentiated epithelium with secretory products and cell debris in the lumina (Fig. 5). The morphology of the pair-fed, zinc-supplemented rat prostates was virtually identical to the zinc-deficient animals (Fig. 6). Those animals given androgen supplementation showed larger acini with secretory epithelium and taller epithelial cells with well formed Golgi regions (Fig. 7), approaching that of control tissue (Fig. 4).

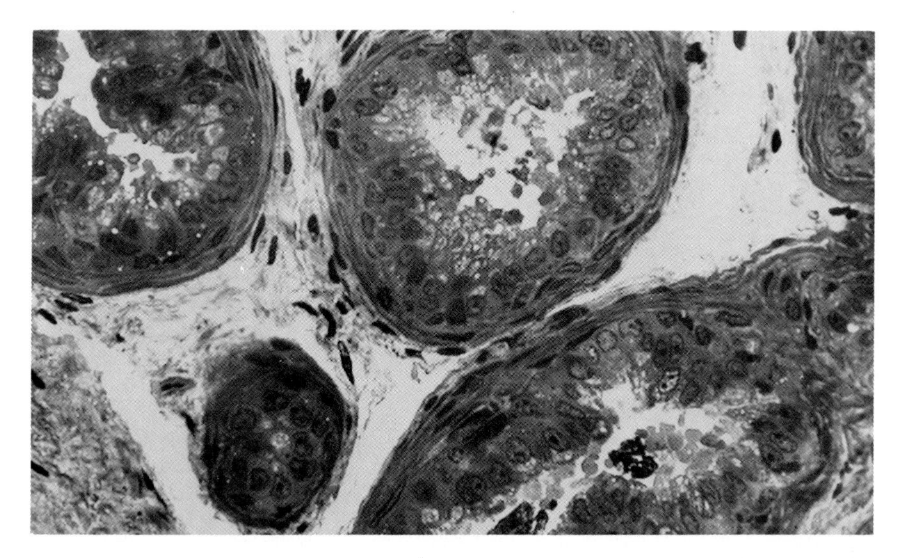

Fig. 6. Semi-thin section of pair-fed, zinc-supplemented rat lateral prostate having virtually identical features to zinc-deficient tissue. There was more cell debris in the lumina but differentiation was advanced.

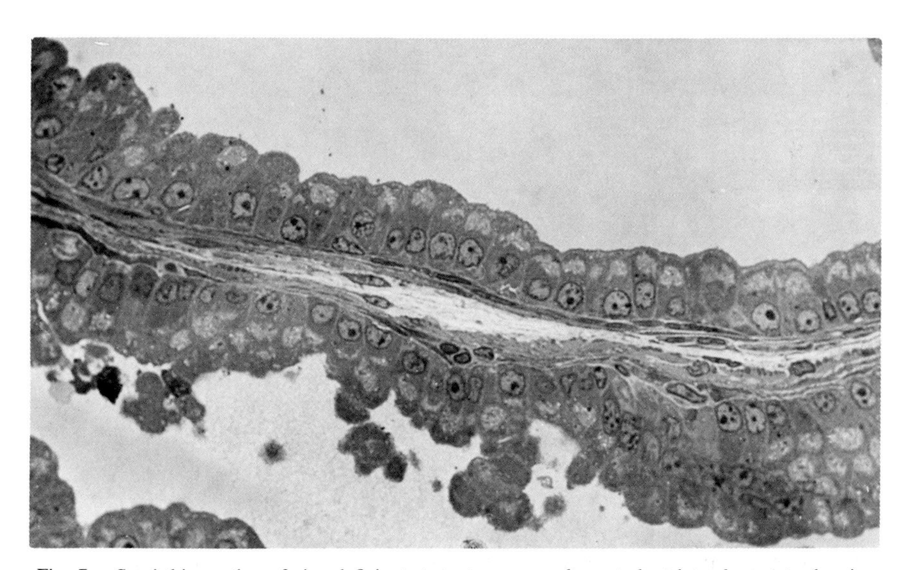

Fig. 7. Semi-thin section of zinc deficient, testosterone supplemented rat lateral prostate showing full differentiation of the epithelium. Cells appeared indistinguishable from controls and had well polarized, columnar cells with large Golgi apparatus and prominent nucleoli.

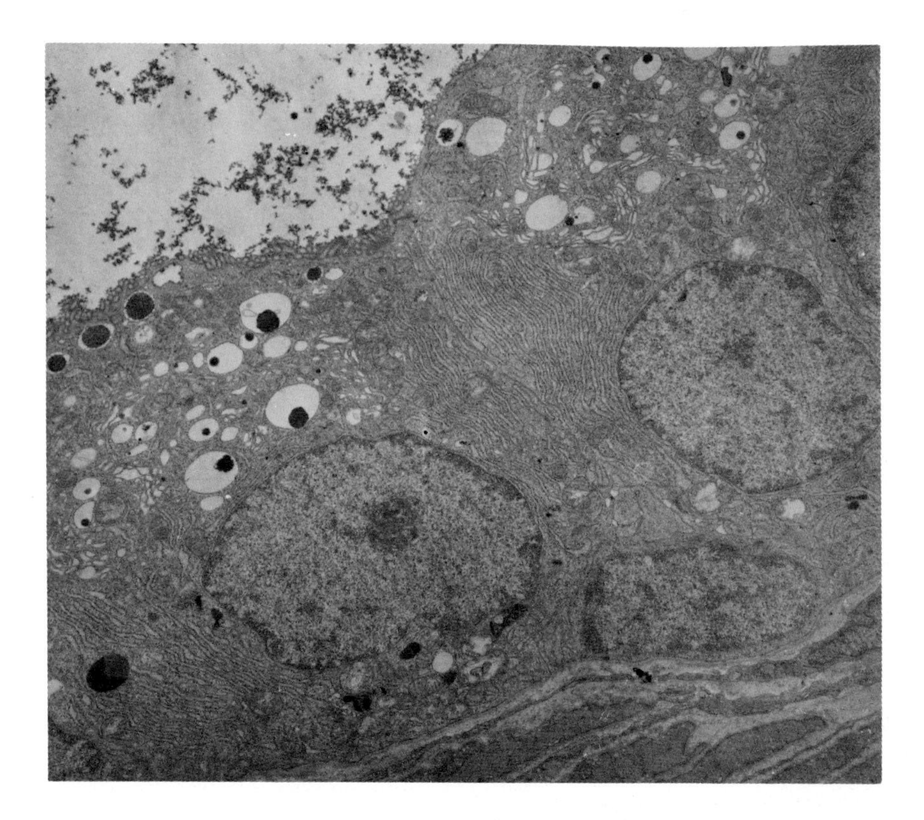

Fig. 8. Ultrastructure of control rat lateral prostate, characterized by large condensed secretory granules, plentiful rough endoplasmic reticulum, active Golgi apparatus, and rich apical microvilli.

At the ultrastructural level the epithelium of the control tissue was characterized by many apical secretory granules with extensive microvilli, and, typical of these protein-synthesizing cells, there was an active Golgi region with abundant endoplasmic reticulum (Fig. 8). The zinc-deficient rat prostate possessed partially differentiated epithelium with secretory and protein-synthesizing activity as in the controls but to a lesser extent (Fig. 9,10). The zinc-supplemented, pair-fed animals were similar in most respects to the zinc deficient animals in prostate ultrastructure.

In those animals, however, which had been administered testosterone for the final phase of their zinc deficient diet, the ultrastructure of the epithelial cells was indistinguishable from control tissue. Microvilli were well formed, the cells were replete with apical secretory granules, and protein synthesis was obviously very active. The cells appeared to be fully differentiated in every respect, and

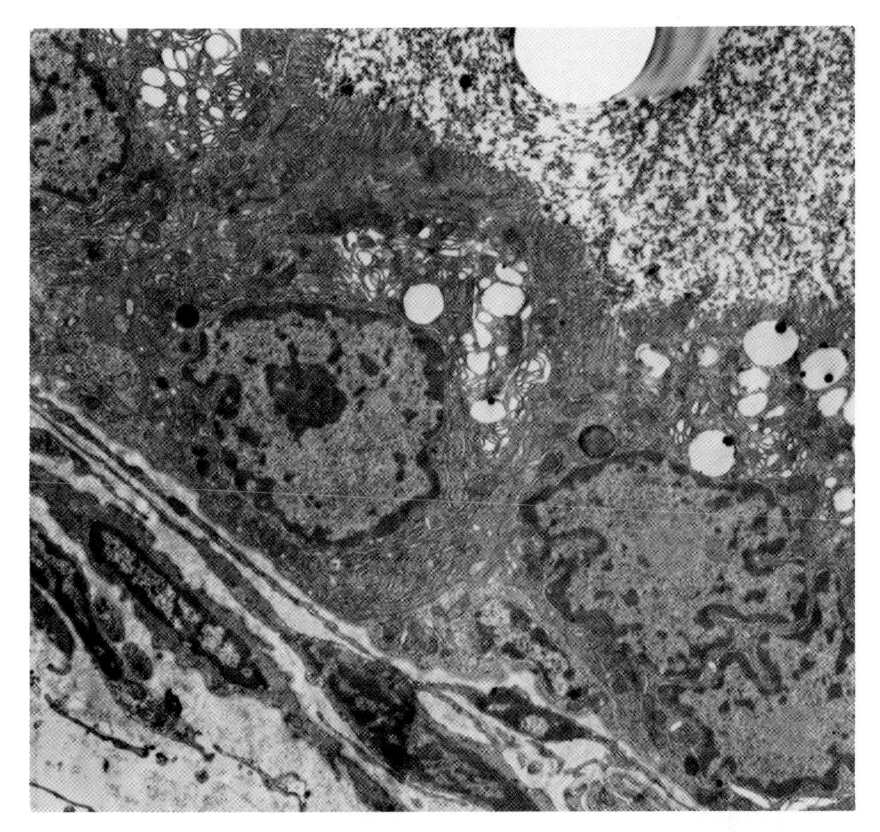

Fig. 9. Ultrastructure of lateral prostate from zinc-deficient rats. The cells are mostly differentiated with all the features of control tissue but with fewer secretory granules, less endoplasmic reticulum, and are shorter. Secretion is plentiful in the lumen.

secretion had increased even though the acini had not yet fully grown to the dimensions of control tissues (Fig. 11).

Zinc Analyses

Whole tissue was analyzed from the lateral prostates of all three groups for zinc content (Fig. 12). In both the zinc-deficient animals and the pair-fed animals, the levels of the metal were less than 1% of control values.

Analysis of plasma for eight elements is shown in Figure 13. While no difference was seen in levels of Na, Mg, P, S, Cl, K, or Ca, the values for Zn in the zinc-deficient and pair-fed zinc supplemented animals was significantly below the levels of control animals.

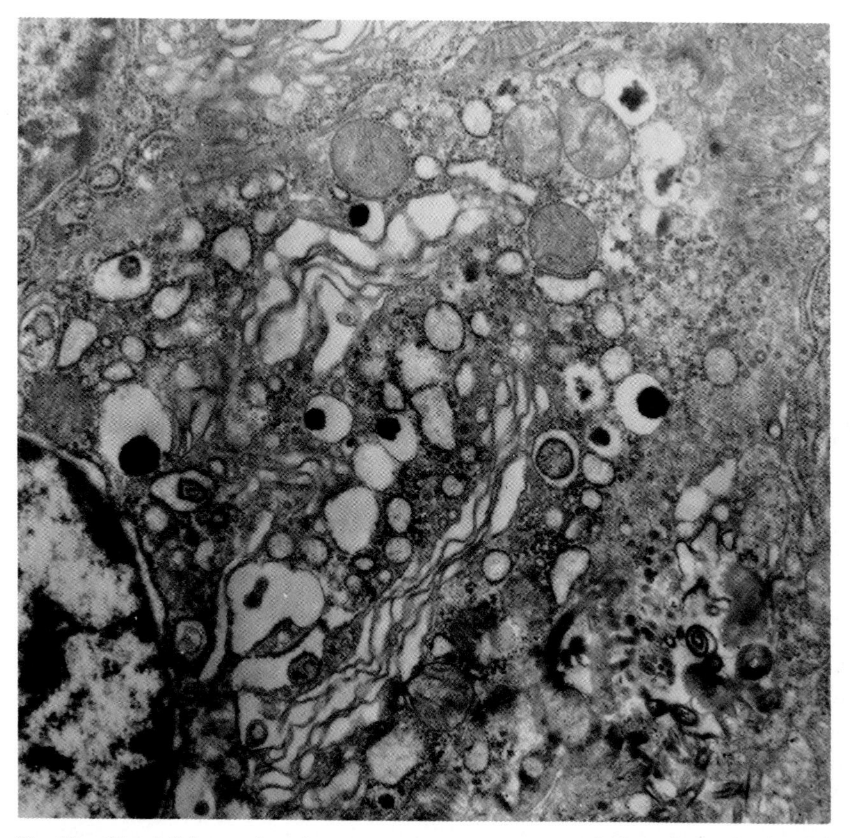

Fig. 10. Zinc-deficient rat lateral prostate showing secretory granule formation and active Golgi apparatus.

Thin sections of the lateral prostate were analyzed in the electron microscope for zinc content of subcellular organelles in the epithelial cells (Fig. 14). Large concentrations (approximately 1% wet weight) were found in the nucleoli, nuclear chromatin, general cytoplasm, and secretory granules of these cells as observed in previous experiments (10). In all other groups, however, zinc could not be detected in any subcellular region except in the nucleoli, the latter concentrations being less than 10% of those seen in control animals.

DISCUSSION

The high concentration of zinc in the mammalian prostate has been the subject of much investigation over the last 10 years. The relationship between tissue

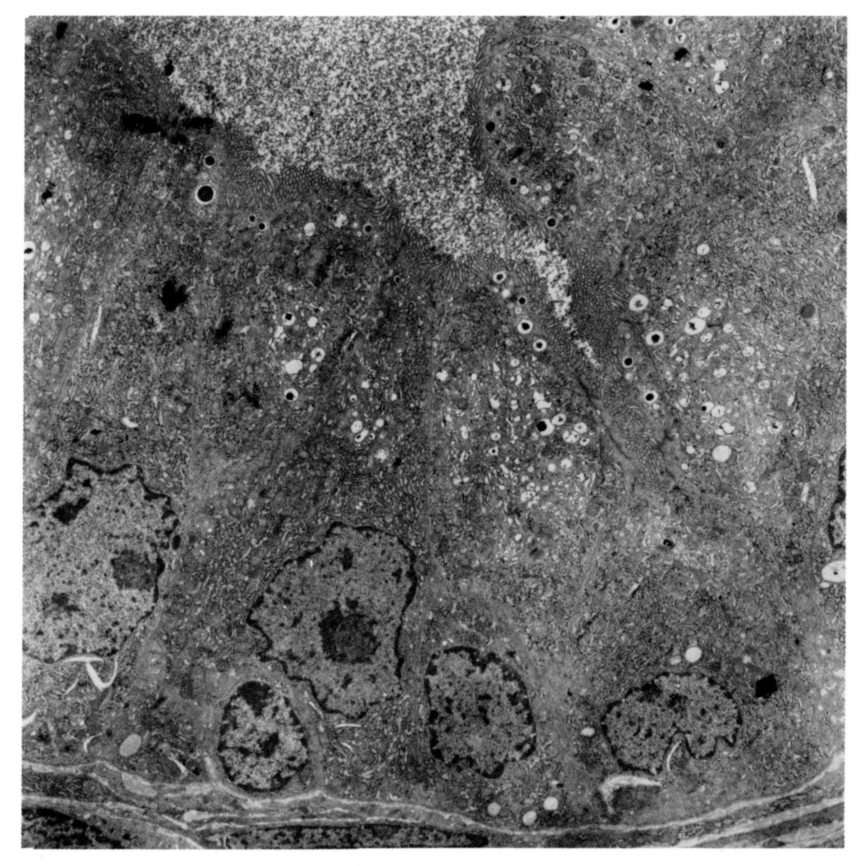

Fig. 11. Zinc-deficient, androgen-maintained rat lateral prostate showing increase in cell height and development of all features of differentiation to become very similar to control tissue.

content of this metal and endocrine status is widely documented but its relationship to prostatic disease remains uncertain [11,12]. Whereas a number of possible roles for the metal in the prostate gland have been postulated, it seems likely that at such high concentrations it can form little else than a transient component of the secretion. In this respect it probably fulfills the role of an antibacterial agent as proposed by Fair et al [4] and may contribute to the regulation of sperm cell viability during ejaculation [13,14].

The studies presented here have shown that high levels of zinc as found in the prostate of normal untreated rats are not necessary for the development of prostatic architecture or epithelial cell differentiation. The lack of growth of the prostate in zinc-deficient rats is due to both inappetance leading to anophagia

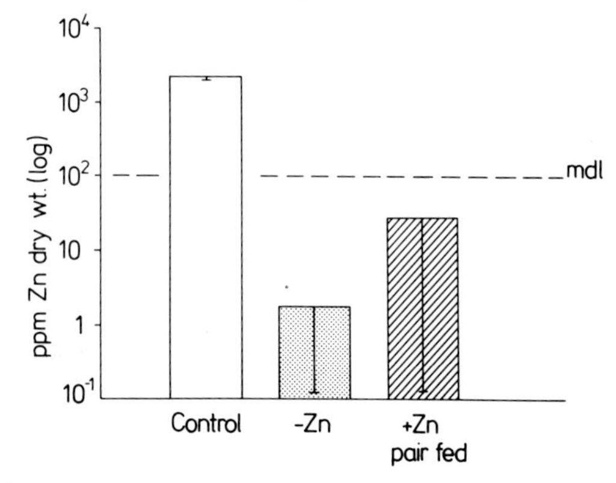

Fig. 12. Whole tissue lateral prostate analysis of zinc by x-ray microanalysis. Concentrations in the zinc-deficient animals were less than 0.1% of control values. mdl, minimum detectable limit.

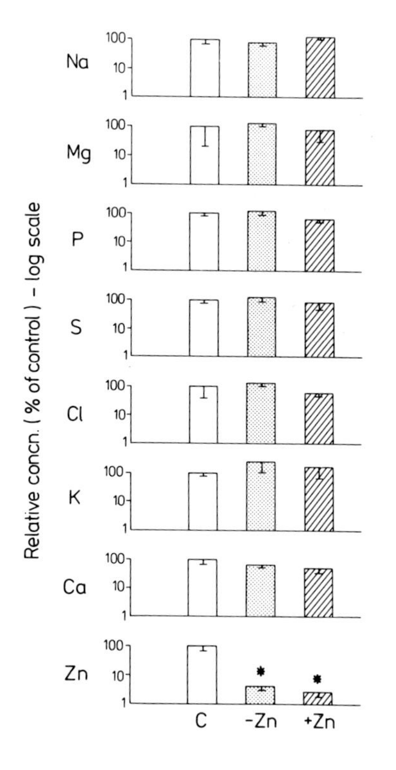

Fig. 13. Elemental concentrations in plasma as determined by x-ray microanalysis. Only zinc concentrations were found to be reduced in both the zinc-deficient and zinc-supplemented, pair-fed groups.

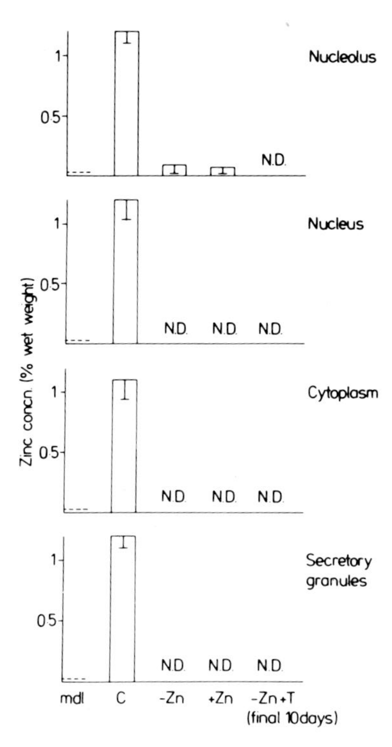

Fig. 14. Subcellular distribution of zinc in epithelial cells of the lateral prostate by x-ray microanalysis. In the experimental groups zinc was detectable only in the nucleoli and then at less than 10% of control values. mdl, minimum detectable limit.

[15] and to reduced androgen synthesis by the testes [16]. This is clear from the similar prostatic development shown in rats given the same weight of food but with zinc supplementation. Provided androgen levels are maintained at those of normal, well-fed rats, the prostate cells fully develop and differentiate to show all the characteristics of protein synthesis and secretion. Whether the secretory products, apart from zinc content, are identical to those of control prostate glands [17] has not been determined. The fertility of these zinc-deficient animals was also not examined but it was seen that sperm cells were formed within the tubules of the testes.

The low levels of zinc found within the nucleoli of zinc-deficient animals were not surprising. Many of the DNA and RNA polymerases, together with thymidine kinase, are zinc-dependent enzymes [18]. It has been shown by a number of workers that zinc deficiency may inhibit DNA synthesis, stop cell division, and block cells at different points in the cell cycle [19–21]. Without any zinc at all in the diet the animals would not survive. While the zinc-deficient group was seen to be suffering from a failure to wound heal, there was a sufficient quantity of the metal in the diet, or accumulated prior to weaning, to service the requirements of subcellular enzymes within individual tissues.

If the elevated concentrations of zinc in the prostate are transient and serve only as a secretory product they may well also provide a protective mechanism against other heavy metals such as cadmium or nickel [22,23]. How the metal is bound in the tissue is not fully clear [7,24,25], but much of it appears to be freely available for histochemical precipitation outside of the epithelial cells in the subepithelial stroma while that in the nucleus appears tightly bound [10,26]. Differences in concentrations of zinc between various pathological and endocrine conditions of the prostate gland may well be explained by this readily displaced, loosely bound zinc fraction. The elevated or normal levels seen in benign human prostatic hyperplasia could be due to the still secretory nature of the epithelium, while the reduced levels seen in carcinoma of the gland may be due to the nondifferentiated, nonsecretory nature of many solid tumors.

If zinc concentrations are a result of prostate pathogenesis rather than a precursor to it, then there appears to be little value in using zinc manipulation as an aid to therapy. There may, however, be some value in using zinc analysis of prostatic tissue, prostatic fluid, or even of semen as an indicator of prostatic disease or of prostatic response to androgens [27].

CONCLUSION

The elevated levels of zinc found in the rat prostate are not required for the growth and development of the gland. Provided the testes synthesize androgen to normal levels, prostatic epithelium is seen to mature and differentiate in the absence of high zinc concentrations. The metal is detected only in the nucleolus of these cells where it would appear to form a necessary function in DNA and RNA synthesis. It is concluded that while zinc uptake is under the influence of hormones, the metal probably functions mainly as a secretory product within the gland.

ACKNOWLEDGMENTS

The authors are grateful to the Tenovus Organisation for generous financial assistance. We are indebted to Mr. Brian Brownsey for help with radioimmunoassay of plasma steroids and to Mr. Doug Mulcuck for expert care of the animals. The diets used in these investigations were kindly supplied by Dr. N. Johnson and Dr. C.F. Mills of the Rowatt Research Institute, Aberdeen, to whom we also owe thanks for much useful communication.

REFERENCES

1. Bertrand G, Vladesco R: Intervention probable du zinc dans les phénomènes de fécondation ches les animaux vertébrés. CR Acad Sci (Paris) 173: 176–179, 1921.
2. Saito S, Bush IM, Whitmore WF: Effects of certain metals and chelating agents on rat and dog epididymal spermatozoan motility. Fertil Steril 18: 517–529, 1967.
3. Lindholmer C: Toxicity of zinc ions to human spermatozoa and the influence of albumen. Andrologia 6: 7–19, 1974.
4. Fair WR, Couch J, Wehner N: Prostatic antibacterial factor. Identity and significance. Urology 7: 169–180, 1976.
5. Gyorkey F, Min KW, Huff JA, Gyorkey P: Zinc and magnesium in human prostate glands: Normal, hyperplastic and neoplastic. Cancer Res 27: 1348–1353, 1967.
6. Schrodt GR, Hall T, Whitmore WF: The concentration of zinc in diseased human prostate glands. Cancer 17: 1555–1566, 1964.
7. Habib FK, Stitch SR: The interrelationship of the metal and androgen binding proteins in normal and cancerous human prostate tissues. Acta Endocrinol 199: 129, 1975.
8. Chandler JA: "X-ray Microanalysis in the Electron Microscope." North Holland Pub. Co., 1977.
9. Chandler JA: A method of preparing absolute standards for quantitative calibration and measurement of section thickness with X-ray microanalysis of biological ultrathin specimens in EMMA. J Microsc 106: 291–302, 1976.
10. Chandler JA, Timms BG, Morton MS: Subcellular distribution of zinc in rat prostate studied by X-ray microanalysis. I. Normal prostate. Hist. J 9: 103–120, 1977.
11. Byar D: Zinc in male accessory sex organs: distribution and hormonal response. In Brandes D (ed): "Male Accessory Sex Organs." New York: Academic Press, 1974, pp 161–171.
12. Habib FK, Hammond GL, Lee IR, Dawson JB, Mason MK, Smith PH, Stitch SR: Metal-androgen interrelationships in carcinoma and hyperplasia of the human prostate. J Endocrinol 71: 133–141, 1976.
13. Eliasson L, Johnson D, Lindholmer C: Effect of zinc on human sperm respiration. Life Sci 10: 1317–1324, 1971.
14. Stankova L, Drach GW, Hicks T, Zukoski CF, Chvapil M: Regulation of some functions of granulocytes by zinc of the prostatic fluid and prostate tissue. J Lab Clin Med 88: 640–648, 1976.
15. Williams RB, Mills CF: The experimental production of zinc deficiency in the rat. Br J Nutr 24: 989–1003, 1970.
16. Hartoma R: Serum testosterone compared with serum zinc in man. Acta Physiol Scand 101: 336–341, 1977.
17. Spring Mills M, Hafez, ESE: The prostate. In Spring Mills E, Hafez ESE (eds): "Male Accessory Sex Glands." North Holland: Elsevier, 1980, pp 79–91.
18. Riordan JF: Biochemistry of zinc. Med Clin N Am 60: 661–674, 1976.
19. Vallee BL: Recent advances in zinc biochemistry. In Delphin D (ed): "Biological Aspects of Inorganic Chemistry." New York: John Wiley & Sons, 1977, pp 37–69.
20. Chesters JK: Biochemical functions of zinc with emphasis on nucleic acid metabolism and cell division. In Hoekstra WG (ed): "Trace Element Metabolism in Animals II." Baltimore: University Park Press, 1974.
21. Williams RB, Chesters JK: The effects of early zinc deficiency on DNA and protein synthesis in the rat. J Nutr 24: 1053–1059, 1970.
22. Timms BG, Chandler JA, Morton MS, Groom GV: The effect of cadmium adminstration in vivo on plasma testosterone and the ultrastructure of rat lateral prostate. Virch Arch B Cell Pathol 25: 33–52, 1977.

23. Chandler JA, Timms BG: The effect of testosterone and cadmium on the rat lateral prostate in organ culture. Virch Arch B Cell Pathol 25: 17–31, 1977.
24. Heathcote JG, Washington RJ: Analysis of the zinc binding protein derived from the human benign hypertrophic prostate. J Endocrinol 58:421–423, 1973.
25. Reed MJ, Stitch SR: The uptake of testosterone and zinc in vitro by the human benign hypertrophic prostate. J Endocrinol 58: 405–419, 1973.
26. Chandler JA, Sinowatz F, Timms BG, Pierrepoint CG: The subcellular distribution of zinc in dog prostate studied by X-ray microanalysis. Cell Tiss Res 185: 89–103, 1977.
27. Homonnai ZT, Matzkin H, Fainman N, Paz G, Kraicer PF: The cation composition of the seminal plasma and prostatic fluid and its correlation to semen quality. Fertil Steril 29: 539–542, 1978.

The Prostatic Cell: Structure and Function
Part A, pages 491-502

Human Malignancy-Associated Nucleolar Antigen (HuMANA) and Zinc in Human Prostatic Tissues

Ferenc Gyorkey

The antigenic differences between isolated nucleoli of malignant tumor cells and non-neoplastic cells [1,2] were followed by the discovery of a putative nucleolar antigen(s) in human malignant tumors which produced nucleolar-specific antibody in rabbits [3–6]. This prompted us to extend our investigation using an antigen from a human prostatic carcinoma cell line [7,8].

Inasmuch as optimal evaluation and diagnostic interpretation in surgical pathology require an integrated study of the tissues submitted for diagnosis, this investigation was designed to evaluate the immunofluorescent results in a combined histopathological and electron microscopic study on a large number of malignant and nonmalignant prostatic tissues. The antigen was also studied and demonstrated by immunoelectron microscopy. Positive nucleolar reaction in prostatic carcinomas was confirmed with this antisera. The antigen was not demonstrable in normal and hyperplastic prostate glands.

Zinc was studied in five cases of normal, hyperplastic, and carcinomatous tissues using light and electron microscopic procedures. Localization was cytoplasmic in the normal and hyperplastic cells and predominantly nucleolar in carcinoma cells. These findings are in agreement with our previous observations [9–12].

MATERIALS AND METHODS

Human prostatic adenocarcinoma verified histologically was grown in tissue culture at 37°C in Eagle's minimum essential medium. There was a multilayered pattern of epithelial cell growth throughout which is now at 66 passages. Chromosomal studies were performed on these cultures at four different time points. Prostatic acid phosphatase was positive by radioimmunoassay in the culture fluid. Samples were studied by electron microscopy and no viral, mycoplasm, or bacterial contamination was found.

Normal prostate cells were also cultured up to six passages, then the cells were preserved frozen and retrieved as needed to serve as control. The nucleoli of the carcinoma cell line were isolated after treatment with NP-40 [13] and purified as described [14]. Highly purified nucleoli were obtained and used as the specific antigenic material.

For the preparation of antisera, 1-year-old, healthy New Zealand white rabbits (male and female) were immunized by simultaneous subcutaneous, intramuscular, and intrapopliteal injections of the nucleolar preparation (10 mg/kg body wt) in Freund's adjuvant. Two booster injections (8 mg/kg body wt) were administered using the original antigen at 12- and 14-day intervals. At various time points, the antisera was tested by the indirect immunofluorescence method on fresh frozen 6 μ cryostat sections and smears, prefixed in absolute ethanol and/or absolute acetone. Routine light microscopic, indirect immunofluorescence, immunoelectron microscopic, and routine electron microscopic studies were carried out on biopsies of 48 cases of normal and hyperplastic human prostatic tissues and of 37 cases of malignant prostatic tumors (primary and metastatic). The established cell line of human prostatic carcinoma and the epithelial cell of a normal prostatic tissue were also studied.

Zinc study was performed in five cases of normal, hyperplastic, and carcinomatous prostatic tissues on fresh frozen cryostat sections using the dithizone and silver sulphide methods [15–17].

RESULTS

Electron microscopic study of prostatic adenocarcinoma showed pleomorphic tumor cells with large and compact nucleoli (Fig. 1). The tissue culture cells of this adenocarcinoma showed multiple large nucleoli, most being compact (Fig. 2). The isolated nucleoli used as the immunogen were pure and well preserved (Fig. 3). The antigen is a protein with an isoelectric point of 6.3 and molecular weight of approximately 54,000 [5].

Applying indirect immunofluorescence, the specific antisera produced bright nucleolar staining in the cryostat section of the original tumor (Fig. 4) and on the coverglass growth of cell culture (Fig. 5). The cryostat section of the hyperplastic prostate (Fig.6) and the coverglass growth of tissue culture of normal prostate epithelial cells (Fig. 7) were devoid of nucleolar staining.

Using the immunoperoxidase method [18] for the immunoelectron microscopic detection and localization of HuMANA, this sensitive method demonstrated the reaction product predominantly in the tumor cell nucleoli, in segregated nucleoli, and focally in the nucleoplasm (Fig. 8). Normal prostate tissue showed no reaction product by immunoelectron microscopy.

Zinc was positive in the cytoplasm of the normal (Fig. 9) and hyperplastic epithelial cells (Fig. 10). In carcinoma, the reaction was preferentially present

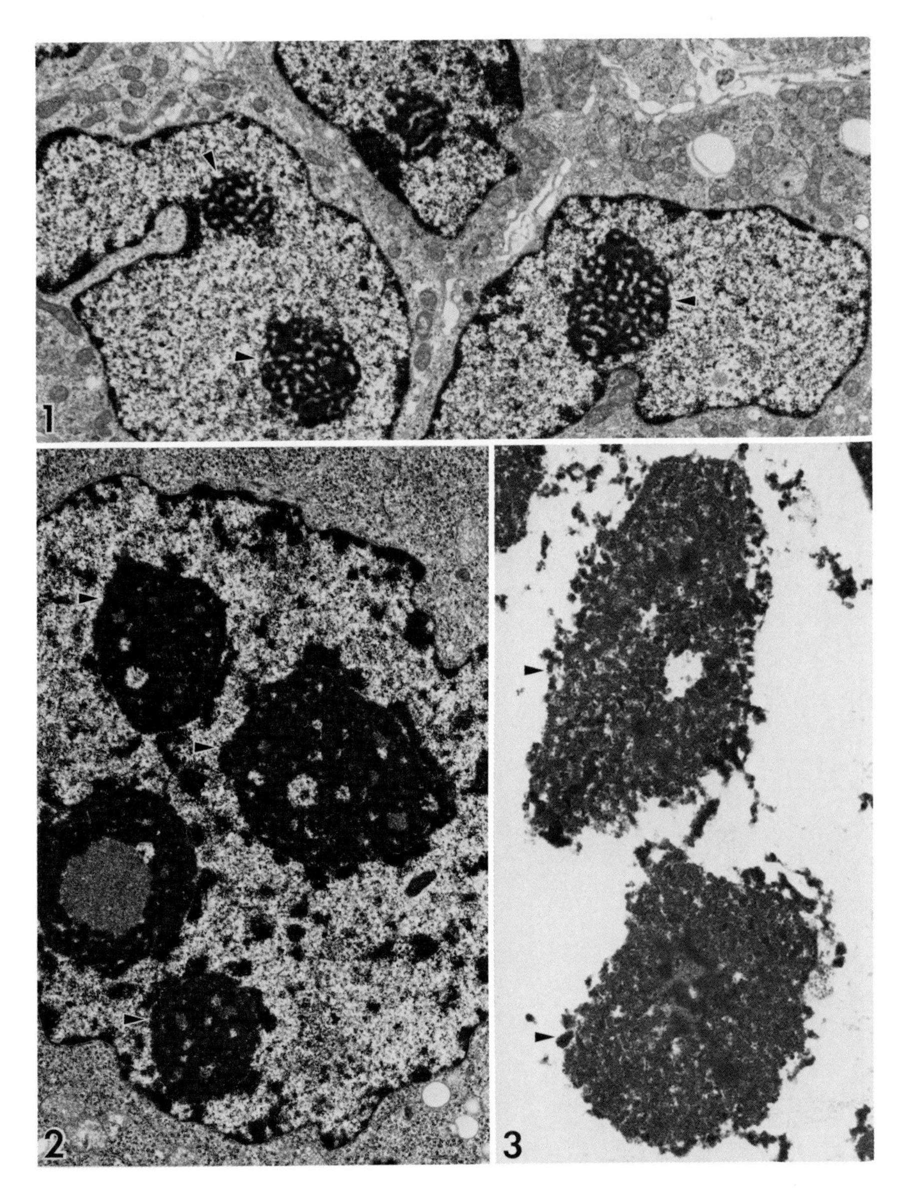

Fig. 1. Electron micrograph of the original prostate carcinoma. Pointers indicate nucleoli. × 8500.

Fig. 2. Electron micrograph of the tissue culture cells of the prostate carcinoma in passage 18. Pointers indicate nucleoli. × 8500.

Fig. 3. Electron micrograph of the isolated nucleoli (pointers) from the tissue culture cells (passage 18). × 27,000.

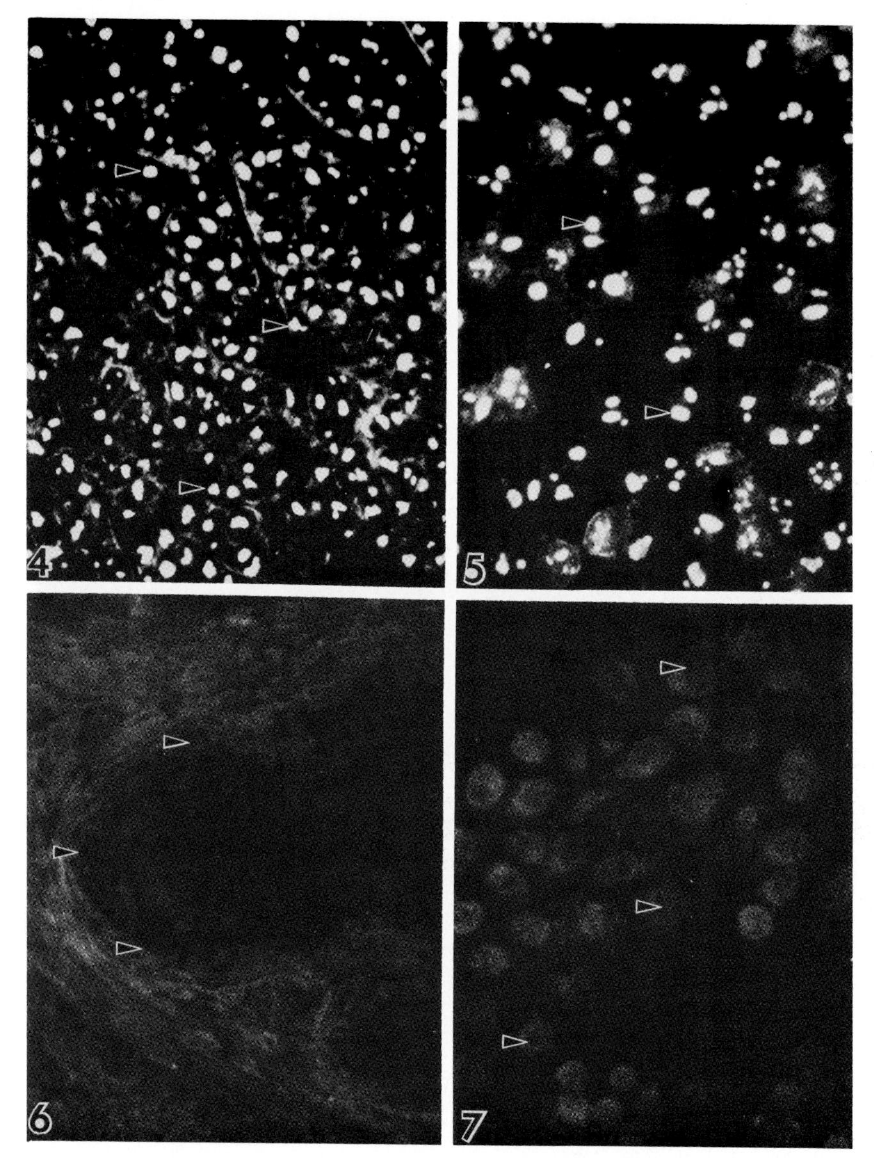

Fig. 4. Bright nucleolar fluorescence (pointers) in the original biopsy using antiserum to human prostate cancer nucleoli on 4-μ sections in a 1:100 dilution of the antiserum. × 1200.

Fig. 5. Bright nucleolar fluorescence (pointers) of the prostate tissue culture cells (passage 18) with antiserum to human prostate cancer nucleoli. × 1200.

Fig. 6. Hyperplastic human prostate (4-μ cryostat sections) treated with antiserum to human prostate cancer nucleoli. Note the lack of fluorescence (pointers). × 600.

Fig. 7. Tissue culture of human hyperplastic prostate gland. The epithelial cells (passage 6) showed no fluorescence (pointers) when treated with antiserum to human prostate cancer nucleoli. × 600.

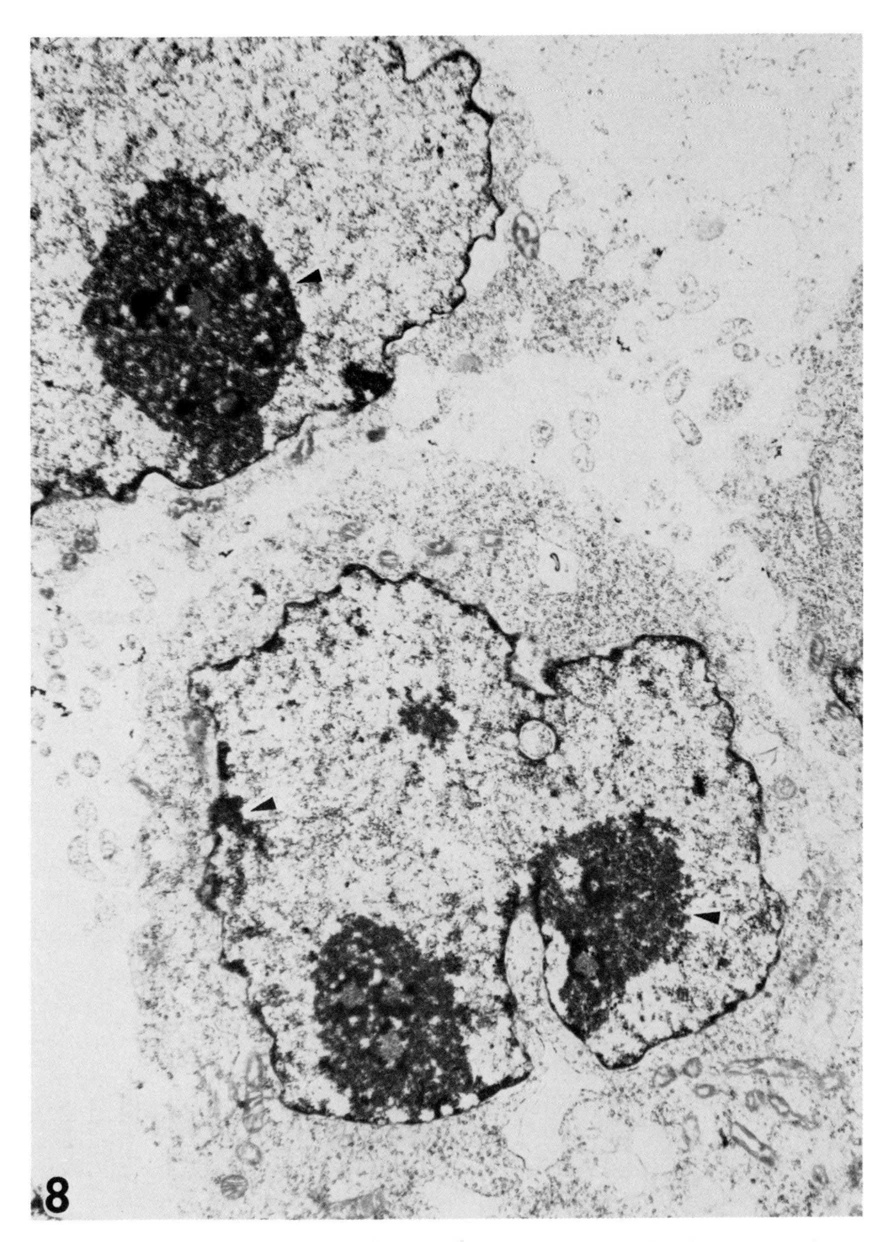

Fig. 8. Immunoelectron microscopic illustration of positive nucleolar antigen in prostate carcinoma cells showing localization in the nucleoli, segregated nucleoli, and perinuclear areas (pointers). × 27,500.

in a nucleolar position (Fig. 11). Figure 12 illustrates the zinc reaction in a prostate tissue section showing both hyperplasia and carcinoma. The application of silver sulphide method revealed positive reaction in the tumor cell nucleoli and occasional granules in the nuclei (Figs. 13, 14).

DISCUSSION

The immunogenicity of the isolated nucleoli from a newly established human prostate cancer tissue culture cell line in our laboratory is established. The results of this study support the concept that HuMANA is a common immunological marker for malignant human tumors and could not be detected in normal tissues and nonmalignant tumors.

In addition to biopsy specimens, our recent studies of smears of fine needle aspirates of various tumors [19, 20) yielded positive nucleolar fluorescence corresponding to our previous observations. This antibody test is valuable in exfoliative cytology diagnosis when a small number of cells are available for examination. Further important application would be to assess the viability of prostatic tumor cells in needle biopsies of patients who have been treated for carcinoma, and followup studies are indicated.

The immunoelectron microscopic study revealed that the antigen was localized in the tumor cell nucleoli. Reactive sites were also observed at the periphery of the nuclei as a narrow rim and in the segregated nucleoli. Furthermore, the antigen was preferentially located in the nucleolar fibrillar areas [11].

The localization of HuMANA and zinc in prostatic carcinoma cell nucleoli are unique immunological and biochemical expressions of this carcinoma since they were not detectable in normal or hyperplastic prostatic tissues. The uniformity of these results suggests that the nucleoli of cancer cells carrying the cancer specific molecules are not present in nonmalignant cells. We cannot exclude, however, the possibility that antigenic molecules responsible for the positive immunological reaction are present also in nonmalignant tumors and in normal cells but in a concentration below the limit of detection of the immunofluorescent technique.

Fig. 9. Fresh-frozen cryostat section. Acinus of normal prostate gland showing the positive dithizone reaction for zinc in the cytoplasm of the epithelial cells. × 600.

Fig. 10. Fresh-frozen cryostat section of hyperplastic prostate gland showing the positive dithizone reaction for zinc in the epithelial cells. × 420.

Fig. 11. Fresh-frozen cryostat section of hyperplastic prostate (arrows) showing the positive dithizone reaction for zinc in the epithelial cells. The adjacent carcinoma showed no reaction for zinc. × 180.

Fig. 12. Fresh-frozen cryostat section of carcinomatous prostate showing the dithizone reaction for zinc in the tumor cell nucleoli (pointer). × 600.

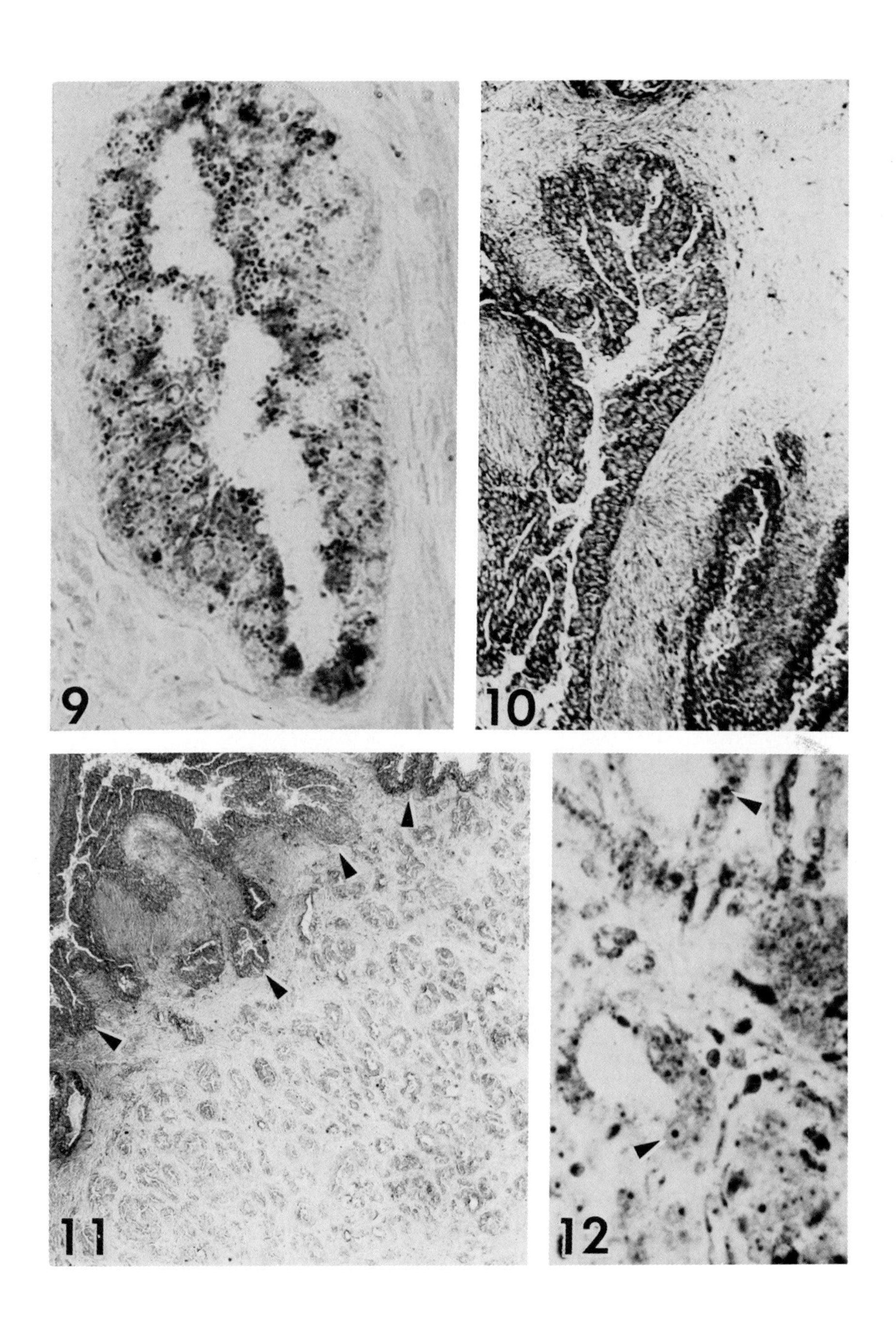
9
10
11
12

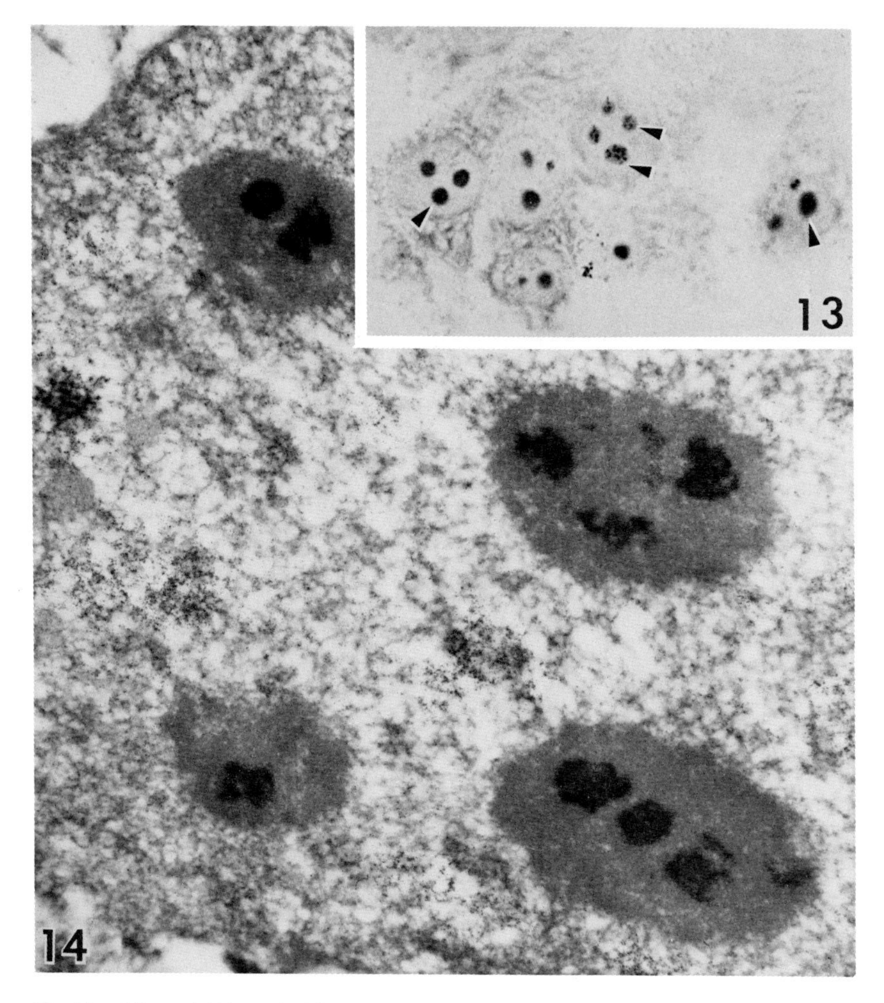

Fig. 13. Silver sulphide method for zinc showing the reaction in the cancer cell nucleoli (pointers). × 800.

Fig. 14. On electron microscopy the reactive product for zinc appears to be localized in the nucleoli of the cancer cells and focally in the nucleoplasm. × 43,750.

At this time we do not know if the molecules responsible for the positive reaction in the malignant cell nucleoli are specific indicators of rapid cellular growth. To obtain evidence for the hypothesis that this antigen is a molecular indicator of the malignant cell transformation, the following experiment was carried out (this was in collaboration with Professor J.L. Melnick).

An epithelial cell line from a normal prostate culture in its sixth passage was infected in petri dishes with 10^5 plaque-forming units (PFU)/ml HSV2 (oncogenic strain 186). After 1 hour at 37°C, the monolayer was washed with Tris buffer (pH 7.2), which was then drained and 5 ml of Eagle's medium with 5% fetal bovine serum was added and incubated at 37°C. At 24 hours, coverslips from the infected cultures and the controls were harvested by washing three times in Tris buffer, dried, and then fixed in absolute ethyl alcohol for 10 minutes for the study of nucleolar antigen by indirect immunofluorescence. Simultaneously, cultures in similar bottles were pelleted, the cells were fixed in 2% buffered glutaraldehyde and were processed for electron microscopy. Another set of cultures was harvested as above at 48 hours and at 72 hours.

The results of these experiments are shown in Table I and in Figures 15–19. At 24 hours the cultures were negative (Fig. 16), but at 48 hours they became positive for nucleolar fluorescence (Fig. 15). Electron microscopic study of the infected cultures at 24 hours showed 1–2% of the cells were replicating the virus; however, at 48 hours about 80% of the cells showed characteristics of viral replication (Fig. 19).

Two uterine cervical squamous cell carcinoma cell lines [21] also gave strongly positive nucleolar reaction for nucleolar antigen (Fig. 17). Dreesman et al [22] found these cells to be positive for DNA-binding antigen (a nonstructural HSV2 polypeptide). The prostate carcinoma cell line served as the positive control (Fig. 15).

The results of this study confirm the presence of HuMANA in cervical cancer (Fig. 17) and prostatic cancer cells in culture (Fig. 18). These cervical cancer cells also carry the DNA-binding antigen of HSV.

Of particular note is the finding that HuMANA can be expressed in normal prostate cells infected by a type 2 oncogenic strain of HSV. Further studies are planned to determine whether HuMANA is coded by the virus genome or whether the antigen is turned on by a derepression event following the entrance of viral nucleic acid into the prostate cells. A means is now available for the laboratory production of the antigen under controlled conditions.

CONCLUSIONS

A tumor nucleolar antigen present in a prostatic carcinoma was successfully isolated from an established cell line. The purified nucleoli were injected into

TABLE I. HuMANA and HSV2 in prostatic cells in culture

	HuMANA (%)	Herpes virions (%)
Normal prostatic cells after herpes virus infection		
0 hr	0	0
24 hr	0	2
48 hr	100	80
Malignant prostatic cells	100	0

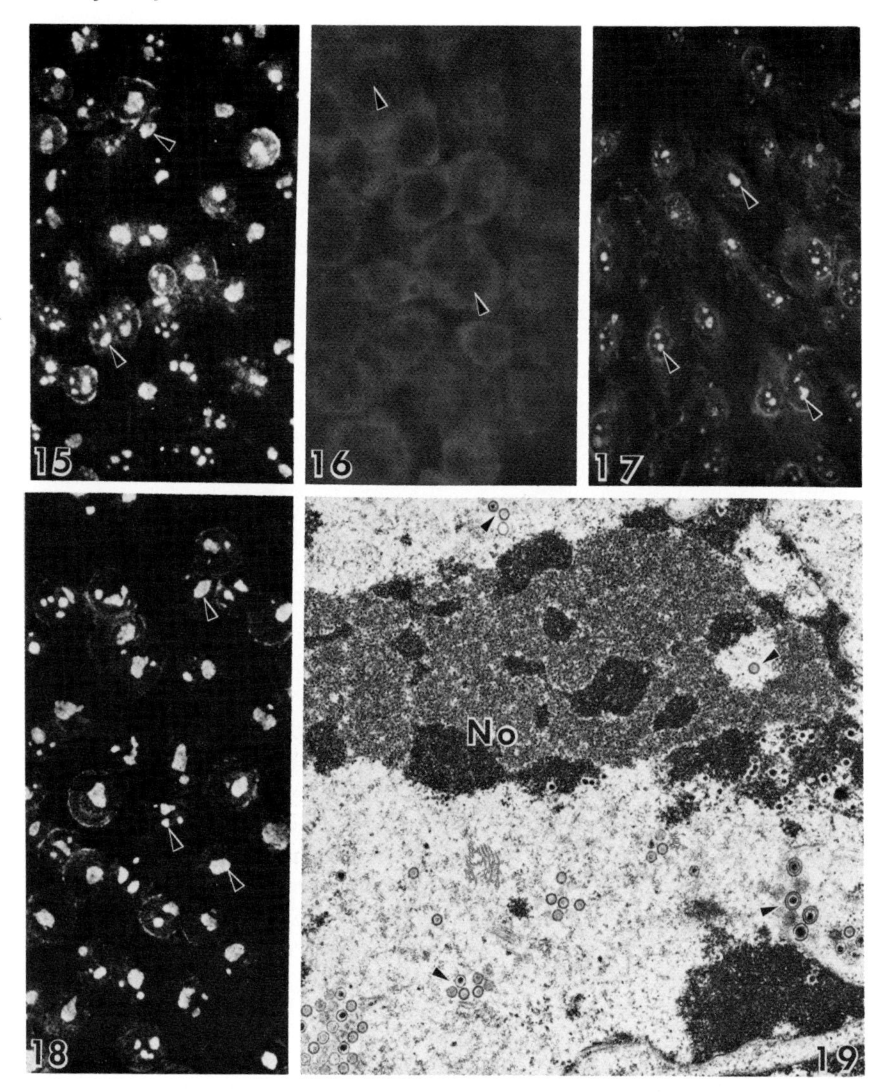

Fig. 15. Human cancer prostate epithelial cell in culture (passage 49) showing positive HuMANA fluorescence reaction. Pointers indicate stained nucleoli. × 760.

Fig. 16. Human normal prostate epithelial cells in culture (passage 6). Note complete absence of fluorescence. Pointers indicate unstained nucleoli. × 1,200.

Fig. 17. Human uterine cervix carcinoma cells in culture (passage 27) showing positive HuMANA fluorescence. Pointers indicate stained nucleoli. × 650.

Fig. 18. Human normal prostate epithelial cells in culture (passage 6) 48 hours after infection with HSV2 showing positive HuMANA fluorescence. Pointers indicate stained nucleoli. × 760.

Fig. 19. Electron micrograph of normal human prostate epithelial cell 48 hours after HSV2 infection showing presence of newly formed virions (pointers). "No" indicates nucleolus. × 37,500.

rabbits as the immunogen, and specific antibody was manufactured in an in vivo system.

The specific rabbit antihuman nucleolar sera 10 days after the second booster injection of the antigen gave strongly positive nucleolar fluorescence in the original tumor, in the tissue culture cell line of the tumor, and in all of the prostatic carcinomas. However, there was no reaction detected in normal tissues, nonmalignant tumors, or a normal prostate epithelial cell culture. The specificity of the reactivity for the antigen was demonstrated in that the preinoculation rabbit serum gave no reaction and all nonmalignant tissues were negative.

It is suggested that this antigen is a molecular indicator of malignant cellular proliferation and has a role in the rapid turnover of the tumor cells as a promoter protein. Since zinc in prostate carcinoma becomes localized in the nucleolus, it may be considered as a component of a malignancy-associated metalloenzyme.

Our data lend support to previous observations that a common nucleolar antigen is present in human malignant tumors.

ACKNOWLEDGMENTS

The support and advice of Dr. H. Busch, Dr. J.L. Melnick, and Dr. J. L. Titus are gratefully acknowledged. The contribution of Phyllis Gyorkey in the technical work and evaluation of data, the technical assistance of Ira Wimberly and Sandor Gergely, and the excellent secretarial work of Ellen Wilson are acknowledged and appreciated.

REFERENCES

1. Busch RK, Busch H: Antigenic proteins of nucleolar chromatin of Novikoff hepatoma ascites cells. Tumori 63:347–357, 1977.
2. Marashi F, Davis FM, Busch RK, Savage HE, Busch H: Purification and partial characterization of nucleolar antigen-1 of the Novikoff hepatoma. Cancer Res 39:59–66, 1979.
3. Davis FM, Gyorkey F, Busch RK, Busch H: A nucleolar antigen found in several human tumors but not in nontumor tissues. Proc Natl Acad Sci USA 76:892–896, 1979.
4. Busch H, Gyorkey F, Busch RK, Davis FM, Gyorkey P, Smetana K: A nucleolar antigen found in a broad range of human malignant tumor specimens. Cancer Res 39:3024–3030, 1979.
5. Busch H, Busch RK, Chan PK, Gyorkey F, Smetana K: The human tumor nucleolar antigen. Trends Pharmacol Sci 1:436–439, 1980.
6. Busch H, Busch RK, Chan PK, Daskal Y, Gyorkey F, Gyorkey P, Kobayashi M, Smetana K, Sudhakar SA: Nucleolar antigen in human malignant tumors. Transplantation Proc 12:99–102, 1980.
7. Gyorkey F, Gyorkey P, Busch H: Human malignancy-associated nucleolar antigen. Hung Acad Sci 19:254–257, 1979.
8. Gyorkey F, Gyorkey P: The fine structure of prostatic tumors. In Spring-Mills E, Hafez ESE (eds): "Male Accessory Sex Glands." Elsevier/North-Holland Biomedical Press, 1980, pp 457–478.
9. Gyorkey F, Min K-W, Huff JA, Gyorkey P: Zinc and magnesium in the human prostate gland: normal, hyperplastic and neoplastic. Cancer Res 27:1348–1353, 1967.

10. Gyorkey F, Sato CS: In vitro ^{65}Zn-binding capacities of normal, hyperplastic and carcinomatous human prostate gland. Exp Mole Pathol 8:216–224, 1968.
11. Gyorkey F, Yazdi E: Cellular and subcellular distribution of zinc in normal, hyperplastic and carcinomatous human prostate gland. Am J Pathol 70 (no. 2), p. 62a, 1973.
12. Gyorkey F: Some aspects of cancer of the prostate gland. In Busch H (ed): "Methods of Cancer Research." New York: Academic Press, 1974, Vol X, pp 279–368.
13. Hodge LD, Mancini P, Davis FM, Heywood P: Nuclear matrix of HeLa S_3 cells. J Cell Biol 72:194–208, 1977.
14. Busch H, Smetana K: The Nucleolus. New York: Academic Press, 1970, pp 448–463.
15. Mager M, McNary WF Jr, Lionette F: The histochemical detection of zinc. J Histochem Cytochem 1:493–504, 1953.
16. Timm F: Zur Histochemie der Schwermettale das Sulfid-Silberverfahren. Deutsche Zeit fur fericht Med Bd 46,S: 706–711, 1958.
17. Kozma M, Ferke A, Kasa P: Ultrastructural identification of neural elements containing trace metals. Acta Histochem Bd 62,S: 142–154, 1978.
18. Daskal Y, Kobayashi M, Gyorkey F, Gyorkey P, Busch RK, Busch H: Immunoelectron microscopic localization of a human tumor nucleolar antigen. Am Assoc Cancer Res, San Diego, California, May 28–31, 1980 (abstr).
19. Gyorkey F, Gomez L, Uribe G, Gyorkey P, Busch RK, Busch H: Clinical application of a human malignancy-associated nucleolar antigen in fine needle aspiration biopsy. Dedication of Dr. Michael DeBakey's Research and Education Center, Baylor College of Medicine, Houston, Texas, October 10, 1980 (Scientific Session: Exhibit).
20. Gyorkey F, Gomez L, Sinkovics JG, Uribe G, Gyorkey P, Busch RK, Busch H: Augmentation of diagnostic efficacy of fine needle aspiration of tumors by staining for human malignancy-associated nucleolar antigen (HuMANA). Am Assoc Cancer Res Washington, D.C., April, 1980 (abstr).
21. Melnick JL, Adam E, Lewis R, Kaufman RH: Cervical cancer cell lines containing herpes virus markers. Intervirology 12:111–114, 1979.
22. Dreesman GR, Burek J, Adam E, Kaufman RH, Melnick JL, Powell KL, Purifoy DJM: Expression of herpes virus-induced antigens in human cervical cancer. Nature 283:591–593, 1980.

Index

PROGRESS IN CLINICAL AND BIOLOGICAL RESEARCH

Vol 1: **Erythrocyte Structure and Function,** George J. Brewer, *Editor*

Vol 2: **Preventability of Perinatal Injury,** Karlis Adamsons and Howard A. Fox, *Editors*

Vol 3: **Infections of the Fetus and the Newborn Infant,** Saul Krugman and Anne A. Gershon, *Editors*

Vol 4: **Conflicts in Childhood Cancer: An Evaluation of Current Management,** Lucius F. Sinks and John O. Godden, *Editors*

Vol 5: **Trace Components of Plasma: Isolation and Clinical Significance,** G.A. Jamieson and T.J. Greenwalt, *Editors*

Vol 6: **Prostatic Disease,** H. Marberger, H. Haschek, H.K.A. Schirmer, J.A.C. Colston, and E. Witkin, *Editors*

Vol 7: **Blood Pressure, Edema and Proteinuria in Pregnancy,** Emanuel A. Friedman, *Editor*

Vol 8: **Cell Surface Receptors,** Garth L. Nicolson, Michael A. Raftery, Martin Rodbell, and C. Fred Fox, *Editors*

Vol 9: **Membranes and Neoplasia: New Approaches and Strategies,** Vincent T. Marchesi, *Editor*

Vol 10: **Diabetes and Other Endocrine Disorders During Pregnancy and in the Newborn,** Maria I. New and Robert H. Fiser, *Editors*

Vol 11: **Clinical Uses of Frozen-Thawed Red Blood Cells,** John A. Griep, *Editor*

Vol 12: **Breast Cancer,** Albert C.W. Montague, Geary L. Stonesifer, Jr., and Edward F. Lewison, *Editors*

Vol 13: **The Granulocyte: Function and Clinical Utilization,** Tibor J. Greenwalt and G.A. Jamieson, *Editors*

Vol 14: **Zinc Metabolism: Current Aspects in Health and Disease,** George J. Brewer and Ananda S. Prasad, *Editors*

Vol 15: **Cellular Neurobiology,** Zach Hall, Regis Kelly, and C. Fred Fox, *Editors*

Vol 16: **HLA and Malignancy,** Gerald P. Murphy, *Editor*

Vol 17: **Cell Shape and Surface Architecture,** Jean Paul Revel, Ulf Henning, and C. Fred Fox, *Editors*

Vol 18: **Tay-Sachs Disease: Screening and Prevention,** Michael M. Kaback, *Editor*

Vol 19: **Blood Substitutes and Plasma Expanders,** G.A. Jamieson and T.J. Greenwalt, *Editors*

Vol 20: **Erythrocyte Membranes: Recent Clinical and Experimental Advances,** Walter C. Kruckeberg, John W. Eaton, and George J. Brewer, *Editors*

Vol 21: **The Red Cell,** George J. Brewer, *Editor*

Vol 22: **Molecular Aspects of Membrane Transport,** Dale Oxender and C. Fred Fox, *Editors*

Vol 23: **Cell Surface Carbohydrates and Biological Recognition,** Vincent T. Marchesi, Victor Ginsburg, Phillips W. Robbins, and C. Fred Fox, *Editors*

Vol 24: **Twin Research,** Proceedings of the Second International Congress on Twin Studies, Walter E. Nance, *Editor*

Published in 3 Volumes:
Part A: Psychology and Methodology
Part B: Biology and Epidemiology
Part C: Clinical Studies

Vol 25: **Recent Advances in Clinical Oncology,** Tapan A. Hazra and Michael C. Beachley, *Editors*

Vol 26: **Origin and Natural History of Cell Lines,** Claudio Barigozzi, *Editor*

Vol 27: **Membrane Mechanisms of Drugs of Abuse,** Charles W. Sharp and Leo G. Abood, *Editors*

Vol 28: **The Blood Platelet in Transfusion Therapy,** Tibor J. Greenwalt and G.A. Jamieson, *Editors*

Vol 29: **Biomedical Applications of the Horseshoe Crab (Limulidae),** Elias Cohen, *Editor-in-Chief*

Vol 30: **Normal and Abnormal Red Cell Membranes,** Samuel E. Lux, Vincent T. Marchesi, and C. Fred Fox, *Editors*

Vol 31: **Transmembrane Signaling,** Mark Bitensky, R. John Collier, Donald F. Steiner, and C. Fred Fox, *Editors*

Vol 32: **Genetic Analysis of Common Diseases: Applications to Predictive Factors in Coronary Disease,** Charles F. Sing and Mark Skolnick, *Editors*

Vol 33: **Prostate Cancer and Hormone Receptors,** Gerald P. Murphy and Avery A. Sandberg, *Editors*

Vol 34: **The Management of Genetic Disorders,** Constantine J. Papadatos and Christos S. Bartsocas, *Editors*

Vol 35: **Antibiotics and Hospitals,** Carlo Grassi and Giuseppe Ostino, *Editors*

Vol 36: **Drug and Chemical Risks to the Fetus and Newborn,** Richard H. Schwarz and Sumner J. Yaffe, *Editors*

Vol 37: **Models for Prostate Cancer,** Gerald P. Murphy, *Editor*

Vol 38: **Ethics, Humanism, and Medicine,** Marc D. Basson, *Editor*

Vol 39: **Neurochemistry and Clinical Neurology,** Leontino Battistin, George Hashim, and Abel Lajtha, *Editors*

Vol 40: **Biological Recognition and Assembly,** David S. Eisenberg, James A. Lake, and C. Fred Fox, *Editors*

Vol 41: **Tumor Cell Surfaces and Malignancy,** Richard O. Hynes and C. Fred Fox, *Editors*

Vol 42: **Membranes, Receptors, and the Immune Response: 80 Years After Ehrlich's Side Chain Theory,** Edward P. Cohen and Heinz Köhler, *Editors*

Vol 43: **Immunobiology of the Erythrocyte,** S. Gerald Sandler, Jacob Nusbacher, and Moses S. Schanfield, *Editors*

Vol 44: **Perinatal Medicine Today,** Bruce K. Young, *Editor*

Vol 45: **Mammalian Genetics and Cancer: The Jackson Laboratory Fiftieth Anniversary Symposium,** Elizabeth S. Russell, *Editor*

Vol 46: **Etiology of Cleft Lip and Cleft Palate,** Michael Melnick, David Bixler, and Edward D. Shields, *Editors*

Vol 47: **New Developments With Human and Veterinary Vaccines,** A. Mizrahi, I. Hertman, M.A. Klingberg, and A. Kohn, *Editors*

Vol 48: **Cloning of Human Tumor Stem Cells,** Sydney E. Salmon, *Editor*

Vol 49: **Myelin: Chemistry and Biology,** George A. Hashim, *Editor*